McGraw-Hill

My Math

Program Overview

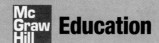 Education

Bothell, WA • Chicago, IL • Columbus, OH • New York, NY

connectED.mcgraw-hill.com

Education

Copyright © 2013 The McGraw-Hill Companies, Inc.

STEM McGraw-Hill is committed to providing instructional materials in Science, Technology, Engineering, and Mathematics (STEM) that give all students a solid foundation, one that prepares them for college and careers in the 21st century.

Send all inquiries to:
McGraw-Hill Education
STEM Learning Solutions Center
8787 Orion Place
Columbus, OH 43240

ISBN: 978-0-02-116201-7 (Teacher Edition, Volume 1)
MHID: 0-02-116201-8 (Teacher Edition, Volume 1)
ISBN: 978-0-02-115021-2 (Student Edition, Volume 1)
MHID: 0-02-115021-4 (Student Edition, Volume 1)

Printed in the United States of America.

5 6 7 8 9 10 RMN 20 19 18 17 16 15 14 13 12

Our mission is to provide educational resources that enable students to become the problem solvers of the 21st century and inspire them to explore careers within Science, Technology, Engineering, and Mathematics (STEM) related fields.

Meet The Artists!

Alyssa Gonzalez

King of the Math Jungle This was a great experience similar to being on a roller coaster. Many friends and family supported me in this competition and many kids at Veterans Elementary will benefit from this. *Volume 1*

Finley Moss

Math is Yummy I came up with the idea because my mom and I love to bake cakes and it takes both time and measurement to do so. I was dreaming about how it would feel to win, so I am very excited! Math is yummy after all! *Volume 2*

Other Finalists

Landre Kate Beeler
Pop Numbers 4 Me

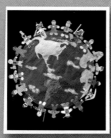

Sherry Bergeron's Class *
Math Makes Our World a Better Place

Sally Barmakian's Class*
Math is a Rainbow of Learning

Kamya Cooperwood
Monkey

Judson Upchurch
I like Numbers

Charles "Greyson" Biggs
Rainbow of Possibilities

Leah Rauch
Connect the Dots

Andrew Morris
Math Designed World

Matthew Saldivat
Math Guy in the Sky

Ngun Za Cin
Three-Dimensional Shape Sculpture

Find out more about the winners and other finalists at www.MHEonline.com.

We wish to congratulate all of the entries in the 2011 *McGraw-Hill My Math* "What Math Means To Me" cover art contest. With over 2,400 entries and more than 20,000 community votes cast, the names mentioned above represent the two winners and ten finalists for this grade.

* Please visit mhmymath.com for a complete list of students who contributed to this artwork.

Plan Your Way

E

very great lesson begins with a plan. Right from the start *My Math* supports you with online lesson planning tools, customizable lessons, and tips for delivering effective instruction.

Your Inspiration + Our Resources

CLASSROOM
SUCCESS!

Customizable Online Lesson Planner

My Math contains hundreds of lessons, activities, online manipulatives, animations, and videos. Use the **online lesson planner** to create highly interactive and engaging lessons by organizing the resources you want, in the order you want, for use when you want.

Visit **www.connectED.mcgraw-hill.com**.

Reading Connections

Math isn't an isolated subject. Use our **Real-World Problem Solving Leveled Readers** to guide students towards discovering the relevance of math across the curriculum and in their daily lives. Students will build reading comprehension skills while developing their mathematical proficiency.

Reading Connections

Real-World Problem Solving Library

Math and Science: Solving the Pyramid Puzzle

Use these leveled books to reinforce and extend problem-solving skills and strategies.

Leveled for:

AL **Approaching Level**

OL **On Level** Also available in Spanish

Beyond Level

My Math — Make it Yours

Short on Time?

Even if you don't have time to tackle every problem in a lesson, *My Math* helps you cover the key concepts. Look for the clock to find streamlining suggestions in the Teacher Edition.

1 LAUNCH THE L

🕐 **If your students are well-versed decomposing numbers, you may begin instruction with Step 2 TE**

You will need
❏ grid paper
❏ crayons, markers, or colored pen

...rs are left? 4 chairs

...g more away each time.

Lunchroom Chat

Building a Learning Community

ELL Ask your colleagues how they differentiate between addition and subtraction situations to help English Language Learners. You may wish to discuss the following.

• Do they use a scaffolding approach to break up questions?

• Do they find that using manipulatives is effective? Which manipulatives are most effective? Which are least effective?

• In which math concepts do ELL students seem to excel?

Lunchroom Chats

We all have moments when we need a little extra inspiration or a new way of explaining a concept. *My Math* provides teaching tips that offer helpful suggestions for effective ways of delivering instruction. Our **Lunchroom Chats** include conversation starters designed to engage your colleagues in developing fresh approaches for tackling challenging teaching situations. Use occasionally or as the foundation for forming discussion groups in your own **Professional Learning Community**.

Prepare
Your Way

Throughout *My Math* you'll find the tools that ensure you're on track, emphasizing the Common Core State Standards and developing Mathematical Practices in your students. With *My Math*, everyone is always on the same page and heading toward the same goal.

MY Common Core State Standards

Number and Operations in Base Ten

4.NBT.1 Recognize that in a multi-digit whole number, a digit in one place represents ten times what it represents in the place to its right.

4.NBT.3 Use place value understanding to round multi-digit whole numbers to any place.

4.NBT.5 Multiply a whole to four digits by a one-digit and multiply two two-digit strategies based on place properties of operations. explain the calculation b rectangular arrays, and

Operations and Algebraic Thinking *This chapter also addresses th*

4.OA.3 Solve multistep word problems posed with whole numbers and having whole-number answers using the four operations, including problems in which remainders must be interpreted. Represent these problems using equations with a letter standing for the unknown quantity. Assess the reasonableness of answers using mental computation and ...tion strategies including round...

The STANDARD in CCSS

Common Core State Standards

My Math was developed from the ground up to meet the new **Common Core State Standards (CCSS)**. *My Math* will confidently guide you through the transition to the **CCSS** and ensure you're teaching the appropriate concepts at the right time.

Mathematical Practices

Students need focused exposure to important concepts and mathematical practices in order to understand them fully and to drive toward mastery. Look for the **Mathematical Practices** icon throughout each lesson which easily identifies those targeted learning opportunities.

Mathematical PRACTICE ➤ Woven Throughout

...ro, how many

Mathematical
16. **PRACTICE 3** **Where Will** scouts need to sell 75 boxes o... gets the same number of boxes be left to sell?

17. **Use the information to solv**

Four zookeepers are resp... the animals in the Cit... four tigers, five c...

Grades 3-5

My Math — Make it Yours

What's the Math?

What's the Math?

CCSS **Common Core State Standards**
DOMAIN: Number and Operations in Base

Standards: 3.NBT.2, 3.OA.8
The wording of these standards can be found on page

The content in this lesson addresses a standard f
Operations and Algebraic Thinking domai
chapter overall addresses standards fr
in **Base Ten** domain. St

A clear understanding of how the math concepts are developed across the domain helps to ensure that learning is on track. Look for **What's the Math?** before each lesson in the *My Math* Teacher Edition for sensible suggestions and strategies for developing skills and understanding in students.

Essential Questions

Students stay motivated and engaged when they know their learning goals. Each chapter of *My Math* is organized around an **Essential Question** that is clearly identified throughout. In every lesson, students build on their knowledge to answer that important question.

ESSENTIAL QUESTION

How can I divide a multi-digit number by a one-digit number?

Teach
Your Way

You've planned. You've prepared. Now the fun begins! With *My Math*'s instructional resources you can guide your students through each new concept, relating it to situations your students will find familiar and interesting. *My Math* allows you to tailor instruction to meet every student's unique needs.

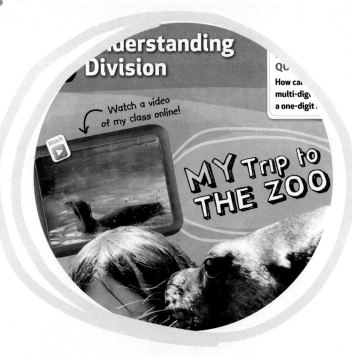

Theme-Based Lessons

Each chapter of *My Math* is built around a **theme** to capture the interest of your students and place mathematical concepts in the context of real-world situations. An entertaining **video** starts each chapter to immediately engage students and to initiate discussion about the concept.

Math in My World

Your students have the opportunity to use math every day and in many different ways. *My Math* uses examples from students' daily lives along with fun problems to help them relate to concepts and make them relevant.

...ty that is left over. You ca... ...emainder in division problems.

 Math in My World

Example 1

Mr. Hein's class is going to the zoo. Each seat o... the bus can hold 2 people. There are 29 student... and 8 adults. How many bus seats are needed f... the field trip?

Find 39 ÷ 3.

Divide the tens.
3 ÷ 2 = 1
Put 1 in the quotient over the tens place.

| 1 |

Grades 3-5

My Math — Make it Yours

Real-World Problem Solving

Students are given the opportunity to solve **real-world problems**. The interactive nature of their Student Editions helps them better illustrate and remember the concepts they're learning by using examples they create and think about.

Problem Solving

15. Marlene makes $4 an hour babysit___
$48, how many hours did she bab___

___

Mathematical
16. **PRACTICE** 3 **Where Will** ___
scouts need to sell 75 boxe___
___ets the same number ___   Grades 3-5

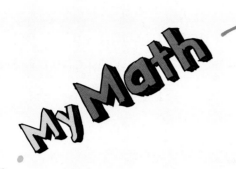

Name

Hands On
Model Division

Explore! Tools Watch

Find 39 ÷ 3.
The **dividend** is _____ and the **divisor** i___

Model the dividend, 39.
Use the base-ten blocks to ___
___nd 9 ones ___   Grades 3-5

Modeling the Math

Student learning is more memorable when models and tools are used to help them visualize their thinking and solidify their understanding. Every *My Math* lesson begins by modeling the math to begin the progression from concrete to pictorial to abstract. You can also use the **virtual manipulatives** to model this thinking with the entire class on an interactive whiteboard.

Differentiated Instruction

My Math is designed for personalized learning. Students arrive at their "a-ha" moments at different times and in different ways. Our **Differentiated Instruction** included in each chapter (and online at **connectED.mcgraw-hill.com**) provides you with strategies and resources to help find the key to unlocking every student's "a-ha" moment.

Rtl **RESPONSE TO INTERVE**___
DIFFERENTIATED INSTRUCTION

AL **APPROACHING LEVEL**

IF **my students struggle with subtracting four-digit numbers,**

THEN **choose a resource:**

→ Use the Reteach worksheet with small groups.
→ Go online for a Differentiated Instruction act___
→ **Using Grid Paper** Give students a list o___
   subtraction problems and grid pape___
   ___ncorrectly because t___

Engage *Your Way*

You'll have no problem capturing students' attention and keeping them engaged whether you're using one of *My Math*'s customizable interactive whiteboard presentations, a virtual manipulative, or reviewing one of the many step-by-step personal tutors.

Your Inspiration
+ *Our Resources*
─────────────
1 EXCITING CLASSROOM!

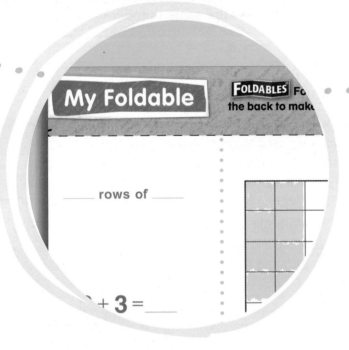

My Foldable

FOLDABLES For
the back to make

____ rows of ____

____ + **3** = ____

Foldables

Sometimes it's the simplest thing that connects with kids. **Foldables** are easy-to-make graphic organizers that enable students to practice and review new concepts in an interactive format. A Foldable template is included in every chapter.

Make one yourself!

Digital Dashboard

Keep your learners captivated during every lesson with the hundreds of digital resources available at **connectED.mcgraw-hill.com.** Each chapter includes recommendations for using such digital resources as virtual manipulatives to demonstrate concepts, animations to show a concept in action, and step-by-step tutorials for problem solving.

Visit **www.connectED.mcgraw-hill.com.**

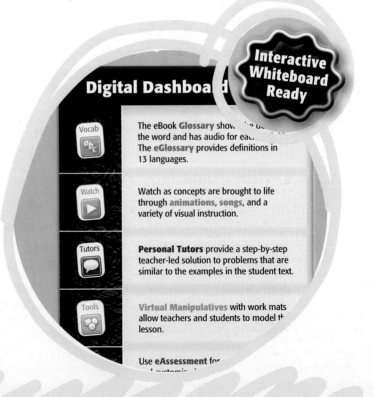

Digital Dashboard

Interactive Whiteboard Ready

Vocab
abc

The eBook **Glossary** show___ the ___ the word and has audio for eac__ The **eGlossary** provides definitions in 13 languages.

Watch

Watch as concepts are brought to life through **animations**, **songs**, and a variety of visual instruction.

Tutors

Personal Tutors provide a step-by-step teacher-led solution to problems that are similar to the examples in the student text.

Tools

Virtual Manipulatives with work mats allow teachers and students to model t__ lesson.

Use **eAssessment** fo__

My Math — Make it Yours

My Math Student Center

Students often need a variety of instruction and resources to gain mathematical fluency and proficiency. What better way to encourage practice than with fun, interactive games? The *My Math* **Student Center** is loaded with online games and digital support resources that students can use at school or at home.

Apps

Mathematics learning is no longer confined to math class. Point your students and their parents to the **STEM App Store** to download the latest math games and other instructional resources. Build fluency and proficiency in a fun and engaging way!

Visit **www.mheonline.com**.

Empower Your Way

Empower students to participate in what and how they're learning. *My Math* provides outlets for personal expression while guiding students toward specific learning goals. Online examples, flashcards, and support resources are all designed to be personalized in ways that fit each student's individual interest and need.

My Math Words / My Vocabulary Cards

Being able to talk about how you've solved a math problem is almost as important as being able to solve it. My Math provides ongoing support for math vocabulary development throughout each chapter. **My Vocabulary Cards** and **My Math Words** build students' mathematical vocabulary by empowering them to create their own unique examples.

Try our 'e-flashcards' app! Visit mheonline.com.

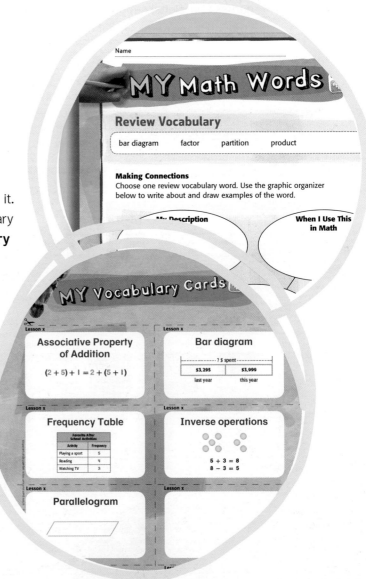

My Math — Make it Yours

Homework

No more loose notebook pages or photocopied worksheets! Homework pages are built right into the *My Math* **Student Edition**. A fully worked out example helps students and parents review the concept before moving to the practice problems.

 If students need help at home, the *My Math* **Online e-Help** provides parents with additional resources to help them support their student's learning.

Name

MY Homework

Homework Helper
Need help?

Find 24 ÷ 2.

1 Model the dividend 24.

the tens.

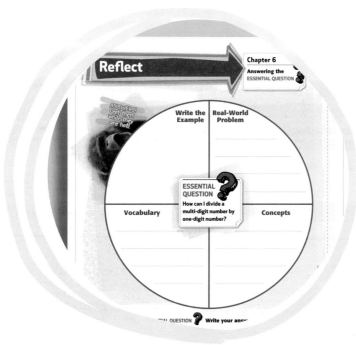

Reflect and Review

Before moving on to the next chapter, make sure students have a final moment to review the vocabulary and reflect on the concepts they've just learned. The **Review** and **Reflect** pages tie back to the Essential Question of the chapter. Students use their own words and examples in a graphic organizer to answer the Essential Question.

Every student progresses at his or her own pace. To help guide individual learning and ensure that every student has an "a-ha" moment, *My Math* offers a variety of assessments that can be used throughout the learning process. You choose the assessment tools that work best, whether it is in print format or online.

Am I Ready?

Knowing what students know and don't know before they dive into a new chapter ensures you're both prepared for the new learning ahead.

The **Am I Ready?** assessment at the start of each chapter identifies whether students have the foundational skills they need in order to successfully learn the new skills and concepts about to be presented.

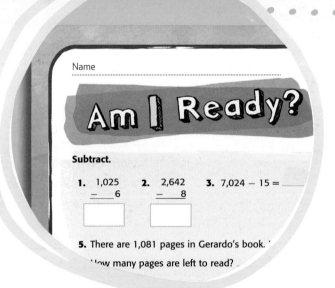

Name

Am I Ready?

Subtract.

1. 1,025
  − 6

2. 2,642
  − 8

3. 7,024 − 15 = _____

5. There are 1,081 pages in Gerardo's book. How many pages are left to read? ___

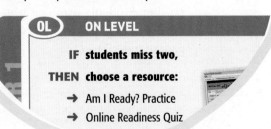

2 Diagnose and Prescribe

Based on the results of the Am I Ready? in the student edition, to address individual needs **before** beginning the chapter.
Use the **ONGOING** resources to support differentiated instruction concepts are presented in the chapter.

| OL | ON LEVEL |

IF students miss two,

THEN choose a resource:
→ Am I Ready? Practice
→ Online Readiness Quiz

Diagnose and Prescribe

If the **Am I Ready?** assessment indicates that a student needs additional support, the **Diagnose and Prescribe** chart in your Teacher Edition provides leveled intervention recommendations that will ensure everyone in your class begins the chapter confidently.

My Math — Make it Yours

Check My Progress

Throughout each chapter, **Check My Progress** assessments allow you to monitor student understanding and to identify where students have gaps in their learning. Based on the results of this assessment, customize your remediation using the correlated **Response to Intervention, (RtI)** guide found in the Teacher Edition.

Assessments

Aligned to the three-tier RtI model, each chapter concludes with **leveled assessment** options. Based on mid-chapter and the final Review and Reflect assessments, you can assign assessments to meet the specific needs of your students.

See our online assessments at **connectED.mcgraw-hill.com** for all grades.

Check My Progress

Vocabulary Check Vocab

1. Label the parts of the division problem with the f

dividend   divisor   quoti

$$11R3$$
$$6\overline{)69}$$

⭐ avorites   🖥 McGraw-Hill My Math: Teacher Center

McGraw-Hill My Math

| Home | Lesson Plan | Manage & Assign | Assess | Res |

Assessment Tool

Chapter 1: Assessment Worksheets   ▶ Resource T

Chapter 2: Assessment Worksheets

Chapter 3: Assessment Worksheets

Chapter 4: Assessment Worksheets

Chapter 5: Assessment Worksheets

Grade 4
Online Assessment

About the Common Core State Standards

What is the goal of the Common Core State Standards?

In 2010, the National Governors Associations Center for Best Practices and the Council of Chief State School Officers released a universal set of standards for mathematics education to be used by all states.

The Common Core State Standards seek to develop both students' mathematical understanding and their procedural skills so that they may be fully prepared for the future in a global economy.

How do I decode the Common Core State Standards?

This diagram provides clarity for decoding the standard identifiers placed on the student pages.

2.OA.4

Grade Level   Domain   Standard

Domain	Abbreviation
Operations and Algebraic Thinking	OA
Number and Operations in Base Ten	NBT
Measurement and Data	MD
Geometry	G

How do I meet the Common Core State Standards by using *My Math*?

My Math was specifically written for the Common Core State Standards (CCSS). The chapters are organized by domain. The domains are color coded in the design of *My Math* so that at any time you can know which domain you are covering when teaching a lesson.

- **On-Page Correlations** Every lesson supports one or more standards. The first page of the lesson tells you which standard(s) are being addressed.

- **Mathematical Practices** The Mathematical Practices are embedded throughout *My Math*, especially present in the hands-on modeling approach, strong problem-solving emphasis in all lessons, and higher-order thinking exercises.

- **What's the Math?** The Teacher Edition contains special sections for every lesson that explain what standard(s) are being addressed, what students should understand, and what students should know how to do.

- **Correlations** The following pages include correlations to both the Content Standards for Mathematics and the Mathematical Practices.

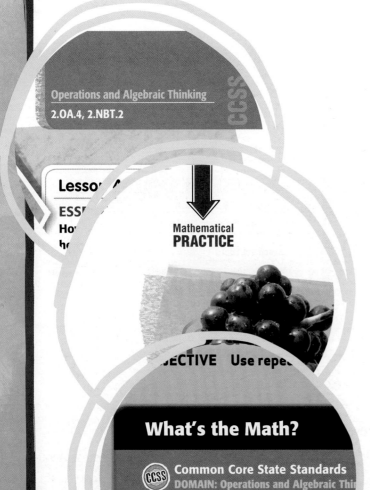

Operations and Algebraic Thinking
2.OA.4, 2.NBT.2

Lesson

ESS
Ho
h

Mathematical
PRACTICE

JECTIVE   Use repe

What's the Math?

CCSS **Common Core State Standards**
DOMAIN: Operations and Algebraic Thin

Standards: 2.OA.4, 2.NBT.2
The wording of these standards can be found on p

What Students Should Underst
finding the total number of

Common Core State Standards (CCSS)

Correlated to *My Math*, Grade 2

CCSS **Common Core State Standards**	Lesson(s)	Page(s)
Domain 2.OA Operations and Algebraic Thinking		
Represent and solve problems involving addition and subtraction.		
2.OA.1 Use addition and subtraction within 100 to solve one- and two-step word problems involving situations of adding to, taking from, putting together, taking apart, and comparing, with unknowns in all positions, e.g., by using drawings and equations with a symbol for the unknown number to represent the problem.	1-1, 1-2, 1-3, 1-4, 1-5, 1-6, 1-7, 1-8, 1-9, 1-10, 1-11, 1-12, 1-13, 2-1, 2-2, 2-3, 3-1, 3-2, 3-3, 3-4, 3-5, 3-6, 3-7, 4-1, 4-2, 4-3, 4-4, 4-5, 4-6, 4-7, 4-8, 4-9	11–16, 17–22, 23–28, 29–34, 35–40, 41–46, 49–54, 55–60, 61–66, 69–74, 76–80, 81–86, 87–92, 107–112, 113–118, 119–124, 165–170, 171–176, 177–182, 185–190, 191–196, 197–202, 203–208, 223–228, 229–234, 235–240, 241–246, 249–254, 255–260, 261–266, 267–272, 273–278
Add and subtract within 20.		
2.OA.2 Fluently add and subtract within 20 using mental strategies. By end of Grade 2, know from memory all sums of two one–digit numbers.	1-1, 1-2, 1-3, 1-4, 1-5, 1-6, 1-7, 1-8, 1-9, 1-10, 1-11, 1-12, 2-1	11–16, 17–22, 23–28, 29–34, 35–40, 41–46, 49–54, 55–60, 61–66, 69–74, 76–80, 81–86, 107–112
Work with equal groups of objects to gain foundations for multiplication.		
2.OA.3 Determine whether a group of objects (up to 20) has an odd or even number of members, e.g., by pairing objects or counting them by 2s; write an equation to express an even number as a sum of two equal addends.	2-6, 2-7	139–144, 145–150
2.OA.4 Use addition to find the total number of objects arranged in rectangular arrays with up to 5 rows and up to 5 columns; write an equation to express the total as a sum of equal addends.	2-4, 2-5	127–132, 133–138

Common Core State Standards | Lesson(s) | Page(s)

Domain 2.NBT Number and Operations in Base Ten

Understand place value.

CCSS		Lesson(s)	Page(s)
2.NBT.1	Understand that the three digits of a three-digit number represent amounts of hundreds, tens, and ones; e.g., 706 equals 7 hundreds, 0 tens, and 6 ones. Understand the following as special cases:	5-1, 5-2, 5-3, 5-4	295–300, 301–306, 307–312, 315–320
2.NBT.1a	100 can be thought of as a bundle of ten tens—called a "hundred."	5-1, 5-2, 5-3, 5-4	295–300, 301–306, 307–312, 315–320
2.NBT.1b	The numbers 100, 200, 300, 400, 500, 600, 700, 800, 900 refer to one, two, three, four, five, six, seven, eight, or nine hundreds (and 0 tens and 0 ones).	5-1, 5-2, 5-3, 5-4	295–300, 301–306, 307–312, 315–320
2.NBT.2	Count within 1000; skip-count by 5s, 10s, and 100s.	2-1, 2-2, 2-3, 2-4, 5-6	107–112, 113–118, 119–124, 127–132, 327–332
2.NBT.3	Read and write numbers to 1000 using base-ten numerals, number names, and expanded form.	2-6, 2-7, 5-2, 5-3, 5-4, 5-5	139–144, 145–150, 301–306, 307–312, 315–320, 321–326
2.NBT.4	Compare two three-digit numbers based on meanings of the hundreds, tens, and ones digits, using >, =, and < symbols to record the results of comparisons.	2-4, 2-5, 5-7	127–132, 133–138, 333–338

Use place value understanding and properties of operations to add and subtract.

CCSS		Lesson(s)	Page(s)
2.NBT.5	Fluently add and subtract within 100 using strategies based on place value, properties of operations, and/or the relationship between addition and subtraction.	1-1, 3-2, 3-3, 3-4, 3-5, 4-1, 4-3, 4-4, 4-5, 4-6, 4-7	11–16, 171– 176, 177–182, 185–190, 191–196, 223–228, 235–240, 241–246, 249–254, 255–260, 261–266
2.NBT.6	Add up to four two-digit numbers using strategies based on place value and properties of operations.	3-5, 3-6	191–196, 197–202
2.NBT.7	Add and subtract within 1000, using concrete models or drawings and strategies based on place value, properties of operations, and/or the relationship between addition and subtraction; relate the strategy to a written method. Understand that in adding or subtracting three-digit numbers, one adds or subtracts hundreds and hundreds, tens and tens, ones and ones; and sometimes it is necessary to compose or decompose tens or hundreds.	6-1, 6-2, 6-4, 6-5, 6-6, 6-7, 6-8, 7-1, 7-2, 7-4, 7-5, 7-6, 7-7, 7-8, 7-9	351–356, 357–362, 371–376, 377–382, 383–388, 389–394, 395–400, 413–418, 419–424, 433–438, 439–444, 445–450, 451–456, 457–462, 463–468
2.NBT.8	Mentally add 10 or 100 to a given number 100–900, and mentally subtract 10 or 100 from a given number 100–900.	5-6, 6-3, 7-3	197–202, 263–268, 425–430
2.NBT.9	Explain why addition and subtraction strategies work, using place value and the properties of operations.	1-1, 1-5, 1-8, 1-12, 3-2, 3-3, 3-4, 3-6, 4-3, 4-4, 4-5, 6-2, 6-4, 6-5, 6-6, 7-2, 7-4, 7-5, 7-6, 7-9	11–16, 35–40, 55–60, 81–86, 171–176, 177–182, 185–190, 197–202, 235–240, 241–246, 249–254, 357–362, 371–376, 377–382, 383–388, 419–424, 433–438, 439–444, 445–450, 463–468

CCSS **Common Core State Standards**	**Lesson(s)**	**Page(s)**

Domain 2.MD **Measurement and Data**

Measure and estimate lengths in standard units.

2.MD.1	Measure the length of an object by selecting and using appropriate tools such as rulers, yardsticks, meter sticks, and measuring tapes.	11-1, 11-2, 11-3, 11-7, 11-8	645–650, 651–656, 657–662, 685–690, 691–696
2.MD.2	Measure the length of an object twice, using length units of different lengths for the two measurements; describe how the two measurements relate to the size of the unit chosen.	11-5, 11-10	671–676, 703–708
2.MD.3	Estimate lengths using units of inches, feet, centimeters, and meters.	11-1, 11-2, 11-3, 11-7, 11-8	645–650, 651–656, 657–662, 685–690, 691–696
2.MD.4	Measure to determine how much longer one object is than another, expressing the length difference in terms of a standard length unit.	11-4, 11-9	665–670, 697–702

Relate addition and subtraction to length.

2.MD.5	Use addition and subtraction within 100 to solve word problems involving lengths that are given in the same units, e.g., by using drawings (such as drawings of rulers) and equations with a symbol for the unknown number to represent the problem.	11-1, 11-2, 11-6, 11-7	645–650, 651–656, 677–682, 685–690
2.MD.6	Represent whole numbers as lengths from 0 on a number line diagram with equally spaced points corresponding to the numbers 0, 1, 2, ..., and represent whole-number sums and differences within 100 on a number line diagram.	11-11	709–714

Work with time and money.

2.MD.7	Tell and write time from analog and digital clocks to the nearest five minutes, using a.m. and p.m.	10-1, 10-2, 10-3, 10-4, 10-5, 10-6	593–598, 599–604, 605–610, 613–618, 619–624, 625–630
2.MD.8	Solve word problems involving dollar bills, quarters, dimes, nickels, and pennies, using $ and ¢ symbols appropriately. Example: *If you have 2 dimes and 3 pennies, how many cents do you have?*	8-1, 8-2, 8-3, 8-4, 8-5	483–488, 489–494, 495–500, 503–508, 509–514

Represent and interpret data.

2.MD.9	Generate measurement data by measuring lengths of several objects to the nearest whole unit, or by making repeated measurements of the same object. Show the measurements by making a line plot, where the horizontal scale is marked off in whole-number units.	9-7, 9-8, 11-12	567–572, 573–578, 715–720
2.MD.10	Draw a picture graph and a bar graph (with single-unit scale) to represent a data set with up to four categories. Solve simple put-together, take-apart, and compare problems using information presented in a bar graph.	9-1, 9-2, 9-3, 9-4, 9-5, 9-6	529–534, 535–540, 541–546, 549–550, 555–560, 561–566

Common Core State Standards	Lesson(s)	Page(s)
Domain 2.G Geometry		
Reason with shapes and their attributes.		
2.G.1 Recognize and draw shapes having specified attributes, such as a given number of angles or a given number of equal faces. Identify triangles, quadrilaterals, pentagons, hexagons, and cubes.	12-1, 12-2, 12-3, 12-4, 12-5, 12-6	739–744, 745–750, 751–756, 759–764, 765–770, 771–776
2.G.2 Partition a rectangle into rows and columns of same-size squares and count to find the total number of them.	12-8	783–788
2.G.3 Partition circles and rectangles into two, three, or four equal shares, describe the shares using the words *halves, thirds, half of, a third of,* etc., and describe the whole as two halves, three thirds, four fourths. Recognize that equal shares of identical wholes need not have the same shape.	12-7	778–782

Common Core State Standards (CCSS)

Correlated to *My Math*, Grade 2

(CCSS) **Mathematical Practices**		**Student Edition**	**Teacher Edition**

Mathematical PRACTICE 1 **Make sense of problems and persevere in solving them.**

Mathematically proficient students start by explaining to themselves the meaning of a problem and looking for entry points to its solution. They analyze givens, constraints, relationships, and goals. They make conjectures about the form and meaning of the solution and plan a solution pathway rather than simply jumping into a solution attempt. They consider analogous problems, and try special cases and simpler forms of the original problem in order to gain insight into its solution. They monitor and evaluate their progress and change course if necessary. Older students might, depending on the context of the problem, transform algebraic expressions or change the viewing window on their graphing calculator to get the information they need. Mathematically proficient students can explain correspondences between equations, verbal descriptions, tables, and graphs or draw diagrams of important features and relationships, graph data, and search for regularity or trends. Younger students might rely on using concrete objects or pictures to help conceptualize and solve a problem. Mathematically proficient students check their answers to problems using a different method, and they continually ask themselves, "Does this make sense?" They can understand the approaches of others to solving complex problems and identify correspondences between different approaches.

A strong problem-solving strand is present throughout the textbook with an emphasis on strategies in the Problem-Solving lessons. Look for additional opportunities within each lesson.
Understand the Problem
Make a Plan
Solve the Problem
Check Your Answer

Student Edition: 14, 20, 26, 32, 38, 41–44, 52, 58, 64, 72, 78, 84, 90, 110, 116, 119–122, 130, 136, 142, 148, 168, 174, 180, 188, 194, 200, 203–206, 226, 232, 238, 243, 252, 258, 264, 267–270, 276, 298, 304, 310, 315–318, 324, 330, 336, 354, 360, 366, 374, 380, 386, 392, 395–398, 416, 422, 428, 436, 442, 448, 454, 457–460, 466, 486, 492, 503–506, 512, 532, 538, 544, 552, 558, 561–564, 570, 576, 596, 602, 605–608, 616, 622, 628, 648, 654, 660, 668, 674, 688, 694, 700, 706, 712, 748, 751–754, 762, 768, 774, 780

Teacher Edition: 19–20, 41–44, 51–52, 63–64, 119–122, 129–130, 147–148, 167–168, 187–188, 203–206, 243–244, 257–258, 267–270, 315–318, 335–336, 359–360, 373–374, 379–380, 391–392, 395–398, 435–436, 441–442, 453–454, 457–460, 465–466, 491–492, 503–506, 537–538, 561–564, 605–608, 667–668, 699–700, 705–706, 717–718, 747–748, 751–754, 785–786

Mathematical PRACTICE 2 **Reason abstractly and quantitatively.**

Mathematically proficient students make sense of quantities and their relationships in problem situations. They bring two complementary abilities to bear on problems involving quantitative relationships: the ability to *decontextualize*—to abstract a given situation and represent it symbolically and manipulate the representing symbols as if they have a life of their own, without necessarily attending to their referents—and the ability to *contextualize*, to pause as needed during the manipulation process in order to probe into the referents for the symbols involved. Quantitative reasoning entails habits of creating a coherent representation of the problem at hand; considering the units involved; attending to the meaning of quantities, not just how to compute them; and knowing and flexibly using different properties of operations and objects.

Students are routinely asked to reason abstractly and quantitatively throughout the textbook. Look for opportunities in the following sections:
Explore and Explain
See and Show
On My Own

Student Edition: 29–31, 61–63, 69–71, 75–77, 107–109, 113–115, 133–135, 139–141, 171–173, 197–199, 223–225, 255–257, 321–323, 333–335, 371–373, 389–391, 425–427, 439–441, 445–447, 463–465, 483–485, 495–497, 529–531, 535–537, 541–543, 567–569, 599–601, 613–615, 625–627, 645–647, 665–667, 671–673, 691–693, 697–699, 715–717, 745–747, 759–761

Teacher Edition: 29–31, 35–37, 69–71, 75–77, 107–109, 113–115, 133–135, 139–141, 141–142, 171–173, 197–199, 223–225, 251–252, 255–257, 321–323, 333–335, 371–373, 389–391, 425–427, 439–441, 445–447, 463–465, 483–485, 495–497, 535–537, 541–543, 567–569, 599–601, 613–615, 625–627, 645–647, 665–667, 671–673, 691–693, 697–699, 715–717, 745–747, 759–761

Note: The Standards for Mathematical Practice are covered throughout the book. For examples, see the page references cited.

		Student Edition	Teacher Edition

Mathematical PRACTICE 3 Construct viable arguments and critique the reasoning of others.

Mathematically proficient students understand and use stated assumptions, definitions, and previously established results in constructing arguments. They make conjectures and build a logical progression of statements to explore the truth of their conjectures. They are able to analyze situations by breaking them into cases, and can recognize and use counterexamples. They justify their conclusions, communicate them to others, and respond to the arguments of others. They reason inductively about data, making plausible arguments that take into account the context from which the data arose. Mathematically proficient students are also able to compare the effectiveness of two plausible arguments, distinguish correct logic or reasoning from that which is flawed, and—if there is a flaw in an argument—explain what it is. Elementary students can construct arguments using concrete referents such as objects, drawings, diagrams, and actions. Such arguments can make sense and be correct, even though they are not generalized or made formal until later grades. Later, students learn to determine domains to which an argument applies. Students at all grades can listen or read the arguments of others, decide whether they make sense, and ask useful questions to clarify or improve the arguments.

Students are required to justify their reasoning in problems and to find the errors in samples of other's work. Look for opportunities in the following sections:
My Vocabulary Cards
Explore and Explain
See and Show
On My Own

Student Edition: 5–8, 11–13, 17–19, 35–37, 61–63, 69–71, 75–77, 139–141, 161–162, 165–167, 177–179, 197–199, 223–225, 229–231, 241–243, 295–297, 321–323, 327–329, 347–348, 363–365, 377–379, 425–427, 439–441, 445–447, 463–465, 483–485, 489–491, 509–511, 529–531, 535–537, 549–551, 613–615, 639–642, 645–647, 665–667, 671–673, 709–711, 715–717, 759–761, 765–767

Teacher Edition: 5–8, 11–13, 17–19, 35–37, 61–63, 69–71, 75–77, 139–141, 161–162, 165–167, 177–179, 197–199, 223–225, 229–231, 241–243, 295–297, 321–323, 327–329, 347–348, 363–365, 377–379, 425–427, 439–441, 445–447, 463–465, 483–485, 489–491, 509–511, 529–531, 535–537, 549–551, 613–615, 639–642, 645–647, 665–667, 671–673, 709–711, 715–717, 759–761, 765–767

Mathematical PRACTICE 4 Model with mathematics.

Mathematically proficient students can apply the mathematics they know to solve problems arising in everyday life, society, and the workplace. In early grades, this might be as simple as writing an addition equation to describe a situation. In middle grades, a student might apply proportional reasoning to plan a school event or analyze a problem in the community. By high school, a student might use geometry to solve a design problem or use a function to describe how one quantity of interest depends on another. Mathematically proficient students who can apply what they know are comfortable making assumptions and approximations to simplify a complicated situation, realizing that these may need revision later. They are able to identify important quantities in a practical situation and map their relationships using such tools as diagrams, two-way tables, graphs, flowcharts and formulas. They can analyze those relationships mathematically to draw conclusions. They routinely interpret their mathematical results in the context of the situation and reflect on whether the results make sense, possibly improving the model if it has not served its purpose.

Real-world applications in problem solving are woven throughout every lesson.
In addition, look for the **Modeling the Math** section in the TE.

Student Edition: 14, 20, 38, 41–44, 52, 72, 78, 84, 90, 130, 136, 142, 148, 168, 174, 180, 188, 194, 200, 203–206, 226, 232, 238, 258, 264, 267–270, 276, 298, 304, 310, 324, 330, 336, 354, 360, 366, 374, 380, 386, 422, 428, 436, 442, 466, 503–506, 512, 532, 538, 544, 552, 605–608, 616, 622, 628, 648, 654, 660, 712, 718, 742, 748, 751–754, 762, 768

Teacher Edition: 11B, 17B, 23B, 29B, 55B, 61B, 69B, 71–72, 75B, 81B, 133B, 139B, 145B, 173–174, 177B, 223B, 229B, 231–232, 235B, 273B, 295B, 301B, 303–304, 307B, 357B, 363B, 371B, 377B, 383B, 389B, 419B, 425B, 433B, 551–552, 555B, 599B, 601–602, 653–654, 657B, 691B, 697B, 703B, 761–762, 765B

Mathematical PRACTICE 5 Use appropriate tools strategically.

Mathematically proficient students consider the available tools when solving a mathematical problem. These tools might include pencil and paper, concrete models, a ruler, a protractor, a calculator, a spreadsheet, a computer algebra system, a statistical package, or dynamic geometry software. Proficient students are sufficiently familiar with tools appropriate for their grade or course to make sound decisions about when each of these tools might be helpful, recognizing both the insight to be gained and their limitations. For example, mathematically proficient high school students analyze graphs of functions and solutions generated using a graphing calculator. They detect possible errors by strategically using estimation and other mathematical knowledge. When making mathematical models, they know that technology can enable them to visualize the results of varying assumptions, explore consequences, and compare predictions with data. Mathematically proficient students at various grade levels are able to identify relevant external mathematical resources, such as digital content located on a website, and use them to pose or solve problems. They are able to use technological tools to explore and deepen their understanding of concepts.

Throughout the textbook, students are exposed to multiple ways to represent and solve problems using various tools, such as connecting cubes, color tiles, two-color counters, base-ten blocks, geometric solids/models, and many more.

Student Edition: 23–28, 113–118, 139–144, 295–300, 419–424, 593–598, 657–662

Teacher Edition: 23–28, 25–26, 113–118, 135–136, 139–144, 263–264, 295–300, 419–424, 593–598, 657–662, 659–660, 687–688, 693–694

		Student Edition	Teacher Edition
Mathematical PRACTICE 6 Attend to precision.	Answers to verbal and written exercises are not just numbers, but include measurements to give the answer meaning. Students are asked to communicate precisely using proper definitions, algorithms, numbers, symbols, etc. Look for opportunities in the following sections: **Explore and Explain See and Show On My Own**	23–25, 29–31, 55–57, 61–63, 81–83, 87–89, 93, 127–129, 133–135, 185–187, 191–193, 197–199, 229–231, 235–237, 241–243, 249–251, 295–297, 301–303, 327–329, 333–335, 351–353, 371–373, 377–379, 383–385, 433–435, 451–453, 463–465, 483–485, 509–511, 529–531, 549–551, 555–557, 593–595, 619–621, 625–627, 657–659, 665–667, 691–693, 697–699, 765–767, 771–773	23–25, 29–31, 55–57, 61–63, 81–83, 87–89, 93, 127–129, 133–135, 185–187, 191–193, 197–199, 229–231, 235–237, 241–243, 249–251, 295–297, 301–303, 327–329, 333–335, 351–353, 371–373, 377–379, 383–385, 433–435, 451–453, 463–465, 483–485, 509–511, 529–531, 549–551, 555–557, 593–595, 595–596, 619–621, 625–627, 657–659, 665–667, 691–693, 697–699, 765–767, 771–773
Mathematical PRACTICE 7 Look for and make use of structure.	Emphasizing the structure of mathematics is present through use of comparing, sorting, classifying, describing, explaining, and giving examples as well as nonexamples.	11–16, 35–40, 75–80, 165–170, 333–338, 361–368	11–16, 13–14, 35–40, 37–38, 75–80, 77–78, 165–170, 179–180, 193–194, 275–276, 309–310, 333–338, 361–368, 531–532, 575–576, 627–628, 767–768, 773–774
Mathematical PRACTICE 8 Look for and express regularity in repeated reasoning.	Patterns in reasoning are demonstrated throughout leading students to sound mathematical conclusions. Look for such patterns when representing and counting numbers, sorting and classifying shapes and objects, etc.	107–112, 127–132, 139–144, 327–332, 413–418, 605–610	107–112, 127–132, 139–144, 327–332, 329–330, 413–418, 605–610, 621–622, 624–625

Mathematical PRACTICE 6 Attend to precision.

Mathematically proficient students try to communicate precisely to others. They try to use clear definitions in discussion with others and in their own reasoning. They state the meaning of the symbols they choose, including using the equal sign consistently and appropriately. They are careful about specifying units of measure, and labeling axes to clarify the correspondence with quantities in a problem. They calculate accurately and efficiently, express numerical answers with a degree of precision appropriate for the problem context. In the elementary grades, students give carefully formulated explanations to each other. By the time they reach high school they have learned to examine claims and make explicit use of definitions.

Mathematical PRACTICE 7 Look for and make use of structure.

Mathematically proficient students look closely to discern a pattern or structure. Young students, for example, might notice that three and seven more is the same amount as seven and three more, or they may sort a collection of shapes according to how many sides the shapes have. Later, students will see 7×8 equals the well remembered $7 \times 5 + 7 \times 3$, in preparation for learning about the distributive property. In the expression $x^2 + 9x + 14$, older students can see the 14 as 2×7 and the 9 as $2 + 7$. They recognize the significance of an existing line in a geometric figure and can use the strategy of drawing an auxiliary line for solving problems. They also can step back for an overview and shift perspective. They can see complicated things, such as some algebraic expressions, as single objects or as being composed of several objects. For example, they can see $5 - 3(x - y)^2$ as 5 minus a positive number times a square and use that to realize that its value cannot be more than 5 for any real numbers x and y.

Mathematical PRACTICE 8 Look for and express regularity in repeated reasoning.

Mathematically proficient students notice if calculations are repeated, and look both for general methods and for shortcuts. Upper elementary students might notice when dividing 25 by 11 that they are repeating the same calculations over and over again, and conclude they have a repeating decimal. By paying attention to the calculation of slope as they repeatedly check whether points are on the line through $(1, 2)$ with slope 3, middle school students might abstract the equation $(y - 2)/(x - 1) = 3$. Noticing the regularity in the way terms cancel when expanding $(x - 1)$ $(x + 1)$, $(x - 1)(x^2 + x + 1)$, and $(x - 1)(x^3 + x^2 + x + 1)$ might lead them to the general formula for the sum of a geometric series. As they work to solve a problem, mathematically proficient students maintain oversight of the process, while attending to the details. They continually evaluate the reasonableness of their intermediate results.

The STANDARD in CCSS

McGraw-Hill

My Math

Grade 2 • Volume 1

Teacher Edition

Carter • Cuevas • Day • Malloy
Altieri • Balka • Gonsalves • Grace • Krulik • Molix-Bailey
Moseley • Mowry • Myren • Price • Reynosa • Santa Cruz
Silbey • Vielhaber

McGraw Hill Education

Bothell, WA • Chicago, IL • Columbus, OH • New York, NY

Table of Contents

GO digital

it's all at
connectED.mcgraw-hill.com

Go to the Teacher Center for all your planning, teaching, assessment, and resource needs.

Write your Username [   ] ✎   Password [   ] ✎

Get your resources online to help you teach in class and plan anywhere.

Vocab

Find activities for building vocabulary.

Watch

Watch animations of key concepts.

Tutor

See a teacher illustrate examples and problems.

Tools

Explore concepts with virtual manipulatives.

Check

Assign, create, and take online assessments.

eHelp

Get targeted homework help.

Games

Reinforce with games and apps.

PD

Watch model lessons and hear best practices.

RtI

Find support for differentiated instruction.

Masters

Print worksheets, work mats, and more.

GO mobile →

Scan this QR code with your smart phone* or visit mheonline.com/stem_apps.

*May require quick response code reader app.

Available on the App Store

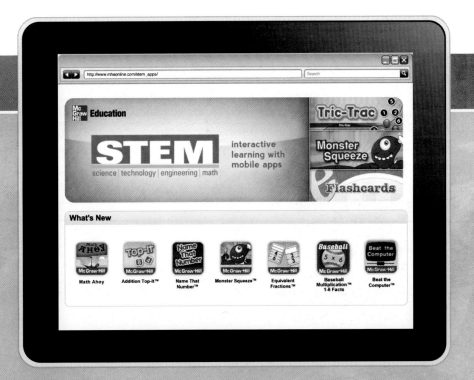

Contents in Brief
Organized by Domain

CCSS

Common Core State Standards

The suggested pacing supports 1 day per lesson for instruction, 2 days per chapter for review and assessment, and includes additional time for remediation and differentiation.

Standards for **Mathematical PRACTICE** → Woven Throughout

Chapter 1
Apply Addition and Subtraction Concepts

ESSENTIAL QUESTION
What strategies can I use to add and subtract?

I ♥ animals!

connectED.mcgraw-hill.com

Look for this! Click online and you can watch videos that will help you learn the lessons.

Chapter 2 Number Patterns

ESSENTIAL QUESTION
How can equal groups help me add?

Getting Started

Lessons and Homework

Wrap Up

Welcome to the desert, cowpoke!

Hi!

connectED.mcgraw-hill.com

Chapter 3
Add Two-Digit Numbers

ESSENTIAL QUESTION
How can I add
two-digit numbers?

Getting Started

Lessons and Homework

Wrap Up

We make a
great pair!

connectED.mcgraw-hill.com

Look for this!
Click online and you
can get more help
while doing your
homework.

eHelp

Chapter 4 Subtract Two-Digit Numbers

ESSENTIAL QUESTION
How can I subtract two-digit numbers?

Getting Started

Lessons and Homework

Wrap Up

Springtime!

connectED.mcgraw-hill.com

Chapter 5 Place Value to 1,000

ESSENTIAL QUESTION
How can I use place value?

Getting Started

Lessons and Homework

Wrap Up

Look how I've grown!

connectED.mcgraw-hill.com

Tools

Look for this!
Click online and you can find tools that will help you explore concepts.

Chapter 6

Add Three-Digit Numbers

ESSENTIAL QUESTION
How can I add three-digit numbers?

Getting Started

Lessons and Homework

Wrap Up

connectED.mcgraw-hill.com

My house

MAIN ST.

LITLER D.

Chapter 7 Subtract Two-Digit Numbers

Getting Started

Lessons and Homework

Wrap Up

Look for this!
Click online and you can find activities to help build your vocabulary.

You + School = Cool

connectED.mcgraw-hill.com

Chapter 8 Money

ESSENTIAL QUESTION
How do I count and use money?

Getting Started

Lessons and Homework

Wrap Up

You make me laugh!

Look for this!
Check
Click online and you can check your progress.

connectED.mcgraw-hill.com

Chapter

 9 Data Analysis

ESSENTIAL QUESTION
How can I record and
analyze data?

Getting Started

Go nuts!

Lessons and Homework

Wrap Up

connectED.mcgraw-hill.com

Chapter 10 — Time

ESSENTIAL QUESTION
How do I use and tell time?

Getting Started

Lessons and Homework

Wrap Up

It's time for our trip!

connectED.mcgraw-hill.com

Chapter 11 Customary and Metric Lengths

ESSENTIAL QUESTION
How can I measure objects?

I love rulers because I'm an inch worm!

Getting Started

Lessons and Homework

Wrap Up

connectED.mcgraw-hill.com

Chapter

12 Geometric Shapes and Equal Shares

ESSENTIAL QUESTION
How do I use shapes and equal parts?

Come on guys. Let's check it out!

connectED.mcgraw-hill.com

Teaching Tools and Resources

connectED.mcgraw-hill.com is your resource for all of your teaching needs. The Teacher Center puts planning, access to printable assets, and presentation tools at your fingertips. The lists below detail only a few of the many tools and resources available, all of which are interactive whiteboard ready.

 ## Assessment

eAssessment: Online Test Generating, Assigning, and Grading
Editable Assessment Masters
Common Core Quick Check Quizzes (Grades 2-5)
Self-Check Quizzes (Grades 1-5)

 ## Visual Learning

Personal Tutors
Lesson Animations
Chapter Opener Videos
Visual Vocabulary Cards
Math Songs *

 ## Response to Intervention

Editable Enrich Worksheets
Editable Reteach Masters
ELL Tiered Instruction
Strategic Intervention Guide

 ## Games and Apps

Math Ahoy! App
eFlashcard App
[EM Apps]

 ## Vocab

eGlossary
Visual Vocabulary Cards *
eBook Glossary

 ## Printable Assets

Problem of the Day
Manipulative Masters
Family Letters and Activities *

 ## Virtual Manipulatives

Base-Ten Blocks
Bucket Balance
Calendar
Clock
Color tiles
Connecting Cubes

Currency
Fraction Circles
Fraction Tiles
Geoboard/Bands
Geometric Solids
Hundred Chart

Number Cubes
(red: 0-5, blue: 5-10)
Number Line
Pattern Blocks
Spinner
Thermometer
Two-Color Counters

 ## MY Learning Stations

This collection of activity cards, literature, games, graphic novels, and problem-solving cards is a ready made center for any classroom.

A Teacher Guide provides differentiated instruction strategies and activities.

Manipulative Kit

Individual Manipulative Kit
Classroom Manipulative Kit

Real-World Problem Solving Readers

Approaching Level
On Level *
Beyond Level
Leveled Reader Database
leveledreaderdatabase.
macmillanmh.com

*Available in Spanish

Authors

Our lead authors ensure that the McGraw-Hill mathematics programs are vertically aligned by beginning with the end in mind—success in Algebra 1 and beyond. By "backmapping" the content from the high school programs, all of our mathematics programs are well articulated in their scope and sequence and solidly support the Common Core State Standards.

Lead Authors

John A. Carter, Ph.D.
Principal
Adlai E. Stevenson High School
Lincolnshire, Illinois
Areas of Expertise: Using technology and
  manipulatives to visualize concepts;
  mathematics achievement of English
  language learners

Gilbert J. Cuevas, Ph.D.
Professor of Mathematics Education
Texas State University—San Marcos
San Marcos, Texas
Areas of Expertise: Use of technology
  in teaching geometry

Roger Day, Ph.D., NBCT
Mathematics Department Chairperson
Pontiac Township High School
Pontiac, Illinois
Areas of Expertise: Understanding and
  applying probability and statistics;
  mathematics teacher education

Carol Malloy, Ph.D.
Associate Professor Emerita
University of North Carolina at Chapel Hill
Chapel Hill, North Carolina
Areas of Expertise: Representations and
  critical thinking; student success in Algebra 1

© The McGraw-Hill Companies, Inc.

Program Authors

Mary Behr Altieri
Putnam/Northern
Westchester BOCES
Yorktown Heights, New York

Don S. Balka
Professor Emeritus
Saint Mary's College
Notre Dame, Indiana

Philip D. Gonsalves
Mathematics Coordinator
Alameda County Office of
  Education and California
  State University East Bay
Hayward, California

Ellen C. Grace
Consultant
Albuquerque, New Mexico

Stephen Krulik
2011 NCTM Lifetime
  Achievement Award
Professor Emeritus
  Mathematics Education
Temple University
Cherry Hill, New Jersey

Rhonda J. Molix-Bailey
Mathematics Consultant
Mathematics by Design
Desoto, Texas

Lois Gordon Moseley
Staff Developer
NUMBERS: Mathematics
  Professional Development
Houston, Texas

Brian Mowry
Independent Math Educational
  Consultant/Part-Time Pre-K
  Instructional Specialist
Austin Independent
  School District
Austin, Texas

Christina L. Myren
Consultant Teacher
Conejo Valley Unified
  School District
Thousand Oaks, California

Jack Price, Ed. D.
Professor Emeritus
California State
  Polytechnic University
Pomona, California

Mary Esther Reynosa
Instructional Specialist for
  Elementary Mathematics
Northside Independent
  School District
San Antonio, Texas

Rafaela M. Santa Cruz
SDSU/CGU Doctoral
  Program in Education
San Diego State University
San Diego, California

Robyn Silbey
Math Content Coach
Montgomery County
  Public Schools (retired)
Gaithersburg, Maryland

Kathleen Vielhaber
Mathematics Consultant
St. Louis, Missouri

Contributing Author

Dinah Zike FOLDABLES
Educational Consultant
Dinah-Might Activities, Inc.
San Antonio, Texas

Consultants and Reviewers

These professionals were instrumental in providing valuable input and suggestions for improving the effectiveness of the mathematics instruction.

Consultants

Instructional Technology

Cheryl Conley
Teacher
2011 National Teacher of the Year
2011 Florida Teacher of the Year Finalist
Vero Beach, Florida

Atsusi "2C"Hirumi, Ph.D.
Associate Professor
University of Central Florida
Orlando, Florida

James Jarvis
Division Manager, Science & Technology
Thomas Jefferson High School
Alexandria, Virginia

Kathy Schrock
Educational Technologist
Eastham, Massachusetts

Family Involvement

Paul Giganti, Jr.
Director, California Math Council Parent Outreach
California Mathematics Council
Albany, California

Response to Intervention (RtI)

Margaret A. Searle
President, Searle Enterprises, Inc.
Perrysburg, Ohio

English Language Learners (ELL)

Kathryn Heinze
Associate Professor
Hamline University, School of Education
St. Paul, Minnesota

Gladis Kersaint, Ph.D.
Associate Professor of Mathematics Education, K-12
University of South Florida
Tampa, Florida

Homework

Richard W. Herrig
Educational Consultant
Consulting Services International
Regina, Saskatchewan

Gifted and Talented

Shelbi K. Cole
Mathematics Consultant
Connecticut State Department of Education
Hartford, Connecticut

Children's Literature/ Reading

David M. Schwartz
Children's author, speaker, storyteller
Oakland, California

Vocabulary Development

Timothy Shanahan, Ph.D.
Professor of Urban Education
University of Illinois at Chicago
Chicago, Illinois

Donald R. Bear, Ph.D.
Professor
University of Nevada, Reno
Reno, Nevada

Douglas Fisher, Ph.D.
Associate Professor in the College of Education
Department of Teacher Education
San Diego State University
San Diego, California

21st Century Skills and Vocabulary Development

Sue Z. Beers
Literacy Consultant
Tools for Learning, Inc.
Jewell, Iowa

Assessment

Cheryl Rose Tobey
Assessment Author and Consultant
Randolph, Maine

STEM Education

Celeste Baine
Director, Engineering Education Service Center
Clinton, Washington

Erleen Braton
Curriculum Integration Coordinator
Roger Elementary School
Rogers, Minnesota

Cindy Hoffner Moss, Ph.D.
Director of STEM
Charlotte-Mecklenburg Schools
Mount Holly, North Carolina

Understanding by Design (UbD)

Jay McTighe
Educational Author and Consultant
Columbia, Maryland
Understanding by Design® is a registered trademark of the Association for Supervision and Curriculum Development ("ASCD").

Differentiated Instruction

Jennifer Taylor-Cox
Educational Consultant
Taylor-Cox Instruction
Severna Park, Maryland

Reviewers

Shawanna G. Anekwe, Ed.S, NBCT
Peer Mathematics Coach
Cleveland Metropolitan School District
Cleveland, Ohio

Kimberly Bess
Mathematics Teacher
Holland Elementary School
Springfield, Missouri

Karen M. Borghi
Mathematics Interventionist
Tracy Elementary School
Easton, Pennsylvania

Jill Carlson
Elementary Principal
Crownhill Elementary School
Bremerton, Washington

Lynda G. D'Angiolillo
Director of Curriculum and Instruction
Wanaque Schools
Wanaque, New Jersey

Patricia Erneste
Mathematics Instructional Coach
Park Hill School District
Kansas City, Missouri

Dana Ferguson
Mathematics Coordinator, K-12
Columbia Public Schools
Columbia, Missouri

Tanjanika Foster
Mathematics Department Chairperson
Collinsville Middle School
Collinsville, Illinois

Robert Gyles, Ph.D.
Professor of Mathematics Education
Hunter College/CUNY
New York, New York

Sr. Helen Lucille Habig, RSM
Assistant Superintendent of Schools
Archdiocese of Cincinnati
Cincinnati, Ohio

Donna M. Hastie
Director of Curriculum and Instruction
North Haledon School District
North Haledon, New Jersey

Karen Henkes
Mathematics Teacher
Bluefield Middle School
Bluefield, West Virginia

Laura Hunovice
Mathematics Resource Teacher
Hampstead Elementary School
Linton Springs Elementary School
Carroll County, Maryland

Sandra Jenoure
Adjunct Professor of
  Mathematics/Science Education
Hunter College
New York, New York

Gail Karle
Lead Teacher
South Elementary
Mt. Healthy City School District
Cincinnati, Ohio

Traci A. Kimball
Mathematics Department Coordinator
Glenwood Middle School
Chatham, Illinois

Jennifer Ledbetter
Teacher
Crownhill Elementary School
Bremerton, Washington

Robert A. LeVien, Jr.
Teacher
Maud S. Sherwood Elementary School
Islip, New York

Stephanie Long
Mathematics Teacher/Curriculum
  Development Council Chairperson
Pleasant View Middle School
Springfield, Missouri

Sara Mahoski
Mathematics Specialist
Cheston Elementary School
Easton, Pennsylvania

Michael R. McGowan
Elementary Supervisor
Allegany County Board of Education
Cumberland, Maryland

Marcy E. Myers
Mathematics Resource Teacher
Robert Moton Elementary School
Westminster, Maryland

Jenni R. Parsons
Mathematics Teacher/Mathematics
  Specialist
Palmer Elementary School
Easton, Pennsylvania

Cary Sikes
Mathematics Chairperson, K-2
Sherwood Elementary
Springfield, Missouri

Liza Starkey
Mathematics Resource Teacher
Taneytown Elementary School
Taneytown, Maryland

Rebecca J. Wilkins
Mathematics Coach and Curriculum
  Specialist
Saginaw Public Schools
Saginaw, Michigan

Heather Youngblood
Teacher
Sherwood Elementary
Springfield, Missouri

Jan Youtz
Mathematics Specialist/Interventionist
Easton Area School District
Easton, Pennsylvania

CHAPTER 1

Apply Addition and Subtraction Concepts

Suggested Pacing		
Instruction*	**Review & Assessment**	**TOTAL**
17 days	2 days	**19 days**

*Includes additional time for remediation and differentiation.

Chapter at a Glance

Lesson	Objective	Materials & Manipulatives	Vocabulary	CCSS Standard
Lesson 1 *pp. 11–16* **Addition Properties**	Use the Commutative Property and the Identity Property to find sums.	• two-color counters • paper • crayons or markers • red and green connecting cubes	**add** **addend** **sum**	2.OA.1 2.OA.2 2.NBT.5 2.NBT.9
Lesson 2 *pp. 17–22* **Count On to Add**	Use a number line to count on when adding.	• construction paper • Work Mat 3 • crayons or markers • number line	**count on**	2.OA.1 2.OA.2
Lesson 3 *pp. 23–28* **Doubles and Near Doubles**	Use doubles and near doubles to find sums.	• number cubes • connecting cubes	**doubles** **near doubles**	2.OA.1 2.OA.2
Lesson 4 *pp. 29–34* **Make a 10**	Make a 10 to solve addition problems.	• number cards (0–9) • two-color counters • cups • Work Mat 2		2.OA.1 2.OA.2
Lesson 5 *pp. 35–40* **Add Three Numbers**	Group addends differently to make the same sum.	• number lines • two-color counters • number cubes • connecting cubes		2.OA.1 2.OA.2
Lesson 6 *pp. 41–46* **Problem-Solving Strategy: Write a Number Sentence**	Write a number sentence to solve problems.	• yellow and red connecting cubes		2.OA.1 2.OA.2

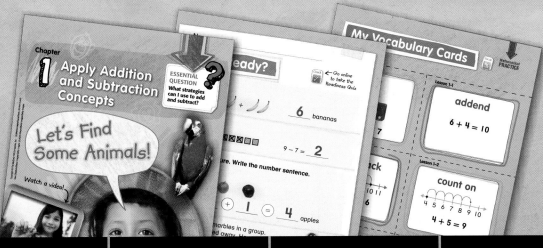

Lesson	Objective	Materials & Manipulatives	Vocabulary	CCSS Standard

✓ Check My Progress

Lesson	Objective	Materials & Manipulatives	Vocabulary	CCSS Standard
Lesson 7 *pp. 49–54* **Count Back to Subtract**	Count back to find the difference (using a number line).	• construction paper • crayons or markers	**count back** **subtract** **difference**	2.OA.1 2.OA.2
Lesson 8 *pp. 55–60* **Subtract All and Subtract Zero**	Subtract all or zero to find the difference.	• two-color counters • crayons or markers		2.OA.1 2.OA.2 2.NBT.9
Lesson 9 *pp. 61–66* **Use Doubles to Subtract**	Use doubles facts to find the difference.	• connecting cubes		2.OA.1 2.OA.2

✓ Check My Progress

Lesson	Objective	Materials & Manipulatives	Vocabulary	CCSS Standard
Lesson 10 *pp. 69–74* **Relate Addition and Subtraction**	Use addition facts to subtract.	• two-color counters	**related facts**	2.OA.1 2.OA.2
Lesson 11 *pp. 75–80* **Missing Addends**	Use subtraction facts to help find missing addends.	• pan balance • connecting cubes	**missing addend**	2.OA.1 2.OA.2
Lesson 12 *pp. 81–86* **Fact Families**	Use related facts to write fact families.	• number cubes • connecting cubes	**fact family**	2.OA.1 2.OA.2 2.NBT.9
Lesson 13 *pp. 87–92* **Two-Step Word Problems**	Solve word problems that involve two steps.	• two-color counters • connecting cubes		2.OA.1 2.OA.2 2.NBT.9

Fluency Practice

✓ My Review and Reflect

 For customizable online assessment, go to **eAssessment** at ⚡ connectED.mcgraw-hill.com.

Planning for Differentiated Instruction

Use these differentiated instruction activity suggestions, along with the ongoing support provided in each lesson of this chapter, to meet individual learning needs.

AL APPROACHING LEVEL

Use with Lesson 2

Materials: connecting cubes, number cubes, crayons, number lines (0-20)

- Have students roll a number cube to determine the starting point on a number.
- The student rolls again to determine how many spaces on the number line to count.
- Students take turns rolling the cube and moving the connecting cubes along the number line.
- The first student to reach 20 scores a point. Repeat until someone has scored 10 points.

AL APPROACHING LEVEL

Use with Lesson 3

Materials: construction paper, scissors, crayons

- Have students work with a partner.
- Tell students to pretend they are in a hot-air balloon looking down on houses.
- Instruct students to draw a house on construction paper, and then cut out the house. Have students draw 1 to 9 windows on their house.
- Have students create and describe an addition story for this situation.

AL APPROACHING LEVEL

Use with Lesson 3

Materials: connecting cubes (two colors)

- Make two large piles of cubes. Have students take a small handful of cubes from one pile.
- Have students count to see how many cubes they have as they connect the cubes. Have them take the same number of cubes from the other pile and connect them.
- Students should place the connected cubes next to each other and write an addition sentence for the doubles fact.

AL APPROACHING LEVEL

Use with Lesson 2

Materials: number cube, spinners labeled 1-3, number lines (0-20)

- Have students work with a partner. Give each pair a number cube, a spinner, and a number line.
- One student rolls the number cube. The number rolled is the first addend. The students should mark this number on the number line.
- The other student spins the spinner. The number spun is the second addend, or the number to count on to find the sum.
- Repeat as needed to practice counting on to find a sum.

OL · ON LEVEL

Use with Lesson 6

Materials: connecting cubes

- Give students several connecting cubes.
- Have students use the connecting cubes to create an addition story of their own.
- Have students write a paragraph to describe their addition story.
- Ask students to exchange addition stories with a partner and use the connecting cubes to solve them.

OL · ON LEVEL

Use with Lesson 5

Materials: number spinner, whiteboard, dry erase marker

- Have students work in small groups.
- Tell students to spin the spinner three times and write the numbers they spin to make an addition number sentence with three addends.
- The student who spun the spinner finds the sum of the three numbers and writes it after the equals sign.
- The second and third students each write a different number sentence using the same three numbers.

BL · BEYOND LEVEL

Use with Lesson 3

Materials: number spinner, whiteboard, dry erase marker

- Have students work in groups of three.
- One student spins the spinner and uses the number the spinner lands on to write a doubles fact on the whiteboard.
- For example, with a spin of 3, the student writes $3 + 3 = 6$ and passes the whiteboard to the next student.
- The next student writes a near doubles fact such as $3 + 4 = 7$ under the doubles fact and passes the board.
- The third student writes another near doubles fact.

ELL · ENGLISH LANGUAGE LEARNERS

Support for English Language Learners is found throughout the chapter and includes:

- ELL strategies at point-of-use in each Teacher Edition lesson
- ELL tiered instruction suggestions for each lesson at connectED.mcgraw-hill.com
- Comprehensive ELL lessons and worksheets for additional instruction at connectED.mcgraw-hill.com
- Non-linguistic representations of concepts on My Math Words, My Vocabulary Cards, and My Foldables

Additional online resources at connectED.mcgraw-hill.com include:

- Visual Vocabulary Cards
- Multilingual eGlossary
- Professional Development support

Looking for more DIFFERENTIATED INSTRUCTION?
Find additional support in each lesson of this chapter and online at connectED.mcgraw-hill.com

 RtI

AL Approaching Level
OL On Level
BL Beyond Level
ELL English Language Learners

What's the Math in This Chapter?

 Points of Intersection

Where
CONTENT STANDARDS

Meet
Mathematical PRACTICE 7

OA
Operations and Algebraic Thinking

Look for and make use of structure.

Most of this chapter concentrates on the **Operations and Algebraic Thinking (OA)** domain. However, aspects of the **Number and Operations in Base Ten (NBT)** domain are also used in the study of **addition and subtraction**.

As you teach addition and subtraction, emphasize the different patterns or structures found within these operations. The Addition and Subtraction Properties can help students learn their addition and subtraction facts. Doubles facts and fact families can also help students add and subtract.

What should my students already know?

In the previous grade, students used **Operations and Algebraic Thinking (OA)** in their study of addition and subtraction:

- Use addition and subtraction within 20 to solve word problems.
  1.OA.1

- Solve word problems that call for addition of three whole numbers whose sum is less than or equal to 20.
  1.OA.2

- Apply properties of operations as strategies to add and subtract.
  1.OA.3

- Understand subtraction as an missing addend problem.
  1.OA.4

- Add and subtract within 20, demonstrating fluency for addition and subtraction within 10.
  1.OA.6

WHAT STUDENTS SHOULD UNDERSTAND

Addition and Subtraction Properties
 2.OA.1

How to use addition and subtraction properties.

- The Commutative Property states that you can add numbers in any order and the sum will be the same.

- The Identity Property states that any number plus zero equals that number.

- When you subtract zero from a number, the difference is that number.

- When you subtract all from a number, the difference is zero.

Count On to Add and Count Back to Subtract
2.OA.1

How to count on and count back to solve addition and subtraction word problems.

- Start by locating the greater number in the number sentence on a number line. Then count on or count back the other number.

WHAT STUDENTS SHOULD BE ABLE TO DO

Use an addition property to find two addition facts that you could use to find the total number of dots on this domino.

$$8 + 4 = 12 \qquad 4 + 8 = 12$$

Commutative Property

Sarah has 8 carrot sticks. She eats 5 carrot sticks. How many carrot sticks does she have left?

Start at 8. Count back 5.

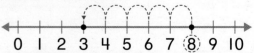

$$8 - 5 = 3$$

Sarah has 3 carrot sticks left.

WHAT STUDENTS SHOULD UNDERSTAND	WHAT STUDENTS SHOULD BE ABLE TO DO

Fact Families

 2.OA.1

How to use related facts to complete fact families.

• Use related facts to complete fact families.

Complete the fact family.

$9 + 4 = 13$
$4 + 9 = 13$
$13 - 9 = 4$
$13 - 4 = 9$

Use Doubles to Add and Subtract

 2.OA.2

How to use doubles to fluently add and subtract.

• Two addends that are the same are called doubles.

Use a doubles fact to find $14 - 7$.

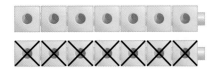

If you know that $7 + 7 = 14$, then $14 - 7 = 7$.

Make a 10 to Add

 2.OA.2

How to make a 10 to help you add.

• Take apart one addend to make the other addend a 10.

Make a ten to find $9 + 4$.

First: Show each addend.

Next: Take apart 4 counters to make 10.

Last: Add.

So, $9 + 4 = 13$.

What will my students do next with these skills?

After this chapter, students will learn to:

• find sums using repeated addition.
2.OA.4

In the next grade, students will learn to:

• find products using repeated addition.
3.OA.3

Reading Connections

Real-World Problem Solving Library

Math and Science: Life Cycles

Use these leveled books to reinforce and extend problem-solving skills and strategies.

Leveled for:

AL **Approaching Level**

OL **On Level** Also available in Spanish

BL **Beyond Level**

For additional support, see the *Real-World Problem Solving Readers Teacher Guide.*

Leveled Reader Database

Available at <u>leveledreaderdatabase.macmillanmh.com</u>
Search by:

• Content Area
• Guided Reading Level
• Lexile Score
• Benchmark Level

Library Books

Check with your school library or your local public library for these titles.

Safari Park
Stuart J. Murphy

Double the Ducks
Stuart J. Murphy

Too Many Kangaroo Things to Do!
Stuart J. Murphy

Each Orange Had 8 Slices
Paul Giganti, Jr.

Divide and Ride
Stuart J. Murphy

One Hundred Hungry Ants
Elinor Pinczes

Reading and Language Arts Support

Math in Our World

Distribute copies of a newspaper's sports section, and have students search for football scores. Ask if anyone can explain the basic rules of scoring in football. If necessary, tell students that a football team can score 6 points by scoring a *touchdown*. They also score an extra point after a touchdown by kicking for the *extra point*. That means if they score the touchdown and get the extra point, they earn 7 points. They can also earn 3 points by kicking the ball through a goal, which is called a *field goal*. Have students find a football score in the paper and explain possible combinations of touchdowns, extra points, and field goals to earn that score.

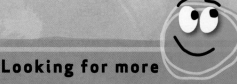

Looking for more Reading and Language Arts Support?
go online to
connectED.mcgraw-hill.com

LAUNCH THE CHAPTER

Chapter 1 Apply Addition and Subtraction Concepts

ESSENTIAL QUESTION
What strategies can I use to add and subtract?

Let's Find Some Animals!

Watch a video!
Watch

Theme:

Let's Find Some Animals!

All of the lessons in Chapter 1 will connect with the theme of Let's Find Some Animals! This is reflected in problem solving and the visuals used throughout the chapter.

Watch ▶ Video

Have students watch the video about animals. You may want to spark a discussion about how math is used in planning a trip to see animals.

❓ Building on the Essential Question

Once students have completed this chapter, they should be able to answer the question "What strategies can I use to add and subtract?" In each lesson, students build upon their understanding of this question by answering a simpler question. These are indicated in the exercises as Building on the Essential Question. At the end of the chapter, students use a graphic organizer to help them answer the Essential Question.

My Common Core State Standards CCSS

Operations and Algebraic Thinking

2.OA.1 Use addition and subtraction within 100 to solve one- and two-step word problems involving situations of adding to, taking from, putting together, taking apart, and comparing, with unknowns in all positions.

2.OA.2 Fluently add and subtract within 20 using mental strategies. By end of Grade 2, know from memory all sums of two one-digit numbers.

Number and Operations in Base Ten *This chapter also addresses these standards:*

2.NBT.5 Fluently add and subtract within 100 using strategies based on place value, properties of operations, and/or the relationship between addition and subtraction.

2.NBT.9 Explain why addition and subtraction strategies work, using place value and the properties of operations.

Standards for
Mathematical PRACTICE ⬇

1. Make sense of problems and persevere in solving them.
2. Reason abstractly and quantitatively.
3. Construct viable arguments and critique the reasoning of others.
4. Model with mathematics.
5. Use appropriate tools strategically.
6. Attend to precision.
7. Look for and make use of structure.
8. Look for and express regularity in repeated reasoning.

✏ = focused on in this chapter

Professional Development

CCSS Common Core State Standards

Learn more about how the Common Core State Standards can be implemented in your classroom at mhpdonline.com.

Look for
- **eImplementation**
- **eVideo Clip Libraries**
- **eTech Training**
- **ePD Webinars**

Watch ▶

Feature video for mathematical content in this chapter:
Addition and Subtraction as Inverse Operations

1 Assess

You have two options for assessing student readiness for this chapter. Use student results to determine which level of instruction is needed to help students get ready for the chapter and to determine what ongoing support they will need during the chapter.

Option 1: Am I Ready?

Have students complete the Am I Ready? page in their student books.

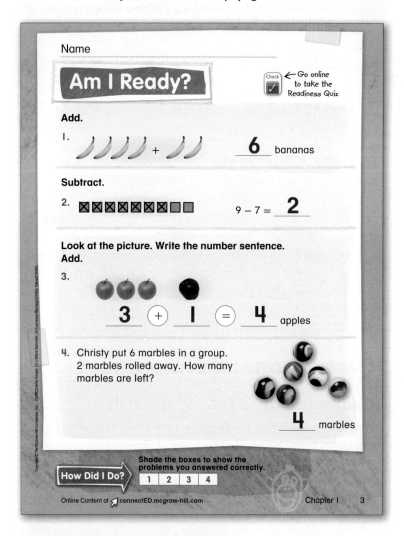

Option 2: Online Readiness Quiz

Have students take the **Online Readiness Quiz.**

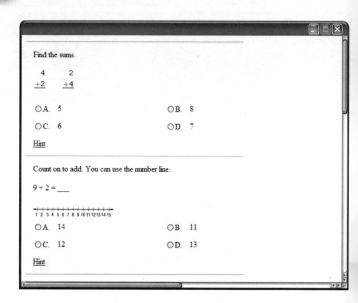

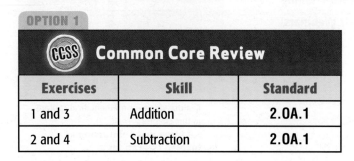

OPTION 2

CCSS Common Core Review

Exercises	Skill	Standard
1–10*	Addition	2.0A.1
	Subtraction	2.0A.1

*These questions are randomly generated from a bank of 15 questions.

OPTION 1

CCSS Common Core Review

Exercises	Skill	Standard
1 and 3	Addition	2.0A.1
2 and 4	Subtraction	2.0A.1

2 Diagnose and Prescribe

Based on the results of the Am I Ready? in the student edition, use the charts below to address individual needs **before** beginning the chapter.

Use the **ONGOING** resources to support differentiated instruction as new skills and concepts are presented in the chapter.

TIER 1

OL   ON LEVEL

IF students miss 2 in Exercises 1–4,

THEN choose a resource:

→ Am I Ready? Practice

→ Online Readiness Quiz

ONGOING Self-Check Quizzes • Chapter Project • Differentiated Assignments • My Learning Stations • Differentiated Instruction activities

TIER 2

AL   STRATEGIC INTERVENTION

(Approaching Grade Level)

IF students miss 3 in Exercises 1–4,

THEN choose a resource:

→ Online Strategic Intervention activity

→ Am I Ready? Review

ONGOING Common Errors • Differentiated Assignments • Online support • Reteach worksheets • Homework Helper • My Learning Stations • RtI lesson support • Differentiated Instruction activities

TIER 3

INTENSIVE INTERVENTION

(2 or more years below grade level)

IF students miss 4 in Exercises 1–4,

THEN use *Math Triumphs,* an intensive math intervention program from McGraw-Hill.

BL   BEYOND LEVEL

IF students miss 1 or less in Exercises 1–4,

THEN choose a resource:

→ Am I Ready? Apply

ONGOING 21st Century Skills • Chapter Project • Differentiated Assignments • Enrich worksheets • My Learning Stations • Differentiated Instruction activities

3 Reassess

If reassessment is necessary, administer the chapter Diagnostic Test in the **Assessment Masters** or go online for eAssessment.

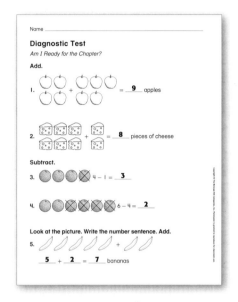

 For additional chapter readiness assessment, go to eAssessment at connectED.mcgraw-hill.com.

My Math Words

Review Vocabulary

Where did they learn it?

- add, subtract   (Kindergarten, Grade 1)
- minus sign (−)   (Grade 1)
- plus sign (+)   (Grade 1)

Making Connections

Ask students what they know about the review vocabulary. Encourage students to describe, draw, or act out, their examples.

Ask students to examine the graphic organizer. Ask them what the space in the center of this graphic organizer represents. Sample answer: The main idea is shown in the center. Have students read the heading for each category. Then ask them to describe what they know about symbols and number sentences.

My Vocabulary Cards

Ask students to browse the words and examples on each of this chapter's cards. Discuss with them what they already know about these words, or the examples shown on the cards. Note on the board any questions or observations students have about these words. Definitions appear on the back of each card.

Students should clip and store their cards in one place, such as a small envelope, where they can access them as needed throughout the chapter.

Mathematical PRACTICE 3 → My Vocabulary Card Activities

The table below and on the next page lists an activity for each card, as well as the answer or sample answer. The activities will include opportunities for students to hear, say, or write the vocabulary words. When applicable, activities will involve drawing or modeling vocabulary. Students' answers can be recorded using various media, such as Notebook Foldables, IWB, electronic tablets, or computers.

Vocabulary Card	Activity/ Activity Answer
add	Add your age to a friend's age. Write the number sentence. Sample answer: $7 + 8 = 15$
addend	Write an addition number sentence. Circle the addends. Sample answer: $\circled{6} + \circled{6} + 12$

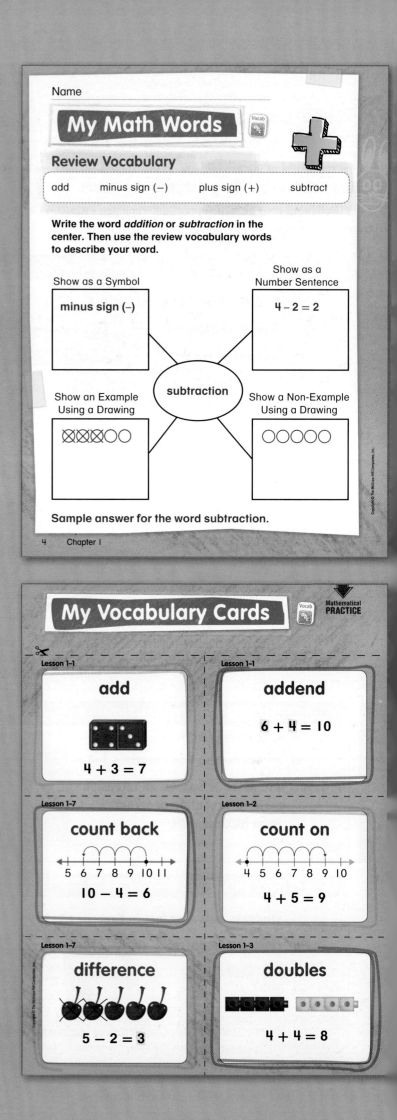

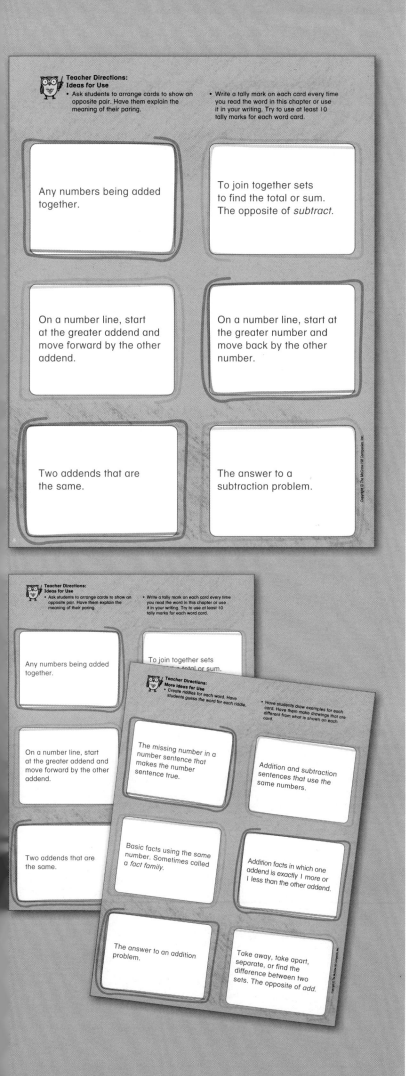

Vocabulary Card	Activity/ Activity Answer
count back	Use the number line to count back 3 from 6. Circle your answer. 3
count on	Use the number line to count on 5 from 3. Circle your answer. 8
difference	What is the difference in the number sentence $7 - 3 = 4$? Draw balloons to illustrate the problem. Students should draw 4 balloons.
doubles	The word *double* can mean "to make twice as much". Write a sentence using *double* with this meaning. Sample answer: Our puppy will double its weight in 6 months.
fact family	How many numbers are in a fact family? Explain your answer. 3
missing addend	Write a subtraction sentence to find the missing addend in $8 + \square = 11$. $11 - 8 = 3$
near doubles	How can knowing doubles facts help you solve near doubles problems? Sample answer: If you know the doubles fact, just add 1.
related facts	A person is related to the people in his or her family. How are math facts related? Sample answer: They have the same numbers in them.
subtract	Anya had 13 stickers. She gave 7 to her sister. Write a number sentence to find how many stickers are left. $13 - 7 = 6$
sum	Count two sets of objects in the room (such as red and blue crayons). Add the two numbers together. What is their sum? See students' work.

My Foldable

What's the Math?

Content Standard: 2.OA.2

Mathematical PRACTICE 7 Look for and make use of structure.

This Foldable encourages use of the Commutative Property of addition to find sums of numbers.

How Do I Make It?

- Tear out the page and cut off the top banner.
- Fold along the green dotted line.
- Cut on the orange dashed lines to make eight tabs.

When Do I Use It?

Use after Lesson 1, and as a review tool at the end of the chapter.

How Could I Use It?

- Have students point to the problem at the top of the Foldable: $2 + 1$.
- Open the first tab. $1 + 2$ is another way to write the problem. $2 + 1$ and $1 + 2$ both equal 3.
- Have students point to the next problem on the Foldable: $6 + 4$. Have students open the tab and write $4 + 6$. $6 + 4$ and $4 + 6$ both equal 10.
- Repeat for the rest of the problems on the Foldable. Have students use the two blank number sentences to write their own problems.

ELL ELL Support Strategy Use this Foldable to visualize what is being taught.

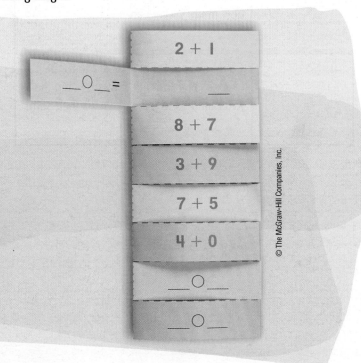

© The McGraw-Hill Companies, Inc.

FOLDABLES

My Foldable

FOLDABLES Follow the steps on the back to make your Foldable.

$2 + 1$

$6 + 4$

$8 + 7$

$3 + 9$

$7 + 5$

$4 + 0$

___ ◯ ___

___ ◯ ___

FOLDABLES Study Organizer ❶ ❷ ❸

$1 + 2 =$	3
$4 \oplus 6 =$	10
$7 \oplus 8 =$	15
$9 \oplus 3 =$	12
$5 \oplus 7 =$	12
$0 \oplus 4 =$	4
___ ◯ ___ =	___
___ ◯ ___ =	___

Project *Express*™

From Dinah Zike, creator of Foldables®

This ready-to-make project format comes in eight bright colors and offers the ability to customize your learning center with different content-based Project Packets. These packets include pre-printed, full color stickers, assorted envelopes and pockets, reproducible templates, and materials needed for quick assembly. You can use these materials as illustrated or use them to design your own learning center.

Order with a McGraw-Hill discount at www.dinah.com.

Subtraction I
(Facts Through 20)

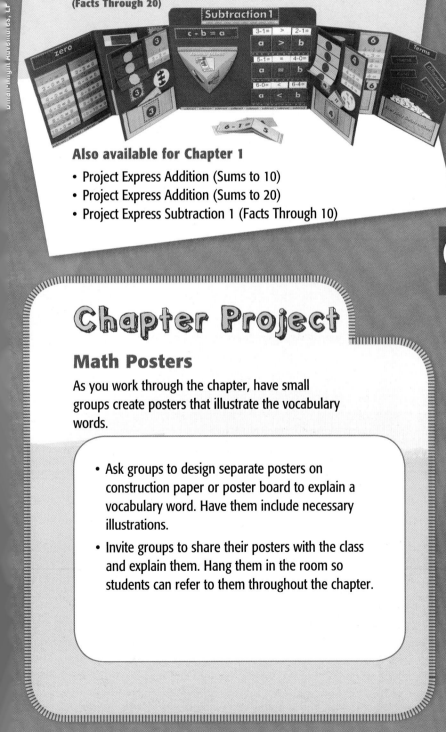

Also available for Chapter 1

• Project Express Addition (Sums to 10)
• Project Express Addition (Sums to 20)
• Project Express Subtraction 1 (Facts Through 10)

MY Learning Stations

Use the following learning stations to differentiate the instruction for Chapter 1. Includes Spanish!

Learning Station	Title	Use after Lesson(s)
Activity Card	*Letter Subtraction*	8
RWPS	*How Many Seeds?*	9
Graphic Novel	*Puppies!*	10
Game	*Switcheroo*	12

RWPS = Real-World Problem-Solving Readers

Chapter Project

Math Posters

As you work through the chapter, have small groups create posters that illustrate the vocabulary words.

• Ask groups to design separate posters on construction paper or poster board to explain a vocabulary word. Have them include necessary illustrations.
• Invite groups to share their posters with the class and explain them. Hang them in the room so students can refer to them throughout the chapter.

📅 CALENDAR TIME

Patterns in the Month

• Have students fill in a blank monthly calendar.
• Have them trace patterns blocks, counters, or attributes blocks in the boxes for the days of the week as listed below.

Sunday = circle   Monday = triangle
Tuesday = square   Wednesday = rectangle
Thursday = trapezoid   Friday = parallelogram
Saturday = hexagon

• Find the repeating pattern. What is it?
• How long is the pattern before it repeats? one week

Sunday	Monday	Tuesday	Wednesday	Thursday	Friday	Saturday

LESSON 1
Addition Properties

OBJECTIVE   Use the Commutative Property and the Identity Property to find sums.

What's the Math?

 Common Core State Standards
DOMAIN: Operations and Algebraic Thinking

Standards: 2.OA.1, 2.OA.2, 2.NBT.5, 2.NBT.9
The wording of these standards can be found on page 2.

What Students Should Understand

- You can use addition properties to find the sums of addition problems.
- The Commutative Property states that you can add numbers in any order and the sum will be the same.
- The Identity Property states that any number plus zero equals that number.

What Students Should be Able to Do

According to the Identity Property, $3 + 0 = 3$ because any number plus zero equals that number.

$3 + 0 = 3$

$$\begin{array}{r} 3 \\ + 0 \\ \hline 3 \end{array}$$

According to the Commutative Property, $2 + 4$ and $4 + 2$ both equal 6 because you can add numbers in any order and the sum will be the same.

$2 + 4 = 6$ $4 + 2 = 6$

Building on the Essential Question

In this lesson, students will build upon the skills and concepts needed to answer the chapter's Essential Question "What strategies can I use to add and subtract?"

Developing Vocabulary

Vocab **New Vocabulary**

add   addend   sum

Activity

- Write *add*, *addend*, and *sum* on the board. Ask students what they know about these words.
- Draw a group of 6 stars and a group of 4 circles. Between the groups, write +. Place = after the second group.
- Point to the group of stars. Tell students this represents an addend. Repeat with the group of circles.
- Tell students to add the addends to find the sum of the shapes.

ELL **ELL Support Strategy** Use this activity to develop oral language with content-specific vocabulary.

My Vocabulary Cards

Ask students to skim the My Vocabulary Cards words. Ask volunteers to tell what they know about each word. Tell students they will learn about these words throughout the chapter. Explain that you will read activities for each card.

IWB **Virtual Word Wall**

Start your IWB Virtual Word Wall for this chapter by adding the new vocabulary words for this chapter.

ELL Refer to the multilingual eGlossary for interactive definitions in 13 languages.

Plan Online

Plan for your lesson by using the resources at
 connectED.mcgraw-hill.com

Digital Dashboard
Interactive Whiteboard Ready

 Vocab
The eBook **Glossary** shows the definition of the word and has audio for each definition. The **eGlossary** provides definitions in 13 languages.

 Watch
Watch as concepts are brought to life through **animations**, **songs**, and a variety of visual instruction.

 Tools
Virtual Manipulatives with work mats allow teachers and students to model the lesson.

 Check
Use **eAssessment** for online assignments and customized assessments.

Use the **Common Core Quick Check** before the lesson to assess students' retention of previously learned concepts.

Use the interactive **Self-Check Quiz** after the lesson to provide immediate feedback on lesson concepts.

 eHelp
Digital and print resources assist students and parents in completing My Homework.

 Games
Online games and **apps** provide extra practice for lesson concepts.

 PD
Professional development videos help teachers gain a deeper understanding of the lesson concepts and strategies.

 RtI
Support for **approaching**, **on-** and **beyond-level** students as well as **English Language Learners**.

Masters
Reteach and **Enrich** worksheets, **Manipulative Masters**, the **Problem of the Day**, and other blackline masters are available for each lesson.

---

1 LAUNCH THE LESSON

 If your students are well-versed in counting counters, you may choose to begin instruction with Step 2, **TEACH**.

You will need
☐ two-color counters

Mathematical PRACTICE 4  **Modeling the Math**

Have each student place 4 counters that are yellow side up on their desk. Have them place 6 counters that are red side up on their desk.

How many yellow counters? 4 *How many red counters?* 6
How many counters in all? 10

Have students place 6 counters in front of them yellow side up and 4 counters red side up.

How many yellow counters? 6 *How many red counters?* 4
How many counters in all? 10

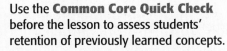

Lunchroom Chat
Tips for New Teachers
Students learn more deeply when they are engaged. For maximized active learning and student engagement, try these:

• Ask open-ended questions and allow time for lively discussion.

• Have students move frequently. Begin and end your lesson on the carpet. Have students move to their seats or to other areas of the room for the lesson body.

• Offer daily opportunities for students to work with another partner or in a small group.

🕐 **Begin core instruction here.**

You will need

☐ paper

☐ crayons or markers

Explore and Explain

Read the directions that are on the bottom of the student page.

To solve problems, you can draw pictures and write number sentences. To find the number of animals Sue and Pat fed, you can draw Xs, shapes, or any other object to represent each type of animal.

Lead students through drawing a picture to find the total number of animals Sue fed. Then guide students through writing the number sentence that tells them how many animals Sue fed.

How do you know which operation to use in the number sentence? Sample answer: You are joining together two sets of objects to find the total number of objects.

Then lead students through solving the other problem.

What do you notice about the addends and the sum in the number sentences? Sample answer: The addends are the same numbers, but are in a different order. The sums are the same.

See and Show

Help students work through the example at the top of the page. Discuss the vocabulary terms. Point out the Commutative Property both in horizontal and vertical form. Also point out the Identity Property. Have them trace the dashed numbers as they work the problems.

Work through Exercises 1–4 as a class.

Mathematical PRACTICE 3 — Talk Math

Discuss with students "Why is the sum the same when you find $3 + 2$ or $2 + 3$?" Sample answer: The sum is the same because you are adding the same numbers. You can add numbers in any order.

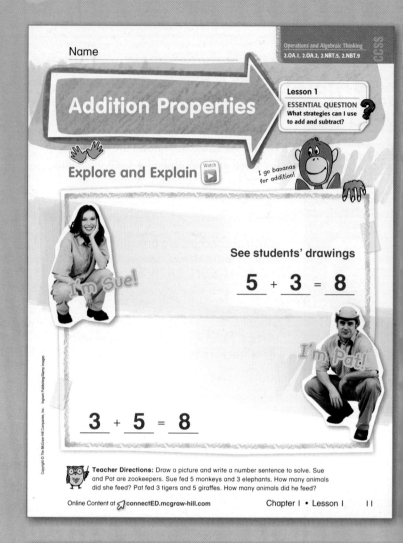

Name _____

Operations and Algebraic Thinking
2.OA.1, 2.OA.2, 2.NBT.5, 2.NBT.9 · CCSS

Addition Properties

Lesson 1
ESSENTIAL QUESTION
What strategies can I use to add and subtract?

Explore and Explain ▶ Watch

I go bananas for addition!

I'm Sue!

See students' drawings

$$5 + 3 = 8$$

I'm Pat!

$$3 + 5 = 8$$

🦉 **Teacher Directions:** Draw a picture and write a number sentence to solve. Sue and Pat are zookeepers. Sue fed 5 monkeys and 3 elephants. How many animals did she feed? Pat fed 3 tigers and 5 giraffes. How many animals did he feed?

Online Content at 🔎 connectED.mcgraw-hill.com   Chapter 1 • Lesson 1   11

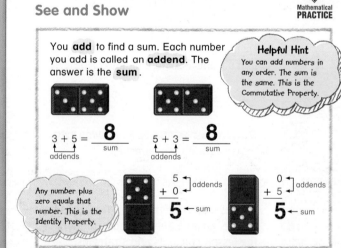

See and Show   Mathematical PRACTICE

You **add** to find a sum. Each number you add is called an **addend**. The answer is the **sum**.

Helpful Hint
You can add numbers in any order. The sum is the same. This is the Commutative Property.

$$3 + 5 = \underset{\text{sum}}{8}$$ $$5 + 3 = \underset{\text{sum}}{8}$$
addends   addends

Any number plus zero equals that number. This is the Identity Property.

$$\begin{array}{r} 5 \\ + 0 \\ \hline 5 \end{array}\right\}\text{addends} \leftarrow \text{sum}$$ $$\begin{array}{r} 0 \\ + 5 \\ \hline 5 \end{array}\right\}\text{addends} \leftarrow \text{sum}$$

Find each sum.

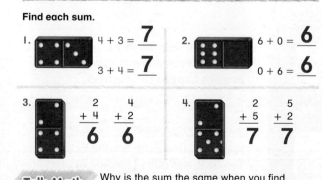

1. $4 + 3 = \mathbf{7}$
     $3 + 4 = \mathbf{7}$

2. $6 + 0 = \mathbf{6}$
     $0 + 6 = \mathbf{6}$

3. $\begin{array}{r} 2 \\ + 4 \\ \hline 6 \end{array}$ $\begin{array}{r} 4 \\ + 2 \\ \hline 6 \end{array}$

4. $\begin{array}{r} 2 \\ + 5 \\ \hline 7 \end{array}$ $\begin{array}{r} 5 \\ + 2 \\ \hline 7 \end{array}$

Talk Math   Why is the sum the same when you find $3 + 2$ or $2 + 3$?

12   Chapter 1 • Lesson 1

Name _____

On My Own

Find each sum.

5. 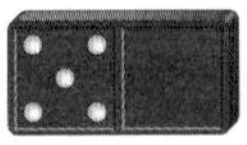 $5 + 1 = \underline{6}$

        $1 + 5 = \underline{6}$

6.
$$\begin{array}{r} 4 \\ +\,5 \\ \hline 9 \end{array} \qquad \begin{array}{r} 5 \\ +\,4 \\ \hline 9 \end{array}$$

7. $\begin{array}{r} 0 \\ +\,3 \\ \hline 3 \end{array} \qquad \begin{array}{r} 3 \\ +\,0 \\ \hline 3 \end{array}$

8. $\begin{array}{r} 6 \\ +\,3 \\ \hline 9 \end{array} \qquad \begin{array}{r} 3 \\ +\,6 \\ \hline 9 \end{array}$

9. $\begin{array}{r} 7 \\ +\,1 \\ \hline 8 \end{array} \qquad \begin{array}{r} 1 \\ +\,7 \\ \hline 8 \end{array}$

10. $6 + 2 = \underline{8}$

     $\underline{8} = 2 + 6$

11. $8 + 0 = \underline{8}$

     $0 + 8 = \underline{8}$

12. $\underline{6} = 4 + 2$

     $2 + 4 = \underline{6}$

13. $3 + 4 = \underline{7}$

     $4 + 3 = \underline{7}$

14. $0 + 9 = \underline{9}$

     $9 + 0 = \underline{9}$

Chapter 1 • Lesson 1   13

Problem Solving

Mathematical **PRACTICE**

15. What two addition facts could you use to find the total number of dots on this domino?

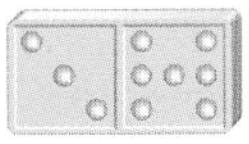

$$\underline{3} + \underline{7} = \underline{10} \qquad \underline{7} + \underline{3} = \underline{10}$$

16. Manuel's team scores 卌 l runs in the first game. They score ||| runs in the second game. Show two ways you can find the total number of runs.

卌 l |||

$$\underline{6} + \underline{3} = \underline{9} \qquad \underline{3} + \underline{6} = \underline{9}$$

Write Math   Write what you know about the order of the addends in an addition problem.

Sample answer: You can add in any order and the sum will be the same.

---

3 PRACTICE & APPLY

CCSS

On My Own

Have students work through the exercises on this page independently. You may choose to assign exercises based on the chart below.

DIFFERENTIATED ASSIGNMENTS

AL   **Approaching Level**   Guide students through the exercises in On My Own. Help them to use manipulatives while working through the exercises.

OL   **On Level**   Complete the exercises independently.

BL   **Beyond Level**   Complete the exercises independently without manipulatives.

Common Error!

When using addition properties to check their work, students may try to use the sum as an addend. Remind them that they need to differentiate between the sum and addend.

Problem Solving

Have students work through the problem-solving exercises on this page independently. If students are struggling, remind them to find the addends first and then determine the sum.

Mathematical **PRACTICE** **7**   In Exercise 16, students **look for and make use of structure.**

Write Math

This exercise asks students to build upon their understanding of concepts needed to answer the chapter's Essential Question.

RtI RESPONSE TO INTERVENTION

DIFFERENTIATED INSTRUCTION

AL **APPROACHING LEVEL**

IF my students struggle with addition properties,

THEN choose a resource:

→ Use the Reteach worksheet with small groups.

→ Go online for a Differentiated Instruction activity.

→ **Connecting Cube Addition** Students join three red connecting cubes and two green cubes. *How many red cubes?* 3 *How many green cubes?* 2 *What number sentence shows the sum?* 3 + 2 = 5 Take apart and rejoin the cubes, putting the green cubes first. *How many green cubes?* 2 *How many red cubes?* 3 *Number sentence?* 2 + 3 = 5 *Does the order of the numbers change the sum?* no

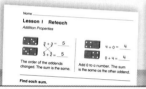

OL **ON LEVEL**

IF my students seem to know addition properties, but need more practice,

THEN choose a resource:

→ Assign My Homework.

→ Go online for a Differentiated Instruction activity.

BL **BEYOND LEVEL**

IF my students have mastered addition properties,

THEN choose a resource:

→ Use the Enrich worksheet in cooperative groups.

→ Assign My Homework.

→ Go online for a Differentiated Instruction activity.

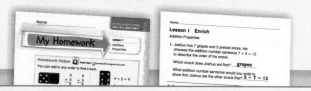

15A **Chapter 1** Apply Addition and Subtraction Concepts

AL Name _____

Lesson 1   Reteach

Addition Properties

 2 + 3 = __5__

3 + 2 = __5__

The order of the addends changed. The sum is the same.

 4 + 0 = __4__

0 + 4 = __4__

Add 0 to a number. The sum is the same as the other addend.

Find each sum.

1. 8 + 4 = __12__

4 + 8 = __12__

2. 5 + 0 = __5__

0 + 5 = __5__

3. 3 + 4 = __7__

4 + 3 = __7__

4. 1 + 8 = __9__

8 + 1 = __9__

5. 5 + 3 = __8__

3 + 5 = __8__

6. 6 + 5 = __11__

5 + 6 = __11__

Copyright © The McGraw-Hill Companies, Inc. Permission is granted to reproduce for classroom use.

BL Name _____

Lesson 1   Enrich

Addition Properties

1. Joshua has 7 grapes and 5 pretzel sticks. He chooses the addition number sentence 7 + 5 = 12 to describe the order of his snack.

   Which snack does Joshua eat first? __**grapes**__

   What addition number sentence would you write to show that Joshua ate the other snack first? **5 + 7 = 12**

2. Devon has 7 apple slices and 7 crackers. She thinks that there is only one addition number sentence to describe her snack.

   Do you agree? __**yes**__

   Write the addition number sentence(s). **7 + 7 = 14**

3. Rico has 8 carrot sticks and 3 celery sticks. Carrots are his favorite snack. Write an addition number sentence to show that he ate his favorite snack first.

   8 + 3 = 11

   Write an addition number sentence to show another way Rico could eat his snack. **3 + 8 = 11**

4. On the back of this page or another piece of paper, combine the sums from problems 1, 2, and 3. How many snacks did the students eat?

   12 + 14 + 11 = 37

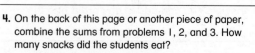

Copyright © The McGraw-Hill Companies, Inc. Permission is granted to reproduce for classroom use.

Name _____

Operations and Algebraic Thinking
2.OA.1, 2.OA.2, 2.NBT.5, 2.NBT.9

CCSS

My Homework

Lesson 1
Addition
Properties

Homework Helper Need help? connectED.mcgraw-hill.com

You can add in any order to find a sum.

$$\begin{array}{r} 5 \\ + 0 \\ \hline 5 \end{array} \qquad \begin{array}{r} 0 \\ + 5 \\ \hline 5 \end{array}$$

$4 + 5 = 9$

$5 + 4 = 9$

Practice

Find each sum.

1.
$$\begin{array}{r} 2 \\ + 4 \\ \hline 6 \end{array} \qquad \begin{array}{r} 4 \\ + 2 \\ \hline 6 \end{array}$$

2.
$$\begin{array}{r} 4 \\ + 1 \\ \hline 5 \end{array} \qquad \begin{array}{r} 1 \\ + 4 \\ \hline 5 \end{array}$$

3.
$$\begin{array}{r} 9 \\ + 0 \\ \hline 9 \end{array} \qquad \begin{array}{r} 0 \\ + 9 \\ \hline 9 \end{array}$$

4.
$$\begin{array}{r} 3 \\ + 4 \\ \hline 7 \end{array} \qquad \begin{array}{r} 4 \\ + 3 \\ \hline 7 \end{array}$$

5. $1 + 7 = $ **8**

   $7 + 1 = $ **8**

6. **3** $= 0 + 3$

   3 $= 3 + 0$

Chapter 1 • Lesson 1   15

Find each sum.

7. $2 + 3 = $ **5**

   $3 + 2 = $ **5**

8. $5 + 3 = $ **8**

   $3 + 5 = $ **8**

9. The zoo has 4 striped snakes. It has 2 yellow snakes. Write two ways you can find how many snakes the zoo has in all.

   Slither!

   2 + **4** = **6**   **4** + **2** = **6**

10. Kathy counts 4 baby goats and 5 baby sheep in the petting zoo. Write two ways you can find how many babies there are in all?

    4 + **5** = **9**   **5** + **4** = **9**

Vocabulary Check

Circle the number sentence that shows the vocabulary word.

11. **addends**   (3 + 1 = 4)   3 + 1 = 4   3 + 1 = 4

 Math at Home Have your child solve the following problem: There are three kittens eating. Two more come over to eat. How many kittens are there in all?

16   Chapter 1 • Lesson 1

---

4 WRAP IT UP

CCSS

My Homework

Assign homework after successful completion of the lesson. Students who understand the concepts may skip the **Homework Helper** section.

Vocabulary Check

Discuss with students that the *s* in *addends* indicates the plural form of the word. Explain the *-s* tells the reader "more than one."

Formative Assessment

Ask students the following question.

How do you know the sum will not change when you switch the order of the addends? The Commutative Property tells me that I can add in any order.

Line Up!

When students line up, have them add the number of girls and boys in line to find the sum.

LESSON 2
Count On to Add

OBJECTIVE   Use a number line to count on when adding.

What's the Math?

 Common Core State Standards
DOMAIN: Operations and Algebraic Thinking

Standards: 2.OA.1, 2.OA.2
The wording of these standards can be found on page 2.

What Students Should Understand

• You can use a number line and count on to add.

• First, find the greater addend on the number line. Then count on the other addend to find the sum.

What Students Should be Able to Do

Use a number line and count on to find $2 + 6$.

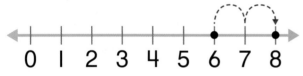

0 1 2 3 4 5 6 7 8

Start with the greater addend, 6. Count on the other addend, 2.
$6 + 2 = 8$

 Building on the Essential Question

In this lesson, students will build upon the skills and concepts needed to answer the chapter's Essential Question "What strategies can I use to add and subtract?"

Developing Vocabulary

New Vocabulary

count on

Activity

• Write *count on* on the board.

• Draw a number line that includes the numbers 0–10.

• Tell students they can use the number line to count on. Tell students that you will start at 5 and count on 2 more.

• To add numbers, point out that you count on, using the numbers that come after 5 on the number line. If you wanted to subtract, you would use the numbers that come before 5.

• *When I start at 5 and count on 2 more, what number do I land on?* 7

• Remind students that when they count on, they should start with the greater addend.

ELL **ELL Support Strategy** Use this vocabulary activity to develop and advance mathematical language skills.

My Vocabulary Cards

Have students work in small groups. Tell each group to identify the *count on* card. Then have them discuss how the visual shows counting on.

IWB **Virtual Word Wall**

Add this vocabulary card to the Virtual Word Wall for the chapter.

ELL Refer to the Multilingual eGlossary for interactive definitions in 13 languages.

Plan Online

Plan for your lesson by using the resources at
connectED.mcgraw-hill.com

Digital Dashboard

Interactive Whiteboard Ready

 Vocab

The eBook **Glossary** shows the definition of the word and has audio for each definition. The **eGlossary** provides definitions in 13 languages.

 Watch

Watch as concepts are brought to life through **animations**, **songs**, and a variety of visual instruction.

 Tools

Virtual Manipulatives with work mats allow teachers and students to model the lesson.

 Check

Use **eAssessment** for online assignments and customized assessments.

Use the **Common Core Quick Check** before the lesson to assess students' retention of previously learned concepts.

Use the interactive **Self-Check Quiz** after the lesson to provide immediate feedback on lesson concepts.

 eHelp

Digital and print resources assist students and parents in completing My Homework.

 Games

Online games and **apps** provide extra practice for lesson concepts.

 PD

Professional development videos help teachers gain a deeper understanding of the lesson concepts and strategies.

 RtI

Support for **approaching**, **on**- and **beyond-level** students as well as **English Language Learners**.

Masters

Reteach and **Enrich** worksheets, **Manipulative Masters**, the **Problem of the Day**, and other blackline masters are available for each lesson.

Online Content at **connectED.mcgraw-hill.com**

 If your students are well-versed in counting on, you may choose to begin instruction with Step 2, **TEACH**.

You will need

☐ construction paper

Mathematical PRACTICE  Modeling the Math

Tape 6 sheets of construction paper together on the floor to make a number line labeled 1—6. Write $3 + 2$ on the board. Ask a volunteer to stand on the number 3, then walk to numbers 4 and 5 as the class counts on aloud. Repeat with other addition problems.

1   2   3   4   5   6

Begin core instruction here.

You will need

☐ Work Mat 3

☐ crayons or markers

Explore and Explain

Read the directions at the bottom of the student page.

In this lesson, you will count on to add. This means that you start at a given number and then count on using the other number to tell you how many times to count on.

Draw a green box around the number 1. Count on 3. This means that you count three over from 1 and land on 4. Draw a purple box around 4.

Draw a green box around number 7. Count on 2. On what number do you land? 9

What do we draw around this number? purple box

Have students work through the last problem independently. Check their work after they have completed the problem.

What number did you draw a purple box around? 12

See and Show

Help students work through the example at the top of the page. Use Work Mat 3 to help practice the skills at their desks while you have volunteers demonstrate at the board. Have them trace the dashed numbers as they find the sums.

Work through Exercises 1–6 as a class.

 **PRACTICE** 3   **Talk Math**

Discuss with students "Why should you count on from the greater addend?" Sample answer: It is easy to count on one, two, or three in your head when you begin with the greater addend.

Name _____

Operations and Algebraic Thinking
2.OA.1, 2.OA.2

Count On to Add

Lesson 2
ESSENTIAL QUESTION
What strategies can I use to add and subtract?

Explore and Explain Watch ▶ Tools

Wow! I'm longer than I thought!

See students' work.

Teacher Directions: Draw a green box around number 1. Count on 3. Draw a purple box around that number. Draw a green box around number 7. Count on 2. Draw a purple box around that number. Draw a green box around number 11. Count on 1. Draw a purple box around that number.

Online Content at ✎ connectED.mcgraw-hill.com   Chapter 1 • Lesson 2   17

See and Show   **Mathematical PRACTICE**

Find 7 + 3. Use a number line. **Count on** to add.
Start with the greater addend.

+1 +1 +1

0 1 2 3 4 5 6 ⑦ 8 9 10 11 12

Start at 7. Count on 3.

7 + 3 = **10**

10 = 7 + 3

Count on to add. Use the number line to help.

0 1 2 3 4 5 6 7 8 9 10 11 12

1. 6 + 3 = **9**   2. **6** = 4 + 2

3. 2 + 9 = **11**   4. 1 + 3 = **4**

5. **9** = 2 + 7   6. **10** = 9 + 1

Talk Math Why should you count on from the greater addend?

18   Chapter 1 • Lesson 2

Name _____

On My Own

Count on to add. Use the number line to help.

Helpful Hint
Start with the greater addend.

0 1 2 3 4 5 6 7 8 9 10 11 12

7. $7 + 1 =$ __8__

8. __7__ $= 5 + 2$

9. $3 + 8 =$ __11__

10. $6 + 1 =$ __7__

11. __12__ $= 9 + 3$

12. $2 + 8 =$ __10__

13. $\begin{array}{r} 2 \\ + 7 \\ \hline 9 \end{array}$

14. $\begin{array}{r} 3 \\ + 2 \\ \hline 5 \end{array}$

15. $\begin{array}{r} 1 \\ + 9 \\ \hline 10 \end{array}$

16. $\begin{array}{r} 5 \\ + 1 \\ \hline 6 \end{array}$

17. $\begin{array}{r} 3 \\ + 6 \\ \hline 9 \end{array}$

18. $\begin{array}{r} 1 \\ + 4 \\ \hline 5 \end{array}$

19. $\begin{array}{r} 3 \\ + 1 \\ \hline 4 \end{array}$

20. $\begin{array}{r} 2 \\ + 6 \\ \hline 8 \end{array}$

21. $\begin{array}{r} 8 \\ + 1 \\ \hline 9 \end{array}$

Chapter 1 • Lesson 2   19

Problem Solving

Mathematical **PRACTICE**

22. Annie buys 6 eggs at the market. She has 3 more eggs at home. How many eggs does she have in all?

Anybody in there?

__9__ eggs

23. Sal's cow gave 3 pails of milk in the morning and 5 pails in the afternoon. How many pails of milk did Sal's cow give?

__8__ pails

24. Joseph has 4 pigs on his farm. One pig has 3 piglets. How many pigs are on the farm?

__7__ pigs

Write Math   How does counting on help you add?
Sample answer: If you start with the greater number

you only have to count on by a small number to find

the sum.

---

③ PRACTICE & APPLY

CCSS

On My Own

Have students work through the exercises on this page independently. You may choose to assign exercises based on the chart below.

DIFFERENTIATED ASSIGNMENTS

AL **Approaching Level** Guide students through the exercises in On My Own. Help them to use a number line while working through the exercises.

OL **On Level** Complete the exercises independently.

BL **Beyond Level** Complete the exercises independently without manipulatives.

Common Error!

Sometimes students may not use the number line correctly when counting on. Watch for students who skip numbers or count backward instead of forward. Show students how to work from left to right on the number line and how to "hop" or "jump" on each number.

Problem Solving

Have students work through the problem-solving exercises on this page independently. Remind students to read the problems carefully to determine what they are trying to find out.

Mathematical **PRACTICE** ➊ In Exercise 23, students **make sense of problems and persevere in solving them.**

Write Math

This exercise asks students to build upon their understanding of concepts needed to answer the chapter's Essential Question.

RESPONSE TO INTERVENTION

DIFFERENTIATED INSTRUCTION

AL APPROACHING LEVEL

IF my students struggle with counting on to add,

THEN choose a resource:

→ Use a Differentiated Instruction activity from p. 1C.

→ Use the Reteach worksheet with small groups.

→ Go online for a Differentiated Instruction activity.

→ **Line Jumps** Write a problem on the board, such as 4 + 3 = ?. Students put a finger above the 4 on a number line. Then they jump three more to count on. Students put a finger where they land. *What number do you land on? 7 What is the sum of 4 + 3? 7*

OL ON LEVEL

IF my students seem to know counting on to add, but need more practice,

THEN choose a resource:

→ Assign My Homework.

→ Go online for a Differentiated Instruction activity.

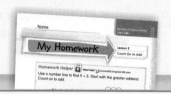

BL BEYOND LEVEL

IF my students have mastered counting on to add,

THEN choose a resource:

→ Use the Enrich worksheet in cooperative groups.

→ Assign My Homework.

→ Go online for a Differentiated Instruction activity.

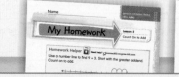

AL Name _____

Lesson 2   Reteach
Count On to Add

You can use squares to count on.

Find 5 + 3. Start at 5. Count on 3.

$5 + 3 = \underline{\ 8\ }$ $\begin{array}{r} 5 \\ +\ 3 \\ \hline 8 \end{array}$

1 2 3 4 5 6 7 8

Use the squares. Add squares to count on.

1. $8 + 1 = \underline{\ 9\ }$

2. $6 + 2 = \underline{\ 8\ }$

3. $7 + 3 = \underline{\ 10\ }$

4. $5 + 1 = \underline{\ 6\ }$

5. $9 + 3 = \underline{\ 12\ }$

6. $7 + 2 = \underline{\ 9\ }$

7. $6 + 3 = \underline{\ 9\ }$

BL Name _____

Lesson 2   Enrich
Count On to Add

This is an addition square. The sum of the numbers is the same for each row, column, and diagonal. They all equal 15.

First, find the sum of the two numbers in each row. Then, count on and use the number line to determine the number hidden behind the critter. Write the number in the box at the end of the row.

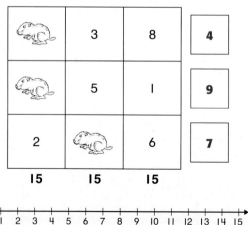

On a separate piece of paper, make your own addition square. The sum of each row, column, and diagonal should be 12.

See students' work.

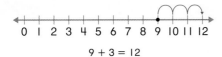

My Homework

Lesson 2
Count On to Add

Homework Helper

Need help? connectED.mcgraw-hill.com

Use a number line to find 9 + 3. Start with the greater addend.
Count on to add.

$$0\ 1\ 2\ 3\ 4\ 5\ 6\ 7\ 8\ 9\ 10\ 11\ 12$$

$$9 + 3 = 12$$

Practice

Count on to add. Use the number line above.

1. $4 + 1 = \underline{5}$

2. $2 + 6 = \underline{8}$

3. $1 + 8 = \underline{9}$

4. $3 + 6 = \underline{9}$

5. $2 + 4 = \underline{6}$

6. $2 + 8 = \underline{10}$

7.
$$\begin{array}{r} 3 \\ + 9 \\ \hline 12 \end{array}$$

8.
$$\begin{array}{r} 4 \\ + 3 \\ \hline 7 \end{array}$$

9.
$$\begin{array}{r} 1 \\ + 4 \\ \hline 5 \end{array}$$

Chapter 1 • Lesson 2   21

Read and then solve the problems.

10. 6 bees are buzzing near a hive.
3 more bees come out of the hive.
How many bees are there now?

$$\underline{9}\ \text{bees}$$

11. Cherie has 5 trading cards. She gets
3 more cards. How many cards does
Cherie have now?

$$\underline{8}\ \text{cards}$$

12. There are 8 butterflies on a bush. 4 more
butterflies fly onto the bush. How many
butterflies are on the bush now?

Me too!

$$\underline{12}\ \text{butterflies}$$

Vocabulary Check

Draw lines to match.

13. **count on** —— 6 + 3 = 9

14. **addend**

$$0\ 1\ 2\ 3\ 4\ 5\ 6\ 7$$

Math at Home Give your child an addition fact. Have him or her count on from the greater number to find the sum.

22   Chapter 1 • Lesson 2

---

4 WRAP IT UP

CCSS

My Homework

Assign homework after successful completion of the lesson.
Students who understand the concepts may skip the
Homework Helper section.

Vocabulary Check

Explain to students that many words can be defined in both
words and drawings.

Formative Assessment

Have students think of the number sentence 2 + 10.

*Which number should you start with when you count on?
Why?* 10; It is easier to count on 2 spaces on the number
line than it is to count on 10 spaces.

Line Up!

Have three students line up. Have three more
students line up behind them. Count on these
additional three students along the line. How
many students are in line? 6 students

LESSON 3
Doubles and Near Doubles

OBJECTIVE Use doubles and near doubles to find sums.

What's the Math?

 Common Core State Standards
DOMAIN: Operations and Algebraic Thinking

Standards: 2.OA.1, 2.OA.2
The wording of these standards can be found on page 2.

What Students Should Understand

- You can use doubles facts to find a sum. Doubles facts have two addends that are the same.
- You can use near doubles facts to find a sum. Near doubles facts have two addends that are almost doubles facts.

What Students Should be Able to Do

Use a doubles fact to find 4 + 4.

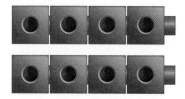

$$4 + 4 = 8$$

Use a near doubles fact to find 4 + 5.

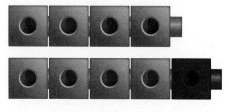

$$4 + 5 = 9$$

 Building on the Essential Question

In this lesson, students will build upon the skills and concepts needed to answer the chapter's Essential Question "What strategies can I use to add and subtract?"

Developing Vocabulary

 New Vocabulary

doubles   near doubles

Activity

- Display 2 cube trains with 4 cubes in each train. Ask students to use doubles to describe the cube trains in an addition sentence. 4 + 4
- Write the doubles fact 4 + 4 = 8 on the board.
- Add a cube to one of the cube trains. *How many cubes are in this train now?* 5 *How do you know?* There were 4 cubes in the train before, and 1 more was added.
- Have students count to verify that there are 5 cubes in the train.
- Ask students why 4 + 5 is called *near doubles.* It is the same as 4 + 4, but one of the 4s has one more.

ELL **ELL Support Strategy** Use this vocabulary activity to visualize what is being taught.

My Vocabulary Cards

Read the activity for the *doubles* and *near doubles* cards. Have students respond.

IWB **Virtual Word Wall**

Add these vocabulary cards to the Virtual Word Wall for the chapter.

ELL Refer to the Multilingual eGlossary for interactive definitions in 13 languages.

Plan Online

Plan for your lesson by using the resources at
connectED.mcgraw-hill.com

Digital Dashboard

Interactive Whiteboard Ready

Vocab

The eBook **Glossary** shows the definition of the word and has audio for each definition. The **eGlossary** provides definitions in 13 languages.

Watch

Watch as concepts are brought to life through **animations**, **songs**, and a variety of visual instruction.

Tools

Virtual Manipulatives with work mats allow teachers and students to model the lesson.

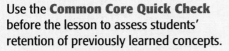
Check

Use **eAssessment** for online assignments and customized assessments.

Use the **Common Core Quick Check** before the lesson to assess students' retention of previously learned concepts.

Use the interactive **Self-Check Quiz** after the lesson to provide immediate feedback on lesson concepts.

eHelp

Digital and print resources assist students and parents in completing My Homework.

Games

Online games and **apps** provide extra practice for lesson concepts.

PD

Professional development videos help teachers gain a deeper understanding of the lesson concepts and strategies.

RtI

Support for **approaching**, **on-** and **beyond-level** students as well as **English Language Learners**.

Masters

Reteach and **Enrich** worksheets, **Manipulative Masters**, the **Problem of the Day**, and other blackline masters are available for each lesson.

---

1 LAUNCH THE LESSON

If your students are well-versed in modeling doubles and modeling one more than a number, you may choose to begin instruction with Step 2, **TEACH**.

You will need

☐ number cubes

Mathematical PRACTICE 4 Modeling the Math

Give each student a number cube. Have students roll the number cube and write the number rolled.

What is that number doubled? What is one more than that number? Write the numbers. See students' work.

Have students find the sum of the numbers.

What is the sum of the numbers? See students' work.

Repeat this procedure two more times.

🕐 **Begin core instruction here.**

You will need
☐ connecting cubes

Explore and Explain

Read the directions that are at the bottom of the student page. Tell students that when two or more connecting cubes are connected, they are called a cube train. Then explain to students that a doubles fact is an addition number sentence that has two addends that are the same number. Guide students through drawing the first cube train and writing the first doubles fact.

How many cubes are in the second cube train? 3

What will the addends be in the doubles fact? 3

What is the sum? 6

Have students work with a partner in drawing the second cube train and writing the second doubles fact.

How many cubes are in the second cube train? 4

What will the addends be in the doubles fact? 4

What is the sum? 8

Have students draw the last cube train and write the last doubles fact independently.

How many cubes are in the last cube train? 5

What will the addends be in the doubles fact? 5

What is the sum? 10

See and Show

Help students work through the example at the top of the page.

Have them trace the dashed numbers as they work through the problems. Practice by having a student name a single digit and then have a second student say "doubles" or "plus one" for the near doubles. The third student says the number sentence and gives the sum. Repeat for each doubles or near doubles problem. For example,

First student:	4	4
Second student:	doubles (or)	plus one
Third student:	$4 + 4 = 8$	$4 + 5 = 9$

Work through Exercises 1 through 6 as a class.

Mathematical PRACTICE 3 ➤ **Talk Math**

Discuss with students "How can you use doubles and near doubles to remember $5 + 5$? $5 + 6$?" Sample answer: $5 + 5$; counting fingers or toes. $5 + 6$; 10 fingers and a toe.

🕐 **CORE INSTRUCTION**

Name _____

Operations and Algebraic Thinking
2.OA.1, 2.OA.2

Doubles and Near Doubles

Lesson 3
ESSENTIAL QUESTION
What strategies can I use to add and subtract?

I am seeing doubles!

Explore and Explain 📺 🔧

$$3 + 3 = 6$$

$$4 + 4 = 8$$

$$5 + 5 = 10$$

🦉 **Teacher Directions:** Look at each cube train. Draw the same train beside it. Write the doubles fact shown by each pair of cube trains.

Online Content at 🔗 **connectED.mcgraw-hill.com**   Chapter 1 • Lesson 3   23

See and Show

Mathematical PRACTICE

Two addends that are the same are called **doubles**.
Use doubles facts to find the sum.

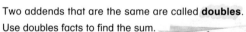

$$\underset{\text{addend}}{6} + \underset{\text{addend}}{6} = \underset{\text{sum}}{12}$$

We're doubles!   *Yeah!*

Two addends that are almost a doubles fact are called **near doubles**.
Use near doubles facts to find the sum.

$$\underset{\text{addend}}{6} + \underset{\text{addend}}{7} = \underset{\text{sum}}{13}$$

Add. Circle the doubles facts.

1. $\left(4 + 4 = \underline{8}\right)$ 2. $3 + 4 = \underline{7}$

3. $\left(\underline{14} = 7 + 7\right)$ 4. $\left(\underline{18} = 9 + 9\right)$

5. $7 + 8 = \underline{15}$ 6. $\left(\underline{16} = 8 + 8\right)$

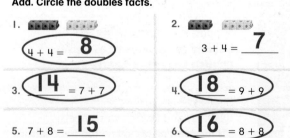

Talk Math How can you use doubles and near doubles to remember $5 + 5$? $5 + 6$?

24   Chapter 1 • Lesson 3

On My Own

Name _____

On My Own

Add. Circle the doubles facts.

7. $0 + 0 =$ ___0___ (circled)

8. $7 + 6 =$ ___13___

9. $2 + 8 =$ ___10___

10. $8 + 9 =$ ___17___

11. $3 + 2 =$ ___5___

12. $2 + 9 =$ ___11___

13. $\begin{array}{r} 2 \\ + 2 \\ \hline 4 \end{array}$ (circled)

14. $\begin{array}{r} 7 \\ + 7 \\ \hline 14 \end{array}$ (circled)

15. $\begin{array}{r} 1 \\ + 1 \\ \hline 2 \end{array}$ (circled)

16. $\begin{array}{r} 9 \\ + 3 \\ \hline 12 \end{array}$

Add. Circle the near doubles facts.

17. $\begin{array}{r} 4 \\ + 3 \\ \hline 7 \end{array}$ (circled)

18. $\begin{array}{r} 2 \\ + 4 \\ \hline 6 \end{array}$

19. $\begin{array}{r} 7 \\ + 8 \\ \hline 15 \end{array}$ (circled)

20. $\begin{array}{r} 3 \\ + 8 \\ \hline 11 \end{array}$

21. $\begin{array}{r} 2 \\ + 7 \\ \hline 9 \end{array}$

22. $\begin{array}{r} 9 \\ + 8 \\ \hline 17 \end{array}$ (circled)

23. $\begin{array}{r} 3 \\ + 5 \\ \hline 8 \end{array}$

24. $\begin{array}{r} 4 \\ + 5 \\ \hline 9 \end{array}$ (circled)

Problem Solving

Mathematical PRACTICE

25. Mr. Bean sells 5 melons to Ed. He sells the same number of melons to Jose. How many melons did Mr. Bean sell in all?

___10___ melons

I'm hungry!

26. Andrea has 3 dogs. Juanita has the same number of dogs. How many dogs do they have in all?

___6___ dogs

27. Anthony has 3 lizards. His cousin has one more lizard than he does. How many lizards do Anthony and his cousin have in all?

___7___ lizards

Write Math How does knowing doubles facts help you with near doubles facts?

Sample answer: Near doubles are just doubles facts plus 1 or minus 1. So if you know the doubles fact you just add 1 or subtract 1.

On My Own

Have students work through the exercises on this page independently. You may choose to assign exercises based on the chart below.

DIFFERENTIATED ASSIGNMENTS

AL **Approaching Level** Guide students through the exercises in On My Own. Help them to use manipulatives while working through the exercises.

OL **On Level** Complete the exercises independently.

BL **Beyond Level** Complete the exercises independently without manipulatives.

Common Error!

Some students will recognize near doubles but have difficulty recognizing two facts simultaneously. Have them write the doubles fact above the near doubles fact until the doubles become automatic.

Problem Solving

Have students work through the problem-solving exercises on this page independently. Remind them that it helps to re-read the problem to be sure they understand it.

Mathematical PRACTICE **5** In Exercise 27, students **use appropriate tools strategically.**

Write Math

This exercise asks students to build upon their understanding of concepts needed to answer the chapter's Essential Question.

AL APPROACHING LEVEL

IF my students struggle with doubles and near doubles,

THEN choose a resource:

→ Use a Differentiated Instruction activity from p. 1C.

→ Use the Reteach worksheet with small groups.

→ Go online for a Differentiated Instruction activity.

→ **Use Counters** Use counters to model doubles and near doubles facts.

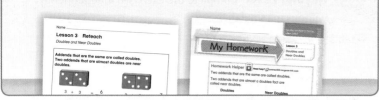

OL ON LEVEL

IF my students seem to know doubles and near doubles, but need more practice,

THEN choose a resource:

→ Assign My Homework.

→ Go online for a Differentiated Instruction activity.

BL BEYOND LEVEL

IF my students have mastered doubles and near doubles,

THEN choose a resource:

→ Use a Differentiated Instruction activity from p. 1D.

→ Use the Enrich worksheet in cooperative groups.

→ Assign My Homework.

→ Go online for a Differentiated Instruction activity.

27A Chapter 1 Apply Addition and Subtraction Concepts

AL

Name _____

Lesson 3   Reteach
Doubles and Near Doubles

Addends that are the same are called doubles.
Two addends that are almost doubles are near doubles.

3 + 3 = __6__   3 + 4 = __7__
addend addend

Add. Use doubles.

1. 4 + 4 = __8__ | 2. 6 + 5 = __11__

3. 2 + 3 = __5__ | 4. 5 + 5 = __10__

BL

Name _____

Lesson 3   Enrich
Doubles and Near Doubles

Do all numbers have doubles in their fact families?

Color the dinosaurs **blue** if they have doubles in one of their fact families.
Color the dinosaurs **green** if they do not have doubles in their fact families.

 15 **green**   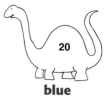 20 **blue**

8 **blue**   11 **green**

14 **blue**   16 **blue**

My Homework

Lesson 3
Doubles and
Near Doubles

Homework Helper
Need help? connectED.mcgraw-hill.com

Two addends that are the same are called doubles.

Two addends that are almost a doubles fact are called near doubles.

Doubles

$4 + 4 = 8$

Near Doubles

$4 + 5 = 9$

Practice

Add. Circle the doubles facts.

1. $5 + 7 = \underline{12}$

2. $2 + 3 = \underline{5}$

3. $\boxed{5 + 5 = \underline{10}}$

4. $8 + 7 = \underline{15}$

5. $\begin{array}{r} 4 \\ + 2 \\ \hline 6 \end{array}$

6. $\boxed{\begin{array}{r} 4 \\ + 4 \\ \hline 8 \end{array}}$

7. $\begin{array}{r} 6 \\ + 7 \\ \hline 13 \end{array}$

8. $\boxed{\begin{array}{r} 8 \\ + 8 \\ \hline 16 \end{array}}$

Chapter 1 • Lesson 3   27

Add. Circle the near doubles facts.

9. $2 + 9 = \underline{11}$

10. $12 + 3 = \underline{15}$

11. $\boxed{4 + 5 = \underline{9}}$

12. $8 + 8 = \underline{16}$

13. $\boxed{9 + 8 = \underline{17}}$

14. $\boxed{7 + 6 = \underline{13}}$

Solve. Then write the doubles fact that helped you solve the problem.

15. 4 frogs are sitting beside a pond. 5 dragon flies land beside them. How many animals are there altogether?

Minus one dragon fly!

$\underline{4} + \underline{5} = \underline{9}$ animals

$\underline{4} + \underline{4} = \underline{8}$

Vocabulary Check

Draw lines to match.

16. **near doubles** $4 + 4 = 8$

17. **doubles** $4 + 5 = 9$

 Math at Home Have your child use objects to make doubles and tell the addition fact.

28   Chapter 1 • Lesson 3

My Homework

Assign homework after successful completion of the lesson. Students who understand the concepts may skip the **Homework Helper** section.

Vocabulary Check

Have students refer to their My Vocabulary Cards for additional support.

Formative Assessment

Ask students the following questions.

What doubles fact can help you find 5 + 4? How would you use it? 4 + 4 or 5 + 5; Add 1 to 4 + 4 = 8; Subtract 1 from 5 + 5 = 10.

Line Up!

Before lining up, assign each student a number 1–10. Tell students that they can line up when they hear you say the double of their number.

LESSON 4
Make a 10
OBJECTIVE Make a 10 to solve addition problems.

What's the Math?

 Common Core State Standards
DOMAIN: Operations and Algebraic Thinking

Standards: 2.OA.1, 2.OA.2
The wording of these standards can be found on page 2.

What Students Should Understand

- You can make a 10 to help you add.
- Take apart the lesser addend so that the greater addend will become a 10. Then add.

What Students Should be Able to Do

Make a ten to help you find $7 + 6$.

First, show 7. Then show 6. Next, take apart 6 to make a 10.

Since $7 + 3 = 10$, take apart 6 so that one addend is 3.

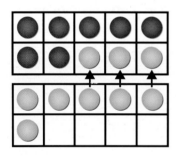

$10 + 3 = 13$
So, $7 + 6 = 13$.

$$7 + 6$$
$$\wedge$$
$$3 + 3$$

Last, add. Now you have $10 + 3$.

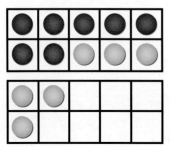

Developing Vocabulary

 Review Vocabulary

sum   ten

Review Activity

- Write *ten* on the board. Ask students what they know about ten. Prompt them with the following questions: How can you make ten? Why is 10 an important number? How is 10 different than other numbers?
- Next, have students volunteer addition sentences that have a sum of ten. Remind them that different sets of addends can make ten.

ELL ELL Support Strategy Use this vocabulary activity to link to familiar contexts and prior knowledge.

My Vocabulary Cards

Have students work in small groups to sort the cards by the number of letters in each word or words.

 Building on the Essential Question
In this lesson, students will build upon the skills and concepts needed to answer the chapter's Essential Question "What strategies can I use to add and subtract?"

Plan Online
Plan for your lesson by using the resources at
connectED.mcgraw-hill.com

Digital Dashboard

Interactive Whiteboard Ready

Vocab The eBook **Glossary** shows the definition of the word and has audio for each definition. The **eGlossary** provides definitions in 13 languages.

Watch Watch as concepts are brought to life through **animations**, **songs**, and a variety of visual instruction.

Tools **Virtual Manipulatives** with work mats allow teachers and students to model the lesson.

Check Use **eAssessment** for online assignments and customized assessments.

Use the **Common Core Quick Check** before the lesson to assess students' retention of previously learned concepts.

Use the interactive **Self-Check Quiz** after the lesson to provide immediate feedback on lesson concepts.

eHelp Digital and print resources assist students and parents in completing My Homework.

Games **Online games** and **apps** provide extra practice for lesson concepts.

PD **Professional development videos** help teachers gain a deeper understanding of the lesson concepts and strategies.

RtI Support for **approaching**, **on-** and **beyond-level** students as well as **English Language Learners**.

Masters **Reteach** and **Enrich** worksheets, **Manipulative Masters**, the **Problem of the Day**, and other blackline masters are available for each lesson.

---

1 LAUNCH THE LESSON

CCSS

🕐 If your students are well-versed in making a 10, you may choose to begin instruction with Step 2, **TEACH**.

You will need
☐ number cards (0–9)

Mathematical PRACTICE  **Modeling the Math**

Place students in pairs. Give each pair a set of shuffled number cards (0–9). Have the pair place the cards face down spread out on the desk or table.

Have the first student draw two cards. The student should determine if the cards make a ten. If so, they earn a point. If they earn a point, have them collect the cards. Have them record the addends and the sums for points earned in a table like the one shown.

Addend 1	Addend 2	Sum
4	6	10
7	3	10

If they did not earn a point, have them place the cards face down again. The second student draws two cards. The second student should determine if the cards make a ten.

Repeat until all the cards are collected, except the cards numbered 0 and 5. The student with the most points wins.

What pairs did you find that had a sum of 10 and earned a point for you? $1 + 9, 2 + 8, 3 + 7, 4 + 6, 5 + 5$

Begin core instruction here.

You will need

☐ two-color counters

☐ cups

☐ Work Mat 2

Explore and Explain

Read the directions that are at the bottom of the student page. Have students shake the cup when the 13 counters are inside to mix up the counters. Guide students through placing red counters in the top ten-frame and yellow counters in the bottom ten-frame.

In the unlikely event that there are 10 or more red or yellow counters, have students place the counters back in the cup, mix them up, and pour them out again.

Write the number of counters that are in the top ten-frame as the first addend in the top addition sentence. Then write the number of counters that are in the bottom ten-frame as the second addend in the top addition sentence. What sum should everyone have? 13

Lead students through moving yellow counters into the top ten-frame to make a ten.

Now write the number of counters that are in the top ten-frame as the first addend in the bottom addition sentence. Then write the number of counters that are in the bottom ten-frame as the second addend in the bottom addition sentence. What number sentence should everyone have?
10 + 3 = 13

See and Show

Help students work through the example at the top of the page.

Have them trace the dashed numbers as they work through the problem. Practice making a ten using the Work Mat and counters for the exercises or additional exercises as needed.

Work through Exercises 1 and 2 as a class.

Mathematical PRACTICE 3 Talk Math

Discuss with students "Name all of the facts you know that have a sum of 10." 0 + 10, 1 + 9, 2 + 8, 3 + 7, 4 + 6, 5 + 5, 6 + 4, 7 + 3, 8 + 2, 9 + 1, 10 + 0

CORE INSTRUCTION

Name _____

Operations and Algebraic Thinking
2.OA.1, 2.OA.2

Make a 10

Lesson 4
ESSENTIAL QUESTION
What strategies can I use to add and subtract?

Explore and Explain

You can count on us!

____ + ____ = ____

See students' work. ____ + ____ = ____

Teacher Directions: Place 13 counters in a cup. Empty the cup onto the page. Place red counters in the top ten-frame. Place yellow counters in the bottom ten-frame. Write the addition sentence. Move yellow counters into the top ten-frame to make ten. Write the new addition sentence.

Online Content at connectED.mcgraw-hill.com   Chapter 1 • Lesson 4   29

See and Show

Mathematical PRACTICE

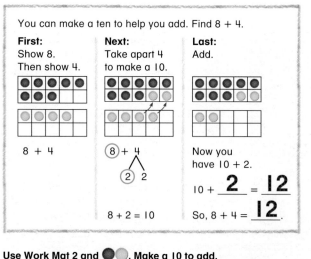

You can make a ten to help you add. Find 8 + 4.

First: Show 8. Then show 4.	**Next:** Take apart 4 to make a 10.	**Last:** Add.
8 + 4	⑧ + 4 / ② 2	Now you have 10 + 2.
	8 + 2 = 10	10 + **2** = **12** / So, 8 + 4 = **12**.

Use Work Mat 2 and ⬤◯. **Make a 10 to add.**

1.

9 + 5 = **14**

2.

7 + 5 = **12**

 **Talk Math**   Name all of the facts you know that have a sum of 10.

30   Chapter 1 • Lesson 4

3 PRACTICE & APPLY

CCSS

Name _____

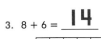

On My Own

Use Work Mat 2 and ●○. Make a 10 to add.

Helpful Hint
Make a 10, count on, or find doubles to add.

3. 8 + 6 = __14__

4. 7 + 8 = __15__

5. 9 + 4 = __13__   6. 7 + 7 = __14__

7. 4 + 8 = __12__   8. 8 + 9 = __17__

9. 3 + 9 = __12__   10. 7 + 5 = __12__

11. 3	12. 4	13. 2
+ 7	+ 9	+ 9
10	**13**	**11**

14. 7	15. 8	16. 4
+ 8	+ 4	+ 6
15	**12**	**10**

Chapter 1 • Lesson 4   31

Problem Solving

Mathematical PRACTICE

17. Ms. Ling's class sees 9 tigers at the zoo. Ms. John's class sees 8 tigers. How many tigers did they see in all?

__17__ tigers

18. There are 6 pigs at the farm. There are 7 sheep at the farm. How many pigs and sheep are there in all?

Did I just see a tiger?

__13__ pigs and sheep

19. 5 goldfish are in the tank. 7 more goldfish are added to the tank. How many goldfish are in the tank now?

__12__ goldfish

Write Math How could you use making a ten when adding?

Sample answer: If you know all the ways to make a ten

then you can mentally make a 10 to solve problems

that have a sum greater than 10.

32   Chapter 1 • Lesson 4

On My Own

Have students work through the exercises on this page independently. You may choose to assign exercises based on the chart below.

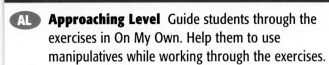

DIFFERENTIATED ASSIGNMENTS

AL **Approaching Level** Guide students through the exercises in On My Own. Help them to use manipulatives while working through the exercises.

OL **On Level** Complete the exercises independently.

BL **Beyond Level** Complete the exercises independently without manipulatives.

Common Error!
Sometimes students may add the wrong number to make 10. Help them avoid this error by reviewing basic addition facts as needed.

Problem Solving

Have students work through the problem-solving exercises on this page independently. Have students use manipulatives if they need help solving the exercises.

Mathematical PRACTICE **4** In Exercise 17, students **model with mathematics.**

Write Math

This exercise asks students to build upon their understanding of concepts needed to answer the chapter's Essential Question.

AL APPROACHING LEVEL

IF my students struggle with making a 10,

THEN choose a resource:

→ Use the Reteach worksheet with small groups.

→ Go online for a Differentiated Instruction activity.

→ **Mental Math** Take apart numbers to make a 10. *How could you take apart 8 + 4 to make a 10?* Take apart 4 into 2 + 2. *How would you solve this problem?* 8 + 2 = 10 and 10 + 2 = 12 Repeat with additional examples.

OL ON LEVEL

IF my students seem to know making a 10, but need more practice,

THEN choose a resource:

→ Assign My Homework.

→ Go online for a Differentiated Instruction activity.

BL BEYOND LEVEL

IF my students have mastered making a 10,

THEN choose a resource:

→ Use the Enrich worksheet in cooperative groups.

→ Assign My Homework.

→ Go online for a Differentiated Instruction activity.

AL

Name _____

Lesson 4   Reteach

Make a 10

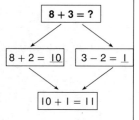

> You can make a 10 to find 8 + 3:
> 1. Add to 8 to make 10.
> 2. Subtract the same number from 3.
> 3. Add the sum and difference.
> 4. The answer is also the sum of 8 + 3.
>
> $8 + 3 = ?$
> $8 + 2 = 10$ $3 - 2 = 1$
> $10 + 1 = 11$
>
> We know that $10 + 1$ equals 11, so $8 + 3$ also equals 11.
> $10 + 1 = 11$ and $8 + 3 = 11$

Make a 10 to add. Use the example above for help.

1.
$9 + 5 = ?$
$9 + \underline{1} = 10$ $5 - \underline{1} = 4$
$10 + \underline{4} = 14$
So, $9 + 5 = \underline{14}$.

2.
$7 + 6 = ?$
$7 + \underline{3} = 10$ $6 - \underline{3} = 3$
$10 + \underline{3} = 13$
So, $7 + 6 = \underline{13}$.

Name _____

BL Lesson 4   Enrich

Make a 10

Circle 5 pairs of numbers that equal 10.
Then fill in the blanks to solve the problems.

Possible answers:

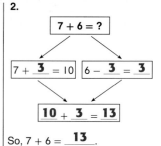

Sample answers:

1. $16 = 6 + \underline{1} + \underline{9}$

2. $19 = 9 + \underline{2} + \underline{8}$

3. $20 = 10 + \underline{3} + \underline{7}$

4. $14 = 4 + \underline{4} + \underline{6}$

5. $18 = 8 + \underline{5} + \underline{5}$

Now find combinations of three numbers to solve these problems.   **See students' work.**

6. _____ + _____ + _____ = 17

7. _____ + _____ + _____ = 19

8. _____ + _____ + _____ = 12

Name

Operations and Algebraic Thinking
2.OA.1, 2.OA.2

My Homework

Lesson 4
Make a 10

Homework Helper 🖥 Need help? connectED.mcgraw-hill.com

Make a ten to help you add.

8 + 6

Think: 8 + 2 = 10
Add: 10 + 4 = 14.
So, 8 + 6 = 14.

Practice

Make a ten to add.

1.

6 + 5 = __11__

2.

8 + 4 = __12__

Chapter 1 • Lesson 4   33

Make a ten to add.

3. 7 + 4 = __11__   4. 4 + 8 = __12__

5. 9 + 7 = __16__   6. 7 + 6 = __13__

7. 3 + 9 = __12__   8. 7 + 5 = __12__

9.   8
    + 8
    __16__

10.   9
     + 4
     __13__

11.   8
     + 5
     __13__

Raul is unstoppable!

12. Raul wins 8 chess matches on Saturday and 5 on Sunday. How many matches did he win?

__13__ matches

Test Practice

13. Which addition sentence can help you find the sum for 8 + 7?

   ○ 5 + 7 = 12   ● 10 + 5 = 15

   ○ 10 + 8 = 18   ○ 10 + 7 = 17

 Math at Home Have your child tell you how to find 8 + 7 by making a 10.

34   Chapter 1 • Lesson 4

---

4 WRAP IT UP

My Homework

Assign homework after successful completion of the lesson.

Students who understand the concepts may skip the **Homework Helper** section.

Test Practice

Diagnose Student Errors

Class trends in wrong answers may indicate common errors or misconceptions.

5 + 7 = 12   5 + 7 does not relate to the problem

10 + 5 = 15   correct

10 + 8 = 18   did not make a 10, just added 10

10 + 7 = 17   did not make a 10, just added 10

Formative Assessment

Ask students the following question.

Does making a 10 make it easier or harder to add in your head? easier to add 10s mentally

Line Up!

As each student lines up, tell him or her a number between 0 and 9. Have the student tell you what number can be added to that number to make 10.

LESSON 5

Add Three Numbers

OBJECTIVE Group addends differently to make the same sum.

What's the Math?

 Common Core State Standards
DOMAIN: Operations and Algebraic Thinking

Standards: 2.OA.1, 2.OA.2
The wording of these standards can be found on page 2.

What Students Should Understand

- You can add three numbers by grouping the addends in different ways. The sum will stay the same.

  Teacher's note: This is the Associative Property of Addition.

- To add three numbers, first decide which two addends are easier to add. Then find their sum. Next, add the third addend to find the total.

What Students Should be Able to Do

Find $3 + 5 + 3$.

$3 + 5 + 3 = $ _____

$$\boxed{6}$$

$5 + 6 = 11$

So, $3 + 5 + 3 = 11$.

Building on the Essential Question

In this lesson, students will build upon the skills and concepts needed to answer the chapter's Essential Question "What strategies can I use to add and subtract?"

Developing Vocabulary

 Review Vocabulary

group

Review Activity

- Display 3 groups of the same object for the whole class to see. One group should contain 3 objects. Another should contain 4 objects. The third group should contain 7 objects.

- Ask students how they could combine two of the groups to make 10.

- Cross out the group of 3 and group of 7.

- Have students explain how the total number of objects represent 14. Then discuss with students how making ten helped make adding the 3 groups of objects easier.

ELL **ELL Support Strategy** Use this vocabulary activity to use non-linguistic representations to support student thinking.

My Vocabulary Cards

Have students use their My Vocabulary Cards to demonstrate *group*. For example, they might group cards that use similar visuals, or that start with the same letter.

Plan Online

Plan for your lesson by using the resources at

↗ connectED.mcgraw-hill.com

Digital Dashboard

Interactive Whiteboard Ready

Vocab

The eBook **Glossary** shows the definition of the word and has audio for each definition. The **eGlossary** provides definitions in 13 languages.

Watch

Watch as concepts are brought to life through **animations**, **songs**, and a variety of visual instruction.

Tools

Virtual Manipulatives with work mats allow teachers and students to model the lesson.

Check

Use **eAssessment** for online assignments and customized assessments.

Use the **Common Core Quick Check** before the lesson to assess students' retention of previously learned concepts.

Use the interactive **Self-Check Quiz** after the lesson to provide immediate feedback on lesson concepts.

eHelp

Digital and print resources assist students and parents in completing My Homework.

Games

Online games and **apps** provide extra practice for lesson concepts.

PD

Professional development videos help teachers gain a deeper understanding of the lesson concepts and strategies.

RtI

Support for **approaching**, **on**- and **beyond-level** students as well as **English Language Learners**.

Masters

Reteach and **Enrich** worksheets, **Manipulative Masters**, the **Problem of the Day**, and other blackline masters are available for each lesson.

1 LAUNCH THE LESSON

 If your students are well-versed in adding three numbers, you may choose to begin instruction with Step 2, **TEACH**.

You will need

☐ number lines

☐ counters

☐ number cubes

Mathematical PRACTICE **Modeling the Math**

Give pairs of students a number line (1–20), a counter, and a number cube.

Have students place the counter at 0. One student rolls the number cube and moves the counter that many spaces on the number line. The other student writes the first number rolled and a plus sign. Students repeat the rolling, moving, and writing twice.

Students then compare where they stopped on the number line with the answer to their number sentence.

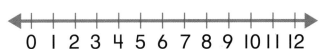

0 1 2 3 4 5 6 7 8 9 10 11 12

21ST CENTURY SKILLS

Critical Thinking

Encourage students to look for ways to combine numbers to make a 10 or to create doubles to add to get the final sum. The ability to combine numbers to make mental addition easier is a valuable tool they will use beyond second grade.

TEACH

 Begin core instruction here.

You will need

☐ counters

Explore and Explain

Read the directions that are at the bottom of the student page.

After you trace the counters, you may write the type of animal or draw the animal in each tracing so that you can keep track of how many fish, frogs, and snakes you drew. How many animals are there in all? 12

See and Show

Help students work through the example at the top of the page. Have them trace the dashed numbers as they work through the problems.

In 4 + 6 + 4, can you group the addends in a different way? Yes; you can add 6 + 4 first to get 10 then add 4 and 10 to get 14.

As a class, discuss the different ways to group the addends in 2 + 3 + 4 and 3 + 1 + 7. Point out that no matter which two numbers are added first, the sum will stay the same.

Work through Exercises 1–6 as a class.

Mathematical PRACTICE ➌   Talk Math

Discuss with students "How do you decide which two numbers to add first when adding three digits?" Sample answer: I look for a fact I know, doubles, or I make a 10.

CORE INSTRUCTION

Name _____

2.OA.1, 2.OA.2

Add Three Numbers

Lesson 5
ESSENTIAL QUESTION
What strategies can I use to add and subtract?

Explore and Explain (Watch) (Tools)

12 animals   See Students' work.

Teacher Directions: Have students use counters to show the following: There are 4 fish, 6 frogs, and 2 snakes in the pond. Trace the counters and write how many in all.

Online Content at connectED.mcgraw-hill.com   Chapter 1 • Lesson 5   35

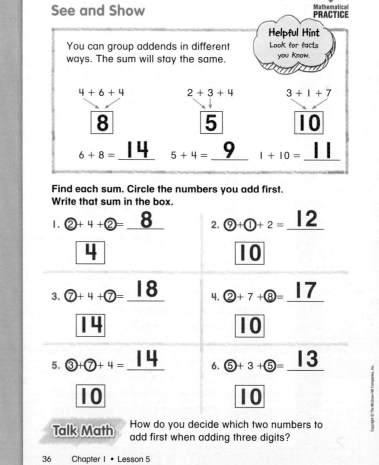

See and Show

Mathematical PRACTICE

Helpful Hint Look for facts you know.

You can group addends in different ways. The sum will stay the same.

4 + 6 + 4   2 + 3 + 4   3 + 1 + 7
  [8]   [5]   [10]
6 + 8 = 14   5 + 4 = 9   1 + 10 = 11

Find each sum. Circle the numbers you add first. Write that sum in the box.

1. ②+ 4 +② = **8**   2. ⑨+①+ 2 = **12**
   [4]   [10]

3. ⑦+ 4 +⑦= **18**   4. ②+ 7 +⑧= **17**
   [14]   [10]

5. ③+⑦+ 4 = **14**   6. ⑤+ 3 +⑤= **13**
   [10]   [10]

Talk Math   How do you decide which two numbers to add first when adding three digits?

36   Chapter 1 • Lesson 5

35-36   Chapter 1 Apply Addition and Subtraction Concepts

On My Own

Name _____

Helpful Hint
Add two numbers first. Look for facts you know.

On My Own

Find each sum. Circle the numbers you add first. Write that sum in the box.

7. ④ + 3 + ④ = __11__
   8

8. 4 + ③ + ⑦ = __14__
   10

9. ② + ⑧ + 3 = __13__
   10

10. ⑥ + 1 + ⑥ = __13__
    12

Find each sum.

11. 5 + 5 + 5 = __15__

12. 6 + 6 + 3 = __15__

13. 7 + 4 + 7 = __18__

14. 9 + 8 + 1 = __18__

15. 1 + 7 + 3 = __11__

16. 5 + 7 + 5 = __17__

17. 3
     5
    + 7
    ___
    15

18. 7
     7
    + 1
    ___
    15

19. 9
     8
    + 1
    ___
    18

Chapter 1 • Lesson 5   37

Problem Solving

20. The zoo has 5 black bears, 5 brown bears and 2 polar bears. How many bears are at the zoo?

    I can't wait to see the answer!

    __12__ bears

21. Lisa saw 4 sheep and 4 goats at the petting zoo. She also saw 6 piglets. How many animals did Lisa see at the petting zoo?

    __14__ animals

    Write the doubles fact that helped you solve the problem.

    __4__ + __4__ = __8__

Write Math Explain how you can group addends in any way to help you solve addition problems that have more than 2 addends.

Sample answer: You can add two numbers that make a 10, add facts you know, or add doubles.

38   Chapter 1 • Lesson 5

---

3 PRACTICE & APPLY

On My Own

Have students work through the exercises on this page independently. You may choose to assign exercises based on the chart below.

DIFFERENTIATED ASSIGNMENTS

AL **Approaching Level** Guide students through the exercises in On My Own. Help them to use manipulatives while working through the exercises.

OL **On Level** Complete the exercises independently.

BL **Beyond Level** Complete the exercises independently without manipulatives.

Common Error!

Sometimes students may forget to add one of the three addends. Have them count the number of addends before they find the sum. Then have them circle the pair of numbers they added first.

Problem Solving

Have students work through the problem-solving exercises on this page independently. If students are struggling, have them solve the doubles fact first and then add the other addend to that sum.

Mathematical PRACTICE 7 In Exercise 21, students **look for and make use of structure.**

Write Math

This exercise asks students to build upon their understanding of concepts needed to answer the chapter's essential question.

AL **APPROACHING LEVEL**

IF my students struggle with adding three numbers,

THEN choose a resource:

→ Use the Reteach worksheet with small groups.

→ Go online for a Differentiated Instruction activity.

→ **Ten-Frame** Students roll a number cube three times. They add a color of connecting cubes to a ten-frame for each number rolled. Students find the sum of the numbers rolled by using their ten-frame and counting any extra cubes.

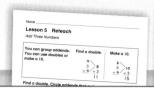

OL **ON LEVEL**

IF my students seem to know adding three numbers, but need more practice,

THEN choose a resource:

→ Use a Differentiated Instruction activity from p. 1D.

→ Assign My Homework.

→ Go online for a Differentiated Instruction activity.

BL **BEYOND LEVEL**

IF my students have mastered adding three numbers,

THEN choose a resource:

→ Use the Enrich worksheet in cooperative groups.

→ Assign My Homework.

→ Go online for a Differentiated Instruction activity.

AL

Name _____

Lesson 5 Reteach

Add Three Numbers

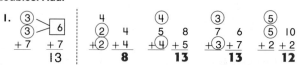

You can group addends. You can use doubles or make a 10.

Find a double.

$$\begin{array}{c}4\\3\\+4\end{array}\Big\rangle 8 \atop +3 \over 11$$

Make a 10.

$$\begin{array}{c}6\\5\\+4\end{array}\Big\rangle 10 \atop +5 \over 15$$

Find a double. Circle addends that make doubles. Add.

1.

$$\begin{array}{c}③\\③\\+7\end{array}\ \boxed{6}\ \begin{array}{c}\\+7\end{array}\ {13}$$

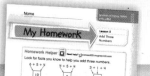

Make a 10. Circle addends that make a 10. Add.

2.

$$\begin{array}{c}⑧\\②\\+4\end{array}\ \boxed{10}\ \begin{array}{c}\\+4\end{array}\ {14}$$

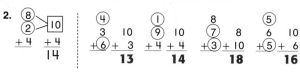

Find the sum.

3.

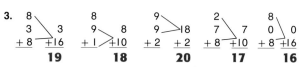

BL

Name _____

Lesson 5 Enrich

Add Three Numbers

Add as quickly as you can.

Write the sum of the first set of numbers in the squares. Then add that sum to the next addend to find the total sum.

1. $2 + 2 + 1 = \boxed{5} + 6 = \underline{11}$

2. $1 + 1 + 1 + 7 = \boxed{10} + 9 = \underline{19}$

3. $3 + 3 + 1 = \boxed{7} + 8 = \underline{15}$

4. $4 + 1 + 1 + 1 = \boxed{7} + 10 = \underline{17}$

5. $2 + 8 + 5 = \boxed{15} + 5 = \underline{20}$

6. $6 + 1 + 1 + 1 + 1 = \boxed{10} + 4 = \underline{14}$

7. Which sum is the greatest? __20__

8. Arrange the total sums in order from *least* to *greatest*.

__11__, __14__, __15__, __17__, __19__, __20__

Name

My Homework

Lesson 5
Add Three
Numbers

Homework Helper
eHelp **Need help?** connectED.mcgraw-hill.com

Look for facts you know to help you add three numbers.

$6 + 5 + 4$

$\boxed{10}$

$10 + 5 = 15$

$4 + 5 + 4$

$\boxed{8}$

$8 + 5 = 13$

$3 + 1 + 4$

$\boxed{4}$

$4 + 4 = 8$

Practice

Find each sum.

1. $6 + 6 + 4 = \underline{16}$

2. $6 + 2 + 8 = \underline{16}$

3. $3 + 3 + 9 = \underline{15}$

4. $7 + 4 + 3 = \underline{14}$

5.
```
   1
   9
 + 4
```
$\underline{14}$

6.
```
   7
   6
 + 6
```
$\underline{19}$

7.
```
   8
   4
 + 2
```
$\underline{14}$

Chapter 1 • Lesson 5   39

Find each sum.

8.
```
   7
   3
 + 5
```
$\underline{15}$

9.
```
   4
   2
 + 6
```
$\underline{12}$

10.
```
   9
   8
 + 1
```
$\underline{18}$

11. The zoo has 3 giraffes, 4 African elephants, and 3 Asian elephants. How many elephants and giraffes are at the zoo?

I've got lots of elephant and giraffe friends!

$\underline{10}$ giraffes and elephants

12. There are 5 tigers, 4 leopards, and 6 lions at the zoo. How many big cats are at the zoo?

$\underline{15}$ big cats

Test Practice

13. Which addition sentence could help solve this problem?

$3 + 5 + 7 = \underline{\quad}$

$2 + 3 = 5$ $\quad$ $5 + 5 = 10$ $\quad$ $3 + 7 = 10$ $\quad$ $5 + 2 = 7$
○ $\quad\quad\quad$ ○ $\quad\quad\quad$ ● $\quad\quad\quad$ ○

 Math at Home Have your child show you how to add $7 + 7 + 1$.

40   Chapter 1 • Lesson 5

---

4 WRAP IT UP

My Homework

Assign homework after successful completion of the lesson. Students who understand the concepts may skip the **Homework Helper** section.

Test Practice

Diagnose Student Errors

Class trends in wrong answers may indicate common errors or misconceptions.

$2 + 3 = 5$ found addends that make 5

$5 + 5 = 10$ found addends that make 10

$3 + 7 = 10$ correct

$5 + 2 = 7$ found addends that make 7

Formative Assessment

Ask students the following question.

What is the sum of $7 + 4 + 3$? 14 *Explain how you found the sum.* Sample answer: $7 + 3$ makes 10, and $10 + 4 = 14$.

Line Up!

Have students line up in groups. For example, have two students line up, then add four students, then add five more. Before the rest of the students line up, ask for the total number of students in line.

Problem Solving
STRATEGY: Write a Number Sentence
OBJECTIVE Write a number sentence to solve problems.

What's the Math?

 Common Core State Standards
DOMAIN: Operations and Algebraic Thinking

Standards: 2.OA.1, 2.OA.2
The wording of these standards can be found on page 2.

Mathematical PRACTICE 4 Model with mathematics.

What Students Should Understand

• You can write a number sentence to solve a real-world problem.

• First, make sure you understand the meaning of the problem. Determine which facts are important and the question being asked.

• Make a plan and follow through to solve the problem.

• Justify your conclusion by checking your answer to determine whether it is correct and makes sense.

What Students Should be Able to Do

Erik and Josh hiked 1 mile in the morning. They hiked 3 miles in the afternoon. Then they hiked 2 miles in the evening. How many miles did they hike in all?

1 Understand

Underline what you know. Circle what you need to find.

2 Plan

How will I solve this problem?
I can write a number sentence.

3 Solve

I will… find $1 + 3 + 2$.
$1 + 3 + 2 = 6$
So, Erik and Josh hiked 6 miles in all.

4 Check

Is my answer reasonable? Explain.
Sample answer: yes; $6 - 1 - 3 - 2 = 0$, so my answer is correct.

Developing the Strategy

What's the Strategy?

Make a Number Sentence Students will write a number sentence to solve a problem. Students translate word problems in this lesson into number sentences to solve.

Other Strategies

Other strategies that have been taught and that can be used are:

• The four-step plan

• Look for a pattern

 **Signal Words** Encourage English-language learners to identify signal words or signal phrases, such as *now* or *how many*, as they read word problems.

Mathematical PRACTICE

The Mathematical Practices are especially evident in problem-solving situations, in which students connect procedures and processes with mathematical understanding. In this lesson, the following Mathematical Practices are addressed.

 Reason abstractly and quantitively.

 Model with mathematics.

Plan Online

Plan for your lesson by using the resources at
connectED.mcgraw-hill.com

Digital Dashboard

Interactive Whiteboard Ready

 Vocab

The eBook **Glossary** shows the definition of the word and has audio for each definition. The **eGlossary** provides definitions in 13 languages.

 Tools

Virtual Manipulatives along with work mats allow teachers and students to model the lesson.

 Check

Use **eAssessment** for online assignments and customized assessments.

Use the **Common Core Quick Check** before the lesson to assess students' retention of previously learned concepts.

 eHelp

Digital and print resources assist students and parents in completing My Homework.

 PD

Professional development videos help teachers gain a deeper understanding of the lesson concepts and strategies.

 RtI

Support for **approaching**, **on**- and **beyond-level** students as well as **English Language Learners**.

Masters

Reteach and **Enrich** worksheets, **Manipulative Masters**, the **Problem of the Day**, and other blackline masters are available for each lesson.

1 LAUNCH THE LESSON

If your students are well-versed in problem solving, you may choose to begin instruction with Step 2, **TEACH**.

You will need

☐ yellow and red connecting cubes

Review

Write and read aloud the following: Rachel planted seven yellow flowers in the garden. She also planted eight red flowers. How many flowers did she plant in all?

What do you know? There are seven yellow flowers and eight red flowers. *What do you want to find?* How many flowers in all

Draw the seven yellow and eight red flowers on the board as shown. Have students use red and yellow connecting cubes to model what you have drawn.

Other than using the connecting cubes, how can you find your answer? Write a number sentence

What is the total number of flowers? 15 flowers; $7 + 8 = 15$

 +

TEACH

Begin core instruction here.

Problem Solving

1 Understand

Reread the problem with the students. Point out information as you read it.

2 Plan

Discuss several ideas. Lead the students toward writing a number sentence to solve the problem.

3 Solve

Work through the problem using the student page with the students. Show how to solve the problem step by step. Discuss with students how they knew to use an addition number sentence.

4 Check

Discuss why the answer makes sense. Try to develop a sense of reasoning.

Practice the Strategy

1 Understand

Reread the problem with the students. Ask students to point out information that is important as you read it.

2 Plan

Lead students in discussing several ideas. Direct the students toward writing a number sentence to solve the problem.

3 Solve

Work through the problem using the student page with the students. Show how to solve step by step. Discuss with class how this problem calls for writing a number sentence using three addends whereas the first problem calls for writing a number sentence using two addends.

4 Check

Discuss why the answer makes sense. Try to develop a sense of reasoning.

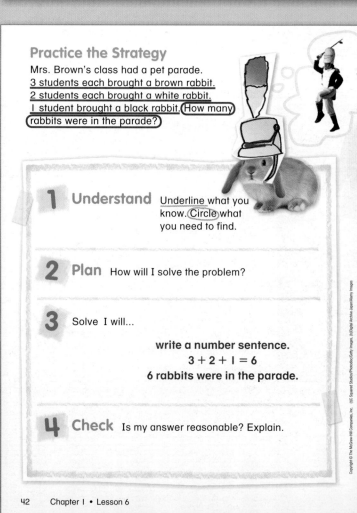

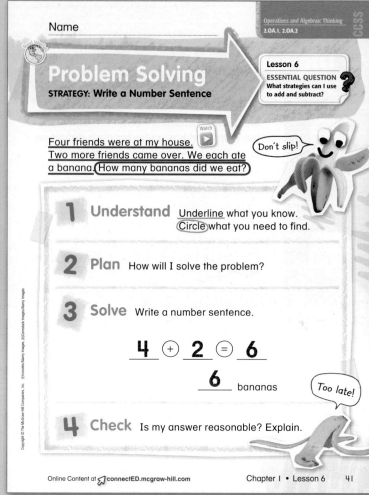

41-42 Chapter 1 Apply Addition and Subtraction Concepts

Name

Apply the Strategy

Write a number sentence to solve.

1. There are 3 rabbits at a farm. The farmer buys 9 more. How many rabbits are there now?

$$3 \oplus 9 \ominus 12 \qquad 12 \text{ rabbits}$$

2. Chung always picks 5 flowers at home after school. How many flowers will he have after 3 days?

$$5 \oplus 5 \oplus 5 \ominus 15 \qquad 15 \text{ flowers}$$

3. Mrs. Lewis has 4 books for her reading group. She finds 2 more books. How many books does she have now?

$$4 \oplus 2 \ominus 6 \qquad 6 \text{ books}$$

Chapter 1 • Lesson 6   43

Review the Strategies

Choose a strategy
- Write a number sentence.
- Act it out.
- Draw a diagram.

4. Steve, Elena, and Ian are playing with toy planes. Steve gave 8 planes to Ian and 8 to Elena. He has 4 planes left. How many planes did Steve start with?

   20 planes

5. Arielle has 4 markers. Julia has 3 more markers than Arielle. How many markers do they have in all?

   11 markers

Parrot books are my favorite!

6. The library has 4 books about parrots and 3 books about swans. There is 1 less book about blue jays than swans. How many books about birds are there in all?

   9 books

Mathematical PRACTICE 1 Apply the Strategy

Have students work through the exercises on these pages independently. You may choose to assign exercises based on the chart below.

DIFFERENTIATED ASSIGNMENTS

AL Approaching Level Guide students through the exercises in Apply the Strategies. Help them to use manipulatives while working through these exercises.

OL On Level Complete the exercises independently.

BL Beyond Level Complete the exercises independently without manipulatives.

Common Error!
Exercise 4 will require students to invoke prior knowledge and use the Act It Out strategy.

Review the Strategies

Students may use other strategies to solve these exercises.

- Act it out
- Draw a diagram

RESPONSE TO INTERVENTION

DIFFERENTIATED INSTRUCTION

AL APPROACHING LEVEL

IF my students struggle with problem solving,

THEN choose a resource:

→ Use the Reteach worksheet with small groups.

→ Go online for a Differentiated Instruction activity.

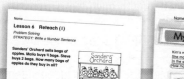

OL ON LEVEL

IF my students seem to know problem solving, but need more practice,

THEN choose a resource:

→ Use a Differentiated Instruction activity from p. 1D.

→ Assign My Homework.

→ Go online for a Differentiated Instruction activity.

BL BEYOND LEVEL

IF my students have mastered problem solving,

THEN choose a resource:

→ Use the Enrich worksheet in cooperative groups.

→ Assign My Homework.

→ Go online for a Differentiated Instruction activity.

45A **Chapter 1** Apply Addition and Subtraction Concepts

Name _____

AL Lesson 6 Reteach (1)

Problem Solving
STRATEGY: *Write a Number Sentence*

Sanders' Orchard sells bags of apples. Malia buys 4 bags. Steve buys 2 bags. How many bags of apples do they buy in all?

Step 1 Understand	**What do I know?** Malia buys 4 bags. Steve buys 2 bags. **What do I need to find?** The total number of bags of apples Steve and Malia buy?
Step 2 Plan	**How will I solve?** I will write a number sentence.
Step 3 Solve	**Write a number sentence.** $4 + 2 = 6$ ___6___ bags of apples
Step 4 Check	Is my answer reasonable? ___yes___

Name _____

AL Lesson 6 Reteach (2)

Problem Solving
STRATEGY: *Write a Number Sentence*

Write a number sentence to solve.

1. A.J., Seth, and Lily each have 1 box of pencils. There are 5 pencils in each box. How many pencils do they have in all? $5 + 5 + 5 = 15$ ___15___ pencils

2. Johnny buys 3 bottles of juice for a party. He decides to buy 6 more bottles. How many total bottles does Johnny buy? $3 + 6 = 9$ ___9___ bottles

3. Steffan has 3 sunflowers and 5 tulips in his garden. How many flowers are there in all? $3 + 5 = 8$ ___8___ flowers

4. Mateo saw 3 red tricycles and 3 blue tricycles coming down the sidewalk. How many tricycles did he see in all? $3 + 3 = 6$ ___6___ tricycles

5. Aiden has 7 robot stickers and 5 alien stickers on his folder. How many stickers in all? $7 + 5 = 12$ ___12___ stickers

---

Name _____

BL Lesson 6 Enrich

Problem Solving
STRATEGY: *Write a Number Sentence*

Write a number sentence to solve.

One cricket has 6 legs.   One spider has 8 legs.

1. How many legs on 3 crickets?
   ___6___ + ___6___ + ___6___ = ___18___ legs

2. How many legs on 4 crickets and 3 spiders?
   ___6___ + ___6___ + ___6___ + ___6___ +
   ___8___ + ___8___ + ___8___ = ___48___ legs

3. How many legs on 2 crickets and 2 spiders?
   ___6___ + ___6___ + ___8___ + ___8___ = ___28___ legs

4. How many legs on 3 spiders and 3 crickets?
   ___8___ + ___8___ + ___8___ + ___6___ +
   ___6___ + ___6___ = ___42___ legs

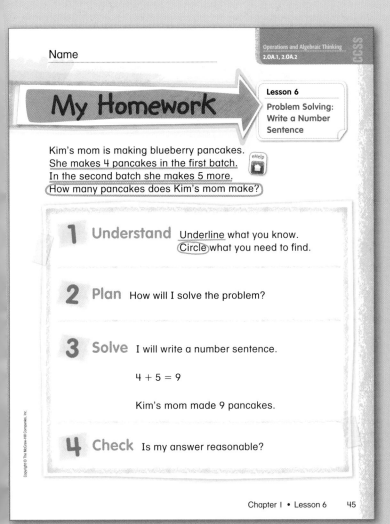

Name _____

My Homework →

Lesson 6
Problem Solving:
Write a Number
Sentence

Kim's mom is making blueberry pancakes.
She makes 4 pancakes in the first batch.
In the second batch she makes 5 more.
How many pancakes does Kim's mom make?

1 Understand Underline what you know.
Circle what you need to find.

2 Plan How will I solve the problem?

3 Solve I will write a number sentence.

$4 + 5 = 9$

Kim's mom made 9 pancakes.

4 Check Is my answer reasonable?

Chapter 1 • Lesson 6   45

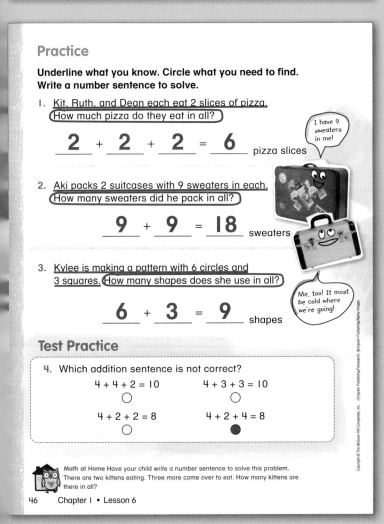

Practice

**Underline what you know. Circle what you need to find.
Write a number sentence to solve.**

1. Kit, Ruth, and Dean each eat 2 slices of pizza.
How much pizza do they eat in all?

$\underline{2} + \underline{2} + \underline{2} = \underline{6}$ pizza slices

I have 9 sweaters in me!

2. Aki packs 2 suitcases with 9 sweaters in each.
How many sweaters did he pack in all?

$\underline{9} + \underline{9} = \underline{18}$ sweaters

3. Kylee is making a pattern with 6 circles and
3 squares. How many shapes does she use in all?

$\underline{6} + \underline{3} = \underline{9}$ shapes

Me, too! It must be cold where we're going!

Test Practice

4. Which addition sentence is not correct?

$4 + 4 + 2 = 10$ ○ $4 + 3 + 3 = 10$ ○

$4 + 2 + 2 = 8$ ○ $4 + 2 + 4 = 8$ ●

Math at Home Have your child write a number sentence to solve this problem.
There are two kittens eating. Three more come over to eat. How many kittens are
there in all?

46   Chapter 1 • Lesson 6

My Homework

Assign homework after successful completion of the lesson.
Students who understand the concepts may skip the
Homework Helper section.

Test Practice

Diagnose Student Errors

Class trends in wrong answers may indicate common errors or
misconceptions.

$4 + 4 + 2 = 10$	added correct
$4 + 3 + 3 = 10$	added correct
$4 + 2 + 2 = 8$	added correct
$4 + 2 + 4 = 8$	added incorrect

Formative Assessment

Ask students the following question.

How can you use number sentences to solve problems?

You can use the information to write an addition or
subtraction number sentence.

Check My Progress

Use this as a formative assessment to determine if your students are struggling, and if so, with which topics they struggle. The criteria for differentiation are on the next page.

Vocabulary Check

Have students point to the number line. Explain that this number line shows the addition sentence that appears above it.

ELL **ELL Support Strategy** Use this information to participate in purposeful, cooperative learning activities.

Concept Check

These concepts are covered in Lessons 1–5.

Exercises	Concept	Review Lesson(s)
5–7	Add	1, 2
8–11	Doubles and Near Doubles	3
12–15	Make a 10	4
16–19	Add Three Numbers	5

Problem Solving

Exercise 20 uses a word problem to check for understanding of the same concepts.

Test Practice

Diagnose Student Errors

Class trends in wrong answers may indicate common errors or misconceptions.

 8 used only the number given
16 correct
18 incorrect
88 placed the two 8's side by side

Name _____

Vocabulary Check

Draw lines to match.

1. **add** — The numbers you add in an addition number sentence.

2. **doubles** — Both addends are the same.

3. **count on** — $3 + 4 = 7$

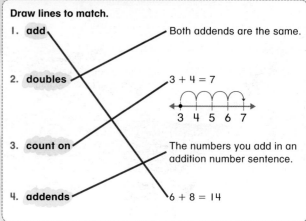

4. **addends** — $6 + 8 = 14$

Concept Check

Find each sum.

5. $7 + 0 = \underline{7}$ 6. $3 + 6 = \underline{9}$ 7. $2 + 5 = \underline{7}$

   $0 + 7 = \underline{7}$ $6 + 3 = \underline{9}$ $5 + 2 = \underline{7}$

Add. Circle the doubles facts.

8. $\begin{array}{r} 0 \\ + 3 \\ \hline 3 \end{array}$ 9. $\begin{array}{r} 1 \\ + 1 \\ \hline 2 \end{array}$ 10. $\begin{array}{r} 3 \\ + 4 \\ \hline 7 \end{array}$ 11. $\begin{array}{r} 9 \\ + 9 \\ \hline 18 \end{array}$

Make a ten to add.

12. $\begin{array}{r} 4 \\ + 8 \\ \hline 12 \end{array}$ 13. $\begin{array}{r} 9 \\ + 5 \\ \hline 14 \end{array}$ 14. $\begin{array}{r} 7 \\ + 6 \\ \hline 13 \end{array}$ 15. $\begin{array}{r} 6 \\ + 8 \\ \hline 14 \end{array}$

Find each sum.

16. $\begin{array}{r} 1 \\ 4 \\ + 6 \\ \hline 11 \end{array}$ 17. $\begin{array}{r} 5 \\ 2 \\ + 8 \\ \hline 15 \end{array}$ 18. $\begin{array}{r} 7 \\ 1 \\ + 2 \\ \hline 10 \end{array}$ 19. $\begin{array}{r} 8 \\ 8 \\ + 2 \\ \hline 18 \end{array}$

20. Lou saw 6 penguins at the zoo. He also saw 3 flamingos and 2 pelicans. How many birds did he see in all?

   $\underline{11}$ birds

Test Practice

21. Ali's dog had 8 puppies. Luca's dog had the same number of puppies. How many puppies are there in all?

   8 ○   16 ●   18 ○   88 ○

Name _____

Check My Progress *(Lessons 1 through 6)*

Find each sum.

1. 2
   +3
   ‾‾
    5

2. 8
   +4
   ‾‾
   12

3. 5
   +6
   ‾‾
   11

Add. Circle the doubles facts.

4. (8
   +8)
   ‾‾
   16

5. 7
   +1
   ‾‾
    8

6. (3
   +3)
   ‾‾
    6

Make a ten to add.

7. 7
   +5
   ‾‾
   12

8. 6
   +9
   ‾‾
   15

9. 8
   +8
   ‾‾
   16

Find each sum.

10. $3 + 4 + 7 =$ __**14**__

11. $5 + 2 + 5 =$ __**12**__

12. $1 + 7 + 9 =$ __**17**__

13. $3 + 4 + 6 =$ __**13**__

Write a number sentence to solve.

14. Charity scored 3 goals in her soccer game on Thursday. She scored 2 goals in her game on Saturday. How many goals did she score in all?

__**$3 + 2 = 5$; 5 goals**__

AL) **STRATEGIC INTERVENTION**

(Approaching Grade Level)

IF students miss 7 or more,

THEN choose a resource:

→ Check My Progress
→ Self-Check Quiz
→ Use the Reteach worksheets.

OL) **ON LEVEL**

IF students miss 5 to 6,

THEN choose a resource:

→ Chapter Project
→ Proceed to the next lesson.

BL) **BEYOND LEVEL**

IF students miss 4 or less,

THEN choose a resource:

→ Chapter Project
→ Use the Enrich worksheets.
→ Proceed to the next lesson.

LESSON 7
Count Back to Subtract

OBJECTIVE Count back to find the difference (using a number line).

What's the Math?

 Common Core State Standards
DOMAIN: Operations and Algebraic Thinking

Standards: 2.OA.1, 2.OA.2
The wording of these standards can be found on page 2.

What Students Should Understand
• You can use a number line and count back to subtract.
• First, find the greater number on the number line. Then count back the other number to find the difference.

What Students Should be Able to Do
Use a number line and count back to find 9 – 4.

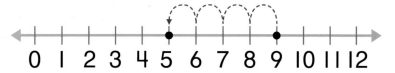

Start with the greater number, 9. Count back the other number, 4.

$9 - 4 = 5$

 Building on the Essential Question

In this lesson, students will build upon the skills and concepts needed to answer the chapter's Essential Question "What strategies can I use to add and subtract?"

Developing Vocabulary

 New Vocabulary

count back   subtract   difference

Activity
• Write *count back, subtract,* and *difference* on the board. Point to these words as you lead the following activity.
• Have 6 students stand up in front of the class. Explain that they can find the difference if 3 students sit down. Have 3 students sit down.
• Tell students they can count back to subtract. Count back from 6, pointing to a seated student for each number.
• Have students describe how this activity helped them understand the meanings of the words.

ELL ELL Support Strategy Use this vocabulary activity to assess students' ability to extend their understanding.

My Vocabulary Cards
Read the activity for the *count back, subtract,* and *difference* cards. Have students respond.

IWB Virtual Word Wall

Add these vocabulary cards to the Virtual Word Wall for this chapter.

ELL Refer to the Multilingual eGlossary for interactive definitions in 13 languages.

Plan Online

Plan for your lesson by using the resources at

connectED.mcgraw-hill.com

Digital Dashboard

Interactive Whiteboard Ready

Vocab

The eBook **Glossary** shows the definition of the word and has audio for each definition. The **eGlossary** provides definitions in 13 languages.

Watch

Watch as concepts are brought to life through **animations**, **songs**, and a variety of visual instruction.

Tools

Virtual Manipulatives with work mats allow teachers and students to model the lesson.

Check

Use **eAssessment** for online assignments and customized assessments.

Use the **Common Core Quick Check** before the lesson to assess students' retention of previously learned concepts.

Use the interactive **Self-Check Quiz** after the lesson to provide immediate feedback on lesson concepts.

eHelp

Digital and print resources assist students and parents in completing My Homework.

Games

Online games and **apps** provide extra practice for lesson concepts.

PD

Professional development videos help teachers gain a deeper understanding of the lesson concepts and strategies.

RtI

Support for **approaching**, **on-** and **beyond-level** students as well as **English Language Learners**.

Masters

Reteach and **Enrich** worksheets, **Manipulative Masters**, the **Problem of the Day**, and other blackline masters are available for each lesson.

 If your students are well-versed in counting back to subtract, you may choose to begin instruction with Step 2, **TEACH**.

You will need

☐ construction paper

Mathematical PRACTICE 4 Modeling the Math

Write large numerals 1 through 10 on construction paper and create a number line on the floor.

Write the subtraction sentence 5 − 2 on the board. Invite a student to stand on the 5.

How many will [student's name] count back? 2 *Why?* The subtraction sentence says 5 − 2.

Have students count as the volunteer moves along the number line. 4, 3

What is 5 − 2? 3

Write 3 to complete the subtraction sentence 5 − 2 = 3. Repeat for other examples.

| 1 | 2 | 3 | 4 | 5 | 6 | 7 | 8 | 9 | 10 |

TEACH

 **Begin core instruction here.**

You will need

☐ crayons or markers

Explore and Explain

You counted on to add in Lesson 2. Now you are going to count back in the opposite direction to subtract.

Read the directions at the bottom of the student page.

Guide students through the first problem.

For the first problem, start at 9. Draw a blue box around it. Then it says to count back 3. This means that you count three to the left from 9 and land on 6. Draw a red circle around 6.

For the second problem, draw a green box around number 19. After you count back 2, what number do you land on? 17

What do we draw around the 17? yellow circle

Have students work through the last problem independently.

What number did you draw an orange circle around? 13

See and Show

Help students work through the example at the top of the page. Have students put a finger or the tip of their pencil on the first number and count back moving each step. Have them trace the dashed numbers as they work through the problems.

Work through Exercises 1–6 as a class.

Mathematical PRACTICE ❸ **Talk Math**

Discuss with students "Explain how you count back on a number line to subtract." Sample answer: Start at the greater number. Count back the number of times you are subtracting. The number on which you land is the difference.

Common Error!

The format of Exercises 6, 8, and 9 may confuse some students. Explain to them that the write on line comes first.

🕐 **CORE INSTRUCTION**

Name _____   Operations and Algebraic Thinking
                               2.OA.1, 2.OA.2

Count Back to Subtract

Lesson 7
ESSENTIAL QUESTION
What strategies can I use to add and subtract?

There are SO many to choose from!

Explore and Explain (Watch) (Tools)

1	2	3	4	5
6	7	8	9	10
11	12	13	14	15
16	17	18	19	20

See students' work.

Teacher Directions: Draw a blue box around number 9. Count back 3. Circle that number red. Draw a green box around number 19. Count back 2. Circle that number yellow. Draw a purple box around 14. Count back 1. Circle that number orange.

Online Content at 🔗 connectED.mcgraw-hill.com   Chapter 1 • Lesson 7   49

See and Show

Mathematical PRACTICE

Find 10 − 3. Use a number line. **Count back** to **subtract**. The answer is the **difference**.

Start with the greater number.

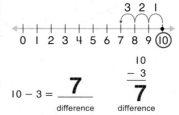

No flowers on this page! I want to go back.

$$10 - 3 = \underline{7}$$
difference

$$\begin{array}{r} 10 \\ -3 \\ \hline 7 \end{array}$$
difference

Count back to subtract. Use the number line.

0 1 2 3 4 5 6 7 8 9 10 11 12

1. $7 - 3 = \underline{4}$ 2. $8 - 1 = \underline{7}$

3. $9 - 2 = \underline{7}$ 4. $10 - 2 = \underline{8}$

5. $8 - 2 = \underline{6}$ 6. $\underline{6} = 7 - 1$

Talk Math Explain how you count back on a number line to subtract.

50   Chapter 1 • Lesson 7

Name

On My Own

Count back to subtract. Use the number line.

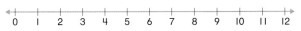

0 1 2 3 4 5 6 7 8 9 10 11 12

7. $3 - 2 = $ __1__

8. __9__ $= 12 - 3$

9. __5__ $= 8 - 3$

10. $11 - 3 = $ __8__

11. $9 - 3 = $ __6__

12. $11 - 2 = $ __9__

13.
  $\begin{array}{r} 9 \\ -\ 1 \\ \hline 8 \end{array}$

14.
  $\begin{array}{r} 5 \\ -\ 3 \\ \hline 2 \end{array}$

15.
  $\begin{array}{r} 10 \\ -\ 1 \\ \hline 9 \end{array}$

16.
  $\begin{array}{r} 4 \\ -\ 2 \\ \hline 2 \end{array}$

17.
  $\begin{array}{r} 12 \\ -\ 2 \\ \hline 10 \end{array}$

18.
  $\begin{array}{r} 4 \\ -\ 3 \\ \hline 1 \end{array}$

19.
  $\begin{array}{r} 8 \\ -\ 1 \\ \hline 7 \end{array}$

20.
  $\begin{array}{r} 7 \\ -\ 2 \\ \hline 5 \end{array}$

21.
  $\begin{array}{r} 5 \\ -\ 2 \\ \hline 3 \end{array}$

Chapter 1 • Lesson 7   51

Problem Solving

 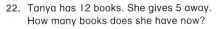

Mathematical **PRACTICE**

22. Tanya has 12 books. She gives 5 away. How many books does she have now?

   __7__ books

23. Hank washes 9 windows at the pet store. He washes 6 windows in the morning. How many windows does he wash in the afternoon?

   __3__ windows

 squawk!

24. The animal shelter had 8 birds. 3 of the birds were adopted. How many birds were left at the animal shelter?

   __5__ birds

Write Math   Explain how counting back can help you subtract.

__Sample answer: If you start with the greater number__
__you only have to count back by a small number to find__
__the answer.__

52   Chapter 1 • Lesson 7

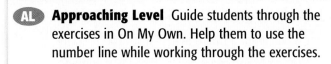

PRACTICE & APPLY

CCSS

On My Own

Have students work through the exercises on this page independently. You may choose to assign exercises based on the chart below.

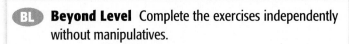

DIFFERENTIATED ASSIGNMENTS

AL **Approaching Level** Guide students through the exercises in On My Own. Help them to use the number line while working through the exercises.

OL **On Level** Complete the exercises independently.

BL **Beyond Level** Complete the exercises independently without manipulatives.

Common Error!

When subtracting on a number line, some students may think: "I'm on 10. I take away numbers: 9 and 8. That leaves 7." Explain to students that "Two steps back from 10 is 8."

Problem Solving

Have students work through the problem-solving exercises on this page independently.

Mathematical **PRACTICE** In Exercise 24, students **make sense of problems and persevere in solving them.**

Write Math

This exercise asks students to build upon their understanding of concepts needed to answer the chapter's Essential Question.

RESPONSE TO INTERVENTION
DIFFERENTIATED INSTRUCTION

AL ▸ **APPROACHING LEVEL**

IF my students struggle with counting back to subtract,

THEN choose a resource:

→ Use the Reteach worksheet with small groups.

→ Go online for a Differentiated Instruction activity.

→ **Virtual Manipulative** Use the virtual number lines and two-color counters to reteach the concept.

OL ▸ **ON LEVEL**

IF my students seem to know counting back to subtract, but need more practice,

THEN choose a resource:

→ Assign My Homework.

→ Go online for a Differentiated Instruction activity.

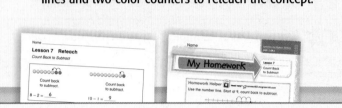

BL ▸ **BEYOND LEVEL**

IF my students have mastered counting back to subtract,

THEN choose a resource:

→ Use the Enrich worksheet in cooperative groups.

→ Assign My Homework.

→ Go online for a Differentiated Instruction activity.

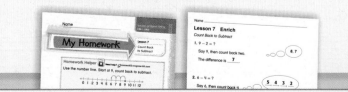

AL

Name _____

Lesson 7   Reteach
Count Back to Subtract

Count back to subtract.

$8 - 2 = \underline{6}$

Count back to subtract.

$10 - 1 = \underline{9}$

Count back to subtract. Show how you use ○ to help.

1. $7 - 4 = \underline{3}$

2. $9 - 3 = \underline{6}$

3. $9 - 2 = \underline{7}$

4. $5 - 1 = \underline{4}$

5. $6 - 2 = \underline{4}$

6. $9 - 1 = \underline{8}$

7. $8 - 6 = \underline{2}$

8. $4 - 3 = \underline{1}$

9. $7 - 3 = \underline{4}$

BL

Name _____

Lesson 7   Enrich
Count Back to Subtract

1. $9 - 2 = ?$

Say 9, then count back two.

8, 7

The difference is $\underline{7}$.

2. $6 - 4 = ?$

5, 4, 3, 2

Say 6, then count back 4.

Write the numbers in the bubble as you say them.

The difference is $\underline{2}$.

3. $15 - 3 = ?$

14, 13, 12

Say 15, then count back 3.

Write the numbers in the bubble as you say them.

The difference is $\underline{12}$.

4. $100 - 5 = ?$

99, 98, 97, 96, 95

Say 100, then count back 5.

Write the numbers in the bubble as you say them.

The difference is $\underline{95}$.

My Homework

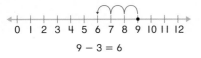

Lesson 7

Count Back
to Subtract

Homework Helper Need help? connectED.mcgraw-hill.com

Use the number line. Start at 9, count back to subtract.

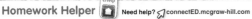

0 1 2 3 4 5 6 7 8 9 10 11 12

$9 - 3 = 6$

Practice

Count back to subtract. Use the number line above.

1. $12 - 4 = \underline{8}$ 2. $11 - 3 = \underline{8}$

3. $8 - 3 = \underline{5}$ 4. $6 - 2 = \underline{4}$

5. $6 - 3 = \underline{3}$ 6. $10 - 2 = \underline{8}$

7.
$$\begin{array}{r} 12 \\ -\ 3 \\ \hline 9 \end{array}$$

8.
$$\begin{array}{r} 11 \\ -\ 1 \\ \hline 10 \end{array}$$

9.
$$\begin{array}{r} 8 \\ -\ 2 \\ \hline 6 \end{array}$$

Chapter 1 • Lesson 7   53

---

10. A paper clip holder has 12 clips.
Alex uses 3 paper clips.
How many paper clips are left?

$\underline{9}$ paper clips

11. Marty buys 11 erasers. He uses 1 eraser.
How many erasers does Marty have left?

$\underline{10}$ erasers

12. Jenny had 9 pencils in her desk. She let
her friends borrow 2 of them. How many
pencils does she have left?

 Pick me! Pick me instead!

$\underline{7}$ pencils

Vocabulary Check

Complete the sentence.

| count back | sum | difference |

13. You can ___count back___ to subtract.

14. The answer to a subtraction problem is
called the ___difference___ .

 Math at Home Have your child count back to subtract. Say a number between 3 and 12. Have you child subtract 1, 2, or 3.

---

4 WRAP IT UP

CCSS

My Homework

Assign homework after successful completion of the lesson. Students who understand the concepts may skip the **Homework Helper** section.

Vocabulary Check

Explain to students that they will not use one of the vocabulary words listed as they answer Exercises 13 and 14.

Formative Assessment

Ask students the following question.

When you count back, which number do you always start with? the greater number

Line Up!

As students line up, give them a doubles fact and state the fact. For example, "I have 5 fingers on each hand: 5 + 5." Ask volunteers for other doubles facts such as 2 legs on each side of a chair: 2 + 2.

LESSON 8
Subtract All and Subtract Zero
OBJECTIVE Subtract all or zero to find the difference.

What's the Math?

 Common Core State Standards
DOMAIN: Operations and Algebraic Thinking

Standards: 2.OA.1, 2.OA.2, 2.NBT.9
The wording of these standards can be found on page 2.

What Students Should Understand
- You can subtract zero from a number and the difference is that number.
- You can subtract all from a number and the difference is zero.

What Students Should be Able to Do
Subtract all to find 4 − 4.

$$4 - 4 = 0$$

Subtract zero to find 4 − 0.

$$4 - 0 = 4$$

 Building on the Essential Question
In this lesson, students will build upon the skills and concepts needed to answer the chapter's Essential Question "What strategies can I use to add and subtract?"

Developing Vocabulary

Review Vocabulary
zero

Review Activity
- Write *zero* and *0* on the board.
- Discuss with students how they can use either drawings or subtraction sentences to show zero. Ask them if there are other ways to show zero.
- Ask volunteers to take turns at the board to demonstrate different ways to represent zero.

ELL **ELL Support Strategy** Use this vocabulary activity to apply mathematical language in situations of personal choice.

My Vocabulary Cards
Have students review the cards they have learned up to this point in the chapter. Ask them to sort the words into two piles. One pile should contain words they know. The second pile should contain words they would like to review. Have students work in small groups to discuss the words they would like to review.

Plan Online

Plan for your lesson by using the resources at
connectED.mcgraw-hill.com

Digital Dashboard

Interactive Whiteboard Ready

Vocab

The eBook **Glossary** shows the definition of the word and has audio for each definition. The **eGlossary** provides definitions in 13 languages.

Watch

Watch as concepts are brought to life through **animations**, **songs**, and a variety of visual instruction.

Tools

Virtual Manipulatives with work mats allow teachers and students to model the lesson.

Check

Use **eAssessment** for online assignments and customized assessments.

Use the **Common Core Quick Check** before the lesson to assess students' retention of previously learned concepts.

Use the interactive **Self-Check Quiz** after the lesson to provide immediate feedback on lesson concepts.

eHelp

Digital and print resources assist students and parents in completing My Homework.

Games

Online games and **apps** provide extra practice for lesson concepts.

PD

Professional development videos help teachers gain a deeper understanding of the lesson concepts and strategies.

RtI

Support for **approaching**, **on**- and **beyond-level** students as well as **English Language Learners**.

Masters

Reteach and **Enrich** worksheets, **Manipulative Masters**, the **Problem of the Day**, and other blackline masters are available for each lesson.

---

1 LAUNCH THE LESSON

CCSS

 If your students are well-versed in subtracting zero and subtracting all, you may choose to begin instruction with Step 2, **TEACH**.

You will need

☐ two-color counters

Mathematical PRACTICE 4 Modeling the Math

Give 5 counters to each student. Tell them to move nothing away from the pile. Point out that this is subtracting zero.

Have students count how many are left.

Tell students to move all of the pile to the side of their desk. Have them count how many are left in the original place. 0 This is subtracting all.

Begin core instruction here.

You will need

☐ crayons or markers

Explore and Explain

Hold up 5 pencils.

How many pencils do I have? 5

Give out all of the pencils to students until you do not have any left.

I gave away 5 pencils to students. Now how many pencils do I have? 0

Write 5 − 5 = 0 on the board. Explain that the first minute represents the 5 pencils that you started with. The second number represents the number of pencils you gave away. The difference represents the number of pencils that you have left.

Read the directions at the bottom of the student page.

You do not actually have to draw dogs when drawing a picture to find the number of dogs that still need to be washed. You can draw the dogs if you want to. You can also draw any object that you want to stand for each dog.

Lead students through drawing a picture to find the total number of dogs that still need to be washed.

You can cross off the dogs one at a time as you are subtracting. The dogs that are not crossed off are the ones that still need to be washed. How many dogs will you cross off? 7 *How many dogs still need to be washed?* 0

See and Show

Help students work through the example at the top of the page. Show examples of subtract all and subtract zero. Have them trace the dashed numbers as they work the problems.

Work through Exercises 1–4 as a class.

Mathematical PRACTICE ③ ➡ **Talk Math**

Discuss with students "Explain how you know 8 − 8 = 0 and 8 − 0 = 8." Sample answer: If there are 8 and you take all of them away, there are none left. If you have 8 and you subtract nothing from it, then you still have 8.

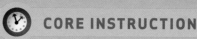

Name _____

Operations and Algebraic Thinking
2.OA.1, 2.OA.2, 2.NBT.9 CCSS

Subtract All and Subtract Zero

Lesson 8
ESSENTIAL QUESTION
What strategies can I use to add and subtract?

Bubbles tickle my nose.

Explore and Explain [Watch ▶] [Tools ▣]

I'm drenched!

$\underline{7} - \underline{7} = \underline{0}$ dogs   See students' work.

Teacher Directions: Draw a picture and write a number sentence to solve the problem. Mary helped wash dogs at the pet store. There were 7 dogs to be washed. Mary washed 7 of them. How many dogs were left to be washed?

Online Content at 🔗 connectED.mcgraw-hill.com   Chapter 1 • Lesson 8   55

See and Show   Mathematical **PRACTICE**

You can subtract to find the difference.
Find how many frogs are left.

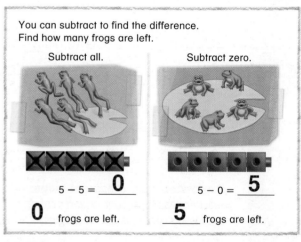

Subtract all.   Subtract zero.

$5 - 5 = \underline{0}$ $5 - 0 = \underline{5}$

$\underline{0}$ frogs are left. $\underline{5}$ frogs are left.

Subtract.

1. $13 - 13 = \underline{0}$ 2. $\underline{7} = 7 - 0$

   $13 - 0 = \underline{13}$ $7 - 7 = \underline{0}$

3. $6 - 6 = \underline{0}$ 4. $8 - 0 = \underline{8}$

   $\underline{6} = 6 - 0$ $8 - 8 = \underline{0}$

Talk Math   Explain how you know 8 − 8 = 0 and 8 − 0 = 8.

PRACTICE & APPLY

CCSS

Name _____

On My Own

Subtract. Circle the problem if the difference is zero.

Helpful Hint
When you subtract zero from a number, the difference is the same as that number.

5. $9 - 3 = $ __6__

6. __7__ $ = 8 - 1$

7. (__0__ $ = 4 - 4$)

8. $7 - 3 = $ __4__

9. (
$\begin{array}{r} 8 \\ -\ 8 \\ \hline 0 \end{array}$
)

10. $\begin{array}{r} 8 \\ -\ 2 \\ \hline 6 \end{array}$

11. $\begin{array}{r} 6 \\ -\ 0 \\ \hline 6 \end{array}$

12. (
$\begin{array}{r} 5 \\ -\ 5 \\ \hline 0 \end{array}$
)

13. $\begin{array}{r} 3 \\ -\ 2 \\ \hline 1 \end{array}$

14. (
$\begin{array}{r} 16 \\ -\ 16 \\ \hline 0 \end{array}$
)

15. $\begin{array}{r} 7 \\ -\ 2 \\ \hline 5 \end{array}$

16. $\begin{array}{r} 4 \\ -\ 0 \\ \hline 4 \end{array}$

17. $\begin{array}{r} 9 \\ -\ 0 \\ \hline 9 \end{array}$

18. $\begin{array}{r} 8 \\ -\ 0 \\ \hline 8 \end{array}$

19. (
$\begin{array}{r} 9 \\ -\ 9 \\ \hline 0 \end{array}$
)

20. $\begin{array}{r} 12 \\ -\ 2 \\ \hline 10 \end{array}$

21. $\begin{array}{r} 11 \\ -\ 6 \\ \hline 5 \end{array}$

22. (
$\begin{array}{r} 3 \\ -\ 3 \\ \hline 0 \end{array}$
)

23. $\begin{array}{r} 7 \\ -\ 1 \\ \hline 6 \end{array}$

24. (
$\begin{array}{r} 6 \\ -\ 6 \\ \hline 0 \end{array}$
)

Copyright © The McGraw-Hill Companies, Inc.

On My Own

Have students work through the exercises on this page independently. You may choose to assign exercises based on the chart below.

DIFFERENTIATED ASSIGNMENTS

AL   Approaching Level Guide students through the exercises in On My Own. Help them to use manipulatives while working through the exercises.

OL   On Level Complete the exercises independently.

BL   Beyond Level Complete the exercises independently without manipulatives.

Common Error!
The concept of zero is important in expressing place value. It might help for students to think of the symbol *0* as representing "empty—there is nothing."

Problem Solving

Have students work through the problem-solving exercises on this page independently.

Mathematical PRACTICE 2 In Exercise 25, students **reason abstractly and quantitatively.**

Write Math

This exercise asks students to build upon their understanding of concepts needed to answer the chapter's Essential Question.

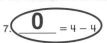

Problem Solving

Mathematical PRACTICE

25. 13 bees buzz near a flower. None fly away. How many bees are near the flower?

__13__ bees

26. 4 sparrows are in the nest. They all fly away. How many sparrows are still in the nest?

Where did everybody go?

__0__ sparrows

27. Todd had 12 beads. He lost some of them. Now he has 7 beads. How many beads did Todd lose?

__5__ beads

Write Math In a subtraction number sentence, which number is the difference?

__Sample answer: The number you get when you__
__subtract the second number from the first number.__

Copyright © The McGraw-Hill Companies, Inc.   Brand X Pictures/PunchStock

---

Online Content at ✐ **connectED.mcgraw-hill.com**

AL) **APPROACHING LEVEL**

IF my students struggle with subtracting zero and subtracting all,

THEN choose a resource:

→ Use the Reteach worksheet with small groups.

→ Go online for a Differentiated Instruction activity.

→ **Domino Math** Give students a domino that has one blank side. Have them count the number of dots on each side. Discuss the word zero to tell that there are no dots on one side.

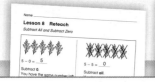 

OL) **ON LEVEL**

IF my students seem to know subtracting zero and subtracting all, but need more practice,

THEN choose a resource:

→ Assign My Homework.

→ Go online for a Differentiated Instruction activity.

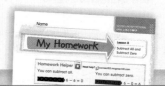

BL) **BEYOND LEVEL**

IF my students have mastered subtracting zero and subtracting all,

THEN choose a resource:

→ Use the Enrich worksheet in cooperative groups.

→ Assign My Homework.

→ Go online for a Differentiated Instruction activity.

 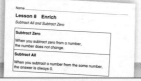

59A **Chapter 1** Apply Addition and Subtraction Concepts

Name _____

Lesson 8 Reteach

Subtract All and Subtract Zero

5 − 0 = __5__	5 − 5 = __0__
Subtract **0**. You have the same number left.	Subtract **all**. You have 0 left.

Subtract. You can cross out pictures to help.

1.
9 − 0 = __9__
9 − 9 = __0__

2.
6 − 0 = __6__
6 − 6 = __0__

3.
4 − 0 = __4__
4 − 4 = __0__

4.
7 − 0 = __7__
7 − 7 = __0__

5.
8 − 0 = __8__
8 − 8 = __0__

6.
5 − 0 = __5__
5 − 5 = __0__

Name _____

Lesson 8 Enrich

Subtract All and Subtract Zero

Subtract Zero
When you subtract zero from a number, the number does not change.

Subtract All
When you subtract a number from the same number, the answer is always 0.

Solve. Then draw a line to connect the subtraction number sentences with the same numbers.

14 − 14 = __0__   5 − 0 = __5__

85 − 0 = __85__   75 − 75 = __0__

5 − 5 = __0__   14 − 0 = __14__

75 − 0 = __75__   85 − 85 = __0__

88 − 88 = __0__   88 − 0 = __88__

My Homework

My Homework

Lesson 8
Subtract All and Subtract Zero

Name _____

Operations and Algebraic Thinking
2.OA.1, 2.OA.2, 2.NBT.9

CCSS

Homework Helper **Need help?** connectED.mcgraw-hill.com

You can subtract all.   You can subtract zero.

XXXXXXX 6 − 6 = 0   ●●●●●● 6 − 0 = 6

Practice

Subtract.

1. $\begin{array}{r} 9 \\ -\ 0 \\ \hline \mathbf{9} \end{array}$	2. $\begin{array}{r} 15 \\ -15 \\ \hline \mathbf{0} \end{array}$	3. $\begin{array}{r} 1 \\ -\ 1 \\ \hline \mathbf{0} \end{array}$	4. $\begin{array}{r} 7 \\ -\ 0 \\ \hline \mathbf{7} \end{array}$
5. $\begin{array}{r} 12 \\ -12 \\ \hline \mathbf{0} \end{array}$	6. $\begin{array}{r} 4 \\ -\ 4 \\ \hline \mathbf{0} \end{array}$	7. $\begin{array}{r} 8 \\ -\ 0 \\ \hline \mathbf{8} \end{array}$	8. $\begin{array}{r} 0 \\ -\ 0 \\ \hline \mathbf{0} \end{array}$

9. $3 - 0 = \underline{\mathbf{3}}$ 10. $17 - 17 = \underline{\mathbf{0}}$

11. $3 - 3 = \underline{\mathbf{0}}$ 12. $2 - 0 = \underline{\mathbf{2}}$

Chapter 1 • Lesson 8   59

13. 10 children play ball. After they finish, all 10 go back to class. How many children keep playing ball?

_____**0**_____ children

14. 8 girls take a walk. When they reach the park, they all keep walking. How many girls are still taking a walk?

_____**8**_____ girls

15. 18 children are at the store. All of them check out and go outside. How many are still shopping?

_____**0**_____ children

Test Practice

16. Find the difference.
$19 - 19 =$

- ● 0
- ○ 18
- ○ 19
- ○ 38

 Math at Home Have your child use small objects to show 5 − 5 and 5 − 0.

60   Chapter 1 • Lesson 8

Test Practice

Diagnose Student Errors

Class trends in wrong answer may indicate common errors or misconceptions.

- **0** correct
- **18** subtracted incorrectly
- **19** subtracted zero
- **38** added

Formative Assessment

Ask students the following question.

Why does subtracting zero leave you with the same number you started with? You are not taking anything away from the number.

 **MY Learning Stations**

Use the activity card **Letter Subtraction** after this lesson. The Teacher Guide provides suggestions for differentiated instruction.

Line Up! When students line up for recess, lunch, or dismissal, have all of them face the front. How many students are facing forward? How many are facing backward?

My Homework

Assign homework after successful completion of the lesson. Students who understand the concepts may skip the **Homework Helper** section.

LESSON 9
Use Doubles to Subtract
OBJECTIVE Use doubles facts to find the difference.

What's the Math?

 Common Core State Standards
DOMAIN: Operations and Algebraic Thinking

Standards: 2.OA.1, 2.OA.2
The wording of these standards can be found on page 2.

What Students Should Understand

- You can use doubles facts to help you subtract.
- First, look at the numbers in the subtraction problem. Then think of a related doubles addition fact to help you subtract.

What Students Should be Able to Do

Use a doubles fact to find 12 − 6.

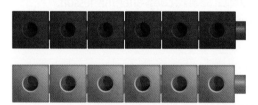

If you know that 6 + 6 = 12,

then 12 − 6 = 6.

 Building on the Essential Question

In this lesson, students will build upon the skills and concepts needed to answer the chapter's Essential Question "What strategies can I use to add and subtract?"

Developing Vocabulary

Review Vocabulary
doubles

Review Activity

- Write *doubles* on the board. Ask students what they know about this word. For example, they might explain that knowing about doubles helps them with addition facts.
- Have students use connecting cubes to show addition sentences that contain doubles.
- Discuss with students how this activity reinforced their understanding of doubles.

ELL **ELL Support Strategy** Use this vocabulary activity to use non-linguistic models to support student thinking.

My Vocabulary Cards

Have students draw examples for each card. Then have them work with a partner. Each partner should guess what word the other student's drawing represents.

Plan Online

Plan for your lesson by using the resources at
connectED.mcgraw-hill.com

Digital Dashboard

Interactive Whiteboard Ready

Vocab

The eBook **Glossary** shows the definition of the word and has audio for each definition. The **eGlossary** provides definitions in 13 languages.

Watch

Watch as concepts are brought to life through **animations**, **songs**, and a variety of visual instruction.

Tools

Virtual Manipulatives with work mats allow teachers and students to model the lesson.

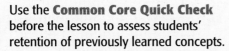

Check

Use **eAssessment** for online assignments and customized assessments.

Use the **Common Core Quick Check** before the lesson to assess students' retention of previously learned concepts.

Use the interactive **Self-Check Quiz** after the lesson to provide immediate feedback on lesson concepts.

eHelp

Digital and print resources assist students and parents in completing My Homework.

Games

Online games and **apps** provide extra practice for lesson concepts.

PD

Professional development videos help teachers gain a deeper understanding of the lesson concepts and strategies.

RtI

Support for **approaching**, **on-** and **beyond-level** students as well as **English Language Learners**.

Masters

Reteach and **Enrich** worksheets, **Manipulative Masters**, the **Problem of the Day**, and other blackline masters are available for each lesson.

1 LAUNCH THE LESSON

CCSS

⏱ If your students are well-versed in using doubles to subtract, you may choose to begin instruction with Step 2, **TEACH**.

Mathematical PRACTICE 4 **Modeling the Math**

Look around the room and name things that are examples of doubles that you either see or know.

Ask students to point to and list all the doubles they see on and around them. Sample answer: such as eyes, nostrils, hands, fingers, feet, shoes, socks, toes, teeth, and so on.

Have students write a number sentence for one of the doubles they just listed. For example, 10 fingers − 5 fingers = 5 fingers.

Repeat with additional examples.

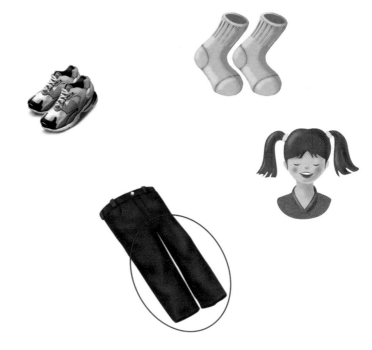

🕐 **Begin core instruction here.**

You will need
☐ connecting cubes

Explore and Explain

Read the directions that are at the bottom of the student page. Guide students through the problem. Show students that you can make sure the cube train has been pulled apart into two equal parts by placing one part on top of the other and comparing the lengths. The lengths should be the same.

How many cubes are in each equal part? 3

3 + 3 = 6 is the inverse or opposite of 6 − 3 = 3. Why is 3 + 3 = 6 called a doubles fact? Sample answer: the addends are the same number *You can use doubles facts to subtract. You can think of the addends in the doubles fact to figure out the difference in the related subtraction fact.*

See and Show

Help students work through the example at the top of the page. Use connecting cubes to demonstrate how you use doubles facts to subtract. Have them trace the dashed number as they work through the problem.

Work through Exercises 1 − 6 as a class using cubes to help subtract.

Mathematical PRACTICE ③ **Talk Math**

Discuss with students "Explain how you can use a doubles fact to subtract." Sample answer: You can use the numbers in a doubles fact to find the difference for a subtraction fact. For example: if 2 + 2 = 4 then 4 − 2 = 2.

Name _____

Operations and Algebraic Thinking
2.OA.1, 2.OA.2

Use Doubles to Subtract

Lesson 9
ESSENTIAL QUESTION
What strategies can I use to add and subtract?

Explore and Explain

Hey! I'm seeing double!

See students' work.

____3____ cubes   ____3____ cubes

Teacher Directions: Place a 6 cube train at the top of the page. Trace it. Separate the train into two equal parts. Draw the parts below the 6 cube train. Write how many cubes are in each part.

Online Content at 🖉 **connectED.mcgraw-hill.com**   Chapter 1 • Lesson 9   61

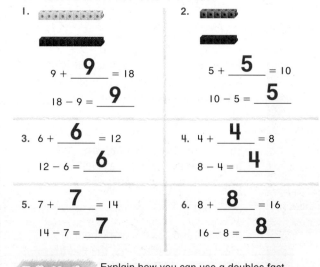

See and Show

Mathematical PRACTICE

You can use doubles facts to help you subtract.
Find 16 − 8.

If you know 8 + 8 = 16,
then 16 − 8 = **8**.

Use cubes and doubles facts to subtract.

1.

9 + **9** = 18

18 − 9 = **9**

2.

5 + **5** = 10

10 − 5 = **5**

3. 6 + **6** = 12

12 − 6 = **6**

4. 4 + **4** = 8

8 − 4 = **4**

5. 7 + **7** = 14

14 − 7 = **7**

6. 8 + **8** = 16

16 − 8 = **8**

Talk Math Explain how you can use a doubles fact to subtract.

62   Chapter 1 • Lesson 9

Name _____

Helpful Hint
I know 5 + 5 = 10, so 10 − 5 = 5.

On My Own

Subtract. Circle the doubles facts.

7. 9 − 3 = **6**

8. 11 − 9 = **2**

9. (6 − **3** = 3)

10. 7 − 3 = **4**

11. (18 − 9 = **9**)

12. 15 − 7 = **8**

13.
16
− **8**
8

14.
7
− 0
7

15.
10
− **5**
5

16.
9
− 8
1

17.
6
− 2
4

18.
8
− 3
5

19.
14
− **7**
7

20.
7
− 6
1

21.
8
− **4**
4

Chapter 1 • Lesson 9   63

Problem Solving

Mathematical PRACTICE

22. Fran and her grandmother pick 16 pumpkins. They use 8 pumpkins for pie. How many pumpkins are left?

8 pumpkins

Pumpkin pie!

23. Delia bakes 18 cherry pies. She sells 9 pies at a farmers' market. How many pies does Delia have left?

9 pies

24. 14 children were playing hide and go seek. 7 children were found. How many children are still hiding?

7 children

Write Math Explain how you can use doubles to help you subtract.

Sample answer: If you know doubles facts then you

will recognize them when you are subtracting and

you can subtract much faster.

On My Own

Have students work through the exercises on this page independently. You may choose to assign exercises based on the chart below.

DIFFERENTIATED ASSIGNMENTS

AL Approaching Level Guide students through the exercises in On My Own. Help them to use manipulatives while working through the exercises.

OL On Level Complete the exercises independently.

BL Beyond Level Complete the exercises independently without manipulatives.

Problem Solving

Have students work through the problem-solving exercises on this page independently.

Mathematical PRACTICE 1 In Exercise 24, students **make sense of problems and persevere in solving them.**

Write Math

This exercise asks students to build upon their understanding of concepts needed to answer the chapter's Essential Question.

RESPONSE TO INTERVENTION

DIFFERENTIATED INSTRUCTION

AL) APPROACHING LEVEL

IF my students struggle with using doubles to subtract,

THEN choose a resource:

→ Use the Reteach worksheet with small groups.

→ Go online for a Differentiated Instruction activity.

→ **Domino Math** Have students use doubles dominoes and count the dots to learn doubles facts.

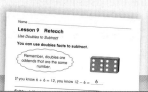

OL) ON LEVEL

IF my students seem to know using doubles to subtract, but need more practice,

THEN choose a resource:

→ Assign My Homework.

→ Go online for a Differentiated Instruction activity.

BL) BEYOND LEVEL

IF my students have mastered using doubles to subtract,

THEN choose a resource:

→ Use the Enrich worksheet in cooperative groups.

→ Assign My Homework.

→ Go online for a Differentiated Instruction activity.

AL)

Name _____

Lesson 9   Reteach

Use Doubles to Subtract

You can use doubles facts to subtract.

> Remember, doubles are addends that are the same number.

If you know $6 + 6 = 12$, you know $12 - 6 = \underline{6}$.

Subtract. Use doubles facts to help.

1.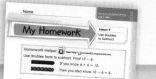

$4 + 4 = \underline{8}$, so
$8 - 4 = \underline{4}$.

2.

$7 + 7 = \underline{14}$, so
$14 - 7 = \underline{7}$.

3.

$3 + 3 = \underline{6}$, so
$6 - 3 = \underline{3}$.

4.

$5 + 5 = \underline{10}$, so
$10 - 5 = \underline{5}$.

5. $8 + 8 = \underline{16}$, so
$16 - 8 = \underline{8}$.

6. $9 + 9 = \underline{18}$, so
$18 - 9 = \underline{9}$.

BL)

Name _____

Lesson 9   Enrich

Use Doubles to Subtract

First, add the doubles.
Then, use the doubles facts to help
you subtract.

$6 + 6 = \underline{12}$ $12 - \underline{6} = \underline{6}$

1. $4 + 4 = \underline{8}$ $8 - \underline{4} = \underline{4}$

2. $7 + 7 = \underline{14}$ $14 - \underline{7} = \underline{7}$

3. $3 + 3 = \underline{6}$ $6 - \underline{3} = \underline{3}$

4. $9 + 9 = \underline{18}$ $18 - \underline{9} = \underline{9}$

5. $5 + 5 = \underline{10}$ $10 - \underline{5} = \underline{5}$

6. $2 + 2 = \underline{4}$ $4 - \underline{2} = \underline{2}$

Name _____

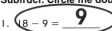
My Homework

Lesson 9
Use Doubles
to Subtract

Homework Helper Need help? connectED.mcgraw-hill.com

Use doubles facts to subtract. Find $12 - 6$.

■■■■■■■ If you know $6 + 6 = 12$,
✗✗✗✗✗✗ then you also know $12 - 6 = 6$.

Practice

Subtract. Circle the doubles facts.

1. (18 − 9 = __9__)

2. $6 - 2 =$ __4__

3. $8 - 2 =$ __6__

4. $5 - 3 =$ __2__

5. (16 − 8 = __8__)

6. $8 - 3 =$ __5__

7. (6 − 3 = __3__)

8. (8 − 8 = __0__)

9.
$$\begin{array}{r} 14 \\ -\ 7 \\ \hline 7 \end{array}$$
(circled)

10.
$$\begin{array}{r} 9 \\ -\ 1 \\ \hline 8 \end{array}$$

11.
$$\begin{array}{r} 10 \\ -\ 4 \\ \hline 6 \end{array}$$

Chapter 1 • Lesson 9   65

Copyright © The McGraw-Hill Companies, Inc.

Subtract. Circle the doubles facts.

12. $14 - 6 =$ __8__

13. $18 - 8 =$ __10__

14. (18 − 9 = __9__)

15. $15 - 7 =$ __8__

16. Anita checks out 14 library books. She reads 7 of the books. How many books does she still have to read?

__7__ books

I love animal stories!

17. Lindsay has 16 cupcakes to hand out. She has given 8 to the girls in her class. How many does she have left?

__8__ cupcakes

Test Practice

18. Mark the number sentence that uses doubles.

$4 - 4 = 0$ ○ $8 - 4 = 4$ ● $8 - 3 = 5$ ○ $8 - 8 = 0$ ○

 Math at Home Call out doubles facts. Have your child name the subtraction problem for each double.

66   Chapter 1 • Lesson 9

Copyright © The McGraw-Hill Companies, Inc.   Brand X Pictures/Punchstock

---

4 WRAP IT UP

CCSS

My Homework

Assign homework after successful completion of the lesson. Students who understand the concepts may skip the **Homework Helper** section.

Test Practice

Diagnose Student Errors

Class trends in wrong answers may indicate common errors or misconceptions.

$4 - 4 = 0$ subtracted all

$8 - 4 = 4$ doubles

$8 - 3 = 5$ correct

$8 - 8 = 0$ subtracted all

Formative Assessment

Ask students the following question.

How can you use $6 + 6 = 12$ to help you find $12 - 6$?

Sample answer: I know $6 + 6 = 12$. Using the doubles fact, I know that if I have 12 and take away 6, there will be 6 remaining.

MY Learning Stations

Use the real-world problem solving reader **How Many Seeds?** after this lesson. The Teacher Guide provides suggestions for differentiated instruction.

Line Up! When students line up for lunch, have them form two lines and then arrange students in pairs. For each pair, ask how many are left if you take one half of the pair away from the other half.

Check My Progress

Use this as a formative assessment to determine if your students are struggling, and if so, with which topics they struggle. The criteria for differentiation are on the next page.

Vocabulary Check

Have a volunteer read aloud the words in the word bank. Ask students what the words in the word bank have in common. Sample answer: They all are used to describe subtraction.

ELL **ELL Support Strategy** Use this vocabulary activity to participate in purposeful, cooperative learning activities.

Concept Check

These concepts are covered in Lessons 7–9.

Exercises	Concept	Review Lesson
4–9	Count back to subtract	7
10–13	Subtract all and subtract zero	8
14–21	Use doubles to subtract	9

Problem Solving

Exercise 22 uses a word problem to check for understanding of the same concepts.

Test Practice

Diagnose Student Errors

Class trends in wrong answers may indicate common errors or misconceptions.

16 used the first number given
10 subtracted six
8 correct
6 subtracted ten

Name _____

Check My Progress

Vocabulary Check

Complete each sentence.

count back   subtract   difference

1. You can ___subtract___ by taking a number away from a greater number.

2. The number you have left after you subtract is called the ___difference___.

3. You can ___count back___ on a number line to help you subtract.

Concept Check

Count back to subtract. Use the number line to help.

0 1 2 3 4 5 6 7 8 9 10 11 12 13 14 15

4. 13 − 3 = **10**   5. 15 − 2 = **13**

6. 7 − 3 = **4**   7. 14 − 3 = **11**

8. 10 − 1 = **9**   9. 12 − 8 = **4**

Chapter 1   67

Subtract.

10.	11.	12.	13.
6 − 0 **6**	8 − 8 **0**	9 − 0 **9**	4 − 4 **0**

Use doubles or near doubles facts to subtract.

14.	15.	16.	17.
16 − 8 **8**	7 − 3 **4**	10 − 4 **6**	18 − 9 **9**

18.	19.	20.	21.
14 − 7 **7**	8 − 5 **3**	6 − 3 **3**	9 − 4 **5**

22. Laine counts 18 fireflies. She counts 9 fireflies in the front yard. How many fireflies does Laine count in the backyard?

18 fireflies

Test Practice

23. Ryder rode his bike around the block 16 times. Violet rode half as many times. How many times did Violet ride her bike around the block?

16 ○   10 ○   8 ●   6 ○

Name _____

Check My Progress *(Lessons 7 through 9)*

```
◄──┼──┼──┼──┼──┼──┼──┼──┼──┼──┼──┼──┼──┼──┼──┼──┼──┼──┼──┼──┼──►
   0  I  2  3  4  5  6  7  8  9 10 11 12 13 14 15 16 17 18 19 20
```

Count back to subtract. Use the number line to help.

1.   10
    − 2
    8
	2. 12
	    − 3
	    9
		3. 11
		    − 4
		    7

4.   8
   − 3
   5
	5. 7
	   − 2
	   5
		6. 9
		   − 3
		   6

Subtract.

7. $7 - 7 =$ __**0**__   8. $6 - 0 =$ __**6**__

9. $8 - 8 =$ __**0**__   10. $10 - 0 =$ __**10**__

11. $8 - 4 =$ __**4**__   12. $6 - 3 =$ __**3**__

13. $14 - 7 =$ __**7**__   14. $12 - 6 =$ __**6**__

RESPONSE TO INTERVENTION

DIFFERENTIATED INSTRUCTION

AL   **STRATEGIC INTERVENTION**

(Approaching Grade Level)

IF students miss 8 or more,

THEN choose a resource:

→ Check My Progress

→ Self-Check Quiz

→ Use the Reteach worksheets.

OL   **ON LEVEL**

IF students miss 6 to 7,

THEN choose a resource:

→ Chapter Project

→ Proceed to the next lesson.

BL   **BEYOND LEVEL**

IF students miss 5 or less,

THEN choose a resource:

→ Chapter Project

→ Use the Enrich worksheets.

→ Proceed to the next lesson.

LESSON 10
Relate Addition and Subtraction
OBJECTIVE Use addition facts to subtract.

What's the Math?

 Common Core State Standards
DOMAIN: Operations and Algebraic Thinking

Standards: 2.OA.1, 2.OA.2
The wording of these standards can be found on page 2.

CCSS

What Students Should Understand
- Addition and subtraction have related facts, or facts that have the same three numbers.
- You can use addition facts to subtract.

What Students Should be Able to Do
Use a related fact to find $8 - 3$.

Think of a related fact that has those numbers.

$3 + 5 = 8 \leftarrow$ related fact

So, $8 - 3 = 5$ because related facts have the same three numbers.

 Building on the Essential Question
In this lesson, students will build upon the skills and concepts needed to answer the chapter's Essential Question "What strategies can I use to add and subtract?"

Developing Vocabulary

 New Vocabulary
related facts

Activity
- Write *related facts* on the board. Explain that related facts are facts that use the same numbers.
- Have students build a two-cube train with cubes of one color, and a three-cube train with cubes of another color. Tell them to join the two-cube and three-cube trains. Then have them separate the trains.
- *What did you do with the cubes?* I did something, then undid it, or did the reverse.

ELL **ELL Support Strategy** Use this vocabulary activity to visualize what is being taught.

My Vocabulary Cards
Have students use the example on the *related facts* card to describe the meaning of *related facts*.

IWB **Virtual Word Wall**
Add this vocabulary card to the Virtual Word Wall for the chapter.

ELL Refer to the Multilingual eGlossary for interactive definitions in 13 languages.

Plan Online
Plan for your lesson by using the resources at
connectED.mcgraw-hill.com

Digital Dashboard

Interactive Whiteboard Ready

 **Vocab**
The eBook **Glossary** shows the definition of the word and has audio for each definition. The **eGlossary** provides definitions in 13 languages.

 Watch
Watch as concepts are brought to life through **animations**, **songs**, and a variety of visual instruction.

 Tools
Virtual Manipulatives with work mats allow teachers and students to model the lesson.

 Check
Use **eAssessment** for online assignments and customized assessments.

Use the **Common Core Quick Check** before the lesson to assess students' retention of previously learned concepts.

Use the interactive **Self-Check Quiz** after the lesson to provide immediate feedback on lesson concepts.

 eHelp
Digital and print resources assist students and parents in completing My Homework.

 Games
Online games and **apps** provide extra practice for lesson concepts.

 PD
Professional development videos help teachers gain a deeper understanding of the lesson concepts and strategies.

 RtI
Support for **approaching**, **on-** and **beyond-level** students as well as **English Language Learners**.

 Masters
Reteach and **Enrich** worksheets, **Manipulative Masters**, the **Problem of the Day**, and other blackline masters are available for each lesson.

LAUNCH THE LESSON

CCSS

 If your students are well-versed in relating addition and subtraction, you may choose to begin instruction with Step 2, **TEACH**.

You will need
☐ two-color counters

Mathematical PRACTICE **Modeling the Math**

Give each student ten two-color counters. Ask them to show seven red and three yellow.

Explain that the counters are related, like members of a family.

How many are in the group? 10 *How many are yellow?* 7 *How many are red?* 3

Ask students to write all related facts with 7, 3, and 10. Remind them that they can use addition and subtraction.

TEACH

 Begin core instruction here.

You will need

☐ counters

Explore and Explain

Read the directions that are at the bottom of the student page. Before students place 4 counters in one part, 3 counters in another part, and move them all to the whole, tell them that they are going to write an addition number sentence to represent this situation. Lead students through the first problem.

> *What numbers are the addends? Why?* 4 and 3; Sample answer: 4 and 3 represent 2 sets of counters that are being joined to find a total
>
> *What number is the sum?* 7 *How is the sum represented by the counters?* Sample answer: the sum is represented by all of the counters being moved to the whole

Before students move the yellow counters back to the part, tell them that they are going to write a subtraction number sentence to represent this situation.

> *What number is being subtracted from?* 7 *How is this number represented by the counters?* the 7 counters that start off on the whole represent the number that is being subtracted from
>
> *What number is being subtracted?* 3 *How is this number represented by the counters?* the yellow counters that are moved to a part represent the number that is being subtracted
>
> *What is the difference?* 4 *How is this number represented by the counters?* the 4 red counters that are still on the whole represent the difference

See and Show

Help students work through the example at the top of the page.

Point out that you are using the same 3 numbers in all three problems. Explain to students that addition and subtraction are opposite or inverse operations. Demonstrate, using connecting cubes, the addition and subtraction problems. Have them trace the dashed numbers as they work through the problems.

Work through Exercises 1–4 as a class.

Mathematical PRACTICE 3 ▶ **Talk Math**

Discuss with students "Explain how addition and subtraction are related." Sample answer: Subtraction is the inverse of addition.

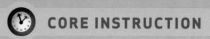

CORE INSTRUCTION

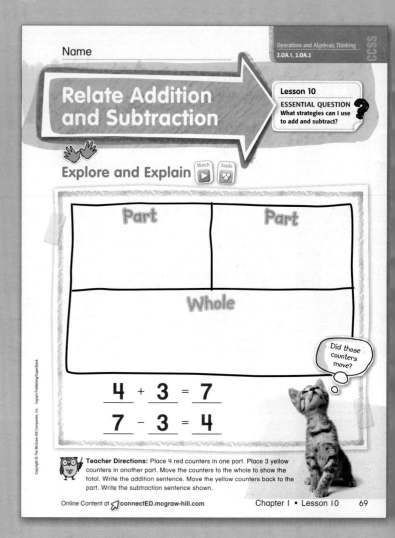

Name _____

Operations and Algebraic Thinking 2.OA.1, 2.OA.2   CCSS

Relate Addition and Subtraction

Lesson 10

ESSENTIAL QUESTION What strategies can I use to add and subtract?

Explore and Explain Watch ▶ Tools 🐾

Part	Part

Whole

4 + 3 = 7
7 − 3 = 4

Did those counters move?

Teacher Directions: Place 4 red counters in one part. Place 3 yellow counters in another part. Move the counters to the whole to show the total. Write the addition sentence. Move the yellow counters back to the part. Write the subtraction sentence shown.

Online Content at 🖥 connectED.mcgraw-hill.com   Chapter 1 • Lesson 10   69

See and Show   **Mathematical PRACTICE**

You can use addition facts to subtract.
Related facts have the same three numbers.

5 + 4 = __9__

Helpful Hint
Addition and subtraction are opposite or inverse operations.

9 − 4 = __5__   9 − 5 = __4__

Use the addition facts to subtract.

1.
6 + 7 = **13**
13 − 6 = **7**
13 − 7 = **6**

2.
5 + 7 = **12**
12 − 7 = **5**
12 − 5 = **7**

3.
5 + 6 = **11**
11 − 6 = **5**
11 − 5 = **6**

4.
7 + 4 = **11**
11 − 4 = **7**
11 − 7 = **4**

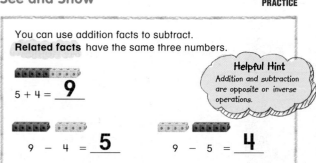

Talk Math Explain how addition and subtraction are related.

70   Chapter 1 • Lesson 10

69-70   Chapter 1 Apply Addition and Subtraction Concepts

Name _____

On My Own

Use addition facts to subtract.

5. $3 + 9 = \underline{12}$
$12 - 9 = \underline{3}$
$12 - 3 = \underline{9}$

6. $4 + 7 = \underline{11}$
$11 - 4 = \underline{7}$
$11 - 7 = \underline{4}$

7. $\begin{array}{r} 8 \\ + 9 \\ \hline 17 \end{array}$ $\begin{array}{r} 17 \\ - 8 \\ \hline 9 \end{array}$

8. $\begin{array}{r} 9 \\ + 6 \\ \hline 15 \end{array}$ $\begin{array}{r} 15 \\ - 9 \\ \hline 6 \end{array}$

9. $\begin{array}{r} 9 \\ + 5 \\ \hline 14 \end{array}$ $\begin{array}{r} 14 \\ - 5 \\ \hline 9 \end{array}$

10. $\begin{array}{r} 8 \\ + 4 \\ \hline 12 \end{array}$ $\begin{array}{r} 12 \\ - 8 \\ \hline 4 \end{array}$

11. $\begin{array}{r} 8 \\ + 7 \\ \hline 15 \end{array}$ $\begin{array}{r} 15 \\ - 7 \\ \hline 8 \end{array}$

12. $\begin{array}{r} 8 \\ + 5 \\ \hline 13 \end{array}$ $\begin{array}{r} 13 \\ - 8 \\ \hline 5 \end{array}$

13. $8 + 9 = \underline{17}$
$17 - 8 = \underline{9}$

14. $6 + 8 = \underline{14}$
$14 - 6 = \underline{8}$

15. $6 + 7 = \underline{13}$
$13 - 6 = \underline{7}$

16. $3 + 8 = \underline{11}$
$11 - 8 = \underline{3}$

17. $8 + 8 = \underline{16}$
$16 - 8 = \underline{8}$

18. $5 + 5 = \underline{10}$
$10 - 5 = \underline{5}$

Problem Solving   See students' work.   **Mathematical PRACTICE**

19. The tennis team has 16 players. 8 players leave the team. How many players are still on the team?

    $\underline{8}$ players

    Write a related fact. **Ex:** $\underline{8} \oplus \underline{8} = \underline{16}$

20. 10 turtles are on a log. 2 turtles jump in the water and swim away. How many turtles are left on the log?

    $\underline{8}$ turtles

    Write a related fact. **Ex:** $\underline{2} \oplus \underline{8} = \underline{10}$

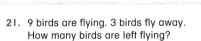

I'm lucky I found this log!

21. 9 birds are flying. 3 birds fly away. How many birds are left flying?

    $\underline{6}$ birds

    Write a related fact. **Ex:** $\underline{9} \ominus \underline{3} = \underline{6}$

Write Math   Write an example of related facts. Use the numbers 4, 6, and 10.

Sample answer: $4 + 6 = 10$; $10 - 6 = 4$; $6 + 4 = 10$;

$10 - 4 = 6$

---

3 PRACTICE & APPLY

On My Own

Have students work through the exercises on this page independently. You may choose to assign exercises based on the chart below.

DIFFERENTIATED ASSIGNMENTS

AL Approaching Level Guide students through the exercises in On My Own. Help them to use manipulatives while working through the exercises.

OL On Level Complete the exercises independently.

BL Beyond Level Complete the exercises independently without manipulatives.

Common Error!
Students may have difficulty with the "fact family" concept. Remind students that in a fact family, all of the facts have the same numbers.

Problem Solving

Have students work through the problem-solving exercises on this page independently.

Mathematical PRACTICE 4   In Exercise 20, students **model with mathematics.**

Write Math

This exercise asks students to build upon their understanding of concepts needed to answer the chapter's Essential Question.

AL ▸ **APPROACHING LEVEL**

IF my students struggle with addition and subtraction,

THEN choose a resource:

→ Use the Reteach worksheet with small groups.

→ Go online for a Differentiated Instruction activity.

→ **Make Models** Have students model the sentences with connecting cubes.

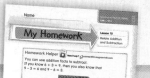

OL ▸ **ON LEVEL**

IF my students seem to know addition and subtraction, but need more practice,

THEN choose a resource:

→ Assign My Homework.

→ Go online for a Differentiated Instruction activity.

BL ▸ **BEYOND LEVEL**

IF my students have mastered addition and subtraction,

THEN choose a resource:

→ Use the Enrich worksheet in cooperative groups.

→ Assign My Homework.

→ Go online for a Differentiated Instruction activity.

73A **Chapter 1** Apply Addition and Subtraction Concepts

Name _____

AL

Lesson 10   Reteach

Relate Addition and Subtraction

●●●● ○○ $8 + 4 = \underline{12}$ ●●●● ○○ $12 - 4 = \underline{8}$	These addition and subtraction facts have the same three numbers.

Use addition facts to subtract.

1. ●● ○○○○
●● ○○○
$4 + 7 = \underline{11}$
$11 - 7 = \underline{4}$

2. ●● ○○○
● ○○○
$3 + 6 = \underline{9}$
$9 - 3 = \underline{6}$

3. ●●●●● ○○
●●●● ○
$9 + 3 = \underline{12}$
$12 - 3 = \underline{9}$

4. ● ○○○
● ○○
$2 + 5 = \underline{7}$
$7 - 5 = \underline{2}$

5. ● ○○○○
● ○○○
$2 + 8 = \underline{10}$
$10 - 2 = \underline{8}$

6. ● ○○○
○○○
$1 + 6 = \underline{7}$
$7 - 6 = \underline{1}$

Name _____

BL

Lesson 10   Enrich

Relate Addition and Subtraction

Draw the missing counters. Fill in the missing numbers.

1. 17
$-\ 8$
9
○○○○○○○○ + ○○○○○○○○○
8   + $\underline{9}$ = 17

2. 14
$-\ 6$
8
○○○○○○ + ○○○○○○○○
6   + $\underline{8}$ = 14

3. 13
$-\ 9$
4
○○○○○○○○○ + ○○○○
9   + $\underline{4}$ = 13

4. 16
$-\ 7$
9
○○○○○○○ + ○○○○○○○○○
7   + $\underline{9}$ = 16

My Homework

Operations and Algebraic Thinking
2.OA.1, 2.OA.2

Lesson 10
Relate Addition
and Subtraction

Homework Helper eHelp Need help? ⟋ connectED.mcgraw-hill.com

You can use addition facts to subtract.
If you know 6 + 3 = 9, then you also know that
9 − 3 = 6 and 9 − 6 = 3.

6 + 3 = 9

9 − 3 = 6   9 − 6 = 3

Practice

Use addition facts to subtract.

1. 7 + 5 = **12**
   12 − 5 = **7**

2. 6 + 9 = **15**
   15 − 9 = **6**

3. 8 + 5 = **13**
   13 − 5 = **8**

4. 4 + 7 = **11**
   11 − 7 = **4**

Chapter 1 • Lesson 10   73

Use addition facts to subtract.

5. 7   10
   + 3   − 3
   10 **7**

6. 4   4
   + 0   − 0
   4   **4**

7. 2   10
   + 8   − 2
   10 **8**

8. Megan sent 12 postcards last week. This week she sent 4 postcards. How many more postcards did she send last week?

   8 _____ postcards

I hope Megan writes to me!

Vocabulary Check

9. **Using 2, 4, and 6, write an example of related facts.**

   4 ⊕ **2** ⊜ **6**
   2 ⊕ **4** ⊜ **6**
   6 ⊖ **2** ⊜ **4**
   6 ⊖ **4** ⊜ **2**

 Math at Home Ask your child to show you an addition sentence with spoons and relate it to subtraction.

74   Chapter 1 • Lesson 10

---

4 WRAP IT UP

My Homework

Assign homework after successful completion of the lesson. Students who understand the concepts may skip the **Homework Helper** section.

Vocabulary Check 🔲 Vocab

Tell students they can refer to the exercises in the lesson for an example.

Formative Assessment

Ask students the following questions.

- *Why are the two number sentences 5 + 2 = 7 and 7 − 5 = 2 called related facts?* They have the same three numbers: 2, 5, and 7.

- *How can the addition sentence 5 + 2 = 7 help you find the difference of 7 + 5?* The second number in the addition sentence, 2, is the missing part of the subtraction sentence.

 MY Learning Stations

Use the graphic novel **Puppies!** after this lesson. The Teacher Guide provides suggestions for differentiated instruction.

Line Up! When students line up for lunch, make a group of five students and add them to a group of three. Then have five students leave the group. Have students say number sentences about the addition and subtraction.

LESSON 11
Missing Addends
OBJECTIVE Use subtraction facts to help find missing addends.

What's the Math?

 Common Core State Standards
DOMAIN: Operations and Algebraic Thinking

Standards: 2.OA.1, 2.OA.2
The wording of these standards can be found on page 2.

What Students Should Understand

• Addition and subtraction have related facts, or facts that have the same three numbers.

• You can use subtraction facts to find a missing addend.

• First, look at the numbers in an addition problem that has a missing addend. Then think of a related subtraction problem that also has those numbers.

What Students Should be Able to Do

Use a related fact to find the missing addend in $4 + \square = 11$.

Think of a related fact that has those numbers.

$11 - 4 = 7$ ⟵——— related fact

$4 + 7 = 11$

So, 7 is the missing addend.

⁇ Building on the Essential Question

In this lesson, students will build upon the skills and concepts needed to answer the chapter's Essential Question "What strategies can I use to add and subtract?"

Developing Vocabulary

 New Vocabulary

missing addend

Activity

• Write *missing addend* on the board. Ask students what they know about this word. Explain that a missing addend is a number missing from an addition sentence.

• Divide the class into half. Have half the students in class roll a red number cube. Have the other half roll a blue number cube.

• Have a pair of volunteers from each group make a subtraction sentence out of the numbers they roll.

• Have the students in the other group write the subtraction sentence shown.

ELL **ELL Support Strategy** Use this vocabulary activity to participate in purposeful, cooperative learning activities.

My Vocabulary Cards

Read the activity for the *missing addend* card. Have students respond.

IWB **Virtual Word Wall**

Add this vocabulary card to the Virtual Word Wall for the chapter.

ELL Refer to the Multilingual eGlossary for interactive definitions in 13 languages.

Digital Dashboard

Interactive Whiteboard Ready

Vocab
The eBook **Glossary** shows the definition of the word and has audio for each definition. The **eGlossary** provides definitions in 13 languages.

Watch
Watch as concepts are brought to life through **animations**, **songs**, and a variety of visual instruction.

Tools
Virtual Manipulatives with work mats allow teachers and students to model the lesson.

Check
Use **eAssessment** for online assignments and customized assessments.

Use the **Common Core Quick Check** before the lesson to assess students' retention of previously learned concepts.

Use the interactive **Self-Check Quiz** after the lesson to provide immediate feedback on lesson concepts.

eHelp
Digital and print resources assist students and parents in completing My Homework.

Games
Online games and **apps** provide extra practice for lesson concepts.

PD
Professional development videos help teachers gain a deeper understanding of the lesson concepts and strategies.

RtI
Support for **approaching**, **on**- and **beyond-level** students as well as **English Language Learners**.

Masters
Reteach and **Enrich** worksheets, **Manipulative Masters**, the **Problem of the Day**, and other blackline masters are available for each lesson.

1 LAUNCH THE LESSON

CCSS

If your students are well-versed in finding missing addends, you may choose to begin instruction with Step 2, **TEACH**.

You will need
☐ pan balance
☐ connecting cubes

Mathematical PRACTICE 4 Modeling the Math

Place 6 connecting cubes on each side of the pan balance.

Do you notice anything about the balance? Is it level? Yes *Since it is level, you know that 6 connecting cubes equals 6 connecting cubes. You can write the number sentence* $6 = 6$.

Remove one connecting cube from one side of the pan balance.

What happens if I take one away from a side? Sample answer: It goes out of balance. One side is higher/lower than the other. *How many cubes are on the first side?* 6 cubes *How many cubes are on the other side?* 5 cubes *What do you need to do to make the balance level again?* Put back the cube to make 6 cubes.

Place the one back on to demonstrate that it will level out.

This tells that $5 + 1 = 6$.

Demonstrate several more examples. This develops a good foundation for future algebraic exploration.

Let's place 3 cubes on one side and 8 cubes on the other side. How many do we need to add to the side with three cubes to make the pan balance level? 5 cubes *What number sentence could I write to show this?* $3 + 5 = 8$

TEACH

 Begin core instruction here.

Explore and Explain

Read the directions that are on the bottom of the student page. Model to students how to draw dots on the right side of the purple domino to determine the missing number in the number sentence. As you draw each dot, have students count on from 4 to say the total number of dots.

> *How many dots did we draw to have a total of 9 dots?* 5
>
> *What number is missing in the number sentence?* 5

Lead students through how to draw dots on the next domino to find the next missing addend.

> *How many dots did you draw to have a total of 8 dots?* 6
>
> *What number is missing in the number sentence?* 6

Then have students find the last two missing addends independently. After students draw the dots on each domino and find the missing addends, ask them how many dots they drew on each domino and what the missing addends were in the number sentences.

See and Show

Help students work through the example at the top of the page. Discuss what is missing and how they might find it. Have them trace the dashed number as they work through the problems.

Work through Exercises 1–4 as a class.

 **Mathematical PRACTICE 3** **Talk Math**

Discuss with students "How do you find the missing addend in $5 + \square = 13$?" Sample answer: You can subtract 5 from 13 to find the missing addend.

 **CORE INSTRUCTION**

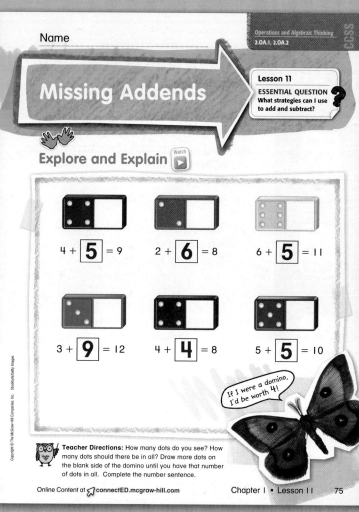

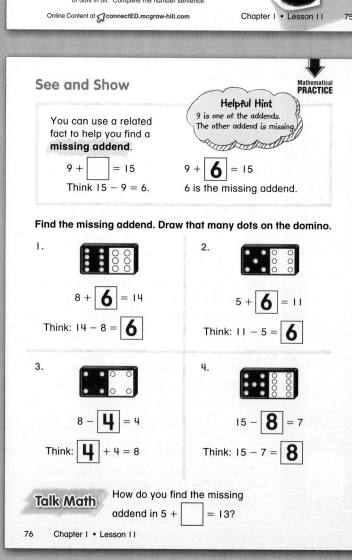

75-76 Chapter 1 Apply Addition and Subtraction Concepts

Name _____

Helpful Hint
To find the missing addend, use related facts.

On My Own

Find the missing addend.

5. $9 + \boxed{3} = 12$

   $12 - 9 = \boxed{3}$

6. $7 + \boxed{1} = 8$

   $8 - 7 = \boxed{1}$

7. $\boxed{6} + 6 = 12$

   $12 - 6 = \boxed{6}$

8. $\boxed{5} + 2 = 7$

   $7 - 2 = \boxed{5}$

9. $15 - \boxed{8} = 7$

   $15 - 7 = \boxed{8}$

10. $\boxed{14} - 7 = 7$

    $7 + 7 = \boxed{14}$

11. $9 - \boxed{9} = 0$

    $9 + 0 = \boxed{9}$

12. $13 - \boxed{7} = 6$

    $13 - 6 = \boxed{7}$

13. $4 + \boxed{8} = 12$

    $12 - 4 = \boxed{8}$

14. $12 - \boxed{7} = 5$

    $12 - 5 = \boxed{7}$

Chapter 1 • Lesson 11   77

Problem Solving

Mathematical
PRACTICE

15. There were 14 seals on a rock. Some seals jumped into the water. 9 seals were left on the rock. How many seals jumped into the water?

    5 seals

16. Anna buys 7 plants. She wants 12 plants. How many more plants does Anna need?

    5 plants

17. J.J. wants 16 fish in his aquarium. He has 6 fish now. How many more fish does J.J. need?

    10 fish

HOT Problem Julie found a missing addend like this:

$7 + \boxed{} = 9 \qquad 9 + 7 = 16$

Tell what she did wrong. Make it right.

Sample answer: Julie added the two numbers to find the missing addend instead of subtracting. $9 - 7 = 2$, so $7 + 2 = 9$.

78   Chapter 1 • Lesson 11

On My Own

Have students work through the exercises on this page independently. You may choose to assign exercises based on the chart below.

DIFFERENTIATED ASSIGNMENTS
AL **Approaching Level** Guide students through the exercises in On My Own. Help them to use manipulatives while working through the exercises.
OL **On Level** Complete the exercises independently.
BL **Beyond Level** Complete the exercises independently without manipulatives.

Problem Solving

Have students work through the problem-solving exercises on this page independently.

Mathematical
PRACTICE **7** In Exercise 16, students **look for and make use of structure.**

HOT Problem This exercise asks students to build upon their understanding of concepts needed to answer the chapter's Essential Question.

RESPONSE TO INTERVENTION

DIFFERENTIATED INSTRUCTION

Copyright © The McGraw-Hill Companies, Inc. Permission is granted to reproduce for classroom use.

AL ▶ APPROACHING LEVEL

IF my students struggle with missing addends,

THEN choose a resource:

→ Use the Reteach worksheet with small groups.

→ Go online for a Differentiated Instruction activity.

OL ▶ ON LEVEL

IF my students seem to know missing addends, but need more practice,

THEN choose a resource:

→ Assign My Homework.

→ Go online for a Differentiated Instruction activity.

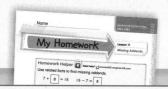

BL ▶ BEYOND LEVEL

IF my students have mastered missing addends,

THEN choose a resource:

→ Use the Enrich worksheet in cooperative groups.

→ Assign My Homework.

→ Go online for a Differentiated Instruction activity.

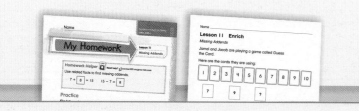

AL

Name _____

Lesson 11   Reteach

Missing Addends

$9 + \boxed{} = 14$

Related facts use the same numbers.

Write a related fact.

$14 - 9 = \underline{\quad 5 \quad}$

So, $9 + \underline{\quad 5 \quad} = 14$.

Find the missing addend. Draw pictures to help.

1. $8 + \boxed{4} = 12$

   $12 - 8 = \boxed{4}$ **1–4. See students' drawings.**

2. $7 + \boxed{5} = 12$

   $12 - 7 = \boxed{5}$

3. $5 + \boxed{8} = 13$

   $13 - 5 = \boxed{8}$

4. $9 + \boxed{8} = 17$

   $17 - 9 = \boxed{8}$

BL

Name _____

Lesson 11   Enrich

Missing Addends

Jamal and Jacob are playing a game called Guess the Card.

Here are the cards they are using:

| 1 | 2 | 3 | 4 | 5 | 6 | 7 | 8 | 9 | 10 |

| 7 | 9 | ? |

Jacob said that the sum of the three cards is 20.

What is the number on the card ? ___**4**___

| ? | 3 | 10 |

Jamal said that his number is the difference between 10 and 3.

What is the number on the card ? ___**7**___

| 5 | 4 | ? |

Jacob said that the number on the card is the difference between 5 and 4.

What is the number on the card? ___**1**___

My Homework

Assign homework after successful completion of the lesson. Students who understand the concepts may skip the **Homework Helper** section.

Vocabulary Check

Have students refer to their My Vocabulary Cards for additional support.

Formative Assessment

Ask students to complete the following problem.

Find the missing addend in 4 + ☐ = 11. 7

Line Up!

When students line up for lunch, make a group of 7 students. Ask how many more students are needed to make 12 students. Write 7 + ☐ = 12 on the board. Have students find the missing addend.

Name _____

Operations and Algebraic Thinking
2.OA.1, 2.OA.2
CCSS

My Homework

Lesson 11
Missing Addends

Homework Helper

Need help? connectED.mcgraw-hill.com

Use related facts to find missing addends.

$7 + \boxed{8} = 15$ $15 - 7 = \boxed{8}$

Practice

Find the missing addend.

1. $8 + \boxed{4} = 12$
   $12 - \boxed{4} = 8$

2. $\boxed{9} + 6 = 15$
   $15 - 6 = \boxed{9}$

3. $8 + \boxed{5} = 13$
   $13 - 8 = \boxed{5}$

4. $\boxed{4} + 7 = 11$
   $11 - \boxed{4} = 7$

5. $17 - \boxed{9} = 8$
   $8 + \boxed{9} = 17$

6. $12 - \boxed{3} = 9$
   $9 + \boxed{3} = 12$

Chapter 1 • Lesson 11   79

---

7. David and his friends are flying 9 kites. Some kites get stuck in a tree. 7 kites are still flying. How many kites are in the tree?

$\underline{9} - \underline{7} = \underline{2}$ $\underline{2}$ kites

I'm really good at playing catch!
Ouch!

8. The Girl Scouts have 15 boats. They put some boats in the pond. 9 boats are left on land. How many boats did the scouts put into the pond?

$\underline{15} - \underline{9} = \underline{6}$ $\underline{6}$ boats

9. 7 boys were riding their bikes. Some of the boys went home. 3 boys are still riding their bikes. How many boys went home?

$\underline{7} - \underline{3} = \underline{4}$ $\underline{4}$ boys

Vocabulary Check

Complete the sentence.

| missing addend | sum |

10. When a number sentence only has one addend, you must find the __missing addend__ to solve it.

 Math at Home Ask your child to tell you the subtraction fact that will help him or her find the missing addend in 7 + ☐ = 15.

LESSON 12
Fact Families
OBJECTIVE Use related facts to write fact families.

What's the Math?

 Common Core State Standards
DOMAIN: Operations and Algebraic Thinking

Standards: 2.OA.1, 2.OA.2, 2.NBT.9
The wording of these standards can be found on page 2.

CCSS

What Students Should Understand

• A fact family is a set of related facts that use the same three numbers.

• When you know the three numbers in a fact family that has addition and subtraction number sentences, you can complete the fact family.

What Students Should be Able to Do

Complete the fact family that has the three numbers shown below.

$$7 + 6 = 13$$
$$6 + 7 = 13$$
$$13 - 7 = 6$$
$$13 - 6 = 7$$

 Building on the Essential Question

In this lesson, students will build upon the skills and concepts needed to answer the chapter's Essential Question "What strategies can I use to add and subtract?"

Developing Vocabulary

 New Vocabulary
fact family

Activity

• Explain that a fact family is a set of addition and subtraction facts with common numbers.

• Write the following on the board as shown:

$$6 + 4 = 10 \qquad 10 - 6 = 4$$
$$7 + 5 = 12 \qquad 5 + 7 = 12$$

$$12 - 5 = 7 \qquad 6 + 4 = 10$$
$$10 - 4 = 6 \qquad 12 - 7 = 5$$

• Ask a student to circle four facts from the same family and put a box around the others.

ELL **ELL Support Strategy** Use this vocabulary activity to show understanding through demonstration.

My Vocabulary Cards

Have students draw a fact family that is different from the one shown on the *fact family* card.

IWB **Virtual Word Wall**

Add this vocabulary card to the Virtual Word Wall for the chapter.

ELL Refer to the Multilingual eGlossary for interactive definitions in 13 languages.

Plan Online

Plan for your lesson by using the resources at
connectED.mcgraw-hill.com

Digital Dashboard

Interactive Whiteboard Ready

Vocab

The eBook **Glossary** shows the definition of the word and has audio for each definition. The **eGlossary** provides definitions in 13 languages.

Watch

Watch as concepts are brought to life through **animations**, **songs**, and a variety of visual instruction.

Tools

Virtual Manipulatives with work mats allow teachers and students to model the lesson.

Check

Use **eAssessment** for online assignments and customized assessments.

Use the **Common Core Quick Check** before the lesson to assess students' retention of previously learned concepts.

Use the interactive **Self-Check Quiz** after the lesson to provide immediate feedback on lesson concepts.

eHelp

Digital and print resources assist students and parents in completing My Homework.

Games

Online games and **apps** provide extra practice for lesson concepts.

PD

Professional development videos help teachers gain a deeper understanding of the lesson concepts and strategies.

RtI

Support for **approaching**, **on-** and **beyond-level** students as well as **English Language Learners**.

Masters

Reteach and **Enrich** worksheets, **Manipulative Masters**, the **Problem of the Day**, and other blackline masters are available for each lesson.

---

1 LAUNCH THE LESSON   CCSS

 If your students are well-versed in fact families, you may choose to begin instruction with Step 2, **TEACH**.

You will need
☐ number cubes
☐ connecting cubes

Mathematical PRACTICE 4 Modeling the Math

Give each pair of students a number cube and two six-cube trains of different colors.

Roll the number cube and remove cubes to create a cube train to show the addition sentence.

Have the pair combine their trains and tell the addition sentence. Then have them flip their train and tell the new addition number sentence.

Now separate your train into two parts and write the two subtraction sentences. See students' responses.

What are the numbers in your fact family? See students' responses.

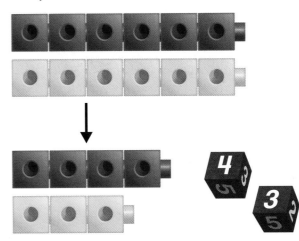

$$4 + 3 = 7$$
$$3 + 4 = 7$$

🕐 **Begin core instruction here.**

You will need

☐ number cubes

Explore and Explain

Explain to students that related number sentences are addition and subtraction number sentences that have the same three numbers in them. Write an example on the board. Model rolling number cubes and write the numbers in the bottom of a triangle. Then write the sum in the top of the triangle. Next, write one addition number sentence on the board.

What is the second addition number sentence? Answers will vary.

What are the related subtraction number sentences? Answers will vary.

Read the directions at the bottom of the student page. Guide students through rolling the number cubes to fill in the top triangle and finding the first set of related number sentences.

Tell students that if they roll doubles, there will be one addition number sentence and one subtraction number sentence that they will write as related number sentences. Work through the example below as you explain it to students.

If I rolled two 3s with my number cubes, I would write two 3s on the bottom of the triangle and a 6 at the top. I would write $3 + 3 = 6$ and $6 - 3 = 3$ as the related number sentences.

Then have students work independently to roll their number cubes to fill in the bottom triangle and find the second set of related number sentences. Invite students to share their related number sentences with the class.

See and Show

Help students work through the example at the top of the page. Discuss the numbers in the triangle. Ask students what they notice about the problems at the top of the page. The triangle is a fact family and the problems are related facts. Have them trace the dashed numbers as they work the problems.

Work through Exercises 1 and 2 as a class.

Mathematical PRACTICE ➌ **Talk Math**

Discuss with students "What are the related facts in the fact family 9, 9, 18? Explain." Sample answer: $9 + 9 = 18$, $18 - 9 = 9$. The addends are the same, so the other addition and subtraction facts are the same.

🕐 **CORE INSTRUCTION**

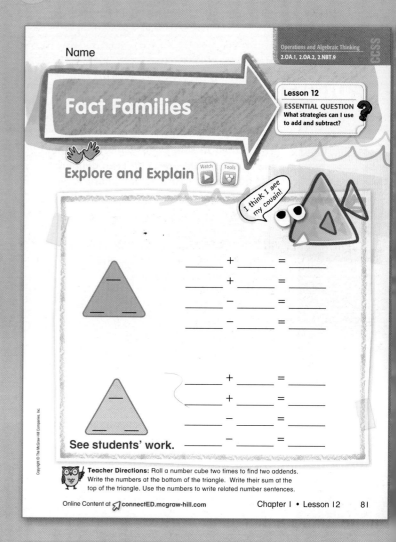

Name _____

Operations and Algebraic Thinking
2.OA.1, 2.OA.2, 2.NBT.9   CCSS

Fact Families

Lesson 12
ESSENTIAL QUESTION
What strategies can I use to add and subtract?

Explore and Explain ▶Watch ⬛Tools

I think I see my cousin!

```
        ___ + ___ = ___
   △    ___ + ___ = ___
        ___ - ___ = ___
        ___ - ___ = ___

        ___ + ___ = ___
   △    ___ + ___ = ___
        ___ - ___ = ___
        ___ - ___ = ___
```

See students' work.

🦉 **Teacher Directions:** Roll a number cube two times to find two addends. Write the numbers at the bottom of the triangle. Write their sum at the top of the triangle. Use the numbers to write related number sentences.

Online Content at 🖊️connectED.mcgraw-hill.com   Chapter 1 • Lesson 12   81

See and Show   Mathematical **PRACTICE**

A **fact family** is a set of related facts using the same three numbers. The numbers in this fact family are 12, 9, and 3.

 Helpful Hint
Use related facts to complete fact families.

```
      12
   △        9 + 3 = 12
  9    3    3 + 9 = 12
           12 - 9 = 3
           12 - 3 = 9
```

Complete each fact family.

1.
```
      16
   △
  7    9
```
$9 + 7 = \underline{16}$
$7 + 9 = \underline{16}$
$16 - 9 = \underline{7}$
$16 - 7 = \underline{9}$

2.
```
      17
   △
  9    8
```
$9 + 8 = \underline{17}$
$\underline{8} + \underline{9} = 17$
$17 - 9 = \underline{8}$
$17 - \underline{8} = \underline{9}$

 Talk Math   What are the related facts in the fact family 9, 9, 18? Explain.

82   Chapter 1 • Lesson 12

Name _____

Helpful Hint
Each fact in a fact family uses the same three numbers.

On My Own

Complete each fact family.

3.

$8 + 6 = 14$
$6 + 8 = 14$
$14 - 8 = 6$
$14 - 6 = 8$

4.
$8 + 5 = 13$
$5 + 8 = 13$
$13 - 5 = 8$
$13 - 8 = 5$

5.

$7 + 3 = 10$
$3 + 7 = 10$
$10 - 7 = 3$
$10 - 3 = 7$

6.

$9 + 6 = 15$
$6 + 9 = 15$
$15 - 9 = 6$
$15 - 6 = 9$

Chapter 1 • Lesson 12   83

🌐 **Problem Solving**

Mathematical PRACTICE

Solve.

7. Linda has 7 fish. She has 5 crabs. How many animals does Linda have?

    __12__ animals

I used to be shy, but I've come out of my shell!

8. There are 8 apples in one basket. The second basket has one more than the first. How many apples are there in all?

    __17__ apples

9. 11 children were on the playground. 3 more children came to the playground. How many children are on the playground now?

    __14__ children

HOT Problem Make a fact family. Use at least one two-digit number. **See students' work.**

☐ + ☐ = ☐   ☐ − ☐ = ☐

☐ + ☐ = ☐   ☐ − ☐ = ☐

84   Chapter 1 • Lesson 12

⬛ **3 PRACTICE & APPLY**

CCSS

On My Own

Have students work through the exercises on this page independently. You may choose to assign exercises based on the chart below.

DIFFERENTIATED ASSIGNMENTS

AL Approaching Level Guide students through the exercises in On My Own. Help them to use manipulatives while working through the exercises.

OL On Level Complete the exercises independently.

BL Beyond Level Complete the exercises independently without manipulatives.

Common Error!
Students sometimes read operation signs too quickly. Encourage students to take their time.

Problem Solving

Have students work through the problem-solving exercises on this page independently.

Mathematical PRACTICE 2 In Exercise 9, students **reason abstractly and quantitatively.**

HOT Problem This exercise asks students to build upon their understanding of concepts needed to answer the chapter's Essential Question.

AL ▸ APPROACHING LEVEL

IF my students struggle with fact families,

THEN choose a resource:

→ Use the Reteach worksheet with small groups.

→ Go online for a Differentiated Instruction activity.

→ **Modeling Fact Families** Use connecting cubes to model problems. As students connect cubes of two colors, direct them to write the addition fact. They can turn the cubes around and write the new addition fact. They snap off 1 color, then the other, to write subtraction facts.

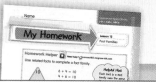

OL ▸ ON LEVEL

IF my students seem to know fact families, but need more practice,

THEN choose a resource:

→ Assign My Homework.

→ Go online for a Differentiated Instruction activity.

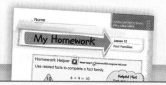

BL ▸ BEYOND LEVEL

IF my students have mastered fact families,

THEN choose a resource:

→ Use the Enrich worksheet in cooperative groups.

→ Assign My Homework.

→ Go online for a Differentiated Instruction activity.

Name _____

AL ▸ Lesson 12   Reteach

Fact Families

Some fact families have two addition facts and two subtraction facts.

$9 + 7 = \underline{16}$ $16 - 7 = \underline{9}$

$7 + 9 = \underline{16}$ $16 - 9 = \underline{7}$

Some fact families have one addition fact and one subtraction fact.

$8 + 8 = \underline{16}$ $16 - 8 = \underline{8}$

Complete each fact family.

1. $9 + 4 = \underline{13}$ $13 - 9 = \underline{4}$

    $4 + 9 = \underline{13}$ $13 - 4 = \underline{9}$

2. $6 + 5 = \underline{11}$ $11 - 5 = \underline{6}$

    $5 + 6 = \underline{11}$ $11 - 6 = \underline{5}$

3. $9 + 8 = \underline{17}$ $17 - 9 = \underline{8}$

    $8 + 9 = \underline{17}$ $17 - 8 = \underline{9}$

4. $7 + 7 = \underline{14}$ $14 - 7 = \underline{7}$

Name _____

BL ▸ Lesson 12   Enrich

Fact Families

The students in the 2nd grade classes choose their lunch each day. Complete the chart.

Class	Choice A	Choice B	Total Number of Students
Mr. Strong	8	9	17
Miss Kim	4	5	**9**
Mrs. West	5	7	**12**
Miss White	6	8	**14**

Use the numbers from the chart to write a fact family.

Mr. Strong's Class

$8 + 9 = 17$

$9 + 8 = 17$

$17 - 9 = 8$

$17 - 8 = 9$

Mrs. West's Class

$5 + 7 = 12$

$7 + 5 = 12$

$12 - 7 = 5$

$12 - 5 = 7$

Miss Kim's Class

$4 + 5 = 9$

$5 + 4 = 9$

$9 - 5 = 4$

$9 - 4 = 5$

Miss White's Class

$6 + 8 = 14$

$8 + 6 = 14$

$14 - 8 = 6$

$14 - 6 = 8$

My Homework

Name _____

Operations and Algebraic Thinking
2.OA.1, 2.OA.2, 2.NBT.9

CCSS

Lesson 12
Fact Families

Homework Helper Need help? connectED.mcgraw-hill.com

Use related facts to complete a fact family.

△ 10 / 6 4

$6 + 4 = 10$
$4 + 6 = 10$
$10 - 4 = 6$
$10 - 6 = 4$

Helpful Hint
Each fact in a fact family uses the same three numbers.

Practice

Complete each fact family.

1.
△ 12 / 8 4

$8 + 4 = 12$
$4 + 8 = 12$
$12 - 4 = 8$
$12 - 8 = 4$

2.
△ 15 / 9 6

$9 + 6 = 15$
$6 + 9 = 15$
$15 - 9 = 6$
$15 - 6 = 9$

Chapter 1 • Lesson 12   85

---

3. There are 8 apples on one tree. There are 7 apples on another tree. How many apples are there in all?

15 apples

4. Sam has 7 toy trucks in one box. He has one less than that number in another box. How many toy trucks does he have in all?

Beep! Beep!

13 toy trucks

Vocabulary Check

Circle the correct answer.

5. Which group shows a fact family?

(2 + 3 = 5)	1 + 4 = 5	2 + 1 = 3
3 + 2 = 5	1 + 5 = 6	2 + 2 = 4
5 - 3 = 2	1 + 7 = 8	2 + 3 = 5
5 - 2 = 3	1 + 8 = 9	2 + 4 = 6

(The first group is circled.)

 Math at Home Have your child write the fact family for the numbers 6, 7, and 13.

86   Chapter 1 • Lesson 12

My Homework

Assign homework after successful completion of the lesson. Students who understand the concepts may skip the **Homework Helper** section.

Vocabulary Check

Have students refer to their My Vocabulary Cards for additional support.

Formative Assessment

Ask students the following questions.

What is the difference between the two addition sentences in a fact family? The addends, or parts, are in different order.

What is the difference between the two subtraction sentences in a fact family? A different part is subtracted from the whole.

MY Learning Stations

Use the game **Switcheroo** after this lesson. The Teacher Guide provides suggestions for differentiated instruction.

Line Up! Make a group of six students. How many more need to join to have 11 students? Write $6 + \_\_ = 11$ on the board. Have students join until there are 11. Ask how many have joined. Repeat with other problems until all have lined up.

LESSON 13
Two-Step Word Problems

OBJECTIVE Solve word problems that involve two steps.

What's the Math?

 Common Core State Standards

DOMAIN: Operations and Algebraic Thinking

Standard: 2.OA.1

The wording of this standard can be found on page 2.

What Students Should Understand

- You can solve two-step word problems by reading the problem very carefully and determining what information is important and what is being asked.

- Since two steps are involved, you must figure out what to do first to get the information you need for the second step.

What Students Should be Able to Do

8 butterflies are in a flower garden. 3 fly away. Then 5 more land in the garden. How many butterflies are in the garden now? Use two steps to solve this problem.

$$
\begin{array}{r} 8 \\ -\ 3 \\ \hline 5 \end{array}
\qquad
\begin{array}{r} 5 \\ +\ 5 \\ \hline 10 \end{array}
$$

So, 10 butterflies are now in the garden.

 Building on the Essential Question

In this lesson, students will build upon the skills and concepts needed to answer the chapter's Essential Question "What strategies can I use to add and subtract?"

Developing Vocabulary

 Review Vocabulary

add   subtract

Review Activity

- Have students skim the first two pages of the lesson. Have them notice how each example is contained within a box. Point out that headings above each box are in a larger and heavier font than the rest of the text.

- Tell students this lesson contains word problems. Explain to students that word problems often contain patterns. These patterns can help readers identify what information is important.

- Have students identify which example shows subtraction, and which example shows addition.

- Encourage students to create visual aids like the vertical blank boxes if it helps them organize their problem solving.

ELL **ELL Support Strategy** Use this vocabulary activity to organize information using visual aids.

My Vocabulary Cards

Ask students to work in small groups to review the words they learned in this chapter.

Plan Online

Plan for your lesson by using the resources at

 connectED.mcgraw-hill.com

Digital Dashboard

Interactive Whiteboard Ready

 Vocab

The eBook **Glossary** shows the definition of the word and has audio for each definition. The **eGlossary** provides definitions in 13 languages.

 Watch

Watch as concepts are brought to life through **animations**, **songs**, and a variety of visual instruction.

 Tools

Virtual Manipulatives with work mats allow teachers and students to model the lesson.

 Check

Use **eAssessment** for online assignments and customized assessments.

Use the **Common Core Quick Check** before the lesson to assess students' retention of previously learned concepts.

Use the interactive **Self-Check Quiz** after the lesson to provide immediate feedback on lesson concepts.

 eHelp

Digital and print resources assist students and parents in completing My Homework.

 Games

Online games and **apps** provide extra practice for lesson concepts.

 PD

Professional development videos help teachers gain a deeper understanding of the lesson concepts and strategies.

 RtI

Support for **approaching**, **on**- and **beyond-level** students as well as **English Language Learners**.

 Masters

Reteach and **Enrich** worksheets, **Manipulative Masters**, the **Problem of the Day**, and other blackline masters are available for each lesson.

---

1 LAUNCH THE LESSON

🕐 **If your students are well-versed in two-step word problems, you may choose to begin instruction with Step 2, TEACH.**

You will need

☐ connecting cubes

Mathematical PRACTICE 4 ➤ Modeling the Math

Model the following problem. Give students 10 connecting cubes.

Listen as I read and use your connecting cubes to act out or model this problem. Adam has 6 books. He gets 3 more books, and then lets his sister have 4 of the books. How many books does Adam have left?

Students should place 6 purple cubes in a row and then add 3 more cubes. *How many are there in all?* 9

Next, they take away 4 purple cubes. *How many are left?* 5

Sometimes word problems will require two steps.

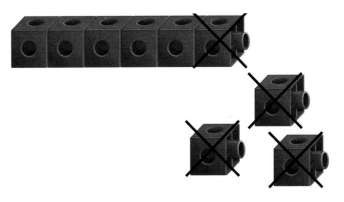

Repeat modeling examples of addition and subtraction using two steps.

2 TEACH

🕐 **Begin core instruction here.**

You will need

☐ two-color counters

Explore and Explain

Read the directions that are on the bottom of the student page.

Sometimes, you will need to use two steps to solve a problem. You can focus on one step at a time. Let's use counters to model the two steps.

Read the example again. Use counters to model what is taking place in the problem.

What question is being asked? **How many dolphins are still following the boat?**

What information do you need to solve the problem? **There is a group of 12 dolphins following the boat. 3 more dolphins join the group. Then 6 of the dolphins swim away.**

What is the first step you will take to solve this problem? **Find 12 + 3.** *Why?* **Sample answer: Two sets of objects are being joined together and I want to find the total amount.**

Write the sum of 12 + 3 in the blank on the left side of the page. What is the sum? **15** *So, now there are 15 dolphins following the boat. You will need this sum to do the next step in this problem.*

What is the next step you will take to solve this problem? **Find 15 − 6.** *Why?* **Sample answer: One set of objects separated from another set.**

Write the difference of 15 − 6 in the blank on the right side of the page. What is the difference? **9** *So, 9 dolphins are still following the boat.*

See and Show

Help students work through the example at the top of the page. Read through the problem together. Discuss what steps are needed to solve the problem. Have them trace the dashed numbers as they work through the problems.

Work through Exercises 1 and 2 as a class.

Mathematical PRACTICE ③ **Talk Math**

Discuss with students "Explain how to solve a two-step word problem." Sample answer: Use the information you have and decide which part to solve first. Then use the rest of the information to solve the next part.

Name _____

Operations and Algebraic Thinking
2.OA.1

Two-Step Word Problems

Lesson 13

ESSENTIAL QUESTION
What strategies can I use to add and subtract?

✋ Explore and Explain 🔧 Tools

I'm a boat chasing champ!

See students' work.

___9___ dolphins

🦉 **Teacher Directions:** Use counters to solve the problem. Trace the counters to show your work. There is a group of 12 dolphins following a boat. 3 more dolphins join the group. Then 6 of the dolphins swim away. How many dolphins are still following the boat?

Online Content at 🔗 connectED.mcgraw-hill.com   Chapter 1 • Lesson 13   87

See and Show

Mathematical PRACTICE

Some word problems take two steps to solve.
Tim's class was having a pizza party. Tim brought 3 pizzas. Jenni brought 2 pizzas. The class ate 4 pizzas. How many pizzas do they have left?

$$\begin{array}{c} 3 \\ +\ 2 \\ \hline 5 \end{array} \quad \begin{array}{c} 5 \\ -\ 4 \\ \hline 1 \end{array} \quad \underline{\quad 1 \quad} \text{ pizza}$$

Solve each two-step word problem.

1. Marla bought 3 books on Monday and 5 books on Wednesday. She returned 4 books today. How many books does Marla have now?

$$\begin{array}{c} 3 \\ +\ 5 \\ \hline 8 \end{array} \quad \begin{array}{c} 8 \\ -\ 4 \\ \hline 4 \end{array} \quad \underline{\quad 4 \quad} \text{ books}$$

2. Carla collected 6 leaves but she lost 3 of them. She has 9 leaves at home. How many leaves does Carla have in all?

_____12_____ leaves

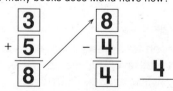

Talk Math Explain how to solve a two-step word problem.

88   Chapter 1 • Lesson 13

CORE INSTRUCTION

Name _____

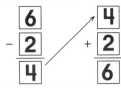

 You can get this one!

On My Own

Solve each two-step word problem.

3. Candice has 6 pencils. She gives 2 away. Then she gets 2 pencils out of her bag. How many pencils does Candice have now?

$$\begin{array}{c} 6 \\ - 2 \\ \hline 4 \end{array} \nearrow \begin{array}{c} 4 \\ + 2 \\ \hline 6 \end{array}$$

___6___ pencils

4. 8 birds land on a tree. 5 of the birds fly to another tree. Then 2 more fly away. How many birds are left in the tree?

___1___ birds

5. Suzie saw 9 ladybugs on her porch. 4 flew away. Then 3 more ladybugs came. How many ladybugs are on the porch now?

___8___ ladybugs

Chapter 1 • Lesson 13   89

Problem Solving

Mathematical PRACTICE

6. 5 seashells were lying on the beach. 8 more shells washed up onto the beach. Sammy picked up 4 shells. How many shells were left on the beach?

___9___ shells

 Cotton tail

7. David counted 6 chipmunks and 7 rabbits in his yard. 5 of the rabbits hopped away. How many animals can David see now?

___8___ animals

8. There were 5 toads in the pond. 3 more toads jumped in. 2 toads jumped out of the pond. How many toads are in the pond now?

___6___ toads

HOT Problem Write a two-step word problem using the number sentences 8 + 2 = 10 and 10 − 4 = 6.

Sample answer: Bob found 8 feathers on the ground.

His brother found 2 feathers. His sister took 4 feathers.

How many feathers do the boys have left?

90   Chapter 1 • Lesson 13

Online Content at 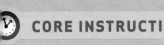 **connectED.mcgraw-hill.com**

---

3 PRACTICE & APPLY

CCSS

On My Own

Have students work through the exercises on this page independently. You may choose to assign exercises based on the chart below.

DIFFERENTIATED ASSIGNMENTS
AL **Approaching Level** Guide students through the exercises in On My Own. Help them to use manipulatives while working through the problems.
OL **On Level** Complete the exercises independently.
BL **Beyond Level** Complete the exercises independently without manipulatives.

Problem Solving

Have students work through the problem-solving exercises on this page independently.

Mathematical PRACTICE 5   In Exercise 8, students **use appropriate tools strategically.**

HOT Problem This exercise asks students to build upon their understanding of concepts needed to answer the chapter's Essential Question.

Lesson 13 Two-Step Word Problems   **89-90**

RESPONSE TO INTERVENTION

DIFFERENTIATED INSTRUCTION

AL **APPROACHING LEVEL**

IF my students struggle with two-step word problems,

THEN choose a resource:

→ Use the Reteach worksheet with small groups.

→ Go online for a Differentiated Instruction activity.

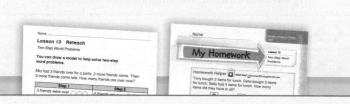

OL **ON LEVEL**

IF my students seem to know two-step word problems but need more practice,

THEN choose a resource:

→ Assign My Homework.

→ Go online for a Differentiated Instruction activity.

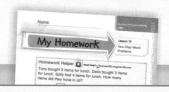

BL **BEYOND LEVEL**

IF my students have mastered two-step word problems,

THEN choose a resource:

→ Use the Enrich worksheet in cooperative groups.

→ Assign My Homework.

→ Go online for a Differentiated Instruction activity.

AL Name _____

Lesson 13   Reteach

Two-Step World Problems

You can draw a model to help solve two-step word problems.

Mia had 3 friends over for a party. 2 more friends came. Then 3 more friends came late. How many friends are over now?

Step 1	Step 2
3 friends were over ○○○ 2 more came ○○ 3 + 2 = 5 friends	5 friends are over ○○○ ○○ 3 more friends came late ○○○ **5 + 3 = 8 friends**

On a separate sheet of paper, draw a model to help solve. Then, write the number sentences.

1. Ella found 2 pens in her room. She found 4 more pens in the kitchen. Ella then found 2 more pens in her brother's room. How many pens did Ella find in all?

Step 1: __2__ + __4__ = __6__ Step 2: __6__ + __2__ = __8__ pens

2. Ryan saw 8 birds in a tree. 2 flew away. Ryan went outside, and 3 more birds flew away. How many birds are left?

Step 1: __8__ – __2__ = __6__ Step 2: __6__ – __3__ = __3__ pens

---

BL Name _____

Lesson 13   Enrich

Two-Step Word Problems

1. Write a two-step addition word problem using the numbers below. Show a partner how to solve it.

   1–2. See students' work.

   13, 6, 3, 4

   _____

   _____

   _____

2. Write a two-step addition word problem using the numbers below. Have a partner solve.

   11, 5, 2, 4

   _____

   _____

   _____

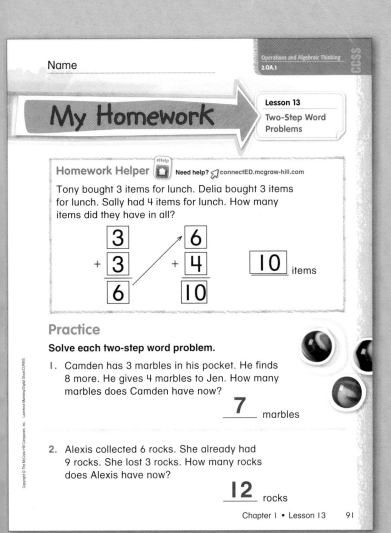

Name _____

My Homework

Lesson 13
Two-Step Word Problems

Homework Helper

Need help? connectED.mcgraw-hill.com

Tony bought 3 items for lunch. Delia bought 3 items for lunch. Sally had 4 items for lunch. How many items did they have in all?

$$\begin{array}{c} \boxed{3} \\ + \boxed{3} \\ \hline \boxed{6} \end{array} \qquad \begin{array}{c} \boxed{6} \\ + \boxed{4} \\ \hline \boxed{10} \end{array} \qquad \boxed{10} \text{ items}$$

Practice

Solve each two-step word problem.

1. Camden has 3 marbles in his pocket. He finds 8 more. He gives 4 marbles to Jen. How many marbles does Camden have now?

   7 marbles

2. Alexis collected 6 rocks. She already had 9 rocks. She lost 3 rocks. How many rocks does Alexis have now?

   12 rocks

Chapter 1 • Lesson 13   91

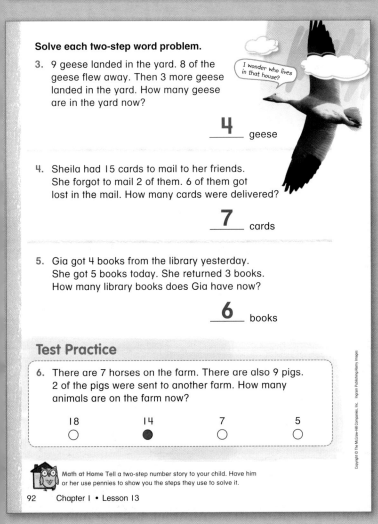

Solve each two-step word problem.

3. 9 geese landed in the yard. 8 of the geese flew away. Then 3 more geese landed in the yard. How many geese are in the yard now?

   I wonder who lives in that house?

   4 geese

4. Sheila had 15 cards to mail to her friends. She forgot to mail 2 of them. 6 of them got lost in the mail. How many cards were delivered?

   7 cards

5. Gia got 4 books from the library yesterday. She got 5 books today. She returned 3 books. How many library books does Gia have now?

   6 books

Test Practice

6. There are 7 horses on the farm. There are also 9 pigs. 2 of the pigs were sent to another farm. How many animals are on the farm now?

   18 ○   14 ●   7 ○   5 ○

Math at Home Tell a two-step number story to your child. Have him or her use pennies to show you the steps they use to solve it.

92   Chapter 1 • Lesson 13

---

4 WRAP IT UP

My Homework

Assign homework after successful completion of the lesson. Students who understand the concepts may skip the **Homework Helper** section.

Test Practice

Diagnose Student Errors

Class trends in wrong answers may indicate common errors or misconceptions.

- **18** added the 3 numbers
- **14** correct
- **7** subtracted 2 from 9
- **5** subtracted 2 from 7

Formative Assessment

Have students explain how to solve this problem: 8 frogs were in the pond. 3 ducks were in the pond. 6 frogs hopped out of the pond. How many frogs and ducks are left in the pond?
Sample answer: First, add the number of frogs and ducks. Then, subtract the number of frogs that hopped out from the total number of frogs and ducks.

Fluency Practice

Mathematical PRACTICE 6 → This page encourages students to become proficient in their calculation abilities. You can use this as a timed or untimed exercise.

Pages 93–94 Students practice addition of whole numbers.

Teaching Tip One approach to build student confidence is to use this page repeatedly. Strive to have students complete a portion of the page correctly in an untimed situation. Then use the rest of the page as a timed test.

Name _____

Fluency Practice

Add.

1. 1 + 8 = **9**	2. 9 + 7 = **16**
3. 3 + 8 = **11**	4. 6 + 5 = **11**
5. 7 + 5 = **12**	6. 8 + 4 = **12**
7. 8 + 5 = **13**	8. 8 + 8 = **16**
9. 7 + 4 = **11**	10. 4 + 8 = **12**
11. 3 + 5 = **8**	12. 6 + 8 = **14**
13. 7 + 9 = **16**	14. 7 + 8 = **15**
15. 7 + 7 = **14**	16. 4 + 4 = **8**
17. 4 + 3 = **7**	18. 5 + 4 = **9**
19. 8 + 8 = **16**	20. 9 + 9 = **18**
21. 7 + 6 = **13**	22. 9 + 8 = **17**
23. 8 + 9 = **17**	24. 5 + 9 = **14**

No monkey business!

Online Content at connectED.mcgraw-hill.com Chapter 1 93

Fluency Practice

Subtract.

1. 8 − 1 = **7**	2. 16 − 7 = **9**
3. 8 − 3 = **5**	4. 11 − 5 = **6**
5. 7 − 5 = **2**	6. 12 − 4 = **8**
7. 8 − 5 = **3**	8. 17 − 8 = **9**
9. 7 − 4 = **3**	10. 12 − 8 = **4**
11. 5 − 3 = **2**	12. 15 − 6 = **9**
13. 16 − 9 = **7**	14. 15 − 8 = **7**
15. 14 − 7 = **7**	16. 8 − 4 = **4**
17. 7 − 3 = **4**	18. 9 − 4 = **5**
19. 16 − 8 = **8**	20. 18 − 8 = **10**
21. 13 − 6 = **7**	22. 17 − 8 = **9**
23. 17 − 9 = **8**	24. 9 − 5 = **4**

94 Chapter 1

Name _____

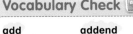

My Review

Chapter 1
Apply Addition and Subtraction Concepts

Vocabulary Check

| add | addend | count back | count on |
| fact family | related facts | subtract | |

**Write the correct word in the blank.
Use words from the box.**

1. When you take one part away from a whole, you _____subtract_____ .

2. Addition and subtraction facts that use the same three numbers can be called a ___fact family___ or ___related facts___ .

3. The two numbers you add together in an addition sentence are called ___addends___ .

4. You can ___count back___ to subtract 2 from a number.

5. To ___add___ , you join two parts together.

6. You can ___count on___ to add 2 to a number.

Chapter 1   95

Concept Check

Add.

7.   9
   + 3
   ‾‾‾‾
    12

8.   8
   + 5
   ‾‾‾‾
    13

9.   9
   + 6
   ‾‾‾‾
    15

10.   7
    + 7
   ‾‾‾‾
    14

Find each sum.

11. 6 + 5 + 4 = **15**   12. 2 + 2 + 8 = **12**

Use addition facts to subtract.

13. 7 + 8 = **15**
    15 − 7 = **8**

14. 6 + 7 = **13**
    13 − 7 = **6**

Complete the fact family.

15.

△ 14
9 5

9 + 5 = 14
5 + 9 = 14
14 − 9 = 5
14 − 5 = 9

96   Chapter 1

My Review

Use these pages to assess your students' understanding of the vocabulary and key concepts in this chapter.

Vocabulary Check

Read aloud the words in the word bank. Ask students how these words are organized. They are organized alphabetically.

ELL **ELL Support Strategy** Use this information to participate in purposeful, cooperative learning activities.

Concept Check

If students need reinforcement of skills after completing this section, use the Reteach worksheet to review the concepts again.

Exercise(s)	Concept	Review Lesson
7–10	Add	1
11–12	Add three numbers	5
13–14	Relate addition and subtraction	10
15	Fact families	12

Problem Solving

Remind students of the four-step plan for problem solving. For students who need help in reading comprehension, have them work with another student to read the problem aloud before attempting the four-step plan.

Test Practice

Diagnose Student Errors

Class trends in wrong answers may indicate common errors or misconceptions.

0	subtracted 5 from 5
5	wrote only the given number
10	correct
15	incorrect

Reflect

Display this chapter's vocabulary on the Virtual Word Wall. Ask students to refer to the words as they complete the graphic organizer.

You may choose to have your students use a different graphic organizer for review.

Summative Assessment

Use these alternate leveled chapter tests from the Assessment Masters to differentiate assessment for the specific needs of your students.

Chapter Tests

Level	Type	Form
AL	Multiple Choice	1A
AL	Multiple Choice	1B
OL	Multiple Choice / Free Choice	2A
OL	Multiple Choice / Free Choice	2B
BL	Free Choice	3A
BL	Free Choice	3B
Additional Chapter Resource Masters		
OL	Vocabulary Test	
OL	Extended Response Test	
OL	Oral Assessment	

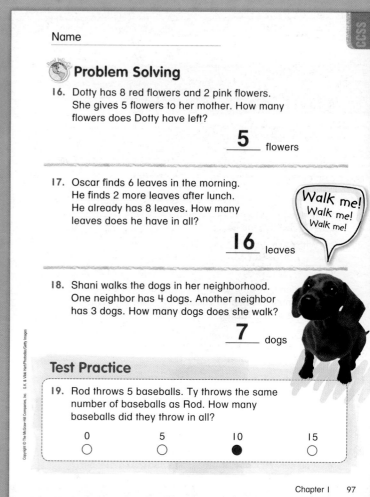

Name _____

🌎 Problem Solving

16. Dotty has 8 red flowers and 2 pink flowers. She gives 5 flowers to her mother. How many flowers does Dotty have left?

        __5__ flowers

17. Oscar finds 6 leaves in the morning. He finds 2 more leaves after lunch. He already has 8 leaves. How many leaves does he have in all?

        _16_ leaves

Walk me! Walk me! Walk me!

18. Shani walks the dogs in her neighborhood. One neighbor has 4 dogs. Another neighbor has 3 dogs. How many dogs does she walk?

        __7__ dogs

Test Practice

19. Rod throws 5 baseballs. Ty throws the same number of baseballs as Rod. How many baseballs did they throw in all?

0	5	10	15
○	○	●	○

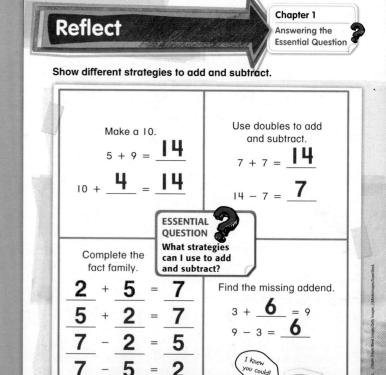

Reflect

Chapter 1
Answering the Essential Question

Show different strategies to add and subtract.

Make a 10.
$5 + 9 = 14$
$10 + 4 = 14$

Use doubles to add and subtract.
$7 + 7 = 14$
$14 - 7 = 7$

ESSENTIAL QUESTION
What strategies can I use to add and subtract?

Complete the fact family.
$2 + 5 = 7$
$5 + 2 = 7$
$7 - 2 = 5$
$7 - 5 = 2$

Find the missing addend.
$3 + 6 = 9$
$9 - 3 = 6$

I knew you could!

See, you can do it!

Notes

CHAPTER 2

Number Patterns

Chapter at a Glance

Suggested Pacing		
Instruction*	Review & Assessment	TOTAL
10 days	2 days	**12 days**

*Includes additional time for remediation and differentiation.

Lesson	Objective	Materials & Manipulatives	Vocabulary	CCSS Standard
Lesson 1 *pp. 107–112* **Skip Count on a Hundred Chart**	Use patterns to skip count.	• long paper • counters • crayons, markers, or colored pencils	**skip count**	2.OA.1 2.OA.2 2.NBT.2
Lesson 2 *pp. 113–118* **Skip Count by 2s, 5s, and 10s**	Model skip counting to find the total in equal groups.	• connecting cubes • base-ten blocks • counters	**equal groups**	2.OA.1 2.NBT.2
Lesson 3 *pp. 119–124* **Problem Solving Strategy: Find a Pattern**	Find a pattern to solve problems.	• connecting cubes		2.OA.1 2.NBT.2
✓ **Check My Progress**				
Lesson 4 *pp. 127–132* **Repeated Addition**	Use repeated addition to add equal groups.	• counters • connecting cubes	**repeated addition**	2.OA.4 2.NBT.2
Lesson 5 *pp. 133–138* **Repeated Addition with Arrays**	Use arrays with repeated addition.	• counters • connecting cubes • crayons or markers	**array**	2.OA.4
Lesson 6 *pp. 139–144* **Even and Odd Numbers**	Find even and odd numbers in number patterns.	• counters • connecting cubes • number cubes	**even** **odd**	2.OA.3
Lesson 7 *pp. 145–150* **Sums of Equal Numbers**	Find sums of equal numbers.	• connecting cubes		2.OA.3
Fluency Practice				
✓ **My Review and Reflect**				

 For customizable online assessment, go to **eAssessment** at connectED.mcgraw-hill.com.

Planning for Differentiated Instruction

Use these differentiated instruction activity suggestions, along with the ongoing support provided in each lesson of this chapter, to meet individual learning needs.

AL APPROACHING LEVEL

Use with Lesson 2

Materials: hundred charts, number cubes, crayons

- Have students work with a partner.
- Have one student roll a number cube to determine where on a hundred chart to start.
- The second student colors the square of the number rolled.
- The first student take picks a number to skip count by 2, 5, or 10.
- The second student colors the number square they land on as they skip count through the chart.

BL BEYOND LEVEL

Use with Lesson 4

Materials: number cubes, two-color counters

- Place students in small groups.
- Students take turns rolling the number cube two times. The first number is the number they will add repeatedly. The second number is how many times they will repeat the addition.
- Have students write the addition sentences.
- Have them work together to model the number sentences using groups of two-color counters.
- Have students create real-world addition stories for each situation.

OL ON LEVEL

Use with Lesson 6

Materials: connecting cubes, hundred charts, crayons

- Have students work with a partner.
- Have partners take turns making a connecting cube train using different numbers of cubes.
- Have students determine whether the number of cubes is even or odd by breaking the trains into pairs of cubes. Remind students that if they can place all the cubes into pairs, the number is even. If they make pairs and there is one left over, the number is odd.
- Each time students break apart a train and discover whether a number is even or odd, have students record their findings on a hundred chart. Have them color even-numbered squares red and odd-numbered squares blue.

ELL ENGLISH LANGUAGE LEARNERS

Support for English Language Learners is found throughout the chapter and includes:

- ELL strategies at point-of-use in each Teacher Edition lesson
- ELL tiered instruction suggestions for each lesson at connectED.mcgraw-hill.com
- Comprehensive ELL lessons and worksheets for additional instruction at connectED.mcgraw-hill.com
- Non-linguistic representations of concepts on My Math Words, My Vocabulary Cards, and My Foldables

Additional online resources at connectED.mcgraw-hill.com include:
- Visual Vocabulary Cards
- Multilingual eGlossary
- Professional Development support

Looking for more DIFFERENTIATED INSTRUCTION?
Find additional support in each lesson of this chapter and online at connectED.mcgraw-hill.com

AL Approaching Level
OL On Level
BL Beyond Level
ELL English Language Learners

What's the Math in This Chapter?

Points of Intersection

Where
CONTENT STANDARDS

Meet
Mathematical PRACTICE **7**

NBT
Number and Operations in Base Ten

Look for and make use of structure.

Most of this chapter concentrates on the **Number and Operations in Base Ten (NBT)** domain. However, aspects of the **Operations and Algebraic Thinking (OA)** domain are also used in the study of **number patterns**.

As you teach different aspects of number patterns, emphasize to students that it is important that they are able to discern patterns because they will continue to use patterns throughout the rest of their mathematics studies and in their everyday lives.

What should my students already know?

In the previous grade, students used **Operations and Algebraic Thinking (OA)** in their study of addition:

- Relate counting to addition.
  1.OA.5

Students also used **Number and Operations in Base Ten (NBT)** in their study of the counting sequence:

- Count to 120, starting at any number less than 120.
  1.NBT.1

WHAT STUDENTS SHOULD UNDERSTAND

Skip Count
CCSS 2.NBT.2

How to skip count by 2s, 5s, and 10s.

- Skip counting involves using patterns to count.
- Skip counting on a hundred chart creates patterns that are easy to see.
- You can find the total number of objects that you have by placing them in equal groups and then skip counting to find the total.

WHAT STUDENTS SHOULD BE ABLE TO DO

Use the hundred chart to skip count by 10s. Write the missing numbers in 20, 30, ___, ___, 60, ___, ___, 90.

1	2	3	4	5	6	7	8	9	10
11	12	13	14	15	16	17	18	19	20
21	22	23	24	25	26	27	28	29	30
31	32	33	34	35	36	37	38	39	40
41	42	43	44	45	46	47	48	49	50
51	52	53	54	55	56	57	58	59	60
61	62	63	64	65	66	67	68	69	70
71	72	73	74	75	76	77	78	79	80
81	82	83	84	85	86	87	88	89	90
91	92	93	94	95	96	97	98	99	100

20, 30, <u>40</u>, <u>50</u>, 60, <u>70</u>, <u>80</u>, 90

Repeated Addition
 CCSS 2.OA.4, 2.NBT.2

How to use repeated addition to find the total number of objects when the objects are in equal groups.

- You can skip count to find the sum in a repeated addition problem.
- You can use a repeated addition number sentence to describe an array.

Describe the array by using a number sentence.

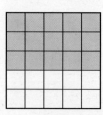

$5 + 5 + 5 = 15$

WHAT STUDENTS SHOULD UNDERSTAND	WHAT STUDENTS SHOULD BE ABLE TO DO

Even and Odd Numbers

 2.OA.3

How to identify even and odd numbers and how to determine two equal addends of an even number.

- Even numbers can be counted by 2s, broken into pairs, or divided into equal groups.
- Odd numbers have 1 left over when counted by 2s, broken into pairs, or divided into equal groups.
- Any even number can be written as the sum of two equal addends.

Use connecting cubes to show the number 3. Then tell whether it is even or odd.

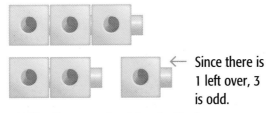

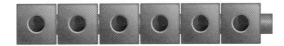

← Since there is 1 left over, 3 is odd.

Write the equal addends that make 6.

First: Create a train of connecting cubes to model 6.

Next: Break the train into two equal groups.

Last: Count the number of connecting cubes in each group. These are the equal addends.

3   3

$6 = 3 + 3$

What will my students do next with these skills?

After this chapter, students will learn to take apart tens and regroup ones
2.OA.1

In the next grade, students will learn to relate addition and multiplication
3.OA.7

Reading Connections

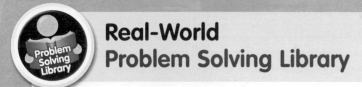

Real-World Problem Solving Library

Math and Science: Geese on the Go

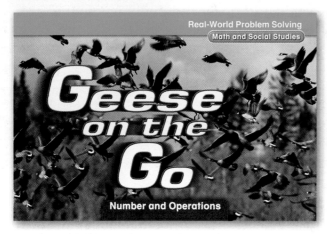

Use these leveled books to reinforce and extend problem-solving skills and strategies.

Leveled for:

AL Approaching Level

OL On Level Also available in Spanish

BL Beyond Level

For additional support, see the *Real-World Problem Solving Readers Teacher Guide.*

Leveled Reader Database

Available at leveledreaderdatabase.macmillanmh.com
Search by:

- Content Area
- Guided Reading Level
- Lexile Score
- Benchmark Level

Library Books

Check with your school library or your local public library for these titles.

Pattern Fish
Trudy Harris

Patterns in Nature
Jennifer Roy

What's Next, Nina?
Sue Kassirer

Dinosaur Deals
Stuart J. Murphy

Safari Park
Stuart J. Murphy

Double the Ducks
Stuart J. Murphy

Reading and Language Arts Support

Math in Our World

Write the word *equal* at the top of the whiteboard. Survey the class to find out which cartoons students like to watch, and create a list on the whiteboard. Work together to rank the cartoons' popularity. Next to the cartoon at the top of the list, write 5 minutes. Tell students that they were going to get to watch that cartoon for 5 minutes, but it isn't available.

Discuss with students if they were allowed to watch the other cartoons, how many more minutes of watching each of those would satisfy their desire getting to watch 5 minutes of the best cartoon. Write their responses as number sentences.

After you are done with the number sentences, discuss if they were now all available, which would they choose. Would they prefer a shorter time of their favorite or a longer time of a less favorite? What is equal? Should they all be treated equally?

Looking for more Reading and Language Arts Support? go online to

connectED.mcgraw-hill.com

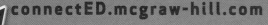

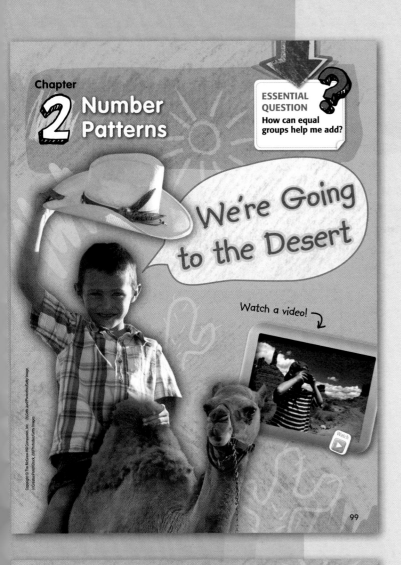

Chapter
2 Number Patterns

ESSENTIAL QUESTION
How can equal groups help me add?

We're Going to the Desert

Watch a video!

99

LAUNCH THE CHAPTER

Theme:
We're Going to the Desert

All of the lessons in Chapter 2 will connect with the theme of We're Going to the Desert, which centers around things found in the desert. This is reflected in problem-solving and the visuals used throughout the chapter.

Video

Have students watch the video about the desert. You may want to spark a discussion about how math is used in planning a trip to the desert.

Building on the Essential Question

Once students have completed this chapter they should be able to answer the question "How can equal groups help me add?" In each lesson, students build on their understanding by answering a simpler question. These are indicated in the exercises as Building on the Essential Question. At the end of the chapter, students use a graphic organizer to help them answer the Essential Question.

My Common Core State Standards (CCSS)

Operations and Algebraic Thinking

2.OA.1 Use addition and subtraction within 100 to solve one-and two-step word problems involving situations of adding to, taking from, putting together, taking apart, and comparing, with unknowns in all positions.

2.OA.2 Fluently add and subtract within 20 using mental strategies. By end of Grade 2, know from memory all sums of two one-digit numbers.

2.OA.3 Determine whether a group of objects (up to 20) has an odd or even number of members.

2.OA.4 Use addition to find the total number of objects arranged in rectangular arrays with up to 5 rows and up to 5 columns; write an equation to express the total as a sum of equal addends.

Number and Operations in Base Ten *This chapter also addresses this standard:*
2.NBT.2 Count within 1000; skip-count by 5s, 10s, and 100s.

Standards for Mathematical PRACTICE

1. Make sense of problems and persevere in solving them.
2. Reason abstractly and quantitatively.
3. Construct viable arguments and critique the reasoning of others.
4. Model with mathematics.
5. Use appropriate tools strategically.
6. Attend to precision.
7. Look for and make use of structure.
8. Look for and express regularity in repeated reasoning.

 = focused on in this chapter

100   Chapter 2

Professional Development

CCSS Common Core State Standards

Learn more about how the Common Core State Standards can be implemented in your classroom at mhpdonline.com.

Look for

- eImplementation
- eVideo Clip Libraries
- eTech Training
- ePD Webinars

Feature video for mathematical content in this chapter:
Modeling Growing Patterns

---

1 Assess

You have two options for assessing student readiness for this chapter. Use student results to determine which level of instruction is needed to help students get ready for the chapter and to determine what ongoing support they will need during the chapter.

Option 1: Am I Ready?

Have students complete the Am I Ready? page in their student books.

Name

Am I Ready?

Check ✓ ← Go online to take the Readiness Quiz

1. Write the missing numbers.

0 1 **2** 3 **4** 5 **6** **7** 8 **9** 10

Write the missing numbers.

2. **1** , 2, **3** , **4** , 5, 6, **7**

3. 11, **12** , **13** , 14, **15** , 16, **17**

4. 10, **12** , **14** , 16, **18** , 20, 22, **24**

Add.

5. 5 + 5 = **10**   6. 2 + 2 + 2 = **6**

7. Alisa has 3 red cups, 3 blue cups, and 3 pink cups. How many cups does she have in all? **9**

How Did I Do?   Shade the boxes to show the problems you answered correctly.
1 2 3 4 5 6 7

Online Content at connectED.mcgraw-hill.com   Chapter 2   101

Option 2: Online Readiness Quiz

Check ✓

Have students take the **Online Readiness Quiz.**

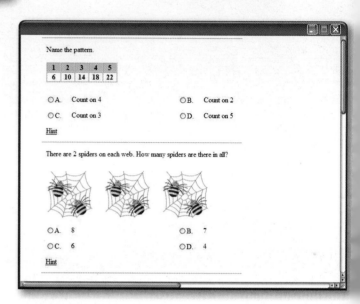

Name the pattern.

1	2	3	4	5
6	10	14	18	22

○ A. Count on 4   ○ B. Count on 2

○ C. Count on 3   ○ D. Count on 5

Hint

There are 2 spiders on each web. How many spiders are there in all?

○ A. 8   ○ B. 7

○ C. 6   ○ D. 4

Hint

OPTION 2

Common Core Review

Exercises	Skill	Standard
1–10*	Counting	2.OA.1
	Addition	2.OA.1

*These questions are randomly generated from a bank of 15 questions.

OPTION 1

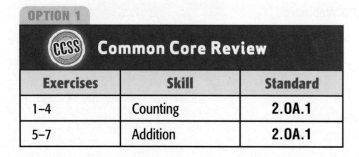

Common Core Review

Exercises	Skill	Standard
1–4	Counting	2.OA.1
5–7	Addition	2.OA.1

2 Diagnose and Prescribe

Rtl

Based on the results of the Am I Ready? in the student edition, use the charts below to address individual needs **before** beginning the chapter.

Use the **ONGOING** resources to support differentiated instruction as new skills and concepts are presented in the chapter.

TIER 1

OL ON LEVEL

IF students miss 2–3 in Exercises 1–7,

THEN choose a resource:
→ Am I Ready? Practice
→ Online Readiness Quiz

ONGOING Self-Check Quizzes • Chapter Project • Differentiated Assignments • My Learning Stations • Differentiated Instruction activities

TIER 2

AL STRATEGIC INTERVENTION

(Approaching Grade Level)

IF students miss 3–4 in Exercises 1–7,

THEN choose a resource:
→ Online Strategic Intervention activity
→ Am I Ready? Review

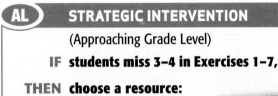

ONGOING Common Errors • Differentiated Assignments • Online support • Reteach worksheets • Homework Helper • My Learning Stations • Rtl lesson support • Differentiated Instruction activities

TIER 3

INTENSIVE INTERVENTION

(2 or more years below grade level)

IF students miss 5 or more in Exercises 1–7,

THEN use *Math Triumphs,* an intensive math intervention program from McGraw-Hill.

TIER 3

BL BEYOND LEVEL

IF students miss 1 or less in Exercises 1–7,

THEN choose a resource:
→ Online Games
→ Am I Ready? Apply

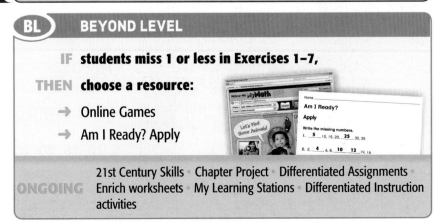

ONGOING 21st Century Skills • Chapter Project • Differentiated Assignments • Enrich worksheets • My Learning Stations • Differentiated Instruction activities

3 Reassess

If reassessment is necessary, administer the chapter Diagnostic Test in the **Assessment Masters** or go online for eAssessment.

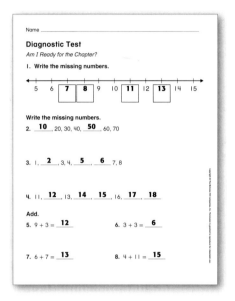

Name _____

Diagnostic Test
Am I Ready for the Chapter?

1. Write the missing numbers.

5 6 **7 8** 9 10 **11** 12 **13** 14 15

Write the missing numbers.

2. __10__, 20, 30, 40, __50__, 60, 70

3. 1, __2__, 3, 4, __5__ __6__, 7, 8

4. 11, __12__, 13, __14__ __15__, 16, __17__ __18__

Add.

5. $9 + 3 =$ __12__   6. $3 + 3 =$ __6__

7. $6 + 7 =$ __13__   8. $4 + 11 =$ __15__

 Check

For additional chapter readiness assessment, go to eAssessment at connectED.mcgraw-hill.com.

DEVELOP VOCABULARY

My Math Words

Review Vocabulary

Where did they learn it?

- addends   (Grade 1)
- sum   (Grade 1)

Making Connections

Ask students what they know about the review vocabulary. Encourage students to describe, draw, act out, or model their examples.

Ask students to examine the graphic organizer. Have them describe the relationship between each addition number sentence and the labels beneath each number. Sample answer: The review vocabulary describes each part of the addition number sentence. Then ask volunteers to point to and name each symbol they see. plus signs, equals signs

My Vocabulary Cards

Ask students to browse the words and examples on each of this chapter's cards. Discuss with them what they already know about these words or the examples shown on the cards. Note on the board any questions or observations students have about these words.

Definitions appear on the back of each card. Discuss the definitions with students.

Students should clip and store their cards in one place, such as a small envelope, where they can access them as needed throughout the chapter.

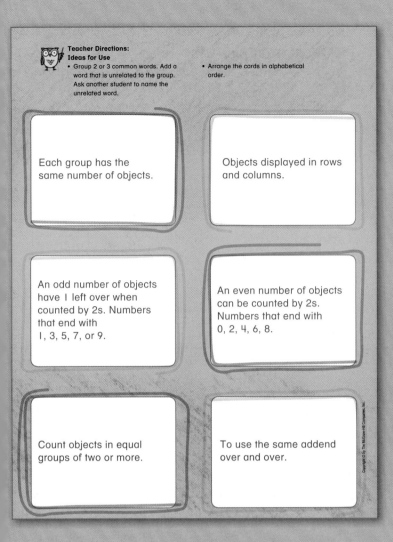

Each group has the same number of objects.

Objects displayed in rows and columns.

An odd number of objects have 1 left over when counted by 2s. Numbers that end with 1, 3, 5, 7, or 9.

An even number of objects can be counted by 2s. Numbers that end with 0, 2, 4, 6, 8.

Count objects in equal groups of two or more.

To use the same addend over and over.

Copyright © by The McGraw-Hill Companies, Inc.

Mathematical PRACTICE ❸ My Vocabulary Card Activities

The table below lists an activity for each card, as well as the answer or sample answer. The activities will include opportunities for students to hear, say, or write the vocabulary words. When applicable, activities will involve drawing or modeling vocabulary. Students' answers can be recorded using various media, such as Notebook Foldables, IWB, electronic tablets, or computers.

Vocabulary Card	Activity/Activity Answer
array	Use the vocabulary cards for this chapter to show 2 groups of 3. See students' work.
equal groups	Imagine you have a jar of 12 marbles. Write a sentence telling how you would place them in four equal groups. Sample answer: I would make four groups of three marbles each.
even	Write a list of four even two-digit numbers. Explain how you know they are even. Sample answer: 20, 24, 28, 30; I can count by 2s to each number with none left over.
odd	How old are you? Is that an even or odd number? How do you know? Sample answer: 7; It is odd. I can take apart a 7-cube train into pairs of cubes and have 1 left over.
repeated addition	Gather a group of 8 objects (such as crayons, connecting cubes, or rubber bands). Arrange them in 4 equal rows. Write a repeated addition problem to describe the arrangement. $2 + 2 + 2 + 2 = 8$
skip count	Write a sentence to explain why skip counting is faster than counting by ones. Sample answer: You don't have to count every single object with skip counting.

STUDY ORGANIZER

My Foldable

What's the Math?

Content Standard: 2.OA.4

Mathematical PRACTICE 5 **Use appropriate tools strategically.**

This Foldable book requires students to use repeated addition to describe arrays.

How Do I Make It?

- Tear out the page and cut off the top banner.
- Fold along the green dotted line.
- Cut along the orange dashed line to cut the paper in half.
- Insert one section into the other to make a book.
- Secure along the fold with staples or glue.

When Do I Use It?

Use after Lesson 5 and as a review tool at the end of the chapter.

How Could I Use It?

- Have students open the book to the first page describe the array shaded in green, and write the repeated addition sentence that expresses it.
- Have students turn the page. Have them write the repeated addition sentence that is described at the top of the page and shade the array to match.
- Have students turn the page and solve the repeated addition sentence at the bottom of the page. Have them shade the array to match and describe it using groups.
- Students can use the back of the book to create and describe their own array.

ELL ELL Support Strategy Use this Foldable to provide multiple exposures to using appropriate tools strategically.

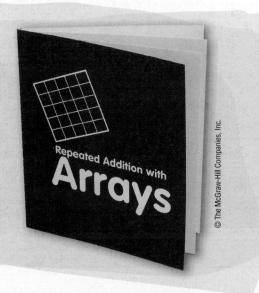

© The McGraw-Hill Companies, Inc.

My Foldable

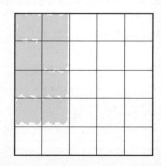
FOLDABLES Follow the steps on the back to make your Foldable.

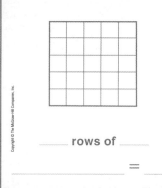

2 rows of **3**

3 + 3 = 6

Copyright © The McGraw-Hill Companies, Inc.

_____ rows of _____

_____ = _____

Repeated Addition with
Arrays

FOLDABLES Study Organizer ① ② ✂ ③ ④

5 rows of 4

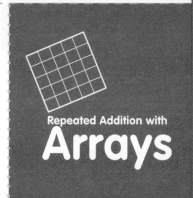

4 + 4 + 4 + 4 + 4 = 20

4 rows of **2**

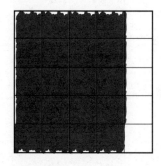

2 + 2 + 2 + 2 = 8

Copyright © The McGraw-Hill Companies, Inc.

Project *Express*™

From Dinah Zike, creator of Foldables®

This ready-to-make project format comes in eight bright colors and offers the ability to customize your learning center with different content-based Project Packets. These packets include pre-printed, full color stickers, assorted envelopes and pockets, reproducible templates, and materials needed for quick assembly. You can use these materials as illustrated or use them to design your own learning center.

Order with a McGraw-Hill discount at www.dinah.com.

Even or Odd

MY Learning Stations

Use the following learning stations to differentiate the instruction for Chapter 2. Includes Spanish!

Learning Station	Title	Use after Lesson
Game	*Count the Stars*	2
Graphic Novel	*Flamingo Fun*	4
RWPS Reader	*Geese on the Go*	5
Activity Card	*High-Frequency Words*	6

RWPS = Real-World Problem-Solving Reader

Chapter Project

Math Posters

As you work through the chapter, have small groups create posters that illustrate math concepts.

- Provide groups with a list of chapter concepts (skip counting, equal groups, repeated addition, even and odd, patterns, sums of equal numbers) and the vocabulary words relevant to each.

- Ask groups to design separate posters on construction paper to explain a concept. Have them include the necessary vocabulary words.

- Invite groups to share their posters with the class and hang them in the room so students can refer to them throughout the chapter.

 CALENDAR TIME

Calendar

- Point to the 12 on the calendar.

- Ask how many tens and ones are in that number. **1 ten 2 ones** What is the date of the day that is 14 days later? **26**

- Ask the students if they can think of 3 ways to figure it out. **Sample answer: count on, add 14, move down 2 rows**

Sunday	Monday	Tuesday	Wednesday	Thursday	Friday	Saturday

Dinah-Might Adventures, LP

LESSON 1
Skip Count on a Hundred Chart
OBJECTIVE   Use patterns to skip count.

What's the Math?

 Common Core State Standards
DOMAIN: Operations and Algebraic Thinking

Standards: 2.OA.1, 2.OA.2, 2.NBT.2
The wording of these standards can be found on page 100.

What Students Should Understand

- Skip counting involves using patterns to count.
- Skip counting on a hundred chart creates patterns that are easy to see.
- You can skip count by 2s, 5s, and 10s.

What Students Should be Able to Do

Use the hundred chart to skip count. Write the missing numbers in 20, 25, __, 35, 40, __, __, 55. Then describe the pattern.

1	2	3	4	5	6	7	8	9	10
11	12	13	14	15	16	17	18	19	20
21	22	23	24	25	26	27	28	29	30
31	32	33	34	35	36	37	38	39	40
41	42	43	44	45	46	47	48	49	50
51	52	53	54	55	56	57	58	59	60

20, 25, 30, 35, 40, 45, 50, 55
The pattern is skip counting by 5s.

Building on the Essential Question

In this lesson, students will build upon the skills and concepts needed to answer the chapter's Essential Question "How can equal groups help me add?"

Developing Vocabulary

 New Vocabulary

skip count

Activity

- Write the word on the board. Ask students what they know about skip counting.
- Write the following sequence of numbers on the board: 5, 10, 15, 20, 25.
- Ask students what pattern they notice in the sequence. For example, they might notice that each number increases by 5.
- Use a hundred chart or number line to model the skips. *What patterns do you notice when we skip count by 5s?* Each number ends in 5 or 0, or has a 5 or 0 in the ones place.

ELL **ELL Support Strategy** Use this vocabulary activity to link familiar contexts and prior knowledge.

My Vocabulary Cards

Read the activity for the *skip count* card. Discuss with the class why skip counting is faster than counting by ones.

IWB **Virtual Word Wall**

Start the Virtual Word Wall for this chapter by adding the new vocabulary words for this chapter.

ELL Refer to the Multilingual eGlossary for interactive definitions in 13 languages.

Plan Online

Plan for your lesson by using the resources at

connectED.mcgraw-hill.com

Digital Dashboard

Interactive Whiteboard Ready

Vocab

The eBook **Glossary** shows the definition of the word and has audio for each definition. The **eGlossary** provides definitions in 13 languages.

Watch

Watch as concepts are brought to life through **animations**, **songs**, and a variety of visual instruction.

Tools

Virtual Manipulatives with work mats allow teachers and students to model the lesson.

Check

Use **eAssessment** for online assignments and customized assessments.

Use the **Common Core Quick Check** before the lesson to assess students' retention of previously learned concepts.

Use the interactive **Self-Check Quiz** after the lesson to provide immediate feedback on lesson concepts.

eHelp

Digital and print resources assist students and parents in completing My Homework.

Games

Online games and **apps** provide extra practice for lesson concepts.

PD

Professional development videos help teachers gain a deeper understanding of the lesson concepts and strategies.

RtI

Support for **approaching**, **on**- and **beyond-level** students as well as **English Language Learners**.

Masters

Reteach and **Enrich** worksheets, **Manipulative Masters**, the **Problem of the Day**, and other blackline masters are available for each lesson.

1 LAUNCH THE LESSON

 If your students are well-versed in skip counting, you may choose to begin instruction with Step 2, **TEACH**.

You will need

- ☐ long paper
- ☐ counters

Mathematical PRACTICE 4 Modeling the Math

Have students create a number line to use for skip counting.

Place your counter on the 2 on your number line. Skip count by 2s on the number line. Use your counter to jump to each new number that you count. On what numbers did you land? 2, 4, 6, 8, 10, 12, 14, 16...

Now, place your counter on 5 and skip count by 5s. Use your counter to jump to each new number that you count. On what numbers did you land? 5, 10, 15, 20, 25,...

Now, place your counter on 10 and skip count by 10s. Use your counter to jump to each new number that you count. On what numbers did you land? 10, 20,...

Depending on how long students drew their number lines, they may not be able to skip count very far.

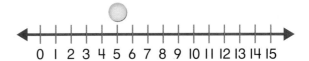

Begin core instruction here.

Vocabulary

Point out the partial hundreds chart on the second page of the lesson. Ask students to explain what patterns they notice.

ELL ELL Support Strategy Use this information to visualize what is being taught.

You will need

☐ crayons, markers, or colored pencils

Explore and Explain

Read the directions that are on the bottom of the student page. Model counting by 1s from 1 to 20.

I just counted by 1s. You can also count by other numbers.

Model skip counting by 2s from 2 to 20.

What number did I count by that time? 2s

Tell students that you are going to skip count by 2s again. Model skip counting by 2s from 2 to 100 slowly. As you skip count, guide students in writing the missing numbers in the hundred chart.

Do you see a pattern in the chart when you count by 2s? yes
What is it? Sample answer: every other number on the chart is filled in when skip counting by 2s.

Model skip counting by 5s from 5 to 50 slowly. Have students join in to skip count by 5s from 55 to 100. Have students color these numbers yellow on the hundred chart.

Do you see a pattern in the chart when you count by 5s? yes
What is it? Sample answer: the fifth and last columns are yellow.

Tell students to skip count by 10s independently. Have them circle these numbers in red on the hundred chart.

Do you see a pattern in the chart this time? yes; Sample answer: the last column of numbers are circled in red.

See and Show

Help students work through the example at the top of the page. Use the hundred chart to practice skip counting. You can have students circle, fill in, or put an "X" on the numbers as they skip count if that helps.

Have them trace the dashed numbers as they skip count by 2s, 5s, and 10s.

Work through Exercises 1 through 3 as a class.

Mathematical PRACTICE 3 **Talk Math**

Discuss with students "When would you use skip counting?" Sample answer: I might use skip counting to count something quicker, when counting money, or when things are grouped in like amounts.

Name _____

Operations and Algebraic Thinking
2.OA.1, 2.OA.2, 2.NBT.2

Skip Count On a Hundred Chart

Lesson 1
ESSENTIAL QUESTION
How can equal groups help me add?

Explore and Explain

1	3	5	7	9
11	13	15	17	19
21	23	25	27	29
31	33	35	37	39
41	43	45	47	49
51	53	55	57	59
61	63	65	67	69
71	73	75	77	79
81	83	85	87	89
91	93	95	97	99

Let's start coloring!

See students' work.

Teacher Directions: Count by 2s. Write the missing numbers. Count by 5s. Color the numbers yellow. Count by 10s. Circle those numbers red.

Online Content at connectED.mcgraw-hill.com   Chapter 2 • Lesson 1   107

See and Show

Mathematical PRACTICE

Helpful Hint
Skip counting on a hundred chart creates patterns.

Use patterns to count. You can **skip count** by 2s, 5s, and 10s.

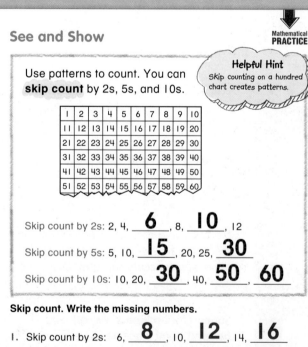

1	2	3	4	5	6	7	8	9	10
11	12	13	14	15	16	17	18	19	20
21	22	23	24	25	26	27	28	29	30
31	32	33	34	35	36	37	38	39	40
41	42	43	44	45	46	47	48	49	50
51	52	53	54	55	56	57	58	59	60

Skip count by 2s: 2, 4, **6**, 8, **10**, 12

Skip count by 5s: 5, 10, **15**, 20, 25, **30**

Skip count by 10s: 10, 20, **30**, 40, **50**, **60**

Skip count. Write the missing numbers.

1. Skip count by 2s: 6, **8**, 10, **12**, 14, **16**

2. Skip count by 5s: 15, 20, **25**, 30, **35**, 40

3. Skip count by 10s: **60**, 50, 40, **30**, 20, **10**

Talk Math When would you use skip counting?

108   Chapter 2 • Lesson 1

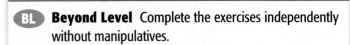

Name _____

On My Own
Use the hundred chart to skip count.

Skip counting is hot!

1	2	3	4	5	6	7	8	9	10
11	12	13	14	15	16	17	18	19	20
21	22	23	24	25	26	27	28	29	30
31	32	33	34	35	36	37	38	39	40
41	42	43	44	45	46	47	48	49	50
51	52	53	54	55	56	57	58	59	60
61	62	63	64	65	66	67	68	69	70
71	72	73	74	75	76	77	78	79	80
81	82	83	84	85	86	87	88	89	90
91	92	93	94	95	96	97	98	99	100

See students' work.

4. Start on 5. Count by 5s. Color the numbers blue.

5. Start on 10. Count by 10s. Circle the numbers red.

See students' work.

Write the missing number. Describe the pattern.

6. 34, 36, 38, **40**

Skip count by **2**.

7. 10, **20**, 30, 40

Skip count by **10**.

8. 24, 22, **20**, 18

Skip count by **2**.

9. 40, 35, **30**, 25

Skip count by **5**.

Chapter 2 • Lesson 1   109

On My Own

Have students work through the exercises on this page independently. You may choose to assign exercises based on the chart below.

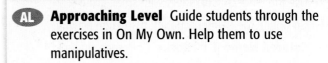
DIFFERENTIATED ASSIGNMENTS

AL **Approaching Level** Guide students through the exercises in On My Own. Help them to use manipulatives.

OL **On Level** Complete the exercises independently.

BL **Beyond Level** Complete the exercises independently without manipulatives.

Common Error!
Students may need to use a number line or hundred chart to help them when they are skip counting, particularly if they are skip counting backwards.

Problem Solving

Have students work through the problem-solving exercises on this page independently.

Mathematical PRACTICE 4 In Exercise 11, students **model with mathematics.**

Write Math

This exercise asks students to build upon their understanding of concepts needed to answer the chapter's Essential Question.

Problem Solving

Mathematical PRACTICE

10. If there are 2 vases with 10 flowers in each vase, how many flowers are there in all?

20 flowers

11. There are 3 fish bowls. How many fish are there in all if there are 5 fish in each bowl?

15 goldfish

12. How many frogs are there in all if there are 3 lily pads and each one has 2 frogs?

6 frogs

Write Math
Write an addition story for the cubes.

Sample answer: Raul put 5 connecting

cubes on each desk. There are 4 desks. Raul

gave out 20 connecting cubes in all.

110   Chapter 2 • Lesson 1

RESPONSE TO INTERVENTION

DIFFERENTIATED INSTRUCTION

AL APPROACHING LEVEL

IF my students struggle with skip counting,

THEN choose a resource:

→ Use the Reteach worksheet with small groups.

→ Go online for a Differentiated Instruction activity.

→ **Colored Number Patterns** Give each student half of a hundred chart with the numbers 0–50.

- Start at 0 and skip count by 2. Color in each square as they land on it. Discuss the pattern.

- Repeat, using the entire hundred chart starting at 0 and skip counting by 10.

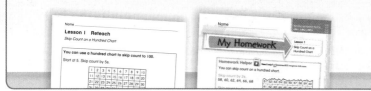

OL ON LEVEL

IF my students seem to know how to skip count, but need more practice,

THEN choose a resource:

→ Assign My Homework.

→ Go online for a Differentiated Instruction activity.

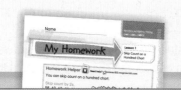

BL BEYOND LEVEL

IF my students have mastered skip counting,

THEN choose a resource:

→ Use the Enrich worksheet in cooperative groups.

→ Assign My Homework.

→ Go online for a Differentiated Instruction activity.

AL

Name _____

Lesson 1   Reteach

Skip Count on a Hundred Chart

You can use a hundred chart to skip count to 100.

Start at 5. Skip count by 5s.

1	2	3	4	5	6	7	8	9	10
11	12	13	14	15	16	17	18	19	20
21	22	23	24	25	26	27	28	29	30
31	32	33	34	35	36	37	38	39	40
41	42	43	44	45	46	47	48	49	50
51	52	53	54	55	56	57	58	59	60
61	62	63	64	65	66	67	68	69	70
71	72	73	74	75	76	77	78	79	80
81	82	83	84	85	86	87	88	89	90
91	92	93	94	95	96	97	98	99	100

Use a hundred chart to skip count.

1. Start at 2. Skip count by 2. Color each square **yellow**.

2. Start at 1. Skip count by 10. Color each square **red**.

3. Which numbers did you color yellow and red?

10, 20, 30, 40, 50, 60, 70, 80, 90, 100

1	2	3	4	5	6	7	8	9	10
11	12	13	14	15	16	17	18	19	20
21	22	23	24	25	26	27	28	29	30
31	32	33	34	35	36	37	38	39	40
41	42	43	44	45	46	47	48	49	50
51	52	53	54	55	56	57	58	59	60
61	62	63	64	65	66	67	68	69	70
71	72	73	74	75	76	77	78	79	80
81	82	83	84	85	86	87	88	89	90
91	92	93	94	95	96	97	98	99	100

BL

Name _____

Lesson 1   Enrich

Skip Count on a Hundred Chart

Mrs. Torrez coaches the girls' swim team. She needs 3 towels for every girl on the team. Use the hundred chart to help her figure out how many towels to bring.

1. 17 girls try out for the team. If they all make the team, how many towels will Mrs. Torrez need?

   51 towels

2. Last year, 26 girls were on the team. How many towels did they need last year?

   78 towels

3. Mrs. Torrez has a total of 90 towels. What is the greatest number of girls that could make the team and still get 3 towels?

   30 girls

1	2	3	4	5	6	7	8	9	10
11	12	13	14	15	16	17	18	19	20
21	22	23	24	25	26	27	28	29	30
31	32	33	34	35	36	37	38	39	40
41	42	43	44	45	46	47	48	49	50
51	52	53	54	55	56	57	58	59	60
61	62	63	64	65	66	67	68	69	70
71	72	73	74	75	76	77	78	79	80
81	82	83	84	85	86	87	88	89	90
91	92	93	94	95	96	97	98	99	100

My Homework

Name _____

Operations and Algebraic Thinking
2.OA.1, 2.OA.2, 2.NBT.2 · CCSS

My Homework → **Lesson 1** Skip Count on a Hundred Chart

Homework Helper
Need help? connectED.mcgraw-hill.com

You can skip count on a hundred chart.

Skip count by 2s.
58, 60, 62, 64, 66, 68

Skip count by 5s.
55, 60, 65, 70, 75, 80

Skip count by 10s.
60, 70, 80, 90, 100

51	52	53	54	55	56	57	58	59	60
61	62	63	64	65	66	67	68	69	70
71	72	73	74	75	76	77	78	79	80
81	82	83	84	85	86	87	88	89	90
91	92	93	94	95	96	97	98	99	100

Practice

Skip count. Write the missing numbers.

1. 62, **64**, 66, **68**, **70**, 72

2. 60, **65**, 70, **75**, 80, **85**

3. 95, **90**, **85**, 80, 75, **70**

4. 88, **86**, 84, **82**, **80**, 78

Write the missing number. Describe the pattern.

5. 50, **60**, 70, 80

   Skip count by **10**.

6. 30, 35, **40**, 45

   Skip count by **5**.

7. 75, **80**, 85, 90

   Skip count by **5**.

8. 90, **80**, **70**, 60

   Skip count by **10**.

9. **Draw a picture to solve.**

   There are 20 wheels on a group of bicycles. Each bike has 2 wheels. How many bikes are there?

   10 bicycles

Vocabulary Check

10. Which is not an example of a way to **skip count**? Circle it.

    (10, 12, 16, 20, 24)   15, 20, 25, 30, 35

    28, 26, 24, 22, 20   40, 50, 60, 70, 80

Adventure time!

 Math at Home Practice skip counting by 2s, 5s and 10s. Use cereal or beans.

My Homework

Assign homework after successful completion of the lesson. Students who understand the concepts may skip the **Homework Helper** section.

Be sure all students understand that bike is the shortened form of the word bicycle.

Test Practice
Diagnose Student Errors

Class trends in wrong answers may indicate common errors or misconceptions. Students needed to read directions carefully to catch the phrase "not an example".

10, 12, 16, 20, 24   correct – it is not skip counting

15, 20, 25, 30, 35   this is skip counting

28, 26, 24, 22, 20   this is skip counting

40, 50, 60, 70, 80   this is skip counting

Formative Assessment

Ask students the following question.

What patterns do you see when you skip count by 10, starting with 10? The digit in the ones place is always 0.

Line Up!

When students are ready to line up for recess, lunch, or dismissal, have only two students line up. Then ask two more students to line up. Continue the pattern, skip counting by 2s as students line up, until all students have lined up. If you have an odd number of students, have 3 students line up at the end.

LESSON 2
Skip Count by 2s, 5s, and 10s
OBJECTIVE Model skip counting to find the total in equal groups.

What's the Math?

 Common Core State Standards
DOMAIN: Operations and Algebraic Thinking

Standards: 2.OA.1, 2.NBT.2
The wording of these standards can be found on page 100.

 CCSS

What Students Should Understand

• You can find the total number of objects that you have by placing them in equal groups and then skip counting to find the total.

What Students Should be Able to Do

Use counters to model 4 groups of 4. Skip count to find the total.

   4,   8,   12,   16   counters in all

 Building on the Essential Question

In this lesson, students will build upon the skills and concepts needed to answer the chapter's Essential Question "How can equal groups help me add?"

Developing Vocabulary

Vocab **New Vocabulary**

equal groups

Activity

• Write the words on the board. Ask students what they know about *equal groups*. For example, they might explain that *equal* means "the same as."

• Draw 2 groups of 4 circles on the board.
  How many groups of circles do you see? 2
  Does each group have an equal number of circles? Yes
  Explain that these are equal groups.

• Draw 12 flowers and 3 vases on the board. Explain that you need to put an equal number of flowers in each vase.
  How many flowers are there in all? 12
  How many groups do we need to make? 3
  How many will be in each group? 4

ELL **ELL Support Strategy** Use this vocabulary activity to apply visual cues to understand concepts.

My Vocabulary Cards

Discuss with students how the visual on the *equal groups* card represents the definition.

IWB **Virtual Word Wall**

Add this vocabulary card to the Virtual Word Wall for the chapter.

ELL Refer to the Multilingual eGlossary for interactive definitions in 13 languages.

Plan Online
Plan for your lesson by using the resources at
connectED.mcgraw-hill.com

Digital Dashboard

Interactive Whiteboard Ready

The eBook **Glossary** shows the definition of the word and has audio for each definition. The **eGlossary** provides definitions in 13 languages.

Watch as concepts are brought to life through **animations**, **songs**, and a variety of visual instruction.

Virtual Manipulatives with work mats allow teachers and students to model the lesson.

Use **eAssessment** for online assignments and customized assessments.

Use the **Common Core Quick Check** before the lesson to assess students' retention of previously learned concepts.

Use the interactive **Self-Check Quiz** after the lesson to provide immediate feedback on lesson concepts.

Digital and print resources assist students and parents in completing My Homework.

Online games and **apps** provide extra practice for lesson concepts.

Professional development videos help teachers gain a deeper understanding of the lesson concepts and strategies.

Support for **approaching**, **on**- and **beyond-level** students as well as **English Language Learners**.

Reteach and **Enrich** worksheets, **Manipulative Masters**, the **Problem of the Day**, and other blackline masters are available for each lesson.

---

1 LAUNCH THE LESSON

CCSS

If your students are well-versed in skip counting, you may choose to begin instruction with Step 2, TEACH.

You will need
☐ connecting cubes
☐ base-ten blocks

Mathematical **PRACTICE** 4 **Modeling the Math**

Give each student 20 connecting cubes.

Make 3 sets with 2 connecting cubes in each group. Count the first group. How many in the first set? 2

For the next group, have the students count up from 2.
How many altogether? 4

For the third group, they will start at 4 and count on by 2.
How many altogether? 6

Repeat the process with 4 groups of 5 and 2 groups of 10.

Use ten rods to demonstrate skip counting by 10s to 100.

Skip count by 10s from 1 to 100. 10, 20, 30, 40...100

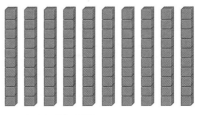

Lunchroom Chat

Building a Learning Community

Students rely on the counting principle to order whole numbers on a number line. Many experiences, not only with counting but with seeing the numbers from 1 to 100 (on a number line, on a ruler or yardstick, in a hundred chart, in literature, on thermometers, clocks, street addresses, etc.), help students see the order of the whole numbers in an increasing pattern. Help students see that the value of the numbers in the patterns increase or decrease by multiples.

🕐 **Begin core instruction here.**

You will need

☐ counters

Explore and Explain

Read the directions that are on the bottom of the student page.

How would you use counters to model 1 group of 5 snakes? Sample answer: place 5 counters in one group.

How would you use counters to model 2 groups of 5 snakes? Sample answer: place 5 counters in each of 2 groups.

How would you use counters to model 3 groups of 5 snakes? Sample answer: place 5 counters in each of 3 groups.

Describe two different ways you can find the total number of snakes. Sample answer: count the number of counters or skip count by 5s

Which is the fastest way to find the total number of snakes? skip count by 5s

When you are finding the total number of objects that you have, you can place them in equal groups and then skip count to find the total.

See and Show

Help students work through the example at the top of the page. Discuss what an equal group is.

Do we have equal groups of boys and girls in this class? Answers will vary.

When we skip count, we are counting equal groups.

Have them trace the dashed numbers as they skip count to find the total.

Work through Exercises 1 through 3 as a class.

Mathematical PRACTICE 3 **Talk Math**

Discuss with students "Create a skip-counting story for Exercise 3." Sample answer: Jen was dyeing eggs. She had four cartons and each carton had ten eggs. How could she skip count to find the total? $10 + 10 + 10 + 10 = 40$ eggs

---

Name _____

Operations and Algebraic Thinking
2.OA.1, 2.NBT.2

Skip Count by 2s, 5s, and 10s

Lesson 2
ESSENTIAL QUESTION
How can equal groups help me add?

Explore and Explain Watch Tools

This desert is not big enough for all of us.

__5__ , __10__ , __15__ snakes

🦉 **Teacher Directions:** Use counters to model. There are 3 groups of snakes in the desert. There are 5 snakes in each group. Skip count. How many snakes in all?

Online Content at 🔗connectED.mcgraw-hill.com   Chapter 2 • Lesson 2   113

See and Show

Mathematical PRACTICE

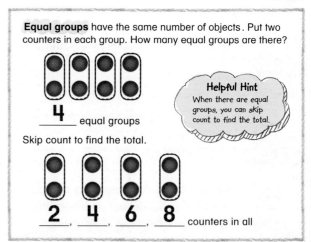

Equal groups have the same number of objects. Put two counters in each group. How many equal groups are there?

__4__ equal groups

Skip count to find the total.

__2__ , __4__ , __6__ , __8__ counters in all

Helpful Hint
When there are equal groups, you can skip count to find the total.

Use to model equal groups.
Skip count to find the total.

1. 3 groups of 2 __6__ in all   2. 4 groups of 5 __20__ in all

Describe the groups. Skip count to find the total.

3.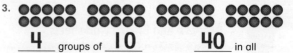

__4__ groups of __10__   __40__ in all

Talk Math Create a skip-counting story for Exercise 3.

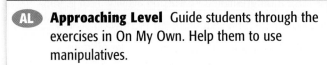

Name _____

On My Own

Use ⬤ to model equal groups.
Skip count to find the total.

4. 2 groups of 10 __20__ in all 5. 6 groups of 2 __12__ in all

Describe the groups. Skip count to find the total.

6.

__3__ groups of __5__ __15__ in all

7.

__3__ groups of __10__ __30__ in all

8.

__5__ groups of __5__ __25__ in all

Chapter 2 • Lesson 2   115

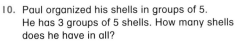 Problem Solving

 Mathematical PRACTICE

Solve. Draw a picture to help, if needed.

9. Lori has 6 bunches of grapes.
Each bunch has 10 grapes.
How many grapes does Lori
have in all?

__60__ grapes

10. Paul organized his shells in groups of 5.
He has 3 groups of 5 shells. How many shells
does he have in all?

__15__ shells

11. Myla put 10 cookies each in 4 bags for a bake
sale. Kate put 10 cookies in each of 3 bags.
How many cookies do they have in all?

__70__ cookies

Write Math How can you find the total number of
tennis balls in 4 groups of 10 tennis balls?
Use your vocabulary word.

Sample answer: There are 4 equal groups

of tennis balls. I can skip count by 10s.

10, 20, 30, 40 so 40 balls in all.

116   Chapter 2 • Lesson 2

On My Own

Have students work through the exercises on this page
independently. You may choose to assign exercises based on the
chart below.

DIFFERENTIATED ASSIGNMENTS

AL **Approaching Level** Guide students through the
exercises in On My Own. Help them to use
manipulatives.

OL **On Level** Complete the exercises independently.

BL **Beyond Level** Complete the exercises independently
without manipulatives.

Common Error!

Some students have difficulty holding more than 3 or
4 groups in their minds. Limit early experiences to 2
and then 3 equal groups.

Problem Solving

Have students work through the problem-solving exercises on
this page independently.

Mathematical PRACTICE 4 In Exercise 10, students **model with
mathematics.**

Write Math

This exercise asks students to build upon their understanding of
concepts needed to answer the chapter's Essential Question.

RESPONSE TO INTERVENTION

DIFFERENTIATED INSTRUCTION

AL **APPROACHING LEVEL**

IF my students struggle with skip counting,

THEN choose a resource:

→ Use a Differentiated Instruction activity from p. 99B.

→ Go online for a Differentiated Instruction activity.

→ **Show a Model** Ask students to take off their shoes and put them in groups of 2.

  • The total number of groups should equal the number of students in the class.

  • Then ask students to put the shoes in groups of 4. How many groups? See students' work.

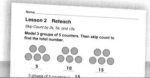 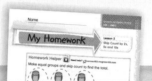

OL **ON LEVEL**

IF my students seem to know skip counting, but need more practice,

THEN choose a resource:

→ Use a Differentiated Instruction activity from p. 99B.

→ Assign My Homework.

→ Go online for a Differentiated Instruction activity.

BL **BEYOND LEVEL**

IF my students have mastered skip counting,

THEN choose a resource:

→ Use the Enrich worksheet in cooperative groups.

→ Assign My Homework.

→ Go online for a Differentiated Instruction activity.

117A **Chapter 2** Number Patterns

AL

Name _____

Lesson 2   Reteach

Skip Count by 2s, 5s, and 10s

Model 3 groups of 5 counters. Then skip count to find the total number.

_____ 5   _____ 10   _____ 15

3 groups of 5 counters is __15__ counters in all.

Use counters to model equal groups. Then skip count to find the total number.

1. 4 groups of 2 is __8__ in all.

2. 3 groups of 10 is __30__ in all.

3. 7 groups of 5 is __35__ in all.

4. 1 group of 5 is __5__ in all.

5. 8 groups of 2 is __16__ in all.

6. 2 groups of 10 is __20__ in all.

7. 1 group of 10 is __10__ in all.

8. 10 groups of 2 is __20__ in all.

9. 8 groups of 5 is __40__ in all.

10. 3 groups of 5 is __15__ in all.

BL

Name _____

Lesson 2   Enrich

Skip Count by 2s, 5s, and 10s

Use the table to answer the questions.

Second Grade Students Who Visited the Zoo	
Class A	X X X X X
Class B	X X X X
Class C	X X
	Each X stands for 2 students.

1. How many students in Class C went to the zoo?
   4 students

2. What number did you skip count by to solve Exercise 1?
   2

3. How many students in Classes A and B went to the zoo? **18 students**

4. What is the total number of students who visited the zoo? **22 students**

What if each X stood for 4 students?

5. How many students in Class C went to the zoo? **8 students**

6. What number did you skip count by to solve Exercise 5? **4**

7. How many students in Classes A and B went to the zoo? **36 students**

8. What is the total number of students who visited the zoo? **44 students**

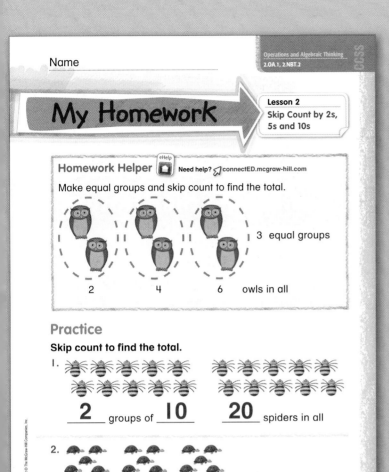

Operations and Algebraic Thinking
2.OA.1, 2.NBT.2

CCSS

My Homework

Lesson 2
Skip Count by 2s,
5s and 10s

Homework Helper
Need help? connectED.mcgraw-hill.com

Make equal groups and skip count to find the total.

3 equal groups

2   4   6   owls in all

Practice

Skip count to find the total.

1.

 2 groups of **10**   **20** spiders in all

2.

 3 groups of **5**   **15** turtles in all

Chapter 2 • Lesson 2   117

Copyright © The McGraw-Hill Companies, Inc.

Solve. Draw a picture to help, if needed.

3. Evan has 6 groups of 5 toy cars. How many toy cars does he have in all?

 30 toy cars

Field Trip!

4. Mrs. Hanes is planning a field trip. There are 6 groups of 10 students going. How many students are going on the field trip?

 60 students

5. Austen has 6 sets of 10 baseball cards. Tim has 3 sets of 10 baseball cards. How many baseball cards do they have in all?

 90 baseball cards

Vocabulary Check

6. Circle **equal groups** of five buttons.

Math at Home Use buttons, macaroni, or pennies. Have your child make equal groups of 2s, 5s, and 10s. Skip count to find the totals.

118   Chapter 2 • Lesson 2

Copyright © The McGraw-Hill Companies, Inc. (t) Lew Robertson/CORBIS, (b) br/Ken Cavanagh/The McGraw-Hill Companies

---

4 WRAP IT UP

CCSS

My Homework

Assign homework after successful completion of the lesson. Students who understand the concepts may skip the **Homework Helper** section.

Vocabulary Check

Have students refer to their My Vocabulary Cards for additional support.

Formative Assessment

Have students use counters to model skip counting by 5s. Answers should show equal groups of 5 counters.

MY Learning Stations

Use the game **Count the Stars** after this lesson. The Teacher Guide provides suggestions for differentiated instruction.

Line Up!   When students line up, have them skip count by 2s aloud, one by one. Then have students skip count in reverse back to the beginning of the line.

LESSON 3
Problem Solving
STRATEGY: Find a Pattern
OBJECTIVE Find a pattern to solve problems.

What's the Math?

 Common Core State Standards
DOMAIN: Operations and Algebraic Thinking

Standards: 2.OA.1, 2.NBT.2
The wording of these standards can be found on page 100.

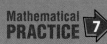 **7** Look for and make use of structure.

What Students Should Understand

- You can find a pattern to solve a real-world word problem.
- First, make sure you understand the meaning of the problem. Determine the facts and what question is being asked.
- Make a plan, solve the problem and follow through.
- Check your answer to see if it is correct and makes sense.

What Students Should be Able to Do

Henry is practicing holding his breath under water. On his first try, he held his breath for 10 seconds. He held his breath for 20 seconds on his second try and 30 seconds on his third try. If this pattern continues, for how many seconds will he hold his breath on his fifth try?

1 Understand

Underline what you know. Circle what you need to find.

2 Plan

How will I solve this problem? I can find a pattern.

3 Solve

I will… find a pattern.

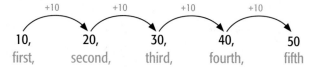

4 Check

Is my answer reasonable? Explain.
Yes; Henry holds his breath for 10 more seconds each try. So, on his fifth try he will hold his breath for 50 seconds.

Developing the Strategy

What's the Strategy?

Find a Pattern Students will find a pattern to solve problems in this lesson. Patterns help students visualize the concepts in a more concrete manner.

Other Strategies

Other strategies that have been taught and that students may choose to use are:

- Write a number sentence
- Act it out

ELL Signal Words Encourage English-language learners to identify signal phrases, such as *if the pattern continues,* as they read word problems.

 **Mathematical PRACTICE**

The Mathematical Practices are especially evident in problem-solving situations, in which students connect procedures and processes with mathematical understanding. In this lesson, the following Mathematical Practices are addressed.

 1 Make sense of problems and persevere in solving them.

 4 Model with mathematics.

 7 Look for and make use of structure.

Plan Online

Plan for your lesson by using the resources at
connectED.mcgraw-hill.com

Digital Dashboard
Interactive Whiteboard Ready

 Vocab
The eBook **Glossary** shows the definition of the word and has audio for each definition. The **eGlossary** provides definitions in 13 languages.

 Tools
Virtual Manipulatives along with work mats allow teachers and students to model the lesson.

 Check
Use **eAssessment** for online assignments and customized assessments.

Use the **Common Core Quick Check** before the lesson to assess students' retention of previously learned concepts.

 eHelp
Digital and print resources assist students and parents in completing My Homework.

 PD
Professional development videos help teachers gain a deeper understanding of the lesson concepts and strategies.

 RtI
Support for **approaching**, **on**- and **beyond-level** students as well as **English Language Learners**.

 Masters
Reteach and **Enrich** worksheets, **Manipulative Masters**, the **Problem of the Day**, and other blackline masters are available for each lesson.

---

1 LAUNCH THE LESSON

If your students are well-versed in finding a pattern, you may choose to begin instruction with Step 2, **TEACH**.

You will need
☐ connecting cubes

Review

Hand out 4 connecting cubes: one green, one red, one yellow, and one purple.

Place the cubes in order according to the following rules:

the red cube is after the purple cube,

the yellow cube comes before the green cube,
the purple cube is after the green cube,

and finally, the green cube is not in front.

Ask for volunteers to show their train of cubes in order yellow, green, purple, red

🕐 **Begin core instruction here.**

Problem Solving

1 Understand

Read the problem with the students. Point out the important information as you read it. Explain to students what the underlined or circled information means.

2 Plan

Discuss several ideas. Lead the students toward the pattern needed to solve the problem.

3 Solve

Work through the problem together as a class. Show students how to solve the problem step-by-step.

4 Check

Discuss why the answer makes sense. Try to develop a sense of reasoning.

Practice the Strategy

1 Understand

Read the problem with the students. Ask students to point out information that is important as you read it. Have students underline what they know. Have them circle what they need to find.

2 Plan

Lead the students in discussing several ideas as to how they might proceed. Direct the students toward a correct plan to solve the problem by using the information given in the problem.

3 Solve

Work through the problem together as a class. Discuss as a class how to solve the problem step-by-step.

4 Check

Discuss why the answer makes sense. Try to develop a sense of reasoning.

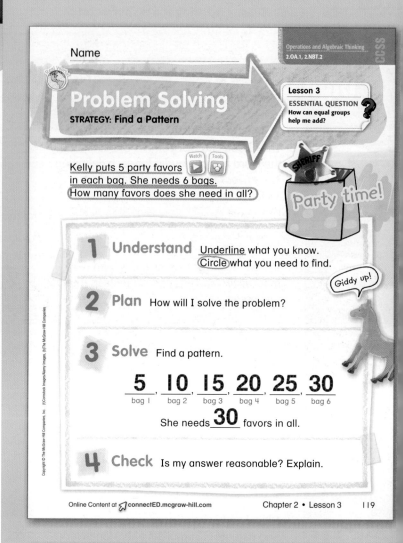

Name _____

Operations and Algebraic Thinking
2.OA.1, 2.NBT.2

Problem Solving
STRATEGY: **Find a Pattern**

Lesson 3
ESSENTIAL QUESTION
How can equal groups help me add?

Kelly puts 5 party favors in each bag. She needs 6 bags. How many favors does she need in all?

Party time!

1 Understand Underline what you know. Circle what you need to find.

Giddy up!

2 Plan How will I solve the problem?

3 Solve Find a pattern.

5, 10, 15, 20, 25, 30
bag 1, bag 2, bag 3, bag 4, bag 5, bag 6

She needs **30** favors in all.

4 Check Is my answer reasonable? Explain.

Online Content at 🖱 connectED.mcgraw-hill.com   Chapter 2 • Lesson 3   119

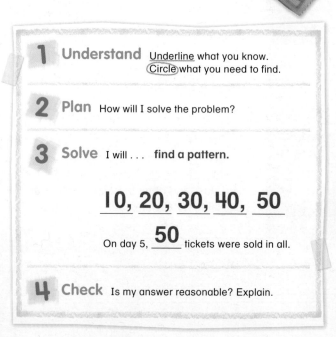

Practice the Strategy

Kate and Pedro count the tickets sold to a museum. They sold 10 tickets each day for 5 days. How many were sold in all?

Let's go to the Wild West Museum!

1 Understand Underline what you know. Circle what you need to find.

2 Plan How will I solve the problem?

3 Solve I will . . . **find a pattern.**

10, 20, 30, 40, 50

On day 5, **50** tickets were sold in all.

4 Check Is my answer reasonable? Explain.

PRACTICE & APPLY

Name

Apply the Strategy

1. Xavier is looking at a map of the desert. He knows that each finger width is about 10 miles. How many miles will he count if he uses 7 finger widths?

   70 miles

2. Sam thinks of the number pattern 15, 20, 25, 30. He continues this pattern. What will be the next four numbers?

   35, 40, 45, 50

Ghost town! Yikes!

3. Amar sees this number pattern. What is the missing number?

   10, **15**, 20, 25, 30

Chapter 2 • Lesson 3   121

Review the Strategies

Choose a strategy
- Write a number sentence.
- Act it out.
- Find a pattern.

4. Justin is stacking books. There are 5 books in the first stack. 10 in the second stack. The third stack has 15 books. The pattern continues. How many books will be in the next stack?

   20 books

5. On the first day of the food drive, Ms. Buckle's class collects 8 cans. Mr. Cline's class collects 6 cans, and Mrs. Brown's class collects 5 cans. How many cans do they collect in all?

   19 cans

6. Josh recorded how many inches of snow fell in each month. Continue the pattern. How many inches fell in January?

Month	Inches
November	14
December	16
January	**18**
February	20

   18 inches

122   Chapter 2 • Lesson 3

Mathematical PRACTICE ① Apply the Strategy

Have students work through the exercises on these pages independently. You may choose to assign exercises based on the chart below.

DIFFERENTIATED ASSIGNMENTS

AL Approaching Level Guide students through the exercises. Help them to use manipulatives.

OL On Level Complete the exercises independently.

BL Beyond Level Complete the exercises independently without manipulatives.

Review the Strategies

Students may use other strategies to solve these exercises.

Other strategies are:
- Act it out
- Find a pattern

RESPONSE TO INTERVENTION

DIFFERENTIATED INSTRUCTION

AL) APPROACHING LEVEL

IF my students struggle with finding a pattern,

THEN choose a resource:

→ Use the Reteach worksheet.

→ Go online for a Differentiated Instruction activity.

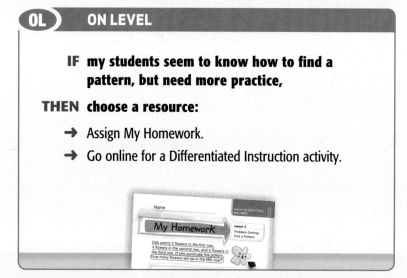

OL) ON LEVEL

IF my students seem to know how to find a pattern, but need more practice,

THEN choose a resource:

→ Assign My Homework.

→ Go online for a Differentiated Instruction activity.

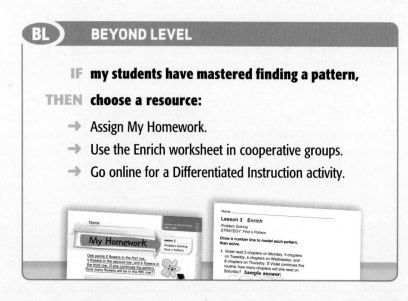

BL) BEYOND LEVEL

IF my students have mastered finding a pattern,

THEN choose a resource:

→ Assign My Homework.

→ Use the Enrich worksheet in cooperative groups.

→ Go online for a Differentiated Instruction activity.

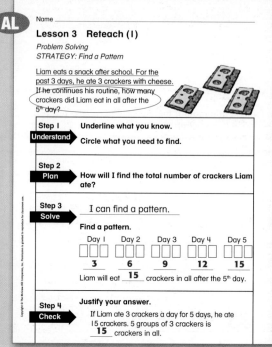

AL) Name _____

Lesson 3 Reteach (1)
Problem Solving
STRATEGY: *Find a Pattern*

Liam eats a snack after school. For the past 3 days, he ate 3 crackers with cheese. If he continues his routine, how many crackers did Liam eat in all after the 5th day?

Step 1 Understand	Underline what you know. Circle what you need to find.
Step 2 Plan	How will I find the total number of crackers Liam ate?
Step 3 Solve	I can find a pattern. Find a pattern.

	Day 1	Day 2	Day 3	Day 4	Day 5
	3	6	9	12	15

Liam will eat **15** crackers in all after the 5th day.

Step 4 Check	Justify your answer. If Liam ate 3 crackers a day for 5 days, he ate 15 crackers. 5 groups of 3 crackers is **15** crackers in all.

AL) Name _____

Lesson 3 Reteach (2)
Problem Solving
STRATEGY: *Find a Pattern*

Find a pattern to solve. Use the number line for help.

1. Evan sent 2 texts on Monday, 4 texts on Tuesday, 6 texts on Wednesday, and 8 texts on Thursday. If Evan continues his texting pattern, how many texts will he send on Friday?

10 texts

2. Last week, Clara walked 2 miles each day. How many miles did she walk in all? (Remember: 1 week is 7 days.)

14 miles

3. Ian read 3 books. Each book had 4 chapters. How many chapters did he read in all?

12 chapters

BL) Name _____

Lesson 3 Enrich
Problem Solving
STRATEGY: *Find a Pattern*

Draw a number line to model each pattern, then solve.

1. Violet read 2 chapters on Monday, 4 chapters on Tuesday, 6 chapters on Wednesday, and 8 chapters on Thursday. If Violet continues this routine, how many chapters will she read on Saturday? **Sample answer:**

0 1 2 3 4 5 6 7 8 9 10 11 12 13

12 chapters

2. Last week, Jada walked 1 mile each day. How many miles did she walk in all? (Remember: 1 week is 7 days.) **Sample answer:**

0 1 2 3 4 5 6 7 8 9 10 11 12 13

7 miles

3. Micah read 2 books. Each book had 6 chapters. He just finished 1 chapter in a third book. How many chapters did he read in all? **Sample answer:**

0 1 2 3 4 5 6 7 8 9 10 11 12 13

13 chapters

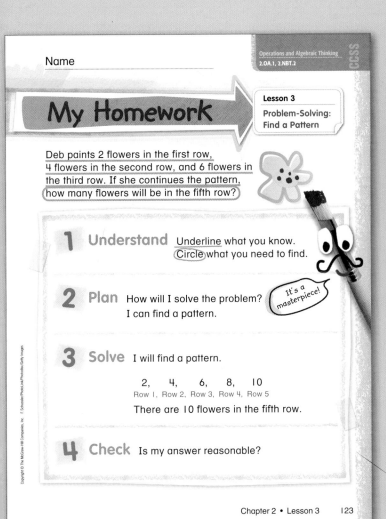

Name _____

Operations and Algebraic Thinking
2.OA.1, 2.NBT.2

My Homework

Lesson 3
Problem-Solving:
Find a Pattern

Deb paints 2 flowers in the first row, 4 flowers in the second row, and 6 flowers in the third row. If she continues the pattern, how many flowers will be in the fifth row?

1 Understand Underline what you know. Circle what you need to find.

2 Plan How will I solve the problem? I can find a pattern.

It's a masterpiece!

3 Solve I will find a pattern.

2,   4,   6,   8,   10
Row 1, Row 2, Row 3, Row 4, Row 5

There are 10 flowers in the fifth row.

4 Check Is my answer reasonable?

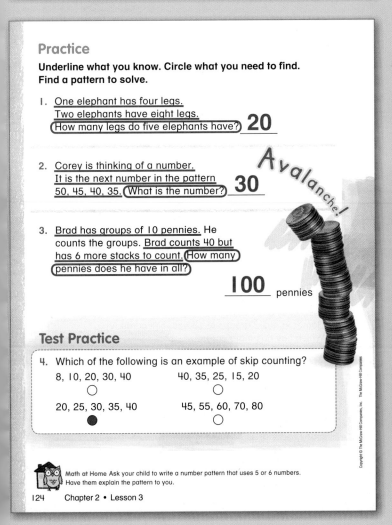

Practice

Underline what you know. Circle what you need to find.
Find a pattern to solve.

1. One elephant has four legs.
   Two elephants have eight legs.
   How many legs do five elephants have? **20**

2. Corey is thinking of a number.
   It is the next number in the pattern
   50, 45, 40, 35. What is the number? **30**

   Avalanche!

3. Brad has groups of 10 pennies. He counts the groups. Brad counts 40 but has 6 more stacks to count. How many pennies does he have in all?
   100 pennies

Test Practice

4. Which of the following is an example of skip counting?

   8, 10, 20, 30, 40   40, 35, 25, 15, 20
        ○   ○

   20, 25, 30, 35, 40   45, 55, 60, 70, 80
        ●   ○

Math at Home Ask your child to write a number pattern that uses 5 or 6 numbers. Have them explain the pattern to you.

My Homework

Assign homework after successful completion of the lesson. Students who understand the concepts may skip the **Homework Helper** section.

Test Practice

Diagnose Student Errors

Class trends in wrong answer may indicate common errors or misconceptions.

8, 10, 20, 30, 40   the 8 was out of place

40, 35, 25, 15, 20   does not skip count

20, 25, 30, 35, 40   correct

45, 55, 60, 70, 80   does not skip count

Formative Assessment

Share this story. *Jason, Lisa, and Rachel are friends. Jason is 12 years old. Rachel is 4 years younger than Jason. Lisa is 2 years older than Rachel. How old are Rachel and Lisa?*

How will you figure out the ages of each child? Jason is 12. Rachel is 4 years younger, so subtract 4 to get 8. Rachel is 8. Lisa is 2 years older, so add 2 to get 10. Lisa is 10.

Check My Progress

Use this as a formative assessment to determine if your students are struggling, and if so, with which topics they struggle. The criteria for differentiation are on the next page.

Vocabulary Check

Have a student read aloud the words in the word bank. Then ask a volunteer to name the vocabulary word that is plural. equal groups

ELL **ELL Support Strategy** Use this information to participate in purposeful, cooperative learning activities.

Concept Check

These concepts are covered in Lessons 1–3.

Exercises	Concept	Review Lessons
3–8	Skip counting by 2s, 5s and 10s	1, 2
9–10	Skip counting using equal groups	1, 2

Problem Solving

Exercise 11 uses a word problem to check for understanding of the same concepts.

Test Practice

Diagnose Student Errors

Class trends in wrong answers may indicate common errors or misconceptions.

10 thought of only one box
13 added 10 + 3
30 only determined how many he has now
40 correct

Name _____

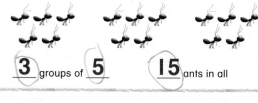
Check My Progress

Vocabulary Check

Complete each sentence.

| skip count | equal groups |

1. When you have sets of the same number of objects you have __equal groups__.
2. You can __skip count__ to help you count equal groups.

Concept Check

Skip count. Write the missing numbers.

3. 6, **8**, **10**, 12, 14, **16**, 18, **20**

4. 15, 20, **25**, 30, **35**, 40, **45**, 50

5. 20, **30**, **40**, 50, **60**, **70**, 80, 90

6. **50**, 55, **60**, 65, **70**, **75**, 80

7. 15, 20, **25**, 30   skip count by **5**.

8. 20, **18**, 16, 14   skip count by **2**.

Chapter 2   125

Describe the groups. Skip count to find the total.

9.

3 groups of **5**   **15** ants in all

10.

4 groups of **2**   **8** lizards in all

11. Jason has 3 groups of 5 baseball cards. Cameron has 2 groups of 10 baseball cards. Which boy has more cards?

Cameron

Test Practice

12. Jose has 3 boxes of rocks in his collection. Each box holds 10 rocks. He fills one more box. How many rocks does he have in all?

   10 ○   13 ○   30 ○   40 ●

126   Chapter 2

Name _____

Check My Progress *(Lessons 1 through 3)*

Write the missing numbers.

1. Count by 2s.
   8, 10, 12, __14__, __16__, __18__, __20__

2. Count by 5s.
   15, 20, 25, __30__, __35__, __40__, __45__

3. Count by 10s.
   40, 50, 60, __70__, __80__, __90__, __100__

4. Circle groups of four.

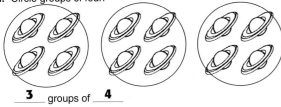

   __3__ groups of __4__

5. Henry saw 6 birds in his backyard. Each bird has two legs. How many legs do all 6 birds have?
   __12 legs__

6. Alana has a stack of nickels. Each nickel is worth 5 cents. Count by 5s to find how much 10 nickels are worth. __50 cents__

RESPONSE TO INTERVENTION

CCSS

DIFFERENTIATED INSTRUCTION

AL **STRATEGIC INTERVENTION**

(Approaching Grade Level)

IF **students miss 6 or more,**

THEN **choose a resource:**

→ Check My Progress
→ Self-Check Quiz
→ Use the Reteach worksheets.

OL **ON LEVEL**

IF **students miss 3 to 4,**

THEN **choose a resource:**

→ Chapter Project
→ Proceed to the next lesson.

BL **BEYOND LEVEL**

IF **students miss 2 or less,**

THEN **choose a resource:**

→ Chapter Project
→ Use the Enrich worksheets.
→ Proceed to the next lesson.

LESSON 4
Repeated Addition

OBJECTIVE Use repeated addition to add equal groups.

What's the Math?

 Common Core State Standards
DOMAIN: Operations and Algebraic Thinking

Standards: 2.OA.4, 2.NBT.2
The wording of these standards can be found on page 100.

What Students Should Understand

- When finding the total number of objects that you have, you can use repeated addition when the objects are in equal groups.
- You can skip count to find the sum in a repeated addition problem.

What Students Should be Able to Do

Use repeated addition to find the total number of connecting cubes shown below.

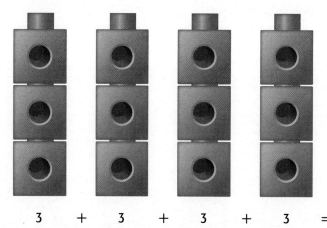

$$3 \ + \ 3 \ + \ 3 \ + \ 3 \ = \ \underline{12}$$

 Building on the Essential Question

In this lesson, students will build upon the skills and concepts needed to answer the chapter's Essential Question "How can equal groups help me add?"

Developing Vocabulary

New Vocabulary

repeated addition

Activity

- Write *repeated addition* and its definition on the board. Tell students that *repeat* means "to do again." Ask students what they think repeated addition means.
- Ask students to provide an example of joining together sets to find the total or sum.
- Display three identical sets, such as 3 cube trains with 5 cubes in each train. *What addition sentence describes the cube trains?*
  $5 + 5 + 5 = 15$ *How do you know?* There are three groups of 5, and their sum is 15.

ELL **ELL Support Strategy** Use this vocabulary activity to assess students' ability to extend their understanding.

My Vocabulary Cards

Have students work in small groups to review the cards they have learned up to this point in the chapter.

IWB **Virtual Word Wall**

Add this vocabulary card to the Virtual Word Wall for the chapter.

ELL Refer to the Multilingual eGlossary for interactive definitions in 13 languages.

Plan Online
Plan for your lesson by using the resources at
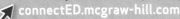 connectED.mcgraw-hill.com

Digital Dashboard

 **Interactive Whiteboard Ready**

 Vocab

The eBook **Glossary** shows the definition of the word and has audio for each definition. The **eGlossary** provides definitions in 13 languages.

 Watch

Watch as concepts are brought to life through **animations**, **songs**, and a variety of visual instruction.

 Tools

Virtual Manipulatives with work mats allow teachers and students to model the lesson.

 Check

Use **eAssessment** for online assignments and customized assessments.

Use the **Common Core Quick Check** before the lesson to assess students' retention of previously learned concepts.

Use the interactive **Self-Check Quiz** after the lesson to provide immediate feedback on lesson concepts.

 eHelp

Digital and print resources assist students and parents in completing My Homework.

 Games

Online games and **apps** provide extra practice for lesson concepts.

 PD

Professional development videos help teachers gain a deeper understanding of the lesson concepts and strategies.

 Rtl

Support for **approaching**, **on**- and **beyond-level** students as well as **English Language Learners**.

 Masters

Reteach and **Enrich** worksheets, **Manipulative Masters**, the **Problem of the Day**, and other blackline masters are available for each lesson.

---

1 LAUNCH THE LESSON

 If your students are well-versed in repeated addition, you may choose to begin instruction with Step 2, TEACH.

You will need

☐ counters

Mathematical PRACTICE 4 Modeling the Math

Give each student 10 counters.

Make 3 groups with 3 counters in each group.

Students count by 3s.

How many altogether? 9 *What addition number sentence can we write to show this?* 3 + 3 + 3

Explain that this is repeated addition because the number of counters in each group is the same, and you add to find how many altogether.

Can anyone else think of a way we have learned that we could use to find the total? skip counting

Explain that skip counting and repeated addition using equal addends are related.

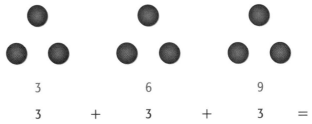

| 3 | | 6 | | 9 | | |
| 3 | + | 3 | + | 3 | = | 9 |

TEACH

Vocabulary

Have students point to the wind turbines. Explain that wind turbines often are grouped together on wind farms. The wind produces energy that is turned into electricity.

ELL **ELL Support Strategy** Use this information to assess students' ability to read for understanding.

You will need

☐ connecting cubes

Explore and Explain

Read the directions that are on the bottom of the student page.

Place a connecting cube on each blade of the wind turbines. How many cubes are on each turbine? 3 *Write that number on the line below each wind turbine.*

Count the total number of connecting cubes. How many are there? 12 *Write that number on the line after the equals sign. What did we just find or do?* Sample answer: We found 4 equal groups of 3 or added the same number 4 times.

Point out the connection to skip counting by 3s.

See and Show

Help students work through the example at the top of the page.

Have them trace the dashed numbers as they work the problems. Use connecting cubes or other manipulatives to demonstrate additional equal groups. Show the groups. Have students write the repeated addition equation on the board.

Work through Exercises 1 through 3 as a class.

 **Mathematical** **PRACTICE** **3** **Talk Math**

Discuss with students "Create a story for $2 + 2 + 2 + 2 + 2$." Sample answer: There are 5 bowls of ice cream. Each bowl contains 2 scoops. $2 + 2 + 2 + 2 + 2 = 10$ scoops in all.

ELL Use tiered questions to informally assess students' progress.

Beginning: Point to an example of 3 connecting cubes.

Intermediate: What do you use to find the total when groups are equal?

Advanced: Explain why repeated addition is used with equal groups.

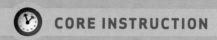
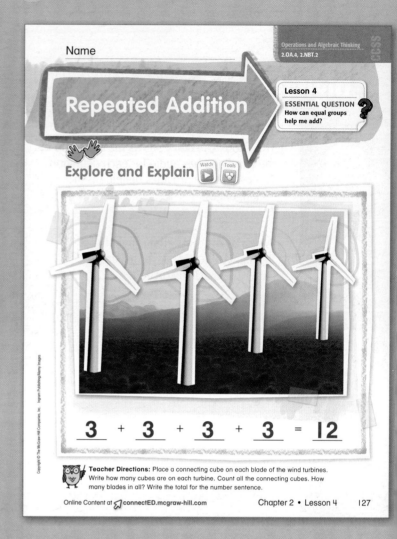

Name _____

Operations and Algebraic Thinking
2.OA.4, 2.NBT.2

Repeated Addition

Lesson 4
ESSENTIAL QUESTION
How can equal groups help me add?

Explore and Explain

$$3 + 3 + 3 + 3 = 12$$

Teacher Directions: Place a connecting cube on each blade of the wind turbines. Write how many cubes are on each turbine. Count all the connecting cubes. How many blades in all? Write the total for the number sentence.

Online Content at connectED.mcgraw-hill.com   Chapter 2 • Lesson 4   127

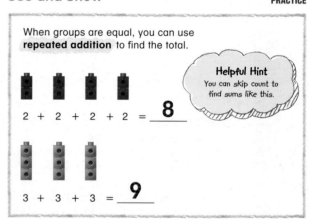

See and Show

When groups are equal, you can use **repeated addition** to find the total.

Helpful Hint
You can skip count to find sums like this.

$$2 + 2 + 2 + 2 = \underline{8}$$

$$3 + 3 + 3 = \underline{9}$$

Use connecting cubes to model equal groups. Add.

1. $$5 + 5 = 10$$

2. $$2 + 2 + 2 = 6$$

3. 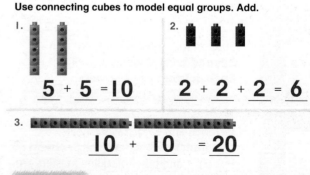 $$10 + 10 = 20$$

Talk Math   Create a story for $2 + 2 + 2 + 2 + 2$.

128   Chapter 2 • Lesson 4

Name

On My Own

Add.

4.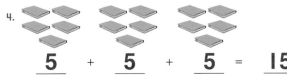

$$\underline{5} + \underline{5} + \underline{5} = 15$$

5.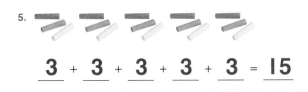

$$\underline{3} + \underline{3} + \underline{3} + \underline{3} + \underline{3} = 15$$

6.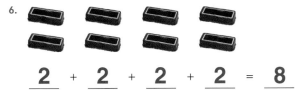

$$\underline{2} + \underline{2} + \underline{2} + \underline{2} = 8$$

7. Draw your own example. Then add.

See students' work.

$$\underline{4} + \underline{4} + \underline{4} + \underline{4} = \underline{16}$$

Problem Solving

Mathematical PRACTICE

Use repeated addition to solve.

8. Mike has five pairs of socks. Each pair has two socks. How many socks does Mike have?

$$\underline{10} \text{ socks}$$

9. Brad makes four groups of animal cards. Each group has three cards. How many cards does he make?

$$\underline{12} \text{ cards}$$

10. There are four balloons in each bunch. Marcy has four bunches. How many balloons are there in all?

Oh, no! a cactus!

$$\underline{16} \text{ balloons}$$

HOT Problem Jaya writes a repeated number sentence. It has three numbers. The sum is 15. What is the number sentence? Explain.

$$5 + 5 + 5 = 15; \text{ three groups of 5 is 15.}$$

---

3 PRACTICE & APPLY

CCSS

On My Own

Have students work through the exercises on this page independently. You may choose to assign exercises based on the chart below.

DIFFERENTIATED ASSIGNMENTS

AL **Approaching Level** Guide students through the exercises in On My Own. Help them to use manipulatives.

OL **On Level** Complete the exercises independently.

BL **Beyond Level** Complete the exercises independently without manipulatives.

Common Error!
Students may add the same number an incorrect number of times when using repeated addition. Try drawing models to represent each group.

Problem Solving

Have students work through the problem-solving exercises on this page independently.

Mathematical PRACTICE 1 In Exercise 10, students **make sense of problems and persevere in solving them.**

HOT Problem This exercise asks students to build upon their understanding of concepts needed to answer the chapter's Essential Question.

RESPONSE TO INTERVENTION

DIFFERENTIATED INSTRUCTION

AL APPROACHING LEVEL

IF my students struggle with repeated addition,

THEN choose a resource:

→ Use the Reteach worksheet with small groups.

→ Go online for a Differentiated Instruction activity.

→ **Show a Model** Lay two pencils on a table. Explain that you want to add more pencils by using repeated addition.

- Place another group of two pencils on the table. *How many pencils in all?* 4 pencils

- *How many pencils will there be if you add another group?* 6 pencils

- Continue until you reach 10.

 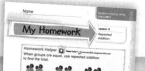

OL ON LEVEL

IF my students seem to know repeated addition, but need more practice,

THEN choose a resource:

→ Assign My Homework.

→ Go online for a Differentiated Instruction activity.

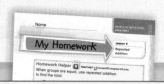

BL BEYOND LEVEL

IF my students have mastered repeated addition,

THEN choose a resource:

→ Use the Differentiated Instruction activity from p. 99B.

→ Use the Enrich worksheet in cooperative groups.

→ Assign My Homework.

→ Go online for a Differentiated Instruction activity.

AL

Name _____

Lesson 4   Reteach

Repeated Addition

Put a ⬤ on each equal group. Count the ◯.

1.

_____3_____ counters

$$\underline{\ 2\ } + \underline{\ 2\ } + \underline{\ 2\ } = \underline{\ 6\ }\ \text{cubes}$$

Use connecting cubes to make equal groups. Add.

2.

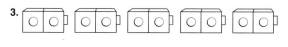

$$\underline{\ 2\ } + \underline{\ 2\ } + \underline{\ 2\ } + \underline{\ 2\ } = \underline{\ 8\ }$$

3.

$$\underline{\ 2\ } + \underline{\ 2\ } + \underline{\ 2\ } + \underline{\ 2\ } + \underline{\ 2\ } = \underline{\ 10\ }$$

BL

Name _____

Lesson 4   Enrich

Repeated Addition

Follow the directions below to draw flowers. Solve.

Each flower has 5 petals, 1 stem, 3 leaves, and 2 dots.

_____

1. Draw 5 petals on each circle.

   $5 + 5 + 5 = \underline{\ 15\ }$ petals

2. Draw 1 long stem on each flower.

   $1 + 1 + 1 = \underline{\ 3\ }$ stems

_____

3. Draw 3 leaves on each stem.

   $3 + 3 + 3 = \underline{\ 9\ }$ leaves

4. Put 2 dots in the center of each flower.

   $2 + 2 + 2 = \underline{\ 6\ }$ dots

Name _____

My Homework →

Lesson 4
Repeated
Addition

Homework Helper Need help? connectED.mcgraw-hill.com

When groups are equal, use repeated addition to find the total.

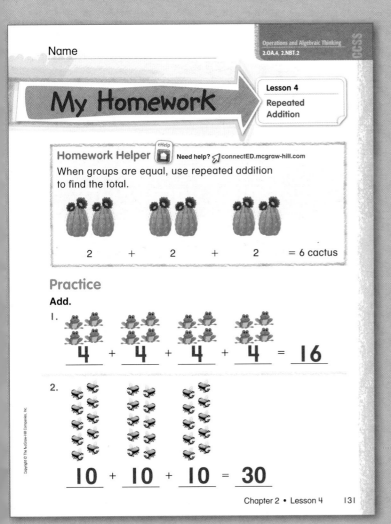

2 + 2 + 2 = 6 cactus

Practice

Add.

1.

4 + 4 + 4 + 4 = 16

2.

10 + 10 + 10 = 30

Chapter 2 • Lesson 4   131

Add.

3.

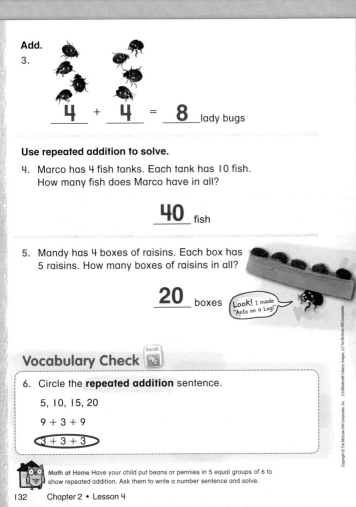

4 + 4 = 8 lady bugs

Use repeated addition to solve.

4. Marco has 4 fish tanks. Each tank has 10 fish. How many fish does Marco have in all?

40 fish

5. Mandy has 4 boxes of raisins. Each box has 5 raisins. How many boxes of raisins in all?

20 boxes   Look! I made "Ants on a Log!"

Vocabulary Check

6. Circle the **repeated addition** sentence.

5, 10, 15, 20

9 + 3 + 9

(3 + 3 + 3)

Math at Home Have your child put beans or pennies in 5 equal groups of 6 to show repeated addition. Ask them to write a number sentence and solve.

132   Chapter 2 • Lesson 4

My Homework

Assign homework after successful completion of the lesson. Students who understand the concepts may skip the **Homework Helper** section.

Vocabulary Check

Discuss with students which example shows repeated addition. Ask how they know the difference between that example and the example showing skip counting.

Formative Assessment

Ask students to represent 4 groups of 5 pencils in a repeated addition sentence. $5 + 5 + 5 + 5 = 20$

MY Learning Stations

Use the graphic novel **Flamingo Fun** after this lesson. The Teacher Guide provides suggestions for differentiated instruction.

Line Up!

When students line up, have them do some repeated addition activities.

• Have students hold up two fingers as they line up one by one.

• The first student who lines up says "2." The second student says "2 + 2 = 4," and so on.

LESSON 5
Repeated Addition with Arrays

OBJECTIVE Use arrays with repeated addition.

What's the Math?

 Common Core State Standards
DOMAIN: Operations and Algebraic Thinking

Standard: 2.OA.4
The wording of this standard can be found on page 100.

What Students Should Understand
- Arrays are groups of objects that are shown in rows and columns of the same length.
- You can describe an array by using a repeated addition number sentence.
- The number of objects in each row is the number that will be added repeatedly. The number of rows tells you how many times to add the number.

What Students Should be Able to Do
Describe the array by using a number sentence.

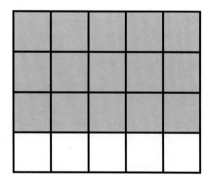

$5 + 5 + 5 = 15$

 Building on the Essential Question

In this lesson, students will build upon the skills and concepts needed to answer the chapter's Essential Question "How can equal groups help me add?"

Developing Vocabulary

New Vocabulary
array

Activity
- Have students look at the array on the first page of the lesson. Explain that each set of boxes in a straight line across is called a *row*. Then explain that each set of boxes in a straight line up and down is called a *column*.
- Explain that an array can be used to display objects in rows and columns. Arrays will help them to show repeated addition.

ELL **ELL Support Strategy** Use this vocabulary activity to visualize what is being taught.

My Vocabulary Cards
Have students work in pairs to use the My Vocabulary Cards for this chapter to show 2, 4, and 5 equal groups.

IWB **Virtual Word Wall**

Add this vocabulary card to the Virtual Word Wall for the chapter.

ELL Refer to the Multilingual eGlossary for interactive definitions in 13 languages.

Plan Online

Plan for your lesson by using the resources at

 connectED.mcgraw-hill.com

Digital Dashboard

Interactive Whiteboard Ready

 Vocab

The eBook **Glossary** shows the definition of the word and has audio for each definition. The **eGlossary** provides definitions in 13 languages.

 Watch

Watch as concepts are brought to life through **animations**, **songs**, and a variety of visual instruction.

 Tools

Virtual Manipulatives with work mats allow teachers and students to model the lesson.

Check

Use **eAssessment** for online assignments and customized assessments.

Use the **Common Core Quick Check** before the lesson to assess students' retention of previously learned concepts.

Use the interactive **Self-Check Quiz** after the lesson to provide immediate feedback on lesson concepts.

eHelp

Digital and print resources assist students and parents in completing My Homework.

Games

Online games and **apps** provide extra practice for lesson concepts.

PD

Professional development videos help teachers gain a deeper understanding of the lesson concepts and strategies.

RtI

Support for **approaching**, **on**- and **beyond-level** students as well as **English Language Learners**.

Masters

Reteach and **Enrich** worksheets, **Manipulative Masters**, the **Problem of the Day**, and other blackline masters are available for each lesson.

---

1 LAUNCH THE LESSON

CCSS

⏱ **If your students are well-versed in repeated addition with equal addends, skip to Step 2, TEACH.**

You will need

☐ counters

Mathematical PRACTICE 4 Modeling the Math

Give each student 20 counters.

Make 4 groups with 3 counters in each group.

Students count by 3s. *How many altogether?* 12

What addition number sentence can you write to show this? $3 + 3 + 3 + 3 = 12$

Explain that this is repeated addition because the number of counters in each group is the same, and we add to find how many altogether.

What do you notice about the number sentence? Sample answer: There are four 3s. *What do we call the addends when all the addends are the same?* equal addends

---

TEACH

🕐 **Begin core instruction here.**

You will need
☐ connecting cubes
☐ crayons or markers

Explore and Explain

Read the directions that are on the bottom of the student page.

How many people collected rocks? Explain. 4 people; Sample answer: Jamar is one of the people and his 3 friends are the other people.

Guide students in placing 4 rows of cube trains in the grid to represent the number of rocks collected by each person. Each cube train should have 2 cubes in it. Then have students color in the grid representing the cube train.

I can use repeated addition to find the total number of rocks Jamar and his friends have in all. What number sentence would I use to find the total number of rocks?
2 + 2 + 2 + 2 = ___

How many rocks do Jamar and his friends have in all?
8 rocks

The connecting cubes that we used to represent the number of rocks collected by each person were placed in an array. An array is a group of objects that are placed in rows and columns of equal length. You can use a repeated addition number sentence to describe the objects in an array.

See and Show

Help students work through the example at the top of the page.

Let's think about things we might see in our everyday life that would be in an array. What are some examples?
Sample answers: eggs in a carton, desks in a classroom, days on a calendar, etc.

We can also draw these displays on paper in a chart called an array. Look at the array on the student page. How many rows did you color? 3 *How many squares are colored in each row?* 4

Have them trace the dashed numbers as they work the problems. You can also have them outline or color over the shaded part of the array.

Work through Exercises 1 through 3 as a class.

Mathematical PRACTICE ➌ **Talk Math**

Discuss with students "How can arrays help you add?"
Sample answer: Arrays can help organize objects into groups, so it is easier to add the groups together.

🕐 **CORE INSTRUCTION**

Name _____

Operations and Algebraic Thinking
2.OA.4

Repeated Addition with Arrays

Lesson 5
ESSENTIAL QUESTION
How can equal groups help me add?

👐 **Explore and Explain** 🧰 Tools

We love collecting rocks!

Jamar

Meko

Kyle

That's easy for her to say. Her rock is the smallest!

Laurel

See students' work

__2__ + __2__ + __2__ + __2__ = __8__ rocks

🦉 **Teacher Directions:** Jamar and 3 of his friends each collect 2 rocks. How many rocks do they have in all? Use connecting cubes to show equal groups of rocks. Color in the grid to show your work. Write a number sentence to show the total.

Online Content at 🖥 connectED.mcgraw-hill.com   Chapter 2 • Lesson 5   133

See and Show   Mathematical **PRACTICE**

In an **array**, objects are shown in rows and columns.

3 rows of 4   3 rows of 4

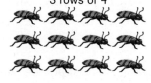

__4__ + __4__ + __4__ = __12__

Describe each array using a number sentence.

1.

__3__ + __3__ + __3__ = __9__
__3__ rows of __3__ turtles

2.

__4__ + __4__ = __8__
__2__ rows of __4__ cacti

3. Shade the grid to show 4 rows of 2.
Write a number sentence to describe it.

__2 + 2 + 2 + 2 = 8__

Talk Math   How can arrays help you add?

134   Chapter 2 • Lesson 5

Name _____

We're 1 group of 3!

On My Own

Describe the array using a number sentence.

4.

$$\underline{5} + \underline{5} + \underline{5} = 15 \qquad \underline{3} \text{ rows of } \underline{5} \text{ lizards}$$

Shade each grid to show the array.
Write a number sentence to describe it.

5. Show 4 rows of 3.

$$3 + 3 + 3 + 3 = 12$$

6. Show 4 rows of 1.

$$1 + 1 + 1 + 1 = 4$$

7. Show 2 rows of 5.

$$5 + 5 = 10$$

8. Show 3 rows of 4.

$$4 + 4 + 4 = 12$$

Chapter 2 • Lesson 5   135

Problem Solving

Mathematical
PRACTICE

Use an array to solve.

9. Kathy puts 5 chairs in one row. She puts the same number of chairs in three more rows. How many chairs are there in all?

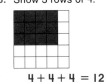

20 chairs

I call dibs on this one.

10. Three hills each have 4 wind turbines. How many wind turbines are there in all?

12 wind turbines

Write Math Describe how this array shows the number sentence 2 + 2 + 2 = 6.

Sample answer: There are 3 rows. Each row has

2 boxes shaded so I add 3 groups of 2 to get 6

136   Chapter 2 • Lesson 5

PRACTICE & APPLY

CCSS

On My Own

Have students work through the exercises on this page independently. You may choose to assign exercises based on the chart below.

DIFFERENTIATED ASSIGNMENTS

AL **Approaching Level** Guide students through the exercises in On My Own. Help them to use manipulatives.

OL **On Level** Complete the exercises independently.

BL **Beyond Level** Complete the exercises independently without manipulatives.

Problem Solving

Have students work through the problem-solving exercises on this page independently.

Mathematical
PRACTICE ➎   In Exercise 10, students **use appropriate tools strategically.**

Write Math

This exercise asks students to build upon their understanding of concepts needed to answer the chapter's Essential Question.

AL **APPROACHING LEVEL**

IF my students struggle with using repeated addition with arrays,

THEN choose a resource:

→ Use the Reteach worksheet with small groups.

→ Go online for a Differentiated Instruction activity.

OL **ON LEVEL**

IF my students seem to know how to use repeated addition with arrays, but need more practice,

THEN choose a resource:

→ Assign My Homework.

→ Go online for a Differentiated Instruction activity.

BL **BEYOND LEVEL**

IF my students have mastered using repeated addition with arrays,

THEN choose a resource:

→ Use the Enrich worksheet in cooperative groups.

→ Assign My Homework.

→ Go online for a Differentiated Instruction activity.

AL Name _____

Lesson 5   Reteach

Repeated Addition with Arrays

Arrays show rows and columns of objects. This array shows equal rows of squares.

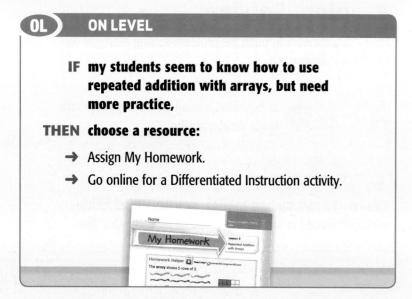

How many rows of 4 squares make this array? __3__ rows

What is the total number of squares? __12__ squares

So, 3 rows of 4 squares equal __12__ squares.

Match each statement to the correct array.

1. 3 rows of 2

2. 2 rows of 6

3. 4 rows of 5

BL Name _____

Lesson 5   Enrich

Repeated Addition with Arrays

An array shows groups of objects in rows and columns. This array shows equal rows of squares in rows.

Use the array to complete this statement:

__3__ rows of __4__ squares equal __12__ squares.

Draw an array of squares to model each statement. Then find the total.

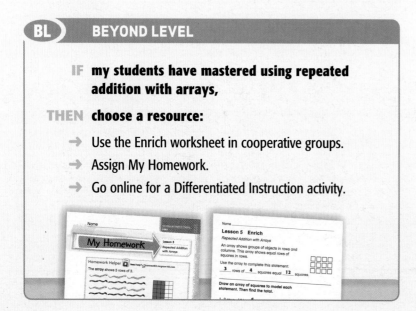

1. 3 rows of 2 is __6__.

2. 2 rows of 4 is __8__.

3. 4 rows of 7 is __28__.

4. 5 rows of 2 is __10__.

My Homework →

Lesson 5
Repeated Addition with Arrays

Homework Helper Need help? ✍ connectED.mcgraw-hill.com

The **array** shows 5 rows of 3.

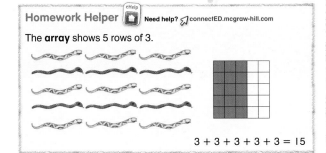

$3 + 3 + 3 + 3 + 3 = 15$

Practice

Describe each array using a number sentence.

1.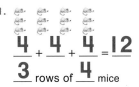

$\underline{4} + \underline{4} + \underline{4} = \underline{12}$

$\underline{3}$ rows of $\underline{4}$ mice

2.

$\underline{5} + \underline{5} = \underline{10}$

$\underline{2}$ rows of $\underline{5}$ owls

3. Show 3 rows of 5.

$5 + 5 + 5 = 15$

4. Show 3 rows of 2.

$2 + 2 + 2 = 6$

Chapter 2 • Lesson 5   137

Describe each array using a number sentence.

5. Show 3 rows of 5.

Hoorah for arrays!

$5 + 5 + 5 = 15$

6. Show 4 rows of 2.

$2 + 2 + 2 + 2 = 8$

7. Show 2 rows of 4.

$4 + 4 = 8$

8. There are 4 legs on 1 camel. How many legs are on 5 camels?

20 legs in all

Vocabulary Check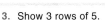

9. Draw an **array** of 2 rows of 3.

See students' work.

---

4 WRAP IT UP

CCSS

My Homework

Assign homework after successful completion of the lesson. Students who understand the concepts may skip the **Homework Helper** section.

Vocabulary Check

Have students refer to their My Vocabulary Cards for additional support.

Formative Assessment

Display counters in 3 groups of 5 counters each. Have students draw an array to represent the equal groups. Have students describe their array with an addition sentence. See students' arrays; $5 + 5 + 5 = 15$

MY Learning Stations

Use the real-world problem-solving reader **Geese on the Go** after this lesson. The Teacher Guide provides suggestions for differentiated instruction.

LESSON 6
Even and Odd Numbers

OBJECTIVE   Find even and odd numbers in number patterns.

What's the Math?

 Common Core State Standards
DOMAIN: Operations and Algebraic Thinking

Standard: 2.OA.3
The wording of this standard can be found on page 100.

What Students Should Understand
- Even numbers can be counted by 2s, broken into pairs, or divided into equal groups.
- Odd numbers have 1 left over when grouped by 2s, broken into pairs, or divided into equal groups.
- You can use connecting cubes to determine if a number is even or odd.
- First, use connecting cubes to show the number. Then place the connecting cubes in groups of 2. If there are no cubes left over, the number is even. If there is 1 cube left over, the number is odd.

What Students Should be Able to Do
Use connecting cubes to show 7. Circle *even* or *odd*.

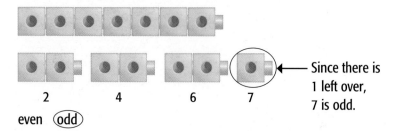

Since there is 1 left over, 7 is odd.

Building on the Essential Question
In this lesson, students will build upon the skills and concepts needed to answer the chapter's Essential Question "How can equal groups help me add?"

Developing Vocabulary

 New Vocabulary
even   odd

Activity
- Write the words on the board. Ask students what they know about each word. For example, they might know that *odd* can mean "unusual."
- Display a number line. Discuss with students that even numbers allow for counting by 2s.
- Have a volunteer place 12 counters on the displayed number line. Ask students how to tell whether 12 is an even or an odd number. even; I counted by 2s to 12, and there were no counters left over.

ELL ELL Support Strategy Use this vocabulary activity to visualize what is being taught.

My Vocabulary Cards
Discuss with students how the visuals on the *even* and *odd* cards show each word's definition.

IWB Virtual Word Wall
Add these vocabulary cards to the Virtual Word Wall for the chapter.

ELL Refer to the Multilingual eGlossary for interactive definitions in 13 languages.

Plan Online

Plan for your lesson by using the resources at
connectED.mcgraw-hill.com

Digital Dashboard

Interactive Whiteboard Ready

Vocab

The eBook **Glossary** shows the definition of the word and has audio for each definition. The **eGlossary** provides definitions in 13 languages.

Watch

Watch as concepts are brought to life through **animations**, **songs**, and a variety of visual instruction.

Tools

Virtual Manipulatives with work mats allow teachers and students to model the lesson.

Check

Use **eAssessment** for online assignments and customized assessments.

Use the **Common Core Quick Check** before the lesson to assess students' retention of previously learned concepts.

Use the interactive **Self-Check Quiz** after the lesson to provide immediate feedback on lesson concepts.

eHelp

Digital and print resources assist students and parents in completing My Homework.

Games

Online games and **apps** provide extra practice for lesson concepts.

PD

Professional development videos help teachers gain a deeper understanding of the lesson concepts and strategies.

RtI

Support for **approaching**, **on-** and **beyond-level** students as well as **English Language Learners**.

Masters

Reteach and **Enrich** worksheets, **Manipulative Masters**, the **Problem of the Day**, and other blackline masters are available for each lesson.

Online Content at connectED.mcgraw-hill.com

---

1 LAUNCH THE LESSON

 If your students are well-versed in even and odd numbers, you may choose to begin instruction with Step 2, **TEACH**.

You will need

☐ counters

Mathematical PRACTICE 4 Modeling the Math

Give each student a handful of counters. Have students count the counters by 2s.

Could you count all the counters by 2s or did you have a counter left over? See students' responses.

Draw two columns on the board; label one **even** and one **odd.**

Tell me how many counters you have and if I should put that number on the even or odd side of our chart.

List the number of counters each student has in the appropriate column. Sample answers:

even	odd
12	9
10	11
14	9
14	
10	

Does anyone see a pattern in the even column?
Even numbers end with 0, 2, 4, 6, or 8.
Do you see a pattern in the odd column?
Odd numbers end with 1, 3, 5, 7, or 9.

🕐 **Begin core instruction here.**

You will need
☐ connecting cubes
☐ number cubes

Explore and Explain

Read the directions that are on the bottom of the student page. Lead students through the example. When students are expected to break the cube train into two equal groups,

What does "break the train into two equal groups" mean? break the train into two groups that have equal numbers

Help them understand how to break the train into two equal groups by taking two cubes from the top lasso and placing one cube in each of the bottom lassos. Have them repeat this until all the cubes are distributed. They may or may not have a cube left over.

This activity will help us decide if numbers are even or odd. The number you rolled is even if there are no extra cubes in that top lasso. Raise your hand if you rolled an even number.

Invite students to share with the class which even numbers they rolled. Sample answers: 2, 4, 6

The number you rolled is odd if there is an extra cube in your top lasso. It is moved to the red cube at the bottom. Raise your hand if you rolled an odd number.

Invite students to share with the class which odd numbers they rolled. Sample answers: 1, 3, 5

See and Show

Help students work through the example at the top of the page. Demonstrate the 4-cube train and then the 5-cube train.

What is the difference between the 4-cube train and the 5-cube train? Sample answer: The 5 cube train has one left over. *What does that tell us?* It is an odd number.

Work through Exercises 1 through 6 as a class.

Mathematical PRACTICE ❸ Talk Math

Discuss with students "When might you use even and odd numbers?" Sample answer: When I need to divide something between two people.

🕐 **CORE INSTRUCTION**

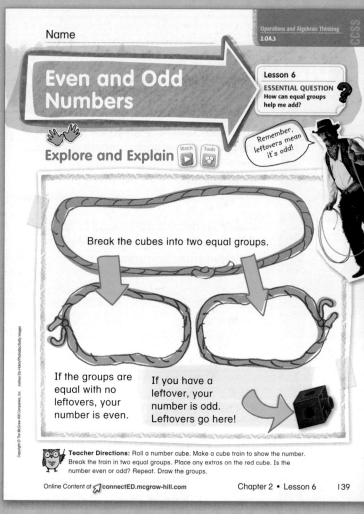

Name _____

Operations and Algebraic Thinking
2.OA.3

Even and Odd Numbers

Lesson 6
ESSENTIAL QUESTION
How can equal groups help me add?

Remember, leftovers mean it's odd!

Explore and Explain 🖥️ 🔧

Break the cubes into two equal groups.

If the groups are equal with no leftovers, your number is even.

If you have a leftover, your number is odd. Leftovers go here!

Teacher Directions: Roll a number cube. Make a cube train to show the number. Break the train in two equal groups. Place any extras on the red cube. Is the number even or odd? Repeat. Draw the groups.

Online Content at connectED.mcgraw-hill.com   Chapter 2 • Lesson 6   139

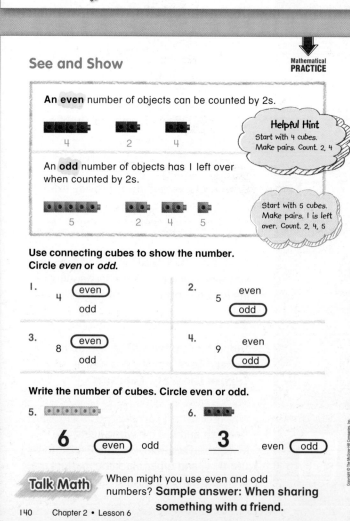

See and Show

An **even** number of objects can be counted by 2s.

4   2   4

Helpful Hint
Start with 4 cubes. Make pairs. Count. 2, 4

An **odd** number of objects has 1 left over when counted by 2s.

5   2   4   5

Start with 5 cubes. Make pairs. 1 is left over. Count. 2, 4, 5

Use connecting cubes to show the number. Circle *even* or *odd*.

1. 4 (even) / odd
2. 5 even / (odd)
3. 8 (even) / odd
4. 9 even / (odd)

Write the number of cubes. Circle even or odd.

5. **6** (even) odd
6. **3** even (odd)

Talk Math When might you use even and odd numbers? **Sample answer: When sharing something with a friend.**

140   Chapter 2 • Lesson 6

CORE INSTRUCTION

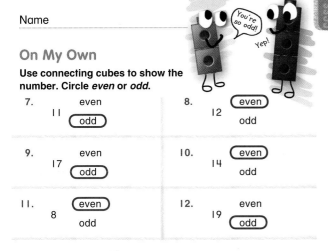

Name _____

On My Own

Use connecting cubes to show the number. Circle even or odd.

7. 11   even
        (odd)

8. 12   (even)
        odd

9. 17   even
        (odd)

10. 14   (even)
        odd

11. 8   (even)
        odd

12. 19   even
        (odd)

Write the number of cubes. Circle even or odd.

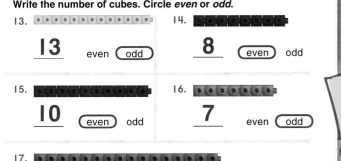

13. **13**   even (odd)

14. **8**   (even) odd

15. **10**   (even) odd

16. **7**   even (odd)

17. **16**   (even) odd

Chapter 2 • Lesson 6   141

Problem Solving

Mathematical PRACTICE

18. Ben has 16 pennies. Does he have an even or odd number of pennies?

    _____even_____

19. Mr. Rice thinks of a number between 14 and 17. The number is even. What is the number?

    16

20. Miss Lee has 18 plants. She wants to split them between two friends. How many plants will she give each friend?

    9 plants

Write Math   Explain how you know 15 is an odd number.

Sample answer: If you break 15 into pairs you will

have have 7 pairs and one extra. This means it is

an odd number.

142   Chapter 2 • Lesson 6

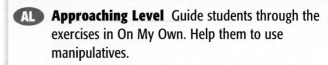

PRACTICE & APPLY

On My Own

Have students work through the exercises on this page independently. You may choose to assign exercises based on the chart below.

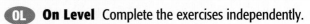

DIFFERENTIATED ASSIGNMENTS
AL **Approaching Level** Guide students through the exercises in On My Own. Help them to use manipulatives.
OL **On Level** Complete the exercises independently.
BL **Beyond Level** Complete the exercises independently without manipulatives.

Common Error!

Students may make an error while counting pairs, which will cause them to incorrectly identify a number as even or odd. Have students use manipulatives and push each pair away from the others so they can clearly see whether or not they have paired all the cubes.

Problem Solving

Have students work through the problem-solving exercises on this page independently.

Mathematical PRACTICE 2   In Exercise 20, students **reason abstractly and quantitatively.**

Write Math

This exercise asks students to build upon their understanding of concepts needed to answer the chapter's Essential Question.

RESPONSE TO INTERVENTION

DIFFERENTIATED INSTRUCTION

AL **APPROACHING LEVEL**

IF **my students struggle with even and odd numbers,**

THEN **choose a resource:**

→ Use the Reteach worksheet with small groups.

→ Go online for a Differentiated Instruction activity.

→ **Equal Groups** Give students connecting cubes. Have them work together to build a number and then break it apart to see if they can make equal groups. Ask students to record if the number is even or odd.

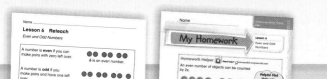

OL **ON LEVEL**

IF **my students seem to know even and odd numbers, but need more practice,**

THEN **choose a resource:**

→ Use the Differentiated Instruction activity from p. 99B.

→ Assign My Homework.

→ Go online for a Differentiated Instruction activity.

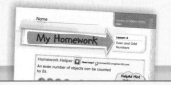

BL **BEYOND LEVEL**

IF **my students have mastered even and odd numbers,**

THEN **choose a resource:**

→ Use the Enrich worksheet in cooperative groups.

→ Assign My Homework.

→ Go online for a Differentiated Instruction activity.

AL

Name _____

Lesson 6   Reteach

Even and Odd Numbers

A number is **even** if you can make pairs with zero left over.

6 is an even number.

A number is **odd** if you make pairs and have one left over.

7 is an odd number.

1	2	3	4	5	6	7	8	9	10
odd	even	odd	even	odd	even	odd	even	odd	even

Look at the numbers. Write them in the table under the correct heading.

4, 7, 9, 15, 18, 22, 25, 26, 31, 34

Even	Odd
4	7
18	9
22	15
26	25
34	31

BL

Name _____

Lesson 6   Enrich

Even and Odd Numbers

Read the clues to find the mystery numbers. Use the chart to help.

1	2	3	4	5	6	7	8	9	10
11	12	13	14	15	16	17	18	19	20
21	22	23	24	25	26	27	28	29	30
31	32	33	34	35	36	37	38	39	40
41	42	43	44	45	46	47	48	49	50

1. Start at 15. Count back 2. Is the number *even* or *odd*? **odd**

   What is the number? **13**

2. Count forward 20 from your answer for Exercise 1. Then count forward 2. Is the number *even* or *odd*? **odd**

   What is the number? **35**

3. Count forward 3. Then count back 10. Is the number *even* or *odd*? **even**

   What is the number? **28**

4. Count back 5. Then count forward 20. Is the number *even* or *odd*? **odd**

   What is the mystery number? **43**

5. Look back at your answers. Which answer is the only even number? **28**

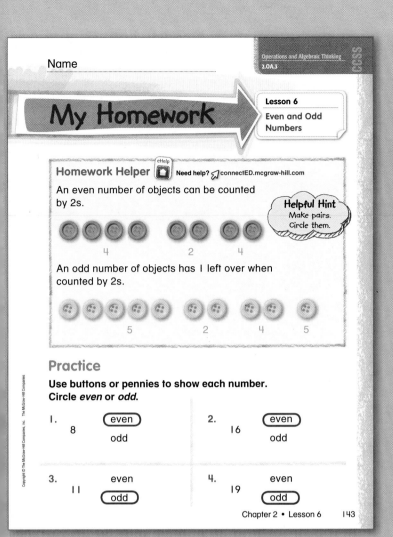

Name _____

Operations and Algebraic Thinking
2.0A.3

CCSS

My Homework

Lesson 6
Even and Odd Numbers

Homework Helper
eHelp
Need help? ⌁ connectED.mcgraw-hill.com

An even number of objects can be counted by 2s.

Helpful Hint
Make pairs.
Circle them.

4   2   4

An odd number of objects has 1 left over when counted by 2s.

5   2   4   5

Practice

Use buttons or pennies to show each number.
Circle *even* or *odd*.

1. 8   (even)
         odd

2. 16   (even)
         odd

3. 11   even
         (odd)

4. 19   even
         (odd)

Chapter 2 • Lesson 6   143

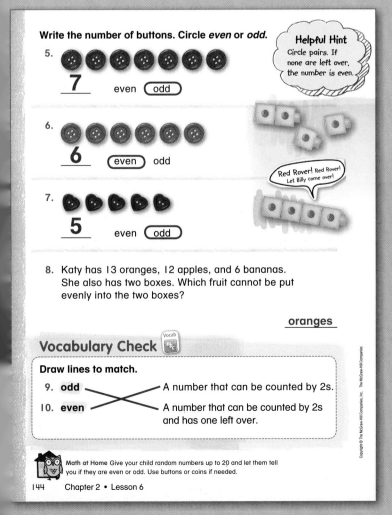

Write the number of buttons. Circle *even* or *odd*.

Helpful Hint
Circle pairs. If none are left over, the number is even.

5. **7**   even (odd)

6. **6**   (even) odd

Red Rover! Red Rover!
Let Billy come over!

7. **5**   even (odd)

8. Katy has 13 oranges, 12 apples, and 6 bananas. She also has two boxes. Which fruit cannot be put evenly into the two boxes?

oranges

Vocabulary Check [Vocab]

Draw lines to match.

9. **odd** ⎯⎯⎯ A number that can be counted by 2s.

10. **even** ⎯⎯⎯ A number that can be counted by 2s and has one left over.

Math at Home Give your child random numbers up to 20 and let them tell you if they are even or odd. Use buttons or coins if needed.

144   Chapter 2 • Lesson 6

My Homework

Assign homework after successful completion of the lesson. Students who understand the concepts may skip the **Homework Helper** section.

Vocabulary Check

Have students refer to the examples at the beginning of the lesson for additional support.

Formative Assessment

Ask the students the following question.

Is 18 an even or odd number? Explain. Sample answer: even; you can count by 2s to 18 or you can break apart an 18-cube train into pairs of cubes with none left over.

MY Learning Stations

Use the activity card **High-Frequency Words** after this lesson. The Teacher Guide provides suggestions for differentiated instruction.

LESSON 7
Sums of Equal Numbers

OBJECTIVE Find sums of equal numbers.

What's the Math?

 Common Core State Standards
DOMAIN: Operations and Algebraic Thinking

Standard: 2.OA.3
The wording of this standard can be found on page 100.

What Students Should Understand

• Any even number can be written as the sum of two equal addends.

• You can use connecting cubes to determine the two equal addends that make a sum.

• First, create a train of connecting cubes to model the sum. Then break the train into two equal groups. These two equal groups represent the two equal addends.

What Students Should be Able to Do

Write the equal addends that make 10.

First: Create a train of connecting cubes to model 10.

Next: Break the train into two equal groups.

Last: Count the number of connecting cubes in each group. These are the equal addends.

$$10 = 5 + 5$$

? Building on the Essential Question

In this lesson, students will build upon the skills and concepts needed to answer the chapter's Essential Question "How can equal groups help me add?"

Developing Vocabulary

Review Vocabulary

addend   sum

Review Activity

• Write each word on the board. Ask students what they know about each word from a previous chapter or grade. For example, they might recall that addends are the numbers added together in an addition sentence.

• Write $6 + 2 = 8$ on the board. Have a volunteer label the addends and the sum.

• Ask volunteers to write addition sentences on the board. Then have students label the addends and sums in each sentence.

ELL ELL Support Strategy Use this vocabulary activity to assess students' ability to extend their understanding.

My Vocabulary Cards

Have students look at the cards for this chapter. Read each word aloud. Survey the class. Ask them to show thumbs-up if they understand, or thumbs-down if they do not understand the word. If they show thumbs-down, review the word.

IWB Virtual Word Wall

You may wish to add these review words to the virtual word wall for the chapter.

Plan Online

Plan for your lesson by using the resources at
connectED.mcgraw-hill.com

Digital Dashboard

Interactive Whiteboard Ready

Vocab
abc

The eBook **Glossary** shows the definition of the word and has audio for each definition. The **eGlossary** provides definitions in 13 languages.

Watch

Watch as concepts are brought to life through **animations**, **songs**, and a variety of visual instruction.

Tools

Virtual Manipulatives with work mats allow teachers and students to model the lesson.

Check

Use **eAssessment** for online assignments and customized assessments.

Use the **Common Core Quick Check** before the lesson to assess students' retention of previously learned concepts.

Use the interactive **Self-Check Quiz** after the lesson to provide immediate feedback on lesson concepts.

eHelp

Digital and print resources assist students and parents in completing My Homework.

Games

Online games and **apps** provide extra practice for lesson concepts.

PD

Professional development videos help teachers gain a deeper understanding of the lesson concepts and strategies.

RtI

Support for **approaching**, **on-** and **beyond-level** students as well as **English Language Learners**.

Masters

Reteach and **Enrich** worksheets, **Manipulative Masters**, the **Problem of the Day**, and other blackline masters are available for each lesson.

1 LAUNCH THE LESSON

CCSS

 If your students are well-versed in sums of equal numbers, you may choose to begin instruction with Step 2, **TEACH**.

Mathematical PRACTICE 4 Modeling the Math

Call two students up to the front. Ask the first student to raise 1 finger. Ask the other student to raise 1 finger.

How many fingers did each student raise? 1 *How many fingers are raised altogether?* 2

Point out that this situation can be represented by an addition sentence. The addends are each 1. The addends are equal. The sum is 2.

Ask each student to now hold up two fingers.

How many fingers did each student raise? 2

How many fingers are raised altogether? 4

Point out that this situation can be represented by an addition sentence.

What are the addends? 2 + 2 *What is the sum?* 4

Have students repeat the activity using 3 fingers, 4 fingers, and so on, until each student has held up 10 fingers.

Have students record the equal addends and sums in a table like the one below.

Even Number		Addend		Addend
2	=	1	+	1
4	=	2	+	2
6	=	3	+	3
8	=	4	+	4
10	=	5	+	5
12	=	6	+	6
14	=	7	+	7
16	=	8	+	8
18	=	9	+	9
20	=	10	+	10

 Begin core instruction here.

You will need

☐ connecting cubes

Explore and Explain

Read the directions that are on the bottom of the student page. Guide students through the activity.

Show students that you can make sure the cube train has been broken into two equal groups by placing one group of cube trains on top of the other group of cube trains. Then compare the lengths. The lengths should be the same.

How many cubes are in each equal group? 3

To complete the addition number sentence, you need to decide which number is the sum and which numbers are the addends.

Which number is the sum? 6 *How was it represented by the connecting cubes?* It was represented by the train of 6 connecting cubes.

What are the addends? 3 *How were they represented by the connecting cubes?* They were represented by the two equal groups of 3 connecting cubes after the train of 6 connecting cubes was broken apart.

Is 6 an even or odd number? even *How do you know?* Sample answer: The train of 6 connecting cubes can be broken into pairs with no extra cubes left over.

Tell students that when the addends are the same number, the sum will always be an even number. Have them break other even numbers of cube trains into two equal groups and find the addends. Ask students to share their results with the class. This will allow students to better understand this concept.

See and Show

Help students work through the example at the top of the page. Practice with other even numbers.

Have them trace the dashed numbers as they write the equal addends.

Work through Exercises 1 through 8 as a class.

Mathematical PRACTICE 3 ▶ **Talk Math**

Discuss with students "How did you find the equal addends that make each sum?" Sample answer: The equal addends are the same number. I can make a cube train to represent the sum. Then I can break apart the cubes into equal groups. The number of cubes in each group represent the equal addends.

Name _____

Operations and Algebraic Thinking
2.OA.3

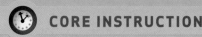

Sums of Equal Numbers

Lesson 7
ESSENTIAL QUESTION
How can equal groups help me add?

Explore and Explain

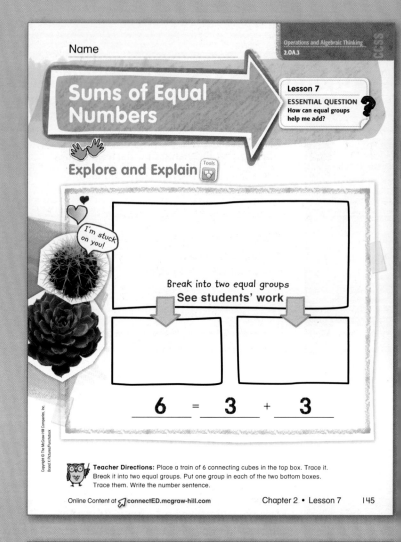

Break into two equal groups
See students' work

___6___ = ___3___ + ___3___

Teacher Directions: Place a train of 6 connecting cubes in the top box. Trace it. Break it into two equal groups. Put one group in each of the two bottom boxes. Trace them. Write the number sentence.

Online Content at connectED.mcgraw-hill.com   Chapter 2 • Lesson 7   145

See and Show

Mathematical PRACTICE

Any even number can be written as the sum of two equal addends.

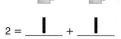

$8 = \underline{4} + \underline{4}$ $2 = \underline{1} + \underline{1}$

Write the equal addends that make each sum.

1. $6 = \underline{3} + \underline{3}$ 2. $4 = \underline{2} + \underline{2}$

3. $\underline{1} + \underline{1} = 2$ 4. $8 = \underline{4} + \underline{4}$

5. $14 = \underline{7} + \underline{7}$ 6. $\underline{9} + \underline{9} = 18$

Find the missing number.

7. $\underline{4} + 4 = 8$ 8. $9 + \underline{9} = 18$

Talk Math How did you find the equal addends that make each sum?

146   Chapter 2 • Lesson 7

CORE INSTRUCTION

Name _____

On My Own

Write the equal addends that make each sum.

9. $2 = \underline{1} + \underline{1}$
10. $12 = \underline{6} + \underline{6}$
11. $10 = \underline{5} + \underline{5}$
12. $14 = \underline{7} + \underline{7}$
13. $18 = \underline{9} + \underline{9}$
14. $8 = \underline{4} + \underline{4}$
15. $\underline{3} + \underline{3} = 6$
16. $\underline{2} + \underline{2} = 4$
17. $\underline{10} + \underline{10} = 20$
18. $\underline{8} + \underline{8} = 16$

Find the missing addends.

19. $10 + \underline{10} = 20$
20. $\underline{6} + 6 = 12$
21. $4 + \underline{4} = 8$
22. $\underline{3} + 3 = 6$
23. $\underline{7} + 7 = 14$

I may live in the desert, but I'm a cool cat!

Problem Solving

24. Henry buys 6 apples. His mother buys the same amount. Write the number sentence. How many do they have in all?

$$\underline{6} + \underline{6} = \underline{12}$$

25. Luke has 10 puppies. An equal number of them are black and brown puppies. How many are brown?

$\underline{5}$ brown puppies

26. Janelle brought 7 magazines. The class now has 14 magazines. How many magazines did they already have?

$\underline{7}$ magazines

Write Math Tamika and Jen have the same number of beads. They have 18 beads in all. How many beads does each girl have? Explain.

Sample answer: They each have 9 because they have an equal amount and 9 + 9 = 18.

_____

---

3 PRACTICE & APPLY

CCSS

On My Own

Have students work through the exercises on this page independently. You may choose to assign exercises based on the chart below.

DIFFERENTIATED ASSIGNMENTS

AL	**Approaching Level** Guide students through the exercises in On My Own. Help them to use manipulatives.
OL	**On Level** Complete the exercises independently.
BL	**Beyond Level** Complete the exercises independently without manipulatives.

Problem Solving

Have students work through the problem-solving exercises on this page independently.

Mathematical PRACTICE 1 In Exercise 25, students **make sense of problems and persevere in solving them.**

Write Math

This exercise asks students to build upon their understanding of concepts needed to answer the chapter's Essential Question.

AL | **APPROACHING LEVEL**

IF my students struggle with sums of equal numbers,

THEN choose a resource:

→ Use the Reteach worksheet with small groups.

→ Go online for a Differentiated Instruction activity.

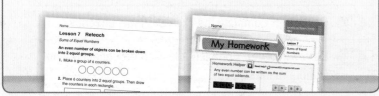

OL | **ON LEVEL**

IF my students seem to know sums of equal numbers, but need more practice,

THEN choose a resource:

→ Assign My Homework.

→ Go online for a Differentiated Instruction activity.

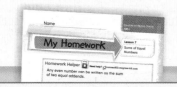

BL | **BEYOND LEVEL**

IF my students have mastered sums of equal numbers,

THEN choose a resource:

→ Use the Enrich worksheet in cooperative groups.

→ Assign My Homework.

→ Go online for a Differentiated Instruction activity.

AL Name _____

Lesson 7 Reteach

Sums of Equal Numbers

An even number of objects can be broken down into 2 equal groups.

1. Make a group of 6 counters.

2. Place 6 counters into 2 equal groups. Then draw the counters in each rectangle.

3. Write the addition number sentence you just modeled.

___**3**___ + ___**3**___ = ___**6**___ counters

1. Make a group of 10 counters.

2. Place 10 counters into 2 equal groups. Then draw the counters in each rectangle.

3. Write the addition number sentence you just modeled.

___**5**___ + ___**5**___ = ___**10**___ counters

BL Name _____

Lesson 7 Enrich

Sums of Equal Numbers

Even numbers can be broken down into two parts that are each the same number.

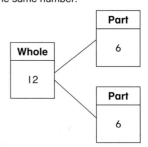

Choose an even number and use it to complete the Part-Part-Whole chart. Then write the addition sentence. **1–2. See students' work.**

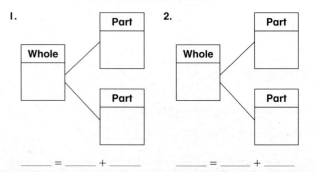

____ = ____ + ____   ____ = ____ + ____

Name _____

Operations and Algebraic Thinking
2.OA.3

My Homework

Lesson 7
Sums of Equal Numbers

Homework Helper
Need help? connectED.mcgraw-hill.com

Any even number can be written as the sum of two equal addends.

6 = 3 + 3   4 = 2 + 2

Practice

Write the equal addends that make each sum.

1. 10 = __5__ + __5__   2. 2 = __1__ + __1__

3. 18 = __9__ + __9__   4. 8 = __4__ + __4__

Find the missing number.

5. 7 + __7__ = 14   6. __3__ + 3 = 6

7. 8 + __8__ = 16   8. __6__ + 6 = 12

Chapter 2 • Lesson 7   149

Find the missing addends.

9. 5 + __5__ = 10   10. __2__ + 2 = 4

11. Maria and Steve each have 8 toys for the toy drive. How many toys do they have in all?

__16__ toys

I couldn't eat another thing. I'm stuffed!

12. Mrs. Miller's class has 18 students. There are an equal number of boys and girls in the class. Write a number sentence to show how many boys and how many girls are in the class.

__18__ = __9__ + __9__

Test Practice

13. Kylie buys 7 bananas. Her mom also buys 7 bananas. How many bananas do they buy in all?

0   7   10   14
○   ○   ○   ●

Math at Home Work with your child to create a number line from 1 to 20. Have them circle the even numbers on the number line. Ask your child to describe a pattern they see.

150   Chapter 2 • Lesson 7

CCSS

4 WRAP IT UP

My Homework

Assign homework after successful completion of the lesson. Students who understand the concepts may skip the **Homework Helper** section.

Test Practice

Diagnose Student Errors

Class trends in wrong answer may indicate common errors or misconceptions.

0 subtracted 7 from 7

7 the number of bananas one person bought

10 added incorrectly

14 correct

Formative Assessment

Keith had 12 shirts. Some are red and an equal number of them are green. How many are red? 6

21ST CENTURY SKILLS

Critical Thinking

The concept of repeated addition is the first step in building the foundation for multiplication and division. Encourage students to use terminology, such as "the sum of three 2s" to lay the groundwork for 3×2.

Online Content at connectED.mcgraw-hill.com

Lesson 7 Sums of Equal Numbers   **149-150**

Fluency Practice

Mathematical **PRACTICE** ⑥ These two pages encourage students to become proficient in their calculation abilities. You can use these as a timed or untimed exercise.

Page 151 Students practice addition of whole numbers.

Page 152 Students practice subtraction of whole numbers.

Teaching Tip One approach to build student confidence is to use these pages repeatedly. Strive for students to complete a portion of each page correctly in an untimed situation. Then use the rest of the page as a timed test.

Name _____   Mathematical **PRACTICE**

Fluency Practice

Add.

1. $2 + 8 =$ **10**	2. $8 + 4 =$ **12**
3. $3 + 6 =$ **9**	4. $5 + 5 =$ **10**
5. $6 + 5 =$ **11**	6. $6 + 4 =$ **10**
7. $6 + 6 =$ **12**	8. $7 + 7 =$ **14**
9. $7 + 6 =$ **13**	10. $4 + 2 =$ **6**
11. $4 + 7 =$ **11**	12. $5 + 8 =$ **13**
13. $8 + 9 =$ **17**	14. $5 + 7 =$ **12**
15. $8 + 8 =$ **16**	16. $2 + 4 =$ **6**
17. $2 + 3 =$ **5**	18. $3 + 4 =$ **7**
19. $5 + 8 =$ **13**	20. $8 + 9 =$ **17**
21. $3 + 5 =$ **8**	22. $9 + 9 =$ **18**
23. $0 + 9 =$ **9**	24. $4 + 8 =$ **12**

Fluency Practice

1. $10 - 1 =$ **9**	2. $9 - 7 =$ **2**
3. $9 - 3 =$ **6**	4. $11 - 4 =$ **7**
5. $6 - 5 =$ **1**	6. $13 - 6 =$ **7**
7. $7 - 4 =$ **3**	8. $19 - 8 =$ **11**
9. $11 - 4 =$ **7**	10. $14 - 7 =$ **7**
11. $5 - 1 =$ **4**	12. $15 - 6 =$ **9**
13. $17 - 9 =$ **8**	14. $11 - 8 =$ **3**
15. $16 - 7 =$ **9**	16. $12 - 5 =$ **7**
17. $12 - 3 =$ **9**	18. $9 - 6 =$ **3**
19. $18 - 9 =$ **9**	20. $15 - 7 =$ **8**
21. $13 - 7 =$ **6**	22. $17 - 9 =$ **8**
23. $17 - 8 =$ **9**	24. $9 - 8 =$ **1**

Name _____

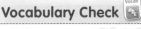 → Chapter 2
Number Patterns

Vocabulary Check

array	equal groups	even
odd	repeated addition	skip count

Complete each sentence.

1. __Equal groups__ have the same number of objects.

2. You can __skip count__ by counting objects in equal groups of two or more.

3. An __odd__ number of objects has 1 left over when counted by 2s.

4. An __array__ is a group of objects arranged in rows and columns of the same length.

Concept Check

Write the missing numbers.

5. 65, __70__, 75, 80, __85__, 90, __95__, 100

6. 30, __40__, 50, 60, __70__, 80, __90__

Fill in the blanks to describe each array.

7.

__3__ rows of __4__

8.

__5__ rows of __5__

Circle *even* or *odd*.

9. 8   (even)   odd

10. 13   even   (odd)

11. 10   (even)   odd

Write the equal addends that make each sum.

12. 8 = __4__ + __4__

13. 16 = __8__ + __8__

14. 12 = __6__ + __6__

15. 18 = __9__ + __9__

Find the missing addends.

16. 7 + __7__ = 14

17. __9__ + 9 = 18

18. __6__ + 6 = 12

19. 3 + __3__ = 6

20. __5__ + 5 = 10

21. 7 + 7 = __14__

My Review

Use these pages to assess your students' understanding of the vocabulary and key concepts in this chapter.

Vocabulary Check

Display this chapter's vocabulary on the virtual word wall. Have students refer to these examples as they complete the exercises.

ELL **ELL Support Strategy** Use this information to participate in purposeful, cooperative learning activities.

Concept Check

If students need reinforcement of skills after completing this section, use the Reteach worksheet to review the concepts again.

Exercises	Concept	Review Lesson(s)
5–6	Skip counting	1, 2
7–8	Repeated addition with arrays	5
9–11	Even and odd numbers	6
12–15	Equal addends	7
16–21	Finding missing addends	7

Problem Solving

Remind students of the four-step plan for problem solving. For students who need help in reading comprehension, have them work with another student to read the problem aloud before attempting the four-step plan.

Test Practice

Diagnose Student Errors

Class trends in wrong answers may indicate common errors or misconceptions.

20	only counted 2 more sets
21	added 16 + 5
24	only counted 4 more sets
26	correct

Reflect

Display this chapter's vocabulary on the Virtual Word Wall. Ask students to refer to the words as they complete the graphic organizer.

You may choose to have your students use a different graphic organizer for review.

Summative Assessment

Use these alternate leveled chapter tests from the Assessment Masters to differentiate assessment for the specific needs of your students.

Chapter Tests		
Level	**Type**	**Form**
AL	Multiple Choice	**1A**
AL	Multiple Choice	**1B**
OL	Multiple Choice / Free Choice	**2A**
OL	Multiple Choice / Free Choice	**2B**
BL	Free Choice	**3A**
BL	Free Choice	**3B**
Additional Chapter Resource Masters		
OL	Vocabulary Test	
OL	Extended Response Test	
OL	Oral Assessment	

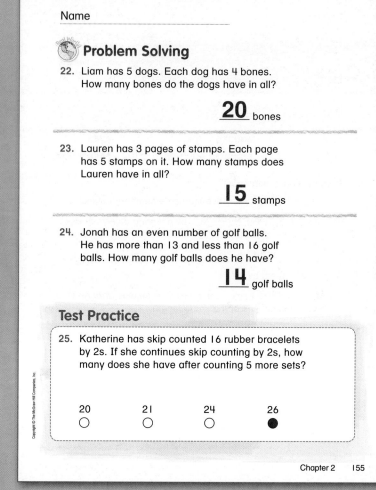

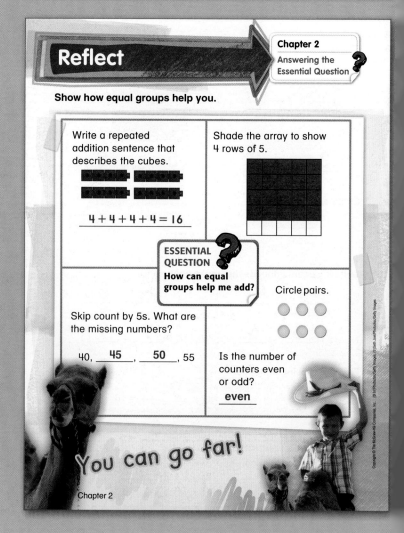

Notes

CHAPTER 3

Add Two-Digit Numbers

Chapter at a Glance

Suggested Pacing		
Instruction*	Review & Assessment	TOTAL
10 days	2 days	**12 days**

*Includes additional time for remediation and differentiation.

Lesson	Objective	Materials & Manipulatives	Vocabulary	CCSS Standard
Lesson 1 *pp. 165–170* **Take Apart Tens to Add**	Take apart an addend to make a ten to add.	• base-ten blocks • craft sticks • Work Mat 6		2.OA.1
Lesson 2 *pp. 171–176* **Regroup Ones as Tens**	Use models to regroup ones as tens to add.	• base-ten blocks	**regroup**	2.OA.1 2.NBT.5 2.NBT.9
Lesson 3 *pp. 177–182* **Add to a Two-Digit Number**	Add one-digit numbers and two-digit numbers.	• base-ten blocks		2.OA.1 2.NBT.5 2.NBT.9

✓ **Check My Progress**

Lesson	Objective	Materials & Manipulatives	Vocabulary	CCSS Standard
Lesson 4 *pp. 185–190* **Add Two-Digit Numbers**	Add two-digit numbers.	• base-ten blocks • Work Mat 6		2.OA.1 2.NBT.5 2.NBT.9
Lesson 5 *pp. 191–196* **Rewrite Two-Digit Addition**	Rewrite horizontal addition problems vertically to add.	• notecards • Work Mat 6		2.OA.1 2.NBT.5
Lesson 6 *pp. 197–202* **Add Three and Four Two-Digit Numbers**	Add three and four two-digit numbers.	• base-ten blocks • number cubes • connecting cubes		2.NBT.6 2.NBT.9
Lesson 7 *pp. 203–208* **Problem-Solving Strategy: Make a Model**	Make a model to solve problems.	• white board		2.OA.1

✓ **My Review and Reflect**

✓ For customizable online assessment, go to **eAssessment** at connectED.mcgraw-hill.com.

Planning for Differentiated Instruction

Use these differentiated instruction activity suggestions, along with the ongoing support provided in each lesson of this chapter, to meet individual learning needs.

AL APPROACHING LEVEL

Use with Lesson 2

Materials: two-color counters, small cups

- Have students work in small groups.
- Give groups of students 24 counters.
- Tell students to make as many groups of ten as they can. Have them put each group of ten in a cup. Find how many tens and how many ones they have. 2 tens and 4 ones
- Use different numbers of counters and repeat.

BL BEYOND LEVEL

Use with Lesson 5

Materials: paper and pencil

- Have students brainstorm real-word situations in which they would add two-digit numbers. Ask students to list the situations on paper. Examples might include: finding the total number of boys and girls in a classroom or finding the total number of days in two months.
- Have students work with a partner to write a story problem based on each situation.
- Groups can present their problems to the class to solve.

OL ON LEVEL

Use with Lesson 2

Materials: base-ten blocks, Work Mat 6: Tens and Ones Chart, spinner labeled 0–9

- Have students work in pairs.
- Instruct students to take turns spinning the spinner. They put the number of units they spin in the ones column of the workmat.
- One student spins the spinner and places that number of unit cubes in the ones column of Work Mat 6.
- The other student spins the spinner and places that number of unit cubes in the ones column of the work mat.
- When there are 10 units in the ones column, students work together to exchange for a tens rod and put 1 in the tens column.
- Students continue until they reach 50 or 5 tens rods.

ELL ENGLISH LANGUAGE LEARNERS

Support for English Language Learners is found throughout the chapter and includes:

- ELL strategies at point-of-use in each Teacher Edition lesson
- ELL tiered instruction suggestions for each lesson at connectED.mcgraw-hill.com
- Comprehensive ELL lessons and worksheets for additional instruction at connectED.mcgraw-hill.com
- Non-linguistic representations of concepts on My Math Words, My Vocabulary Cards, and My Foldables

Additional online resources at connectED.mcgraw-hill.com include:

- Visual Vocabulary Cards
- Multilingual eGlossary
- Professional Development support

Looking for more DIFFERENTIATED INSTRUCTION? Find additional support in **each lesson** of this chapter and **online** at **connectED.mcgraw-hill.com**

RtI

AL Approaching Level
OL On Level
BL Beyond Level
ELL English Language Learners

What's the Math in This Chapter?

Points of Intersection

Where
CONTENT STANDARDS

Meet
Mathematical
PRACTICE ➤ 8

NBT
Number and Operations in Base Ten

Look for and express regularity in repeated reasoning.

Most of this chapter concentrates on the **Number and Operations in Base Ten (NBT)** domain. However, aspects of the **Operations and Algebraic Thinking (OA)** domain are also used in the study of **addition**.

As you teach different aspects of addition, emphasize that addition of two-digit numbers is a process of repeated calculation: add the ones digits, regroup if needed, then add the tens digits. Once students memorize this process they can later apply it to addition of greater numbers.

What should my students already know?

In the previous grade, students used **Operations and Algebraic Thinking (OA)** in their study of addition:

- Use addition within 20 to solve word problems.
  1.OA.1, 1.OA.6

- Solve word problems that involve adding three whole numbers whose sum is less than or equal to 20.
  1.OA.2

Students used **Number and Operations in Base Ten (NBT)** in their study of place value and addition:

- Understand that the two digits of a two-digit number represent amounts of tens and ones.
  1.NBT.2

- Add within 100, using concrete models or drawings and strategies based on place value. Understand that in adding two-digit numbers, one adds tens and tens, ones and ones; and sometimes it is necessary to compose a ten.
  1.NBT.4

WHAT STUDENTS SHOULD UNDERSTAND

Add Two Two-Digit Numbers

CCSS 2.OA.1, 2.NBT.9

How to add two two-digit numbers by taking apart and making numbers that end in zero.

- Numbers that end in zero are easier to add.

- You can take apart an addend to make a number that ends in zero.

WHAT STUDENTS SHOULD BE ABLE TO DO

Ryan has 37 apples and 45 oranges. How many pieces of fruit does he have in all?

Find $37 + 45$.

Take apart 37 as $32 + 5$.

Then, make $5 + 45$ into 50.

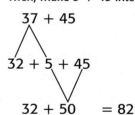

$37 + 45$

$32 + 5 + 45$

$32 + 50 \quad = 82$

So, he has 82 pieces of fruit.

WHAT STUDENTS SHOULD UNDERSTAND	WHAT STUDENTS SHOULD BE ABLE TO DO

Regroup When Adding Two-Digit Numbers

 2.OA.1, 2.NBT.5, 2.NBT.9

How to regroup ones as tens when adding two-digit numbers.

- When adding two-digit numbers, add the ones and then the tens.
- Regroup if there are ten or more ones. You can use base-ten blocks to help you regroup and find the sum.

Find 16 + 29.

Step 1 Add the ones.

$6 + 9 = 15$ ones

Step 2 Regroup if needed. Write how many.

tens	ones
1	6
+ 2	9
	5

Step 3 Add the tens.

1 ten + 1 ten + 2 tens = 4 tens

tens	ones
1	
1	6
+ 2	9
4	5

So, 16 + 29 = 45

Add Three and Four Two-Digit Numbers

 2.OA.1, 2.NBT.6

How to add three and four two-digit numbers.

- You can use the same steps to add three and four two-digit numbers as you used when you added two two-digit numbers.
- First, line up the ones and tens digits. Add the ones. Regroup if needed. Add the tens.

Add four numbers.

```
  1
 21
 13  > 3 + 7 = 10
 37
+25    10 + 1 = 11
 96    11 + 5 = 16
```

What will my students do next with these skills?

After this chapter, students will learn to:

- subtract two-digit numbers
  2.OA.1, 2.NBT.5, 2.NBT.9

In the next grade, students will learn to:

- add and subtract within 1,000
  3.NBT.2

Reading Connections

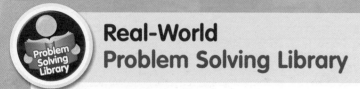

Real-World Problem Solving Library

Math and Social Studies: Baseball's Hero

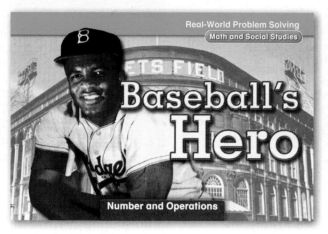

Real-World Problem Solving
Math and Social Studies

Baseball's **Hero**

Number and Operations

Use these leveled books to reinforce and extend problem-solving skills and strategies.

Leveled for:

AL Approaching Level

OL On Level Also available in Spanish

BL Beyond Level

For additional support, see the
Real-World Problem Solving Readers Teacher Guide.

Leveled Reader Database

Available at leveledreaderdatabase.macmillanmh.com
Search by:

• Content Area   • Lexile Score
• Guided Reading Level • Benchmark Level

Library Books

Check with your school library or your local public library for these titles.

Coyotes All Around
Stuart J. Murphy

One Duck Stuck
Phyllis Root

Sea Sums
Joy N. Hulme

A Fair Bear Share
Stuart J. Murphy

Mall Mania
Stuart J. Murphy

Toasty Toes: Counting by Tens
Michael Dahl

Tail Feather Fun: Counting by Tens
Michael Dahl

Reading and Language Arts Support

Math in Our World

Divide the class into groups of 4. Distribute copies of a newspaper to each group. Have students search for and circle 2-digit numbers. Have students create a poster telling a story behind a situation that uses the numbers they have found. The situation should include an instance in which two of the numbers need to be added. Have students display their posters and tell their story. Then have the class solve the problem presented in the story.

Looking for more
Reading and Language Arts Support?
go online to
connectED.mcgraw-hill.com

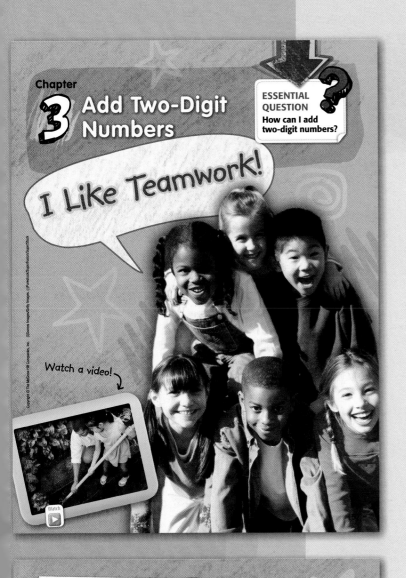

Chapter

3 Add Two-Digit Numbers

ESSENTIAL QUESTION
How can I add two-digit numbers?

I Like Teamwork!

Watch a video!

LAUNCH THE CHAPTER

Theme:

I Like Teamwork!

All of the lessons in Chapter 3 will connect with the theme of I Like Teamwork!, which centers around fund-raisers and working and playing together. This is reflected in problem solving and the visuals used throughout the chapter.

Video

Have students watch the video about teamwork. You may want to spark a discussion about how math is used in teamwork.

Building on the Essential Question

Once students have completed this chapter they should be able to answer the question "How can I add two-digit numbers?" In each lesson, students build upon their understanding by answering a simpler question. These are indicated in the exercises as Building on the Essential Question. At the end of the chapter, students use a graphic organizer to help them answer the Essential Question.

My Common Core State Standards (CCSS)

Operations and Algebraic Thinking

2.OA.1 Use addition and subtraction within 100 to solve one-and two-step word problems involving situations of adding to, taking from, putting together, taking apart, and comparing, with unknowns in all positions

Number and Operations in Base Ten *This chapter also addresses these standards:*

2.NBT.5 Fluently add and subtract within 100 using strategies based on place value, properties of operations, and/or the relationship between addition and subtraction.

2.NBT.6 Add up to four two-digit numbers using strategies based on place value and properties of operations.

2.NBT.9 Explain why addition and subtraction strategies work, using place value and the properties of operations.

Standards for Mathematical PRACTICE

1. Make sense of problems and persevere in solving them.
2. Reason abstractly and quantitatively.
3. Construct viable arguments and critique the reasoning of others.
4. Model with mathematics.
5. Use appropriate tools strategically.
6. Attend to precision.
7. Look for and make use of structure.
8. Look for and express regularity in repeated reasoning.

= focused on in this chapter

Professional Development

CCSS Common Core State Standards

Learn more about how the Common Core State Standards can be implemented in your classroom at mhpdonline.com.

Look for
- **eImplementation**
- **eVideo Clip Libraries**
- **eTech Training**
- **ePD Webinars**

Feature video for mathematical content in this chapter:
CGI-Join Result Unknown—Direct Modeling-01

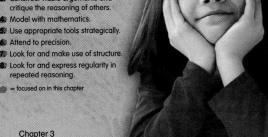

1 Assess

You have two options for assessing student readiness for this chapter. Use student results to determine which level of instruction is needed to help students get ready for the chapter and to determine what ongoing support they will need during the chapter.

Option 1: Am I Ready?

Have students complete the Am I Ready? in their student books.

Name _____

Am I Ready?

Check ✓ → Go online to take the Readiness Quiz

Write each number two ways.

1. 18 ones = **18**
   1 ten **8** ones

2. 26 ones = **26**
   2 tens **6** ones

Add.

3. 2
   + 7
   ‾‾‾
    9

4. 3
   + 4
   ‾‾‾
    7

5. 2
   + 2
   ‾‾‾
    4

6. 9
   + 6
   ‾‾‾
   15

7. 3 + 3 + 1 = **7**

8. 4 + 2 + 3 = **9**

9. Jack has 5 red marbles. Trent has 3 blue marbles. Lien has 2 green marbles. How many marbles do they have altogether?

   10 marbles

How Did I Do? →
Shade the boxes to show the problems you answered correctly.
| 1 | 2 | 3 | 4 | 5 | 6 | 7 | 8 | 9 |

Online Content at connectED.mcgraw-hill.com   Chapter 3   159

Check ✓ Option 2: Online Readiness Quiz

Have students take the **Online Readiness Quiz.**

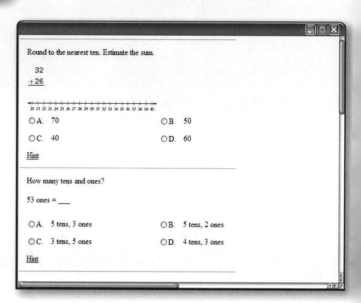

Round to the nearest ten. Estimate the sum.

  32
+26

20 21 22 23 24 25 26 27 28 29 30 31 32 33 34 35 36 37 38 39 40

○A. 70   ○B. 50

○C. 40   ○D. 60

Hint

How many tens and ones?

53 ones = ___

○A. 5 tens, 3 ones   ○B. 5 tens, 2 ones

○C. 3 tens, 5 ones   ○D. 4 tens, 3 ones

Hint

OPTION 2

CCSS Common Core Review

Exercises	Skill	Standard
1–10*	Number sense	2.OA.1
	Addition	2.OA.1
	Addition of three numbers	2.OA.1

*These questions are randomly generated from a bank of 15 questions.

OPTION 1

CCSS Common Core Review

Exercises	Skill	Standard
1–2	Number sense	2.OA.1
3–6	Addition	2.OA.1
7–9	Addition of three numbers	2.OA.1

2 Diagnose and Prescribe

3 Reassess

Based on the results of the Am I Ready? in the student edition, use the charts below to address individual needs **before** beginning the chapter.

Use the **ONGOING** resources to support differentiated instruction as new skills and concepts are presented in the chapter.

If reassessment is necessary, administer the chapter Diagnostic Test in the **Assessment Masters** or go online for eAssessment.

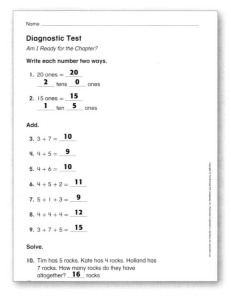

TIER 1

OL ON LEVEL

IF students miss 2–3 in Exercises 1–9,

THEN choose a resource:

→ Am I Ready? Practice

→ Online Readiness Quiz

ONGOING Self-Check Quizzes • Chapter Project • Differentiated Assignments • My Learning Stations • Differentiated Instruction activities

TIER 2

AL STRATEGIC INTERVENTION

(Approaching Grade Level)

IF students miss 4–5 in Exercises 1–9,

THEN choose a resource:

→ Online Strategic Intervention activity

→ Am I Ready? Review

ONGOING Common Errors • Differentiated Assignments • Online support • Reteach worksheets • Homework Helper • My Learning Stations • RtI lesson support • Differentiated Instruction activities

TIER 3

INTENSIVE INTERVENTION

(2 or more years below grade level)

IF students miss 6 or more in Exercises 1–9,

THEN use *Math Triumphs,* an intensive math intervention program from McGraw-Hill.

BL BEYOND LEVEL

IF students miss 1 or less in Exercises 1–9,

THEN choose a resource:

→ Online Games

→ Am I Ready? Apply

ONGOING 21st Century Skills • Chapter Project • Differentiated Assignments • Enrich worksheets • My Learning Stations • Differentiated Instruction activities

 For additional chapter readiness assessment, go to eAssessment at connectED.mcgraw-hill.com.

DEVELOP VOCABULARY

My Math Words

Review Vocabulary

Where did they learn it?

- addends   (Lesson 1-1)
- sum   (Lesson 1-1)
- add   (Lesson 1-1)

Making Connections

Ask students to describe or show what they know about the review vocabulary. For example, they might recognize these words are used to describe an addition sentence.

Ask students to examine the graphic organizer. Have a volunteer describe the addition sentence. Sample answer: Blue and red numbers are used to show the addition sentence.

After students complete the graphic organizer, ask them to read the word problem they wrote at the bottom of the page to another student.

My Vocabulary Cards

Ask students to browse the word and example on the card. Discuss with them what they already know about the word or the example shown on the card. Note on the board any questions or observations students have about the word.

The definition appears on the back of the card. Discuss the definition with students.

Students should clip and store their cards in one place, such as a small envelope, where they can access them as needed throughout the chapter.

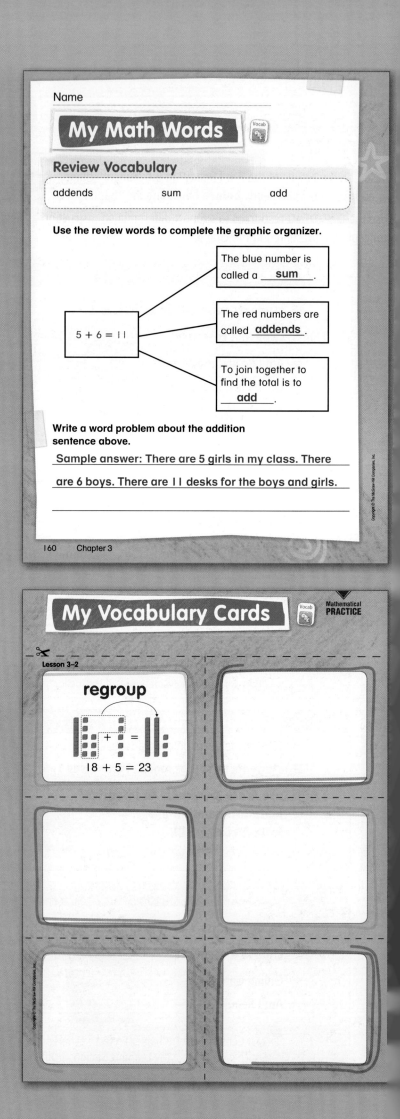

Directions:
Ideas for Use
- Have students write a tally mark on the card each time they read the word in this chapter.
- Ask students to use the blank cards to write their own vocabulary cards.

Take apart a number to write it in a new way.

Copyright © The McGraw-Hill Companies, Inc.

Mathematical PRACTICE 3 — My Vocabulary Card Activities

The table below lists the activity for this chapter's card, as well as the answer. The activities will include opportunities for students to hear, say, or write the vocabulary words. When applicable, activities will involve drawing or modeling vocabulary. Students' answers can be recorded using various media, such as Notebook Foldables, IWB, electronic tablets, or computers. Suggestions for using blank cards appear in some Developing Vocabulary activities.

Vocabulary Card	Activity/Activity Answer
regroup	How would you regroup the number 24? 2 tens and 4 ones

STUDY ORGANIZER

My Foldable

What's the Math?

Content Standard: 2.OA.1

Mathematical PRACTICE 5 **Use appropriate tools strategically.**

This Foldable provides guidance for students in regrouping ones as tens when adding two two-digit numbers.

How Do I Make It?

- Tear out the page and cut off the top banner.
- Fold along the green dotted line to make a pocket.
- Glue or staple in the center and at each end to make the pocket more secure.
- Give each student a minimum of 5 index cards. To make number cards, have them cut each index card in half and label the cards with one number 0-9 on each side.

When Do I Use It?

Use after Lesson 2 and as a review tool throughout the chapter.

How Could I Use It?

- Have students look at the problem in the green square. Have them show 15 by placing the appropriate number cards in the tens and ones pockets. Have them show 28 by placing those cards in the tens and ones pockets.
- Have students add the ones, $5 + 8$, to make 13. Then have them place just a 3 card in the ones pocket and adding a 1 card in the tens pocket.
- Have students add the tens, $1 + 2 + 1$, and place the new number card in the tens pocket, 4. The answer is 43.
- Empty the pockets and try another problem.

ELL ELL Support Strategy Use this vocabulary activity to practice 2-digit addition.

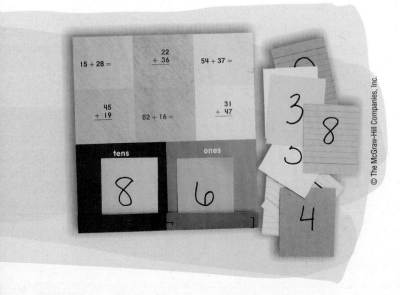

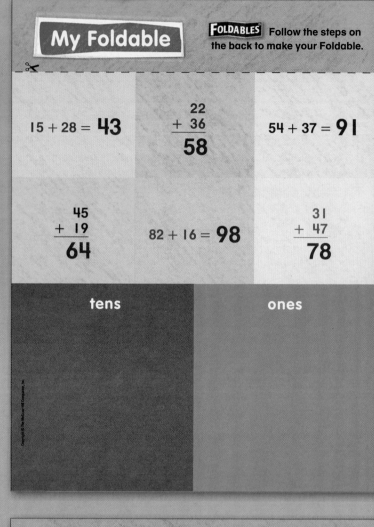

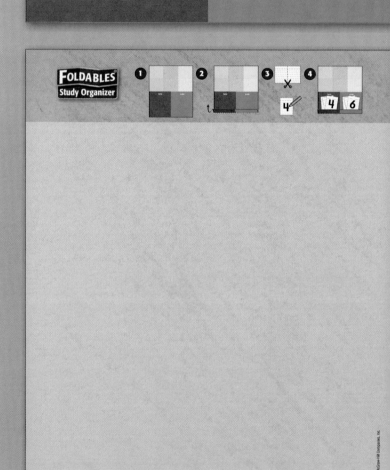

Project *Express*™

From Dinah Zike, creator of Foldables®

This ready-to-make project format comes in eight bright colors and offers the ability to customize your learning center with different content-based Project Packets. These packets include pre-printed, full color stickers, assorted envelopes and pockets, reproducible templates, and materials needed for quick assembly. You can use these materials as illustrated or use them to design your own learning center.

Order with a McGraw-Hill discount at www.dinah.com.

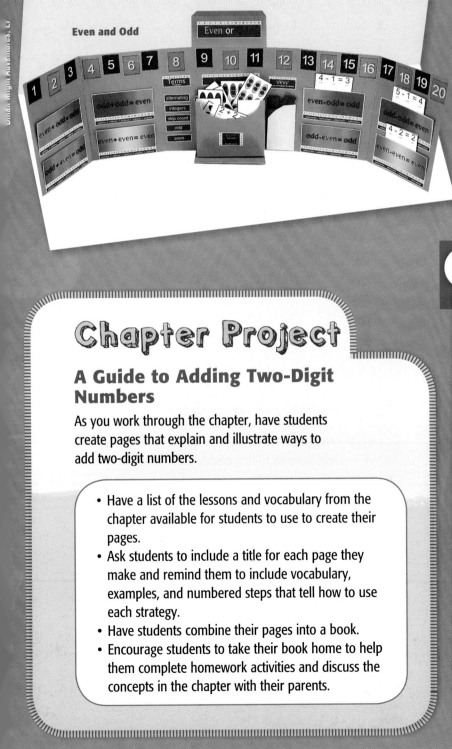

MY Learning Stations

Use the following learning stations to differentiate the instruction for Chapter 3. Includes Spanish!

Learning Station	Title	Use after Lesson(s)
Game	*Pick Your Path*	4
Graphic Novel	*Tickets to the Puppet Show*	4
Activity Card	*Telephone Words*	5

Chapter Project

A Guide to Adding Two-Digit Numbers

As you work through the chapter, have students create pages that explain and illustrate ways to add two-digit numbers.

- Have a list of the lessons and vocabulary from the chapter available for students to use to create their pages.
- Ask students to include a title for each page they make and remind them to include vocabulary, examples, and numbered steps that tell how to use each strategy.
- Have students combine their pages into a book.
- Encourage students to take their book home to help them complete homework activities and discuss the concepts in the chapter with their parents.

📅 CALENDAR TIME

Work Backward on the Calendar

- Write the name of the current month on the calendar poster. Have students fill in the numbers for the days of the month.
- Have them choose one number from a stack of index cards. This number is the sum.
- Have students look at the calendar. Ask what two numbers they can add to get the sum on the index card. Direct them to write a number sentence on the board or on paper.

LESSON 1
Take Apart Tens to Add

OBJECTIVE Take apart an addend to make a ten to add.

What's the Math?

 Common Core State Standards
DOMAIN: Operations and Algebraic Thinking

Standard: 2.OA.1

The wording of this standard can be found on page 158.

What Students Should Understand

- It is easier to add two two-digit numbers if one of the numbers ends in a zero.
- You can take apart an addend to make a number that ends in zero.

What Students Should be Able to Do

Find 27 + 34 by taking apart an addend.

One Way:

Take apart 34 as 3 + 31.

Then make 3 + 27 into 30.

27 + 34

27 + 3 + 31

30 + 31 = 61

Another Way:

Take apart 27 as 21 + 6.

Then make 6 + 34 into 40.

27 + 34

21 + 6 + 34

21 + 40 = 61

So, 27 + 34 = 61.

 Building on the Essential Question

In this lesson, students will build upon the skills and concepts needed to answer the chapter's Essential Question "How can I add two-digit numbers?"

Developing Vocabulary

Review Vocabulary

addend

Review Activity

- Write *addend* on the board. Ask students what they recall about addends from previous chapters.
- Have students skim the lesson. Ask volunteers to point to exercises showing two-digit addends.
- Explain to students they will learn a way to make adding two-digit addends easier in this lesson.

ELL **ELL Support Strategy** Use this information to develop oral language with content-specific vocabulary.

My Vocabulary Cards

Have students use the blank cards to write any word or words they would like to review.

IWB **Virtual Word Wall**

You may wish to add this review word to begin the Virtual Word Wall for this chapter.

ELL Refer to the Multilingual eGlossary for interactive definitions in 13 languages.

Plan Online

Plan for your lesson by using the resources at

connectED.mcgraw-hill.com

Digital Dashboard

Interactive Whiteboard Ready

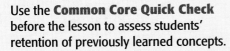

Vocab

The eBook **Glossary** shows the definition of the word and has audio for each definition. The **eGlossary** provides definitions in 13 languages.

Watch

Watch as concepts are brought to life through **animations**, **songs**, and a variety of visual instruction.

Tools

Virtual Manipulatives with work mats allow teachers and students to model the lesson.

Check

Use **eAssessment** for online assignments and customized assessments.

Use the **Common Core Quick Check** before the lesson to assess students' retention of previously learned concepts.

Use the interactive **Self-Check Quiz** after the lesson to provide immediate feedback on lesson concepts.

eHelp

Digital and print resources assist students and parents in completing My Homework.

Games

Online games and **apps** provide extra practice for lesson concepts.

PD

Professional development videos help teachers gain a deeper understanding of the lesson concepts and strategies.

RtI

Support for **approaching**, **on-** and **beyond-level** students as well as **English Language Learners**.

Masters

Reteach and **Enrich** worksheets, **Manipulative Masters**, the **Problem of the Day**, and other blackline masters are available for each lesson.

1 LAUNCH THE LESSON

 CCSS

If your students are well-versed in taking apart tens to add, you may choose to begin instruction with Step 2, **TEACH**.

You will need

☐ craft sticks
☐ Work Mat 6

Mathematical PRACTICE 4 Modeling the Math

Give each student 30 craft sticks and Work Mat 6.

Count out 15 craft sticks. Place 10 sticks in the tens column of the mat.

How many sticks do you have left? 5

Have students place the 5 sticks in the ones column of the mat.

Tell students to clear their mat and repeat the procedure using the numbers 20, 17, 13, and 11.

tens	ones

Lunchroom Chat

Tips for New Teachers

Taking apart numbers is a new concept to many of your students. It is important to stress that there is more than one way this can be accomplished. Work in small groups to identify the number that students think might be the easier number to take apart to make a ten. Once students feel comfortable with this strategy, let them work independently.

© The McGraw-Hill Companies, Inc., photographed by Ken Cavanagh

Online Content at connectED.mcgraw-hill.com

 Begin core instruction here.

You will need

☐ base-ten blocks

Explore and Explain

Read the directions that are at the bottom of the student page. Guide students to use base-ten blocks to show 48 and 16. Then guide them to move some base-ten blocks from the yellow box to the red box to make 50.

How many base-ten blocks do you need to move from the yellow box to the red box to make 50 in the red box? 2

How many base-ten blocks are left in the yellow box? 14

Have the students write the numbers shown in the boxes as the addends in the addition number sentence. *What did you write? What is the sum of 50 + 14?* 64

Is it easier to find 48 + 16 or 50 + 14? Why? 50 + 14; Sample answer: One of the addends ends in 0.

See and Show

Help students work through the example at the top of the page.

Discuss with students the two ways shown to find 28 + 36. Be sure students understand the thinking behind each composition and/or decomposition. That is, in One Way, the goal is to change 28 to 30, its closest ten. So, you take apart 36 as 2 + 34 since 28 + 2 = 30. In Another Way, the goal is to change 36 to 40, its closest ten. So, you take apart 28 as 24 + 4 since 36 + 4 = 40.

Why is it easier to add a number that ends in zero? You add only the tens.

Why do they show two different ways to work this problem? You can take apart either addend to make a ten.

Have them trace the dashed numbers as they work the problems.

Work through Exercises 1 and 2 as a class.

Mathematical PRACTICE 3 ➤ **Talk Math**

Discuss with students "How do you decide which addend to take apart when adding?" Sample answer: You can break apart either number, but it is easier to break apart the addend that is farthest from a ten.

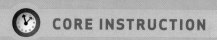

Name _____

Operations and Algebraic Thinking
2.OA.1

Take Apart Tens to Add

Lesson 1
ESSENTIAL QUESTION
How can I add two-digit numbers?

Explore and Explain [Watch] [Tools]

We'll win if we pull together!

$$50 + 14 = 64$$

Teacher Directions: Use base-ten blocks. Show 48 in the red box. Show 16 in the yellow box. Move some base-ten blocks from the yellow box to the red box to make 50. Write the number shown in each box. Add. Write the sum.

Online Content at 🖉 connectED.mcgraw-hill.com   Chapter 3 • Lesson 1   165

See and Show

Mathematical **PRACTICE**

Numbers that end in zero are easier to add.
Take apart addends to make numbers that end in zero.

Find 28 + 36.

One Way:
Take apart 36 as 2 + 34.
Then make 28 + 2 into 30.

28 + 36

28 + 2 + 34

30 + 34 = **64**

Another Way:
Take apart 28 as 24 + 4.
Then make 4 + 36 into 40.

28 + 36

24 + 4 + 36

24 + 40 = **64**

So, 28 + 36 = **64**.

Take apart an addend to solve.

1.   18 + 35

18 + **2** + **33**

20 + **33** = **53**

So, 18 + 35 = **53**.

2.   44 + 26

44 + **6** + **20**

50 + **20** = **70**

So, 44 + 26 = **70**.

Talk Math   How do you decide which addend to take apart when adding?

166   Chapter 3 • Lesson 1

Name _____

I wonder what this take apart will be?

On My Own

Take apart an addend to solve.

3.   36 + 45

$$36 + \underline{4} + 41$$

$$40 + 41 = 81$$

So, 36 + 45 = $\underline{81}$.

4.   25 + 58

$$\underline{23} + \underline{2} + 58$$

$$23 + 60 = 83$$

So, 25 + 58 = $\underline{83}$.

5.   67 + 26

$$67 + \underline{3} + \underline{23}$$

$$70 + \underline{23} = 93$$

So, 67 + 26 = $\underline{93}$.

6.   38 + 14

$$38 + \underline{2} + \underline{12}$$

$$40 + 12 = 52$$

So, 38 + 14 = $\underline{52}$.

🌎 **Problem Solving**

Mathematical
PRACTICE

7. 28 people came to the bake sale in the morning. 34 people came to the bake sale in the afternoon. How many people came in all?

My granola bars are a hit!

$\underline{62}$ people

8. Bill collected 16 toys for the toy drive. Lisa collected 37 toys. How many toys did Bill and Lisa collect in all?

She's right. I'm yummy!

$\underline{53}$ toys

Write Math Explain how you would find 65 + 18 by taking apart an addend.

Sample answer: Take apart 65 as 2 + 63. Next, add 2 to

18 to get 20. Lastly, add 20 to 63 to get 83. So, 65 + 18 =

83.

On My Own

Have students work through the exercises on this page independently. You may choose to assign exercises based on the chart below.

DIFFERENTIATED ASSIGNMENTS

AL **Approaching Level** Guide students through the exercises in On My Own. Help them to use manipulatives while working through the exercises.

OL **On Level** Complete the exercises independently.

BL **Beyond Level** Complete the exercises independently without manipulatives.

Common Error!
Students may have difficulty correctly taking apart numbers. If needed, allow them to use counters to take apart large numbers.

Problem Solving

Have students work through the problem-solving exercises on this page independently.

Mathematical **PRACTICE** **1** In Exercise 7, students **make sense of problems and persevere in solving them.**

Write Math

This exercise asks students to build upon their understanding of concepts needed to answer the chapter's Essential Question.

RESPONSE TO INTERVENTION

DIFFERENTIATED INSTRUCTION

AL APPROACHING LEVEL

IF my students struggle with another way to add,

THEN choose a resource:

→ Use the Reteach worksheet with small groups.

→ Go online for a Differentiated Instruction activity.

OL ON LEVEL

IF my students seem to know another way to add, but need more practice,

THEN choose a resource:

→ Assign My Homework.

→ Go online for a Differentiated Instruction activity.

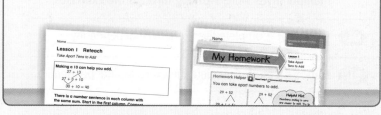

BL BEYOND LEVEL

IF my students have mastered another way to add,

THEN choose a resource:

→ Use the Enrich worksheet in cooperative groups.

→ Assign My Homework.

→ Go online for a Differentiated Instruction activity.

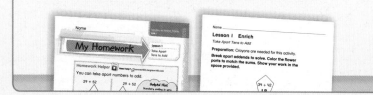

AL

Name

Lesson 1   Reteach
Take Apart Tens to Add

Making a 10 can help you add.

27 + 13

27 + 3 + 10

30 + 10 = 40

There is a number sentence in each column with the same sum. Start in the first column. Connect number sentences with the same sum.

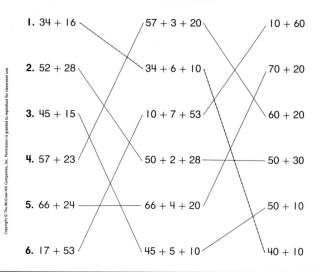

1. 34 + 16   57 + 3 + 20   10 + 60
2. 52 + 28   34 + 6 + 10   70 + 20
3. 45 + 15   10 + 7 + 53   60 + 20
4. 57 + 23   50 + 2 + 28   50 + 30
5. 66 + 24   66 + 4 + 20   50 + 10
6. 17 + 53   45 + 5 + 10   40 + 10

BL

Name

Lesson 1   Enrich
Take Apart Tens to Add

Preparation: Crayons are needed for this activity.

Break apart addends to solve. Color the flower parts to match the sums. Show your work in the space provided.

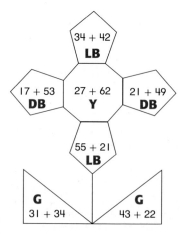

Color parts with sums of 65 green.

Color parts with sums of 70 dark blue.

Color parts with sums of 76 light blue.

Color parts with sums of 89 yellow.

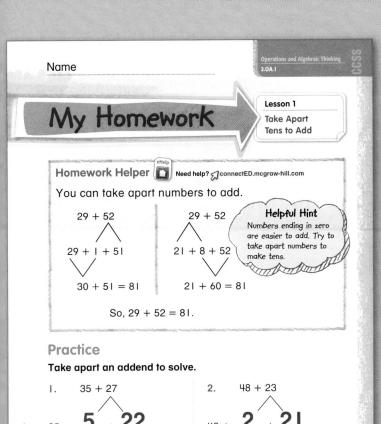

My Homework →

Lesson 1
Take Apart
Tens to Add

Homework Helper eHelp Need help? ⤢ connectED.mcgraw-hill.com

You can take apart numbers to add.

29 + 52

29 + 1 + 51

30 + 51 = 81

29 + 52

21 + 8 + 52

21 + 60 = 81

Helpful Hint
Numbers ending in zero are easier to add. Try to take apart numbers to make tens.

So, 29 + 52 = 81.

Practice

Take apart an addend to solve.

1.   35 + 27

35 + **5** + **22**

40 + **22** = **62**

So, 35 + 27 = **62**.

2.   48 + 23

48 + **2** + **21**

50 + **21** = **71**

So, 48 + 23 = **71**.

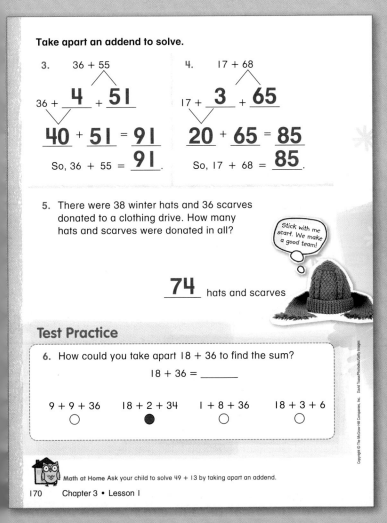

Take apart an addend to solve.

3.   36 + 55

36 + **4** + **51**

40 + **51** = **91**

So, 36 + 55 = **91**.

4.   17 + 68

17 + **3** + **65**

20 + **65** = **85**

So, 17 + 68 = **85**.

5. There were 38 winter hats and 36 scarves donated to a clothing drive. How many hats and scarves were donated in all?

Stick with me scarf. We make a good team!

74 hats and scarves

Test Practice

6. How could you take apart 18 + 36 to find the sum?

18 + 36 = _____

9 + 9 + 36   18 + 2 + 34   1 + 8 + 36   18 + 3 + 6
   ○   ●   ○   ○

🦉 Math at Home Ask your child to solve 49 + 13 by taking apart an addend.

---

4 WRAP IT UP

My Homework

Assign homework after successful completion of the lesson. Students who understand the concepts may skip the **Homework Helper** section.

Test Practice

Diagnose Student Errors

Class trends in wrong answers may indicate common errors or misconceptions.

9 + 9 + 36   did not make a ten

18 + 2 + 34 correct

1 + 8 + 36   did not make a ten

18 + 3 + 6   did not make a ten

Formative Assessment

If you have the numbers 43 and 37, which number would you take apart to help you make a ten? What would it be? 43 could be 40 and 3 or 37 could be 30 and 7.

Line Up!

When students line up, have them practice finding another way to add.

• Write several two-digit addition problems on the board.

• Have two students at a time come up and break apart an addend to solve. Continue until all students are lined up.

LESSON 2
Regroup Ones as Tens
OBJECTIVE Use models to regroup ones as tens to add.

What's the Math?

 Common Core State Standards
DOMAIN: Operations and Algebraic Thinking

Standards: 2.OA.1, 2.NBT.5, 2.NBT.9
The wording of these standards can be found on page 158.

CCSS

What Students Should Understand

• When adding two-digit numbers, regroup 10 ones as 1 ten if there are ten or more ones.

• You can use base-ten blocks to help you regroup and find the sum.

What Students Should be Able to Do

Use base-ten blocks to find 18 + 6.

Step 1

Use base-ten blocks to show 18 and 6.

tens	ones

Step 2

If there are ten or more ones, regroup 10 ones as 1 ten.

tens	ones

Step 3

Write the number of tens and ones.

tens	ones

There are 2 tens and 4 ones.
So, 18 + 6 = 24.

Developing Vocabulary

 New Vocabulary

regroup

Activity

• Have students use a place-value chart and base-ten blocks to learn about the meaning of regroup. Explain that *regroup* means to take apart a number to write it in a new way.

• Demonstrate using the base-ten blocks that 10 ones is the same as 1 ten. Explain that when there are 10 or more ones, regrouping is needed.

• Have students use the unit cubes to show 17 ones.

> *Are there 10 or more ones?* yes
> *How else can we show 17?* 1 ten and 7 ones

ELL **ELL Support Strategy** Use this vocabulary activity to visualize what is being taught.

My Vocabulary Cards

Read the activity for *regroup*. Have students complete the activity.

IWB **Virtual Word Wall**

Add this vocabulary card to the virtual word wall for the chapter.

ELL Refer to the Multilingual eGlossary for interactive definitions in 13 languages.

 Building on the Essential Question

In this lesson, students will build upon the skills and concepts needed to answer the chapter's Essential Question "How can I add two-digit numbers?"

Plan Online
Plan for your lesson by using the resources at
 connectED.mcgraw-hill.com

Digital Dashboard

Interactive Whiteboard Ready

 Vocab

The eBook **Glossary** shows the definition of the word and has audio for each definition. The **eGlossary** provides definitions in 13 languages.

 Watch

Watch as concepts are brought to life through **animations**, **songs**, and a variety of visual instruction.

 Tools

Virtual Manipulatives with work mats allow teachers and students to model the lesson.

 Check

Use **eAssessment** for online assignments and customized assessments.

Use the **Common Core Quick Check** before the lesson to assess students' retention of previously learned concepts.

Use the interactive **Self-Check Quiz** after the lesson to provide immediate feedback on lesson concepts.

 eHelp

Digital and print resources assist students and parents in completing My Homework.

 Games

Online games and **apps** provide extra practice for lesson concepts.

 PD

Professional development videos help teachers gain a deeper understanding of the lesson concepts and strategies.

 RtI

Support for **approaching**, **on**- and **beyond-level** students as well as **English Language Learners**.

Masters

Reteach and **Enrich** worksheets, **Manipulative Masters**, the **Problem of the Day**, and other blackline masters are available for each lesson.

---

1 LAUNCH THE LESSON CCSS

 If your students are well-versed in regrouping ones as tens, you may choose to begin instruction with Step 2, **TEACH**.

You will need
☐ base-ten blocks

Mathematical PRACTICE 4 Modeling the Math

Write addition problems on the board. Some should require regrouping and some should not.

Point to the first problem. Have students stand up if it is necessary to regroup. Have them raise their hands if it is *not* necessary to regroup.

Have students use base-ten blocks to prove their responses.

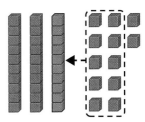

Lunchroom Chat

Invented strategies are critical for the development of understanding any addition algorithm. The critical transformation is from thinking of each of the numbers as a collection of ones to numbers that are collections of tens and ones. Counting up still works, but is inefficient. This understanding of tens and ones is crucial.

2 TEACH

⏱ Begin core instruction here.

You will need

☐ base-ten blocks

Explore and Explain

Read the directions that are on the bottom of the student page.

To find 19 + 3, you can first use base-ten blocks to represent each addend. Then you can determine how many base-ten blocks you have in all.

Guide students in using base-ten blocks to show 19 and 3.

It will be easier to determine how many base-ten blocks there are if you trade 10 ones for 1 ten. This is called regrouping. Can you do this here? **yes** *Why were you able to trade some ones for a ten?* **Sample answer: There were more than 10 ones, and 10 ones equals 1 ten.**

Explain to students that there were 12 ones before the regrouping took place. Ten of the ones were traded for 1 ten. The remaining 2 ones stay in the ones place.

How many base-ten blocks are in the chart now? **22** *This number is the sum. Fill in the blanks.*

Vocabulary

Explain to students that *steps* has more than one meaning. In a textbook, information is often presented in steps. In this sense, *steps* means "a series of actions taken to achieve something." Ask students how many steps are in See and Show. **3**

See and Show

Help students work through the example at the top of the page. Use base-ten blocks either in actual or virtual manipulatives to demonstrate the steps with the students. Ask the following questions.

What do you notice about the number of ones blocks in the ones column? **There are more than 10.**

What do you do when you have more than 10 ones blocks in the ones column? **regroup**

How many tens and ones do you have after regrouping? **3 tens and 2 ones**

Have students trace the dashed numbers as they work.

Work through Exercises 1 and 2 as a class.

Discuss with students "How do you know if you need to regroup?" Sample answer: When there are 10 or more ones, you need to regroup.

⏱ CORE INSTRUCTION

Name _____

Operations and Algebraic Thinking
2.OA.1, 2.NBT.5, 2.NBT.9

Regroup Ones as Tens

Lesson 2
ESSENTIAL QUESTION
How can I add two-digit numbers?

Explore and Explain 📺 🔧

We make a great pair!

tens	ones

Fresh Lemonade 50¢

We make a great pair too!

19 + 3 = **22**
Also, **2** tens
and **2** ones.

We're not pears. We're lemons!

🦉 **Teacher Directions:** Show the number 19 in the chart using base-ten blocks. In the ones column, below the first number, show 3 more ones cubes. Count all of the ones. Make a group of 10. Trade it for a tens rod and place the rod in the tens column. Write the sum. Write how many tens and ones.

Online Content at 🔗 connectED.mcgraw-hill.com   Chapter 3 • Lesson 2   171

See and Show

Mathematical **PRACTICE**

Find 27 + 5.

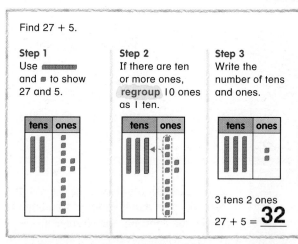

Step 1
Use ▭ and ▪ to show 27 and 5.

tens	ones

Step 2
If there are ten or more ones, **regroup** 10 ones as 1 ten.

tens	ones

Step 3
Write the number of tens and ones.

tens	ones

3 tens 2 ones
27 + 5 = **32**

Use Work Mat 6 and base-ten blocks to add.

	Add the ones. Add the tens.	Do you regroup?	Write the sum.
1. 15 + 8	**1** ten **13** ones	(yes) no	**23**
2. 23 + 6	**2** tens **9** ones	yes (no)	**29**

Talk Math   How do you know if you need to regroup?

172   Chapter 3 • Lesson 2

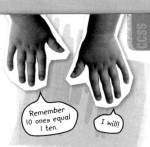

Name _____

On My Own
Use Work Mat 6 and base-ten blocks to add.

Remember 10 ones equal 1 ten.

I will!

	Add the ones. Add the tens.	Do you regroup?	Write the sum.
3. 76 + 4	**7** tens **10** ones	(yes) no	**80**
4. 17 + 7	**1** ten **14** ones	(yes) no	**24**
5. 32 + 6	**3** tens **8** ones	yes (no)	**38**
6. 59 + 5	**5** tens **14** ones	(yes) no	**64**
7. 13 + 9	**1** ten **12** ones	(yes) no	**22**
8. 31 + 8	**3** tens **9** ones	yes (no)	**39**
9. 25 + 6	**2** tens **11** ones	(yes) no	**31**
10. 62 + 7	**6** tens **9** ones	yes (no)	**69**

Chapter 3 • Lesson 2   173

 ## Problem Solving
Use Work Mat 6 and base-ten blocks to solve.

Mathematical PRACTICE

11. In April, it rained 18 days. It rained 6 days in May. How many days did it rain in April and May?

24 days

12. John sold 17 bottles of water. Later, he sold 8 bottles of water. How many bottles of water did John sell in all?

25 bottles of water

13. The runners ate 6 bananas before the race. They ate 14 bananas after the race. How many bananas did the runners eat in all?

20 bananas

Write Math Explain how you can regroup 19 + 7 to find the sum.

Sample answer: There is 1 ten, 9 ones, and 7 ones.

Put 10 ones together. Move that ten to the tens side.

6 ones are left. 2 tens and 6 ones make 26.

---

3 PRACTICE & APPLY

CCSS

On My Own
Have students work through the exercises on this page independently. You may choose to assign exercises based on the chart below.

DIFFERENTIATED ASSIGNMENTS

AL **Approaching Level** Guide students through the exercises in On My Own. Help them to use manipulatives while working through the exercises.

OL **On Level** Complete the exercises independently.

BL **Beyond Level** Complete the exercises independently without manipulatives.

Common Error!
Students may have difficulty understanding how to add and subtract with multiple digits. Guide them in lots of practice with base-ten blocks.

Problem Solving
Have students work through the problem-solving exercises on this page independently.

Mathematical PRACTICE 4 In Exercise 12, students **model with mathematics.**

Write Math
This exercise asks students to build upon their understanding of concepts needed to answer the chapter's Essential Question.

RESPONSE TO INTERVENTION

DIFFERENTIATED INSTRUCTION

 AL APPROACHING LEVEL

IF my students struggle with regroup ones as tens,

THEN choose a resource:

→ Use the Differentiated Instruction activity on p. 157B.

→ Use the Reteach Worksheet with small groups.

→ Go online for a Differentiated Instruction activity.

→ **Make a Ten** Have students find 28 + 7 mentally. Break apart 7 to include 2 and 5. Add 28 + 2 to find 30, and 30 + 5 to find the sum of 35.

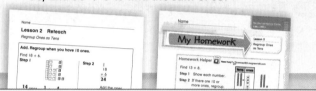

OL ON LEVEL

IF my students seem to know regroup ones as tens, but need more practice,

THEN choose a resource:

→ Use the Differentiated Instruction activity on p. 157B.

→ Assign My Homework.

→ Go online for a Differentiated Instruction activity.

BL BEYOND LEVEL

IF my students have mastered regroup ones as tens,

THEN choose a resource:

→ Use the Enrich Worksheet in cooperative groups.

→ Assign My Homework.

→ Go online for a Differentiated Instruction activity.

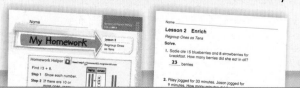

AL Name _____

Lesson 2 Reteach

Regroup Ones as Tens

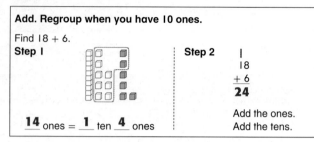

Add. Regroup when you have 10 ones.

Find 18 + 6.

Step 1

Step 2
```
  1
  18
+  6
  24
```
Add the ones.
Add the tens.

__14__ ones = __1__ ten __4__ ones

Add. Regroup when you have 10 ones.

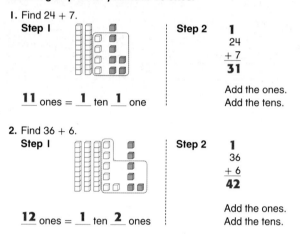

1. Find 24 + 7.

Step 1

Step 2
```
  1
  24
+  7
  31
```
Add the ones.
Add the tens.

__11__ ones = __1__ ten __1__ one

2. Find 36 + 6.

Step 1

Step 2
```
  1
  36
+  6
  42
```
Add the ones.
Add the tens.

__12__ ones = __1__ ten __2__ ones

BL Name _____

Lesson 2 Enrich

Regroup Ones as Tens

Solve.

1. Sadie ate 15 blueberries and 8 strawberries for breakfast. How many berries did she eat in all?

__23__ berries

2. Riley jogged for 33 minutes. Jason jogged for 9 minutes. How many minutes did they jog altogether?

__42__ minutes

3. Draw a picture with symbols or base-ten blocks to show how to regroup 44 + 8. Then use words to explain how you regrouped.

See students' drawing

Sample answer: There were 4 and 8 ones. I put them together to make 1 ten. I moved the ten over to the tens side, and I had 2 ones left. There were 5 tens and 2 ones making 52.

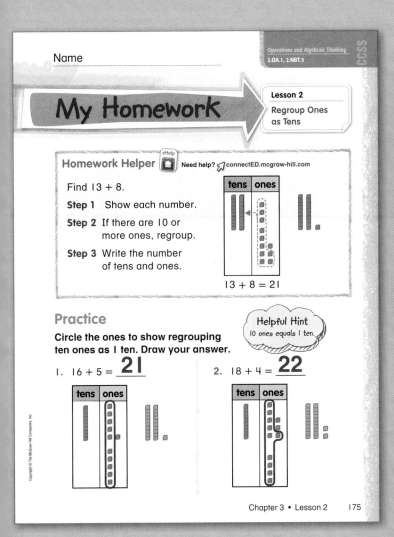

Name _____

Operations and Algebraic Thinking
2.OA.1, 2.NBT.5

My Homework

Lesson 2
Regroup Ones
as Tens

Homework Helper 📱 eHelp   Need help? ✏ connectED.mcgraw-hill.com

Find 13 + 8.

Step 1 Show each number.

Step 2 If there are 10 or more ones, regroup.

Step 3 Write the number of tens and ones.

13 + 8 = 21

Practice

Circle the ones to show regrouping ten ones as 1 ten. Draw your answer.

Helpful Hint
10 ones equals 1 ten.

1. 16 + 5 = **21**

2. 18 + 4 = **22**

Copyright © The McGraw-Hill Companies, Inc.

Chapter 3 • Lesson 2   175

Circle the ones to show regrouping ten ones as 1 ten. Draw your answer.

3. 14 + 8 = **22**

4. 15 + 5 = **20**

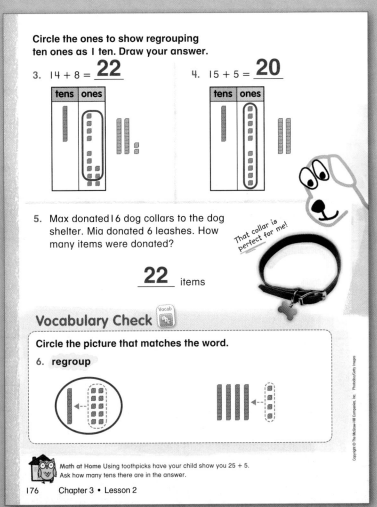

5. Max donated 16 dog collars to the dog shelter. Mia donated 6 leashes. How many items were donated?

That collar is perfect for me!

22 items

Vocabulary Check 📇

Circle the picture that matches the word.

6. **regroup**

🦉 **Math at Home** Using toothpicks have your child show you 25 + 5. Ask how many tens there are in the answer.

176   Chapter 3 • Lesson 2

---

⁴WRAP IT UP

CCSS

My Homework

Assign homework after successful completion of the lesson. Students who understand the concepts may skip the **Homework Helper** section.

Vocabulary Check

If they need additional support, have students refer to the lesson for other examples of regrouping.

Formative Assessment

Ask students to model regrouping 9 + 4.

Line Up!

When students line up, have them solve addition problems that have two-digit and one-digit numbers that do not require regrouping.

Online Content at ✏ **connectED.mcgraw-hill.com**

Lesson 2 Regroup Ones as Tens   **175-176**

LESSON 3
Add to a Two-Digit Number

OBJECTIVE Add one-digit numbers and two-digit numbers.

What's the Math?

CCSS **Common Core State Standards**
DOMAIN: Operations and Algebraic Thinking

Standards: 2.OA.1, 2.NBT.5, 2.NBT.9
The wording of these standards can be found on page 158.

CCSS

What Students Should Understand

- When adding with two-digit numbers, add the ones and then the tens.
- Regroup if there are ten or more ones. You can use base-ten blocks to help you regroup and find the sum.

What Students Should be Able to Do

Find 26 + 8.

Step 1
Add the ones.
6 + 8 = 14 ones

tens	ones
☐	
2	6
+	8

Step 2
Regroup if needed.
Write how many.

tens	ones
1	
2	6
+	8
	4

Step 3
Add the tens.
1 ten + 2 tens = 3 tens

tens	ones
1	
2	6
+	8
3	4

So, 26 + 8 = 34

Developing Vocabulary

 Review Vocabulary
add

Review Activity

- Ask students what they have learned about adding. For example, they might recall the regrouping lesson in this chapter.
- Have students skim the lesson. Call on volunteers to identify any symbols or words that indicate adding.
- Discuss the responses. Ask students whether some examples were easier to identify than others.

ELL **ELL Support Strategy** Use this vocabulary activity to develop oral language with content specific vocabulary.

My Vocabulary Cards

Have students use the blank card to write a tip about regrouping.

IWB **Virtual Word Wall**

You may wish to add this review word to the Virtual Word Wall for the chapter.

ELL Refer to the Multilingual eGlossary for interactive definitions in 13 languages.

 Building on the Essential Question

In this lesson, students will build upon the skills and concepts needed to answer the chapter's Essential Question "How can I add two-digit numbers?"

Plan Online
Plan for your lesson by using the resources at
 connectED.mcgraw-hill.com

Digital Dashboard
Interactive Whiteboard Ready

The eBook **Glossary** shows the definition of the word and has audio for each definition. The **eGlossary** provides definitions in 13 languages.

Watch as concepts are brought to life through **animations**, **songs**, and a variety of visual instruction.

Virtual Manipulatives with work mats allow teachers and students to model the lesson.

Use **eAssessment** for online assignments and customized assessments.

Use the **Common Core Quick Check** before the lesson to assess students' retention of previously learned concepts.

Use the interactive **Self-Check Quiz** after the lesson to provide immediate feedback on lesson concepts.

Digital and print resources assist students and parents in completing My Homework.

Online games and **apps** provide extra practice for lesson concepts.

Professional development videos help teachers gain a deeper understanding of the lesson concepts and strategies.

Support for **approaching**, **on**- and **beyond-level** students as well as **English Language Learners**.

Reteach and **Enrich** worksheets, **Manipulative Masters**, the **Problem of the Day**, and other blackline masters are available for each lesson.

---

1 LAUNCH THE LESSON

 If your students are well-versed in adding to a two-digit number, you may choose to begin instruction with Step 2, **TEACH**.

You will need
☐ base-ten blocks

Mathematical PRACTICE 4 Modeling the Math

Give half of the class two-digit numbers. Give the other half of the class one-digit numbers.

Have each student find a partner from the opposite group.

Have the pairs use base-ten blocks to model adding their numbers.

Tell students they can also use the number line to help them add.

$$22 + 9$$

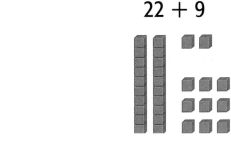

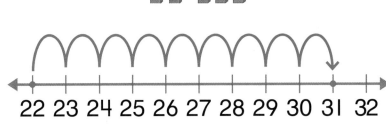

22 23 24 25 26 27 28 29 30 31 32

🕐 **Begin core instruction here.**

You will need
☐ base-ten blocks

Explore and Explain

Read the directions that are on the bottom of the student page.

You need to find the total number of newspapers that were collected. How can you do that? Add 7 and 15.

Guide students in using base-ten blocks to show 7 and 15 in the chart.

When you add with a two-digit number, add the ones first. Then add the tens.

First, you need to find how many ones there are. How many ones are there in all? 12 ones

What do you do when there are 10 or more ones? Regroup or trade 10 ones for 1 ten.

Guide students to make a group of 10 ones, and trading it for 1 tens rod.

How many ones will remain in the ones place? 2 ones

How many tens and ones are there? 2 tens and 2 ones

What number does 2 tens and 2 ones represent? 22

How can you write the number sentence to solve this problem? 7 + 15 = 22 newspapers

See and Show

Help students work through the example at the top of the page.

Work through the steps together. Use actual or virtual base-ten manipulatives to help students visualize the process. Have them trace the dashed numbers as they work the problems.

Work through Exercises 1–5 as a class.

Vocabulary

Direct students' attention to *regrouped*. Explain that *regroup* is the root word in this word, and *–ed* is its ending. Tell students that this ending signals to readers that the action occurred in the past.

Mathematical PRACTICE 3 **Talk Math**

Discuss with students "How do you show that you regrouped?" Sample answer: The 1 in the box in the tens column shows 10 ones regrouped as 1 ten.

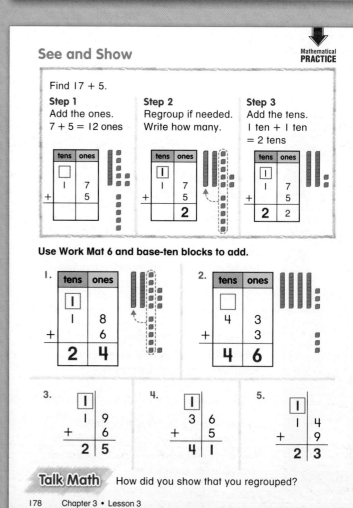

Name _____

On My Own

Use Work Mat 6 and base-ten blocks to add.

6.
```
    [ ]|
    5 | 6
+     | 1
-------
    5 | 7
```

7.
```
    [1]|
    7 | 2
+     | 8
-------
    8 | 0
```

8.
```
    [1]|
    3 | 8
+     | 8
-------
    4 | 6
```

9.
```
    [ ]|
    2 | 4
+     | 4
-------
    2 | 8
```

10.
```
    [1]|
    4 | 3
+     | 9
-------
    5 | 2
```

11.
```
    [1]|
    1 | 3
+     | 7
-------
    2 | 0
```

12.
```
    [1]|
    5 | 1
+     | 9
-------
    6 | 0
```

13.
```
    [1]|
    1 | 7
+     | 6
-------
    2 | 3
```

14.
```
    [1]|
    3 | 8
+     | 4
-------
    4 | 2
```

15.
```
    3 3
+     7
------
    4 0
```

16.
```
    2 2
+     9
------
    3 1
```

17.
```
    6 8
+     3
------
    7 1
```

Chapter 3 • Lesson 3   179

Problem Solving

Mathematical PRACTICE

18. Jaya has 25 stickers on her paper. She adds 4 more stickers. How many stickers does Jaya have now?

29 stickers

19. Micah does 19 cartwheels. Then he does 8 more. How many cartwheels does Micah do altogether?

27 cartwheels

20. 13 children are waiting for the bus. 5 more children get in line for the bus. How many children are waiting for the bus now?

18 children

Write Math Explain how you can solve 14 + 7.
Sample answer: I can regroup the ones. There will be

2 tens and 1 one, or 21.

On My Own

Have students work through the exercises on this page independently. You may choose to assign exercises based on the chart below.

DIFFERENTIATED ASSIGNMENTS
AL **Approaching Level** Guide students through the exercises in On My Own. Help them to use manipulatives while working through the exercises.
OL **On Level** Complete the exercises independently.
BL **Beyond Level** Complete the exercises independently without manipulatives.

Common Error!
Students may have difficulty adding one-digit and two-digit numbers when more than 1 ten is involved. Allow students to use rods and units as they work. When students regroup, encourage them to exchange 10 units for 1 rod each time it is necessary.

Problem Solving

Have students work through the problem-solving exercises on this page independently.

Mathematical PRACTICE 7 In Exercise 19, students **look for and make use of structure.**

Write Math

This exercise asks students to build upon their understanding of concepts needed to answer the chapter's Essential Question.

RESPONSE TO INTERVENTION

DIFFERENTIATED INSTRUCTION

AL APPROACHING LEVEL

IF my students struggle with adding to a two-digit number,

THEN choose a resource:

→ Use the Reteach worksheet with small groups.

→ Go online for a Differentiated Instruction activity.

→ **Show a Model** Write the problem 15 + 9 on the board. Have students draw a picture to show how they can regroup to solve. Students may draw fifteen circles and nine circles. Then they can put rings around groups of ten. 2 tens and 4 ones.

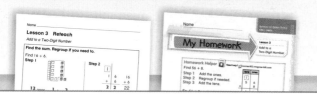

OL ON LEVEL

IF my students seem to know how to add to a two-digit number, but need more practice,

THEN choose a resource:

→ Assign My Homework.

→ Go online for a Differentiated Instruction activity.

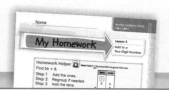

BL BEYOND LEVEL

IF my students have mastered adding to a two-digit number,

THEN choose a resource:

→ Use the Enrich worksheet in cooperative groups.

→ Assign My Homework.

→ Go online for a Differentiated Instruction activity.

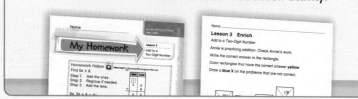

AL Name _____

Lesson 3 Reteach

Add to a Two-Digit Number

Find the sum. Regroup if you need to.

Find 16 + 6.

Step 1

__12__ ones = __1__ ten __2__ ones

Step 2

	1	
1	6	16
+	6	+ 6
2	2	22

Add the ones.
Add the tens.

Add. Regroup if you need to.

1. Find 35 + 6.

Step 1

Step 2

1		
3	5	35
+	6	+ 6
4	1	41

__11__ ones = __1__ ten __1__ one

Add the ones.
Add the tens.

2. Find 24 + 9.

Step 1

Step 2

1		
2	4	24
+	9	+ 9
3	3	33

__13__ ones = __1__ ten __3__ ones

Add the ones.
Add the tens.

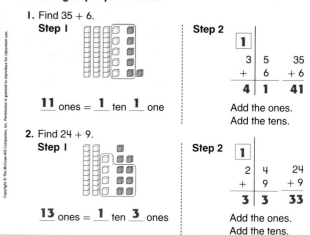

BL Name _____

Lesson 3 Enrich

Add to a Two-Digit Number

Annie is practicing addition. Check Annie's work.

Write the correct answer in the rectangle.

Color rectangles that have the correct answer **yellow**.

Draw a **blue X** on the problems that are not correct.

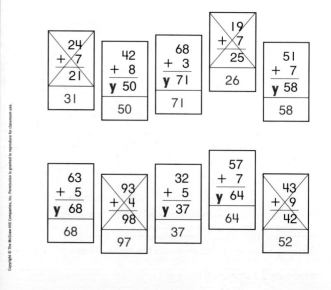

Annie has __6__ correct problems.

Name _____

My Homework →

Lesson 3
Add to a
Two-Digit Number

Homework Helper  **Need help?** connectED.mcgraw-hill.com

Find 56 + 8.

Step 1   Add the ones.
Step 2   Regroup if needed.
Step 3   Add the tens.

	tens	ones
	1	
	5	6
+		8
	6	4

So, 56 + 8 = 64.

Practice

Add.

1.
```
  |1|
   6 6
 +   6
 ─────
   7 2
```

2.
```
  |□|
   8 4
 +   3
 ─────
   8 7
```

3.
```
  |1|
   2 9
 +   4
 ─────
   3 3
```

4.
```
  |1|
   3 7
 +   9
 ─────
   4 6
```

5.
```
  |1|
   2 1
 +   9
 ─────
   3 0
```

6.
```
  |1|
   4 5
 +   6
 ─────
   5 1
```

Chapter 3 • Lesson 3   181

Add.

7.
```
  |1|
   3 8
 +   3
 ─────
   4 1
```

8.
```
  |1|
   7 8
 +   7
 ─────
   8 5
```

9.
```
  |1|
   8 3
 +   8
 ─────
   8 1
```

10. There are 24 students in Ms. Ito's class. 5 more students join her class. How many students are there now?

Coach Harry is awesome!

29 students

11. Harry coaches 25 children on Wednesday. On Saturday, he coaches 9 more children. How many children does he coach in all?

34 children

Test Practice

12. Fifty-four people were early for the Tigers' game. Nine people were late. How many people came to the game?

63 ●   52 ○   44 ○   20 ○

 Math at Home Ask your child to show you how to add 14 and 8. Then ask your child to show you how to add 27 and 2.

182   Chapter 3 • Lesson 3

---

4 WRAP IT UP

My Homework

Assign homework after successful completion of the lesson. Students who understand the concepts may skip the **Homework Helper** section.

Test Practice
Diagnose Student Errors

Class trends in wrong answers may indicate common errors or misconceptions.

63 correct

52 error in computation

44 misunderstood concept; subtracted instead of adding

20 did not read the question

Formative Assessment

Ask students to find the sum of 18 + 8. Have them draw pictures to show one way to find the sum.

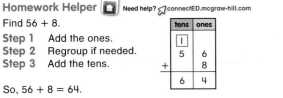

Line Up!

When students line up for recess, lunch, or dismissal, practice strategies for addition facts. Give students numbers and have them count on 1, 2, or 3 more numbers.

Check My Progress

Use this as a formative assessment to determine if your students are struggling, and if so, with which topics they struggle. The criteria for differentiation are on the next page.

Vocabulary Check

Have a student read aloud the words in the word bank. Ask volunteers to use each word in a sentence.

ELL **ELL Support Strategy** Use this information to participate in purposeful, cooperative learning activities.

Concept Check

These concepts are covered in Lesson 1–3.

Exercises	Concept	Review Lesson
5–6	Take apart tens to add	1
7–9	Regroup ones as tens	2
10-12	Add two-digit numbers	3

Problem Solving

Exercise 13 uses a word problem to check for understanding of adding a one-digit and a two-digit number.

Test Practice

Diagnose Student Errors

Class trends in wrong answers may indicate common errors or misconceptions.

40 correct
31 used first number
22 subtracted 31−9
 9 used the second number

Name _____

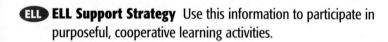
Check My Progress

Vocabulary Check

Complete each sentence.

    sum   add   **regroup**   addends

1. You can **regroup** 10 ones into 1 ten.
2. The __sum__ is the answer to an addition problem.
3. You __add__ by joining two numbers together.
4. The numbers you join when adding are called __addends__ .

Concept Check

Take apart an addend to solve.

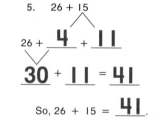

5.   26 + 15

$26 + $ **4** $ + $ **11**

30 $ + $ **11** $ = $ **41**

So, 26 + 15 = **41** .

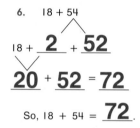

6.   18 + 54

$18 + $ **2** $ + $ **52**

20 $ + $ **52** $ = $ **72**

So, 18 + 54 = **72** .

Chapter 3   183

Add.

7.
```
   1
   4 | 5
 + | 9
   5 | 4
```

8.
```
   1
   7 | 3
 + | 8
   8 | 1
```

9.
```
   □
   2 | 6
 + | 3
   2 | 9
```

10.   24
   + 9
   33

11.   43
   + 7
   50

12.   18
   + 4
   22

13. Liam's boy scout troop collected 18 bins of plastic bottles to recycle. Landon's troop collected 9 bins. How many bins did the boy scouts collect in all?

        27 bins

Test Practice

14. 31 people are in the store. 9 more people come into the store. How many people are in the store now?

    40   31   22   9
    ●   ○   ○   ○

184   Chapter 3

Name _____

Check My Progress *(Lessons 1 through 3)*

Break apart an addend to solve.

1. 46 + 35

    46 + __4__ + __31__

    __50__ + __31__ = __81__

    So, 46 + 35 = __81__

2. 28 + 64

    28 + __2__ + __62__

    __30__ + __62__ = __92__

    So, 28 + 64 = __92__

Circle the ones to show regrouping. Draw your answer.

3. 15 + 7 = __22__

4. 26 + 6 = __32__

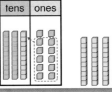

RESPONSE TO INTERVENTION

Rtl

CCSS

DIFFERENTIATED INSTRUCTION

AL **STRATEGIC INTERVENTION**

IF **students miss 5 or more,**

THEN **choose a resource:**

→ Check My Progress

→ Self-Check Quiz

→ Use the Reteach worksheets.

OL **ON LEVEL**

IF **students miss 3 to 4,**

THEN **choose a resource:**

→ Chapter Project

→ Proceed to the next lesson.

BL **BEYOND LEVEL**

IF **students miss 2 or less,**

THEN **choose a resource:**

→ Chapter Project

→ Use the Enrich worksheets.

→ Proceed to the next lesson.

LESSON 4
Add Two-Digit Numbers

OBJECTIVE Add two-digit numbers.

What's the Math?

Common Core State Standards
DOMAIN: Operations and Algebraic Thinking
Standards: 2.OA.1, 2.NBT.5, 2.NBT.9
The wording of these standards can be found on page 158.

What Students Should Understand

- When adding two two-digit numbers, add the ones and then the tens.
- Regroup if there are ten or more ones. You can use base-ten blocks to help you regroup and find the sum.

What Students Should be Able to Do

Find $15 + 27$.

Step 1
Add the ones.
$5 + 7 = 12$ ones

tens	ones
☐	
1	5
+ 2	7

Step 2
Regroup if needed.
Write how many.

tens	ones
1	
1	5
+ 2	7
	2

Step 3
Add the tens.
1 ten + 1 ten + 2 tens = 4 tens

tens	ones
1	
1	5
+ 2	7
4	2

So, $15 + 27 = 42$

Developing Vocabulary

 Review Vocabulary

regroup

Review Activity

- Have students skim the lesson. Point out the tens and ones chart. Ask students how the exercises in these charts differ from the charts used in the previous lesson. Both addends in this lesson contain two digits.

- Ask volunteers to explain how the place-value charts help them regroup addition problems.

ELL ELL Support Strategy Use this vocabulary activity to participate in purposeful cooperative learning activities.

My Vocabulary Cards

Have students use blank cards to write a question they have about adding two-digit numbers. Collect the cards to informally assess students' comprehension of this chapter.

ELL Refer to the Multilingual eGlossary for interactive definitions in 13 languages.

? Building on the Essential Question

In this lesson, students will build upon the skills and concepts needed to answer the chapter's Essential Question "How can I add two-digit numbers?"

Digital Dashboard

 Interactive Whiteboard Ready

 Vocab
The eBook **Glossary** shows the definition of the word and has audio for each definition. The **eGlossary** provides definitions in 13 languages.

 Watch
Watch as concepts are brought to life through **animations**, **songs**, and a variety of visual instruction.

 Tools
Virtual Manipulatives with work mats allow teachers and students to model the lesson.

 Check
Use **eAssessment** for online assignments and customized assessments.

Use the **Common Core Quick Check** before the lesson to assess students' retention of previously learned concepts.

Use the interactive **Self-Check Quiz** after the lesson to provide immediate feedback on lesson concepts.

 eHelp
Digital and print resources assist students and parents in completing My Homework.

 Games
Online games and **apps** provide extra practice for lesson concepts.

 PD
Professional development videos help teachers gain a deeper understanding of the lesson concepts and strategies.

 RtI
Support for **approaching**, **on-** and **beyond-level** students as well as **English Language Learners**.

 Masters
Reteach and **Enrich** worksheets, **Manipulative Masters**, the **Problem of the Day**, and other blackline masters are available for each lesson.

---

1 LAUNCH THE LESSON

 If your students are well-versed in adding two-digit numbers, you may choose to begin instruction with Step 2, **TEACH**.

Mathematical **PRACTICE 4** **Modeling the Math**

How do football players show how many touchdowns they have made? Sample answer: Some like to put a football sticker on their helmets each time they get a touchdown.

Ask small groups of students to determine a way to show this problem without using individual football stickers: *Jason put stickers on his helmet for each touchdown he made. There are 14 stickers on the left side and 10 stickers on the right side. How many did he get altogether?* 24; See students' responses.

Tell students they can also use a number line similar to the one below to help them add.

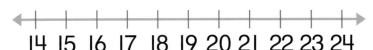

14 15 16 17 18 19 20 21 22 23 24

 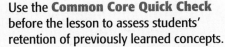

TEACH

🕐 **Begin core instruction here.**

You will need

☐ base-ten blocks

Explore and Explain

Read the directions that are on the bottom of the student page.

What do we need to find? The total number of flowers that Mr. Kay's class sold in all. *How can we do that?* Add 45 and 26.

Guide students to use base-ten blocks to show 45 in the box that says Week 1, and show 26 in the box that says Week 2.

When you add with a two-digit number, do you add the ones or tens first? ones

How many ones are there in all? 11 ones

What do you do when there are 10 or more ones? Regroup or trade 10 ones for 1 ten.

Guide students to make a group of 10 ones and trading it for 1 tens rod.

How many ones will remain in the ones place? 1

How many tens and ones are there now? 7 tens and 1 one

How should you write the number sentence to solve this problem? 45 + 26 = 71 flowers

See and Show

Help students work through the example at the top of the page. Write the problem 18 + 25 on the board. Rewrite the problem vertically. Add the ones.

What does 8 + 5 equal? 13

Write 3 and then regroup the ten ones over to the tens column.

Add the tens.

What does 1 + 1+ 2 equal? 4

So, 18 + 25 = 43. Have students look at the demonstration of this with the base-ten blocks. Use base-ten blocks in class if they help students to visualize the math. Have them trace the dashed numbers as they work the problems.

Work through Exercises 1–5 as a class.

Mathematical PRACTICE 3 → **Talk Math**

Discuss with students "What do you do first when you add two-digit numbers?" Sample answer: I add the ones.

CORE INSTRUCTION

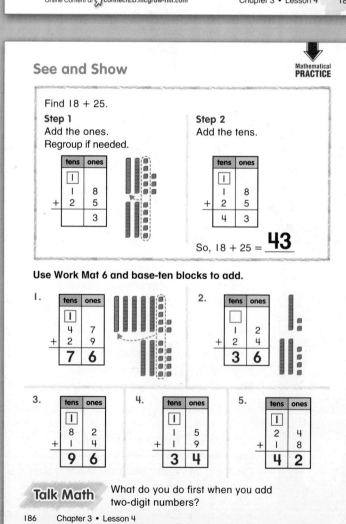

185-186 **Chapter 3** Add Two-Digit Numbers

Name _____

On My Own

Use Work Mat 6 and base-ten blocks to add.

6.
tens	ones
[1]	
3	3
+ 1	8
5	**1**

7.
tens	ones
[1]	
6	4
+ 2	6
9	**0**

8.
tens	ones
[1]	
5	8
+ 1	2
7	**0**

9.
[1]	
3	6
+ 2	7
6	**3**

10.
☐	
2	2
+ 1	0
3	**2**

11.
[1]	
5	9
+ 1	3
7	**2**

12.
[1]	
4	6
+ 2	6
7	**2**

13.
[1]	
2	8
+ 1	8
4	**6**

14.
[1]	
	9
+ 3	2
4	**1**

15.
```
   42
+  42
   84
```

16.
```
    7
+  27
   34
```

17.
```
    8
+  11
   19
```

Problem Solving

18. Tia fed her turtle 30 times in June and 31 times in July. How many times did she feed her turtle?

61 times

Is it lunch time yet?

19. There are 25 chairs in one classroom. There are 28 chairs in another classroom. How many chairs are there in all?

53 chairs

20. The pet store has 14 small lizards. There are also 16 large lizards. How many lizards are at the pet store in all?

30 lizards

Write Math How is adding 21 + 9 different than adding 21 + 19?

Sample answer: You may have 3 digits in the tens

column to add instead of 2.

On My Own

Have students work through the exercises on this page independently. You may choose to assign exercises based on the chart below.

DIFFERENTIATED ASSIGNMENTS

AL Approaching Level Guide students through the exercises in On My Own. Help them to use manipulatives.

OL On Level Complete the exercises independently.

BL Beyond Level Complete the exercises independently without manipulatives.

Common Error!

Students may have difficulty lining up the numerals to add them correctly. You may want to make photocopies of several place-value charts for students to write on as they solve the problems.

Problem Solving

Have students work through the problem-solving exercises on this page independently.

Mathematical PRACTICE 1 In Exercise 19, students **make sense of problems and persevere in solving them.**

Write Math

This exercise asks students to build upon their understanding of concepts needed to answer the chapter's Essential Question.

AL   APPROACHING LEVEL

IF my students struggle with adding two-digit numbers,

THEN choose a resource:

→ Use the Reteach worksheet with small groups.

→ Go online for a Differentiated Instruction activity.

→ **Show a Model** Write the problem 15 + 16 on the board. Model how to write the numbers correctly on a place-value chart. Next to each numeral, draw a picture to represent the value of that numeral. You can draw ten stars next to the 1 digit in 15 and five stars next to the 5.

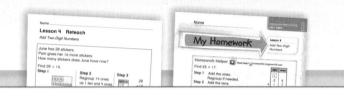

OL   ON LEVEL

IF my students seem to know how to add two-digit numbers, but need more practice,

THEN choose a resource:

→ Assign My Homework.

→ Go online for a Differentiated Instruction activity.

BL   BEYOND LEVEL

IF my students have mastered adding two-digit numbers,

THEN choose a resource:

→ Use the Enrich worksheet in cooperative groups.

→ Assign My Homework.

→ Go online for a Differentiated Instruction activity.

AL   Name _____

Lesson 4   Reteach

Add Two-Digit Numbers

June has 28 stickers.
Pam gives her 16 more stickers.
How many stickers does June have now?

Find 28 + 16.

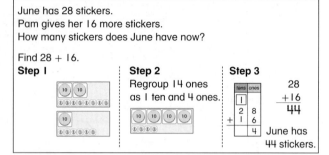

Step 1

Step 2
Regroup 14 ones
as 1 ten and 4 ones.

Step 3

$$\begin{array}{r} 28 \\ +16 \\ \hline 44 \end{array}$$

June has 44 stickers.

Add. You can use counters to help. Regroup if you need to.

1.
tens	ones
1	
3	7
+ 2	7
6	**4**

2.
tens	ones
1	
3	5
+ 1	5
5	**0**

3.
tens	ones
1	
4	8
+ 2	5
7	**3**

4.
tens	ones
1	
1	9
+ 6	8
8	**7**

5.
tens	ones
3	6
+ 4	3
7	**9**

6.
tens	ones
1	
5	4
+ 2	7
8	**1**

BL   Name _____

Lesson 4   Enrich

Add Two-Digit Numbers

Drop a counter on the game board two times. On another piece of paper, add the two numbers.

The person with the greater sum gets one point.

You get two points if you have to regroup when you add and get the greater sum.

Make a score sheet, and use tally marks to keep score.

The first player to get 10 points or more wins the game.

14	37	52	38
25	46	17	21
43	33	28	39
27	11	42	30
65	27	92	86

Name _____

Operations and Algebraic Thinking
2.OA.1, 2.NBT.5

CCSS

My Homework

Lesson 4
Add Two-Digit
Numbers

Homework Helper Need help? connectED.mcgraw-hill.com

Find 25 + 17.

	tens	ones
	1	
	2	5
+	1	7
	4	2

Step 1   Add the ones.
             Regroup if needed.
Step 2   Add the tens.

So, 25 + 17 = 42.

Practice
Add.

1.

tens	ones
1	
3	5
+ 2	5
6	**0**

2.

tens	ones
1	
4	8
+ 1	8
6	**6**

3.

tens	ones
1	
1	5
+ 5	9
7	**4**

4.

1	
5	6
+ 3	5
9	**1**

5.

1	
2	7
+ 2	8
5	**5**

6.

1	4
+ 3	3
4	**7**

Chapter 3 • Lesson 4   189

Add.

7.
```
   53
 + 35
 ----
   88
```

8.
```
   23
 + 58
 ----
   81
```

9.
```
   83
 + 13
 ----
   96
```

10.
```
   62
 + 28
 ----
   90
```

11.
```
   53
 + 39
 ----
   92
```

12.
```
   49
 + 24
 ----
   73
```

13. Brad's family picks 22 pounds of cherries.
Seth's family picks 43 pounds. How many
pounds of cherries did they pick in all?

_**65**_ pounds

Test Practice

14. 46 people came to the museum early. 39 more
people came late. How many people came to the
museum in all?

86 ○   85 ●   39 ○   7 ○

 Math at Home Take two 2-digit numbers from your phone number and have your
child add them. Example: 555-1234; 12 + 34 = 46

190   Chapter 3 • Lesson 4

My Homework

Assign homework after successful completion of the lesson.
Students who understand the concepts may skip the
Homework Helper section.

Test Practice
Diagnose Student Errors

Class trends in wrong answers may indicate common errors or
misconceptions.

86   added incorrectly

85   correct

39   identified an addend

7   subtracted

Formative Assessment

Ask students to find the sum of 36 + 15. Have students draw
a place-value chart and put each numeral in the correct place
before adding. 51

 MY Learning Stations

Use the game **Pick Your Path** and the graphic novel **Tickets
to the Puppet Show** after this lesson. The Teacher Guide
provides suggestions for differentiated instruction.

Line Up!

When students line up for recess, lunch, or
dismissal, have them add one-digit and two-digit
numbers. Tell them to snap eleven times. Then
have them tap their heads seven times. *How
many taps and snaps?* 18

LESSON 5
Rewrite Two-Digit Addition

OBJECTIVE Rewrite horizontal addition problems vertically to add.

What's the Math?

Common Core State Standards
DOMAIN: Operations and Algebraic Thinking

Standards: 2.OA.1, 2.NBT.5
The wording of these standards can be found on page 158.

CCSS

What Students Should Understand

- You can rewrite a horizontal addition problem vertically before finding the sum.
- After rewriting the problem, add the ones, regroup if needed, and then add the tens.

What Students Should be Able to Do

Find $39 + 22$.
Write the ones digits in the ones column.
Write the tens digits in the tens column.
Add the ones. Regroup if needed.
Then add the tens.

tens	ones
1	
3	9
+ 2	2
6	1

 Building on the Essential Question

In this lesson, students will build upon the skills and concepts needed to answer the chapter's Essential Question "How can I add two-digit numbers?"

Developing Vocabulary

 Review Vocabulary
add

Review Activity

- Ask students to skim the chapter. Tell them to identify any words, phrases, or symbols that indicate addition.
- Have students explain how these words contribute to their knowledge of addition.

ELL **ELL Support Strategy** Use this vocabulary activity to develop and advance mathematical language skills.

My Vocabulary Cards

Have students work in small groups to discuss the examples they have written on the blank cards in this chapter.

ELL Refer to the Multilingual eGlossary for interactive definitions in 13 languages.

Plan Online

Plan for your lesson by using the resources at

 connectED.mcgraw-hill.com

Digital Dashboard

Interactive Whiteboard Ready

 Vocab

The eBook **Glossary** shows the definition of the word and has audio for each definition. The **eGlossary** provides definitions in 13 languages.

 Watch

Watch as concepts are brought to life through **animations**, **songs**, and a variety of visual instruction.

 Tools

Virtual Manipulatives with work mats allow teachers and students to model the lesson.

 Check

Use **eAssessment** for online assignments and customized assessments.

Use the **Common Core Quick Check** before the lesson to assess students' retention of previously learned concepts.

Use the interactive **Self-Check Quiz** after the lesson to provide immediate feedback on lesson concepts.

 eHelp

Digital and print resources assist students and parents in completing My Homework.

 Games

Online games and **apps** provide extra practice for lesson concepts.

 PD

Professional development videos help teachers gain a deeper understanding of the lesson concepts and strategies.

 RtI

Support for **approaching**, **on-** and **beyond-level** students as well as **English Language Learners**.

 Masters

Reteach and **Enrich** worksheets, **Manipulative Masters**, the **Problem of the Day**, and other blackline masters are available for each lesson.

---

1 LAUNCH THE LESSON

 If your students are well-versed in rewriting two-digit addition, you may choose to begin instruction with Step 2, TEACH.

You will need

☐ notecards or papers the size of note cards

Mathematical PRACTICE 4 Modeling the Math

Create cards with two-digit numbers on them.

Write a blank horizontal and vertical number sentence on the board. Have two cards with two-digit numbers on them ready to give to students.

I would like two students to tape these two cards in their places in the number sentence on the board.

Discuss the placement of the cards with the class.

Now I would like two more students to move those number cards to the vertical number sentence.

Have a volunteer solve the problem. Ask him or her which form of the problem they prefer to use. After they solve the problem, discuss which problem is easier to solve, vertical or horizontal.

$$ \boxed{15} \quad + \quad \boxed{22} \quad = \quad \underline{\qquad} $$

$$
\begin{array}{r}
\boxed{15} \\
+ \ \boxed{22} \\
\hline
\end{array}
$$

Richard Hutchings/Digital Light Source, Inc.

 **TEACH**

 Begin core instruction here.

You will need

☐ tens and ones place-value chart or Work Mat 6

Explore and Explain

Read the directions that are on the bottom of the student page.

We need to find how many runs were scored in all. How can we do that? Add 11 and 8.

Write 11 + 8 = ___ on the board horizontally.

We can rewrite this addition problem in the place-value chart with one addend on top of the other.

Guide students in writing 11 + 8 vertically in the place-value chart.

Which place value should we add first, ones or tens? ones

How many ones are there in all? 9 ones

Do we need to regroup the ones? no *Why not?* There are less than 10 ones.

Lead students in writing 9 in the sum in the ones place

How many tens are there in all? 1 ten

Guide students in writing 1 in the sum in the tens place.

How many runs were scored in all? 19 runs

ELL Use tiered questions to informally assess students' progress.

Beginning: What is the title of this lesson?

Intermediate: Which two words are shown in the place-value chart on page 191?

Advanced: Summarize the steps used to rewrite two-digit addition problems.

See and Show

Help students work through the example at the top of the page. Guide students to rewriting the horizontal addition problem vertically before adding. Have students trace the dashed numbers as they work the problems.

Work through Exercises 1–6 as a class.

Mathematical PRACTICE ③ **Talk Math**

Discuss with students "Why is it helpful to rewrite addition?" Sample answer: It is easier to show regrouping when the ones and tens are lined up in columns.

 **CORE INSTRUCTION**

Name _____

Operations and Algebraic Thinking
2.OA.1, 2.NBT.5 **CCSS**

Rewrite Two-Digit Addition

Lesson 5

ESSENTIAL QUESTION
How can I add two-digit numbers?

Explore and Explain 🔧 Tools

Emily's going to get a hit. Just watch!

11 + 8

tens	ones
+	

19 runs

That's Emily.

Teacher Directions: Emily's baseball team is playing a baseball game to raise money for a children's hospital. Emily's team scored 11 runs in the game. The other team scored 8 runs. How many runs were scored in all? Write the numbers in the place-value chart and add.

Online Content at 🖱 connectED.mcgraw-hill.com   Chapter 3 • Lesson 5   191

See and Show

Mathematical PRACTICE

You can rewrite a problem to add.

Find 35 + 26.

Step 1 Write one addend below the other addend. Line up the tens and the ones.

Step 2 Add. Regroup if necessary.

```
  1
  3 | 5
+ 2 | 6
  6 | 1
```

Rewrite the problem. Add.

1. 64 + 22
```
  6 | 4
+ 2 | 2
  8 | 6
```

2. 26 + 65
```
  2 | 6
+ 6 | 5
  9 | 1
```

3. 36 + 36
```
  3 | 6
+ 3 | 6
  7 | 2
```

4. 73 + 19
```
  7 | 3
+ 1 | 9
  9 | 2
```

5. 47 + 18
```
  4 | 7
+ 1 | 8
  6 | 5
```

6. 56 + 37
```
  5 | 6
+ 3 | 7
  9 | 3
```

Talk Math Why is it helpful to rewrite addition?

192   Chapter 3 • Lesson 5

3 PRACTICE & APPLY

Name _____

Bring it home!

On My Own

Rewrite the problem. Add.

7. 26 + 36

$$\begin{array}{r} 2\,6 \\ +\,3\,6 \\ \hline 6\,2 \end{array}$$

8. 17 + 19

$$\begin{array}{r} 1\,7 \\ +\,1\,9 \\ \hline 3\,6 \end{array}$$

9. 74 + 16

$$\begin{array}{r} 7\,4 \\ +\,1\,6 \\ \hline 9\,0 \end{array}$$

10. 18 + 63

$$\begin{array}{r} 1\,8 \\ +\,6\,3 \\ \hline 8\,1 \end{array}$$

11. 64 + 27

$$\begin{array}{r} 6\,4 \\ +\,2\,7 \\ \hline 9\,1 \end{array}$$

12. 73 + 18

$$\begin{array}{r} 7\,3 \\ +\,1\,8 \\ \hline 9\,1 \end{array}$$

13. 56 + 23

$$\begin{array}{r} 5\,6 \\ +\,2\,3 \\ \hline 7\,9 \end{array}$$

14. 37 + 39

$$\begin{array}{r} 3\,7 \\ +\,3\,9 \\ \hline 7\,6 \end{array}$$

15. 28 + 33

$$\begin{array}{r} 2\,8 \\ +\,3\,3 \\ \hline 6\,1 \end{array}$$

Chapter 3 • Lesson 5   193

On My Own

Have students work through the exercises on this page independently. You may choose to assign exercises based on the chart below.

DIFFERENTIATED ASSIGNMENTS
AL **Approaching Level** Guide students through the exercises in On My Own. Help them to use manipulatives while working through the exercises.
OL **On Level** Complete the exercises independently.
BL **Beyond Level** Complete the exercises independently without manipulatives.

Problem Solving

Have students work through the problem-solving exercises on this page independently.

Mathematical **PRACTICE** **7** — In Exercise 16, students **look for and make use of structure.**

HOT Problem This exercise asks students to build upon their understanding of concepts needed to answer the chapter's Essential Question.

Problem Solving

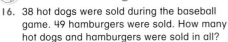 Mathematical **PRACTICE**

16. 38 hot dogs were sold during the baseball game. 49 hamburgers were sold. How many hot dogs and hamburgers were sold in all?

87 hot dogs and hamburgers

17. 65 boys and 29 girls came to watch the baseball game. How many boys and girls came to watch the game?

 All for one!

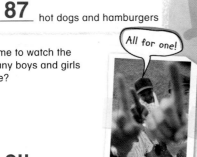

94 boys and girls

HOT Problem There are 13 players on the Panthers baseball team, 15 players on the Eagles team, and 14 players on the Lions team. How many players are on all three teams? Explain.

Sample answer: 13 + 15 = 28. 28 + 14 = 42 players in all.

194   Chapter 3 • Lesson 5

RtI RESPONSE TO INTERVENTION

DIFFERENTIATED INSTRUCTION

AL) APPROACHING LEVEL

IF my students struggle with rewriting two-digit addition,

THEN choose a resource:

→ Use the Reteach worksheet with small groups.

→ Go online for a Differentiated Instruction activity.

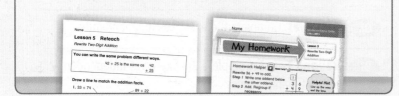

OL) ON LEVEL

IF my students seem to know how to rewrite two-digit addition, but need more practice,

THEN choose a resource:

→ Assign My Homework.

→ Go online for a Differentiated Instruction activity.

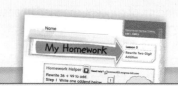

BL) BEYOND LEVEL

IF my students have mastered rewriting two-digit addition,

THEN choose a resource:

→ Use the Differentiated Instruction activity on p. 157B.

→ Use the Enrich Worksheet in cooperative groups.

→ Assign My Homework.

→ Go online for a Differentiated Instruction activity.

AL

Name _____

Lesson 5   Reteach

Rewrite Two-Digit Addition

> **You can write the same problem different ways.**
>
> 42 + 25 is the same as   42
>   + 25

Draw a line to match the addition facts.

1. 33 + 74   89 + 22

2.   89   53 + 99
   + 22

3. 75 + 48   33
                            + 74

4. 19 + 56   19
                            + 56

5.   67   75
   + 15   + 48

6.   53   67 + 15
   + 99

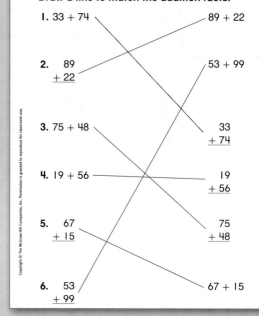

BL

Name _____

Lesson 5   Enrich

Rewrite Two-Digit Addition

Follow the directions.

1. Place an **X** on the problem if the answer is 87.

2. Draw a **rectangle** around the problem that is the same as 45 + 70.

3. Draw a **trapezoid** around the problems with a sum of 60.

4. Draw a **triangle** around the problem that is equal to   66
                                                            + 33

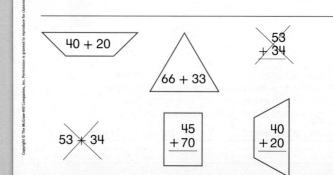

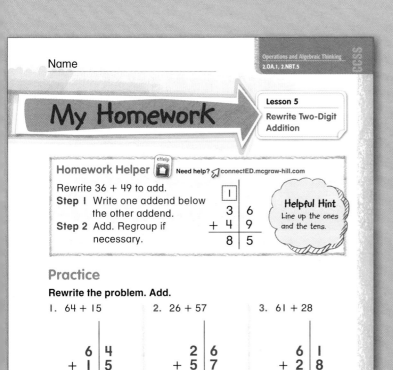

Name _____

Operations and Algebraic Thinking
2.OA.1, 2.NBT.5

My Homework

Lesson 5
Rewrite Two-Digit
Addition

Homework Helper 🖥 Need help? ⤢ connectED.mcgraw-hill.com

Rewrite 36 + 49 to add.
Step 1 Write one addend below the other addend.
Step 2 Add. Regroup if necessary.

	1	
	3	6
+	4	9
	8	5

Helpful Hint
Line up the ones and the tens.

Practice

Rewrite the problem. Add.

1. 64 + 15

	6	4
+	1	5
	7	9

2. 26 + 57

	2	6
+	5	7
	8	3

3. 61 + 28

	6	1
+	2	8
	8	9

4. 37 + 47

```
  37
+ 47
────
  84
```

5. 49 + 38

```
  49
+ 38
────
  87
```

6. 34 + 18

```
  34
+ 18
────
  52
```

Chapter 3 • Lesson 5   195

Rewrite the problem. Add.

7. 72 + 17

```
  72
+ 17
────
  89
```

8. 19 + 18

```
  19
+ 18
────
  37
```

9. 29 + 35

```
  29
+ 35
────
  64
```

10. 43 girls ran the race. 38 boys ran the race. How many people ran the race in all?

Gosh, I hope they don't drop me!

Relay!

_81_ people

Test Practice

11. Mark the answer that shows how to rewrite and solve 46 + 38.

```
              316
   46          4̶6̶          46          46
 +38         −38         +38         +38
 ────        ────        ────        ────
  74           8          84          85
  ○            ○           ●           ○
```

 Math at Home Write 35 + 38 on a piece of paper. Have your child rewrite the problem and solve it.

196   Chapter 3 • Lesson 5

4 WRAP IT UP

CCSS

My Homework

Assign homework after successful completion of the lesson. Students who understand the concepts may skip the **Homework Helper** section.

Test Practice
Diagnose Student Errors

Class trends in wrong answers may indicate common errors or misconceptions.

```
  46
+ 38
────
  74
```
did not regroup correctly

```
   3
  4̶6̶
− 38
────
   8
```
subtracted

```
   1
  46
+ 38
────
  84
```
correct

```
   1
  46
+ 38
────
  85
```
added incorrectly

Formative Assessment

Write a horizontal addition problem on the board. Have students rewrite it vertically and solve.

 MY Learning Stations

Use the activity card **Telephone Words** after this lesson. The Teacher Guide provides suggestions for differentiated instruction.

LESSON 6
Add Three or Four Two-Digit Numbers

OBJECTIVE   Add three and four two-digit numbers.

What's the Math?

Common Core State Standards
DOMAIN: Operations and Algebraic Thinking
Standards: 2.NBT.6, 2.NBT.9
The wording of these standards can be found on page 158.

CCSS

What Students Should Understand
- You can add three or four two-digit numbers.
- You can use the same steps to add three or four two-digit numbers that you use to add two two-digit numbers. First, line up the ones and tens digits. Add the ones. Regroup if needed. Add the tens.
- When you add the ones digits, look for facts that you know.

What Students Should be Able to Do
Add four numbers.

$$
\begin{array}{r}
\overset{\text{\tiny 1}}{38} \\
12 \\
23 \\
+\ 14 \\
\hline
87
\end{array}
\qquad
\begin{array}{l}
8 + 2 = 10 \\
10 + 3 = 13 \\
13 + 4 = 17
\end{array}
$$

 Building on the Essential Question
In this lesson, students will build upon the skills and concepts needed to answer the chapter's Essential Question "How can I add two-digit numbers?"

Developing Vocabulary

Vocab
Review Vocabulary
ones   tens

Review Activity
- Skim the lesson with students. Have them point out examples or exercises showing ones and tens lined up.
- Explain that it is important that ones and tens are lined up clearly when adding two-digit addends.
- Have students compare the two examples in the text box on the second page of the lesson.

ELL **ELL Support Strategy** Use this vocabulary activity to provide non-linguistic representations by students of their comprehension.

My Vocabulary Cards
Ask students which of the activities using blank cards was most helpful in understanding this chapter.

IWB **Virtual Word Wall**
You may wish to add these review words to the Virtual Word Wall for the chapter.

ELL Refer to the Multilingual eGlossary for interactive definitions in 13 languages.

Plan Online

Plan for your lesson by using the resources at

 connectED.mcgraw-hill.com

Digital Dashboard
Interactive Whiteboard Ready

 Vocab
The eBook **Glossary** shows the definition of the word and has audio for each definition. The **eGlossary** provides definitions in 13 languages.

 Watch
Watch as concepts are brought to life through **animations**, **songs**, and a variety of visual instruction.

 Tools
Virtual Manipulatives with work mats allow teachers and students to model the lesson.

 Check
Use **eAssessment** for online assignments and customized assessments.

Use the **Common Core Quick Check** before the lesson to assess students' retention of previously learned concepts.

Use the interactive **Self-Check Quiz** after the lesson to provide immediate feedback on lesson concepts.

 eHelp
Digital and print resources assist students and parents in completing My Homework.

 Games
Online games and **apps** provide extra practice for lesson concepts.

 PD
Professional development videos help teachers gain a deeper understanding of the lesson concepts and strategies.

 RtI
Support for **approaching**, **on**- and **beyond-level** students as well as **English Language Learners**.

 Masters
Reteach and **Enrich** worksheets, **Manipulative Masters**, the **Problem of the Day**, and other blackline masters are available for each lesson.

---

1 LAUNCH THE LESSON

 If your students are well-versed in adding three and four two-digit numbers, you may choose to begin instruction with Step 2, **TEACH**.

You will need
☐ number cubes
☐ connecting cubes

Mathematical PRACTICE 4 Modeling the Math

Provide groups of three students with three number cubes and 20 connecting cubes. Assign the roles of recorder, manipulator, and calculator in each group.

Have each student roll the number cube and take the corresponding number of connecting cubes.

The recorder writes the numbers to create a column addition problem. The manipulator combines the cubes to make a ten, if possible. The calculator tells how many ones and tens in all, and the recorder writes the sum.

 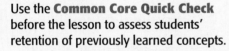

Begin core instruction here.

You will need

☐ base-ten blocks

Explore and Explain

Read the directions that are on the bottom of the student page.

We need to find how many cars were washed in all. How can we do that? Add 13, 22, and 14. *To find 13 + 22 + 14, you can use base-ten blocks to represent each addend. Then figure out how many base-ten blocks you have in all.*

Guide students in using base-ten blocks to represent 13, 22, and 14.

How many ones are there in all? 9 ones

Do we need to regroup the ones? no *Why not?* There are less than 10 ones.

How many tens are there in all? 4 tens

How many cars were washed in all? 49 cars

Another way that we could have added these three numbers is we could have used the same steps that we have used in previous lessons. We could have added the ones first and then added the tens.

See and Show

Help students work through the example at the top of the page. Discuss the helpful hint. Have students look for any other options of facts they know. Have them trace the dashed numbers as they work the problems.

Work through Exercises 1–8 as a class. As you work through the first couple of exercises, remind students to look for facts they know.

Mathematical PRACTICE 3   **Talk Math**

Discuss with students "How is adding 3 two-digit numbers like adding 2 two-digit numbers?" Sample answer: You add the ones first, then regroup, then add the tens.

Name _____

Operations and Algebraic Thinking
2.NBT.6, 2.NBT.9   CCSS

Add Three and Four Two-Digit Numbers

Lesson 6
ESSENTIAL QUESTION
How can I add two-digit numbers?

Explore and Explain   Watch ▶ Tools

CANNONBALL!

tens	ones

49 cars

Teacher Directions: Miley's class is having a car wash. They washed 13 blue cars, 22 red cars, and 14 white cars. How many cars did they wash in all? Use base-ten blocks to show each number. Trace the blocks. Write the number.

Online Content at ⤻ connectED.mcgraw-hill.com   Chapter 3 • Lesson 6   197

See and Show

Mathematical **PRACTICE**

You can add three and four two-digit numbers. Line up the ones and the tens. Add the ones first, then add the tens.

Helpful Hint
Remember, when you add the ones, look for a fact you know.

Add three numbers.

```
  3 ⑥
  1 4 ⟩ 6 + 4 = 10
+ 2 ④
─────
  74    10 + 4 = 14
```

Add four numbers.

```
  1 2
  3 5 ⟩ 4 + 4 = 8
  1 ④   8 + 5 = 13
+ 2 ④   13 + 2 = 15
─────
  85
```

Add.

1.	17	2.	22	3.	31	4.	18
	23		12		19		10
	+14		+15		+25		+32
	54		**49**		**75**		**60**

5.	12	6.	13	7.	11	8.	13
	19		22		25		42
	21		42		33		8
	+17		+16		+13		+36
	69		**93**		**82**		**99**

Talk Math   How is adding three two-digit numbers like adding two two-digit numbers?

198   Chapter 3 • Lesson 6

Name _____

Everyone stick together now!

On My Own

Add.

9.	25 11 + 15 **51**	10.	51 12 + 32 **95**	11.	2 25 + 42 **69**	12.	13 33 + 45 **91**
13.	22 18 32 + 13 **85**	14.	15 31 19 + 20 **85**	15.	31 34 14 + 17 **96**	16.	11 15 46 + 15 **87**
17.	34 13 + 13 **60**	18.	16 27 + 36 **79**	19.	61 10 + 19 **90**	20.	32 15 + 38 **85**
21.	12 34 14 + 26 **86**	22.	10 43 17 + 20 **90**	23.	11 28 24 + 36 **99**	24.	22 36 14 + 23 **95**

Chapter 3 • Lesson 6   199

Problem Solving

Mathematical PRACTICE

25. Logan has 11 paper clips. Amanda has 31 paper clips. Nate has 26 paper clips. How many paper clips do they have altogether?

We'll need a lot of teamwork to untangle this mess!

68 paper clips

26. Ben sold 28 tickets to the harvest party. Sunny sold 12 tickets. Jill sold 18 tickets. Tom sold 32 tickets. How many tickets did they sell in all?

90 tickets

HOT Problem 14 boys play basketball. 12 boys play soccer. 16 boys play baseball. How many boys play basketball, soccer, or baseball?

Jayden solved the problem like this:
14 + 12 + 16 = 312 boys

Tell why he is wrong. Make it right. Explain.

Sample answer: Jayden did not regroup the

ones into a 10 after he added the ones column.

14 + 12 + 16 = 42.

200   Chapter 3 • Lesson 6

---

3 PRACTICE & APPLY

On My Own

Have students work through the exercises on this page independently. You may choose to assign exercises based on the chart below.

DIFFERENTIATED ASSIGNMENTS

AL **Approaching Level** Guide students through the exercises in On My Own. Help them to use manipulatives while working through the exercises.

OL **On Level** Complete the exercises independently.

BL **Beyond Level** Complete the exercises independently without manipulatives.

Common Error!
Students may have trouble keeping the three addends lined up to add them correctly. Allow students to use a place-value chart.

Problem Solving

Have students work through the problem-solving exercises on this page independently.

Mathematical PRACTICE 6 In Exercise 26, students **attend to precision.**

HOT Problem This exercise asks students to build upon their understanding of concepts needed to answer the chapter's Essential Question.

Online Content at connectED.mcgraw-hill.com

AL **APPROACHING LEVEL**

IF my students struggle with three and four two-digit numbers,

THEN choose a resource:

→ Use the Reteach worksheet with small groups.

→ Go online for a Differentiated Instruction activity.

→ **Use Manipulatives** Write $36 + 14 + 24$ on a place-value chart. Have students use base-ten blocks to show each addend. Tell them to count ones and tens to find the sum. For example, $30 + 10 + 20 = 60$ and $6 + 4 + 4 = 14$. Finally, $60 + 14 = 74$.

OL **ON LEVEL**

IF my students seem to know three and four two-digit numbers, but need more practice,

THEN choose a resource:

→ Assign My Homework.

→ Go online for a Differentiated Instruction activity.

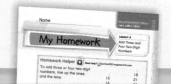

BL **BEYOND LEVEL**

IF my students have mastered three and four two-digit numbers,

THEN choose a resource:

→ Use the Enrich worksheet in cooperative groups.

→ Assign My Homework.

→ Go online for a Differentiated Instruction activity.

AL Name _____

Lesson 6   Reteach
Add Three or Four Two-Digit Numbers

You can make a ten when you are adding three or four two-digit numbers.

1. Make a ten with two numbers from the ones column.

2. Add the 10 to the number(s) left in the ones column.

3. Add the ones.

4. Add the tens.

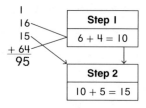

```
    1
   16
   15
 + 64
 ─────
   95
```

Step 1
$6 + 4 = 10$

Step 2
$10 + 5 = 15$

Make a ten to add.

```
1.   15          2.   41
     10               19
   + 5              + 33
   ────             ────
     30               93
```

```
3.   34          4.   14
     26                6
   + 20                3
   ────             + 50
     80             ────
                      73
```

BL Name _____

Lesson 6   Enrich
Add Three or Four Two-Digit Numbers

Add.

```
1.   41          2.   24
     19                6
   + 35                3
   ────             + 50
     95             ────
                      83
```

3. Sofia, Juan, and Max played a computer game. Sofia scored 40 points. Juan scored 3 less points than Max. Max scored 30 points. How many points did they score in all?

   40 + **27** + **30** = **97** points

4. Jorge's fruit salad has 6 cups of blueberries, 6 cups of strawberries, 2 cups of blackberries, and 3 cups of raspberries. How many cups of berries did Jorge use?

   6 + **6** + **2** + **3** = **17** cups

5. Hailey has 4 piles of pennies. There are 12 pennies in each pile. How many pennies does she have in all?

   12 + **12** + **12** + **12** = **48** pennies

My Homework

Assign homework after successful completion of the lesson. Students who understand the concepts may skip the **Homework Helper** section.

Test Practice

Diagnose Student Errors

Class trends in wrong answers may indicate common errors or misconceptions.

10 subtracted instead of adding

20 identified an addend

30 correct

35 misunderstood problem

Formative Assessment

Add 38 + 41 + 18. **97** *How did you find the sum?* Add the ones, looking for a ten or a double. Then add the tens.

Line Up! When students line up, call out three one-digit numbers for students to add mentally. Ask students to share the strategy they used for finding the sum mentally.

Name _____

Operations and Algebraic Thinking
2.OA.1, 2.NBT.6, 2.NBT.9
CCSS

My Homework

Lesson 6
Add Three and Four Two-Digit Numbers

Homework Helper eHelp   Need help? connectED.mcgraw-hill.com

To add three or four two-digit numbers, line up the ones and the tens.

Add the ones, then add the tens.

```
  15        18
  16        21
+ 46        46
----      + 12
  77      ----
            97
```

Helpful Hint
Look for a fact you know or doubles.

Practice

Add.

1.
```
  53
  27
+ 10
----
  90
```

2.
```
  52
  23
+ 18
----
  93
```

3.
```
  11
  19
+ 24
----
  54
```

4.
```
  26
  35
  24
+ 11
----
  96
```

5.
```
  23
  36
  16
+ 11
----
  86
```

6.
```
  23
  33
  13
+ 15
----
  84
```

Chapter 3 • Lesson 6   201

Read and solve the problem.

7. 13 students play the bells. 16 students play the drums. 24 students play the recorder. 14 students play trumpet. How many students play instruments?

67 students

8. Mr. Tan picks 24 apples. Mrs. Tan picks 35 apples. Their son picks 26 apples. How many apples do the Tans pick in all?

"Take us to your toy drive earthling!"

85 apples

Test Practice

9. A class collects 20 toys on Monday, 15 toys on Tuesday and 10 toys on Wednesday. How many toys did they collect on Monday and Wednesday?

10 ○   20 ○   30 ●   35 ○

 Math at Home Have your child explain how to add 28 + 12 + 35.

202   Chapter 3 • Lesson 6

Online Content at connectED.mcgraw-hill.com

Lesson 6 Add Three or Four Two-Digit Numbers   **201-202**

LESSON 7
Problem Solving
STRATEGY: Make a Model
OBJECTIVE Make a model to solve problems.

What's the Math?

 Common Core State Standards
DOMAIN: Operations and Algebraic Thinking

Standard: 2.OA.1
The wording of this standard can be found on page 158.

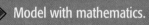 **4** Model with mathematics.

CCSS

What Students Should Understand
• You can make a model to solve real-world problems.

What Students Should be Able to Do
Amy, Jason, and Kendra are collecting money for camp. Amy has collected $24, Jason has collected $16, and Kendra has collected $38. How much money have they collected in all?

1 Understand

Underline what you know. Circle what you need to find.

2 Plan

How will I solve this problem?
I can make a model.

3 Solve

I will... make a model using base-ten blocks.

Have students work in groups to show 24, 16, and 38 using base-ten blocks. They can then use the models to find that
$24 + 16 + 38 = 78$.
So, $24 + $16 + $36 = 78
They have collected $78 in all.

4 Check

Is my answer reasonable? Explain.

Developing the Strategy

What's the Strategy?
Make a Model Students will us models to solve problems in this lesson. Models will help students visualize the numbers in a more concrete manner.

Other Strategies
Other strategies that have been taught and that students may choose to use are:
• *The four-step plan*
• *Look for a pattern*

ELL **Signal Words** Encourage English-language learners to identify signal words or signal phrases, such as *already* or *if this pattern continues*, as they read word problems.

Mathematical PRACTICE ➡

The Mathematical Practices are especially evident in problem-solving situations, in which students connect procedures and processes with mathematical understanding. In this lesson the following Mathematical Practices are addressed.

1 Make sense of problems and persevere in solving them.
4 Model with mathematics.
6 Attend to precision.

Plan Online

Plan for your lesson by using the resources at

 connectED.mcgraw-hill.com

Digital Dashboard

Interactive Whiteboard Ready

Vocab

The eBook **Glossary** shows the definition of the word and has audio for each definition. The **eGlossary** provides definitions in 13 languages.

Tools

Virtual Manipulatives along with work mats allow teachers and students to model the lesson.

Check

Use **eAssessment** for online assignments and customized assessments.

Use the **Common Core Quick Check** before the lesson to assess students' retention of previously learned concepts.

eHelp

Digital and print resources assist students and parents in completing My Homework.

PD

Professional development videos help teachers gain a deeper understanding of the lesson concepts and strategies.

RtI

Support for **approaching**, **on-** and **beyond-level** students as well as **English Language Learners**.

Masters

Reteach and **Enrich** worksheets, **Manipulative Masters**, the **Problem of the Day**, and other blackline masters are available for each lesson.

1 LAUNCH THE LESSON

 CCSS

If your students are well-versed in making a model, you may choose to begin instruction with Step 2, **TEACH**.

You will need

☐ white board

Review

Cathy has 12 cakes and 14 pies to sell at the bake sale. How many cakes and pies does she have to sell in all?

How could we solve this using a model?

Have a student or students use squares and circles or Xs and Os to represent the cakes and pies and draw a model.

What is the total? 26; cakes and pies

🕐 **Begin core instruction here.**

Problem Solving

1 Understand

Reread the problem with the students. Point out information as you read it.

2 Plan

Discuss several ideas. Guide students toward making a model to solve the problem.

3 Solve

Work through the problem using the student page with the students. Show how to solve the problem step-by-step. Have students use and then draw base-ten blocks.

4 Check

Discuss why the answer makes sense. Try to develop a sense of reasoning.

Practice the Strategy

1 Understand

Reread the problem with the students. Ask students to point out information that is important as you read it.

2 Plan

Lead students in discussing several ideas. Direct the students toward making a model to solve the problem.

3 Solve

Work through the problem using the student page with the class. Show how to solve it step-by-step. Have students use and then draw base-ten blocks.

4 Check

Discuss why the answer makes sense. Try to develop a sense of reasoning.

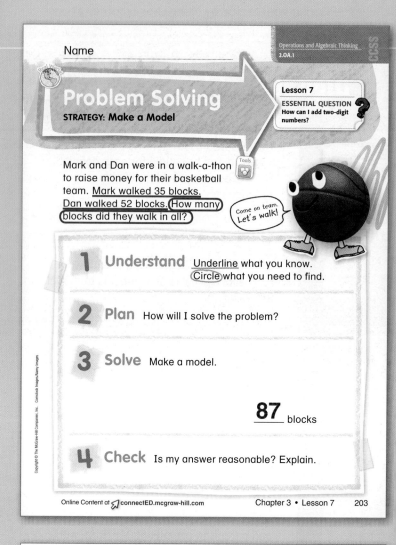

Name _____

Operations and Algebraic Thinking
2.OA.1

Problem Solving
STRATEGY: Make a Model

Lesson 7
ESSENTIAL QUESTION
How can I add two-digit numbers?

Mark and Dan were in a walk-a-thon to raise money for their basketball team. Mark walked 35 blocks. Dan walked 52 blocks. How many blocks did they walk in all?

Come on team. Let's walk!

1 Understand Underline what you know. Circle what you need to find.

2 Plan How will I solve the problem?

3 Solve Make a model.

87 blocks

4 Check Is my answer reasonable? Explain.

Online Content at connectED.mcgraw-hill.com   Chapter 3 • Lesson 7   203

Practice the Strategy

I can hear the ocean Jonny!

Sara, Mary, and Jonny are collecting shells at the beach. Sara has 45 shells. Jonny has 23 shells. Mary has 15 shells. How many shells do they have in all?

1 Understand Underline what you know. Circle what you need to find.

2 Plan How will I solve the problem?

3 Solve I will...
make a model. See students' work.

4 Check Is my answer reasonable? Explain.
See students' explanations.

204   Chapter 3 • Lesson 7

Name _____

Apply the Strategy

1. Karenna ran 15 blocks Tuesday.
   She ran 20 blocks on Wednesday.
   How many blocks did she run in all?

   35 blocks

2. Bradley got 33 action figures for his birthday.
   He had 12 already. How many will he have
   if he buys 15 more?

   60 action figures

3. Nora made 16 points in her basketball game.
   Jenna made 24 points and Alicia made 22.
   No one else scored on their team.
   What was their final score?

   Great shooting team!

   62 points

Review the Strategies

Choose a strategy
- Write a number sentence.
- Find a pattern.
- Make a model.

4. Melissa has 23 pairs of earrings.
   She buys 2 more pairs. Then she is given
   6 more pairs for her birthday. How many
   pairs of earrings does she have in all?

   31 pairs

5. Jessica made muffins for the bake sale.
   She made 24 blueberry muffins and
   10 strawberry muffins. She also made
   12 banana muffins. How many muffins
   did she make in all?

   Bake sale!

   46 muffins

6. Jacob and Luis collected glass bottles to
   recycle. The first day they collected 12 bottles.
   The second day they collected 15. The third
   day they collected 18. If this pattern continues,
   how many will they collect on the fourth day?

   21 bottles

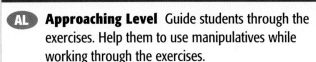

Mathematical PRACTICE **1** Apply the Strategy

Have students work through the exercises on these pages independently. You may choose to assign exercises based on the chart below.

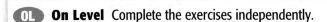

DIFFERENTIATED ASSIGNMENTS

AL **Approaching Level** Guide students through the exercises. Help them to use manipulatives while working through the exercises.

OL **On Level** Complete the exercises independently.

BL **Beyond Level** Complete the exercises independently without manipulatives.

Review the Strategies

Students may use other strategies to solve these exercises.

- *Write a number sentence*
- *Find a pattern*

21ST CENTURY SKILLS

Collaboration

Working together is a skill that is valuable throughout a person's life. When students work together in this problem solving lesson, encourage them to listen to all ideas of what model would work best for each problem and come to a consensus before solving the problem. Also have them evaluate whether their chosen model was a good one or whether they might reconsider another.

RESPONSE TO INTERVENTION
DIFFERENTIATED INSTRUCTION

AL · APPROACHING LEVEL

IF my students struggle with making a model,

THEN choose a resource:

→ Use the Reteach worksheet with small groups.

→ Go online for a Differentiated Instruction activity.

OL · ON LEVEL

IF my students seem to know how to make a model, but need more practice,

THEN choose a resource:

→ Assign My Homework.

→ Go online for a Differentiated Instruction activity.

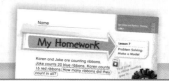

BL · BEYOND LEVEL

IF my students have mastered making a model,

THEN choose a resource:

→ Use the Enrich worksheet in cooperative groups.

→ Assign My Homework.

→ Go online for a Differentiated Instruction activity.

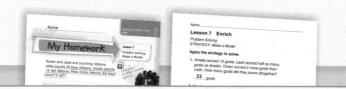

AL

Name _____

Lesson 7   Reteach (1)

Problem Solving
STRATEGY: Make a Model

Gabe rode his scooter 4 blocks to Carters's house. Then, Gabe rode to soccer practice and back home. The soccer field is 10 blocks away from Carter's house and 8 blocks away from Gabe's house. What is the total number of blocks Gabe rode his scooter?

Step 1 Understand	**What do I know?**
	Gabe rode __4__ blocks to Carter's house.
	Gabe rode __10__ blocks to the soccer field from Carter's house.
	Gabe rode __8__ blocks from the soccer field back to his house.
	What do I need to find?
	The total number of blocks Gabe rode his scooter.
Step 2 Plan	**How will I solve the problem?**
	I will __make a model__
Step 3 Solve	**Make a model with base-ten blocks.**
	Gabe rode __22__ blocks in all.
Step 4 Check	**How do I know my answer is reasonable?**
	__4__ + __10__ + __8__ = __22__ blocks

AL

Name _____

Lesson 7   Reteach (2)

Problem Solving
STRATEGY: Make a Model

Apply the strategy to solve.

1. Emily, Logan, and Carlos just finished their soccer season. Emily and Logan each scored 8 goals. Carlos scored 10 goals. How many goals did they score altogether?

   __26__ goals

2. Madison, Caden, and Lucas each walked 3 miles. How many miles did they walk in all?

   __9__ miles

3. Bella read 3 chapters. Eli read 1 more chapter than Bella. Austin and Sarah each read 1 less chapter than Bella. How many chapters did they read in all?

   __11__ chapters

4. Claire saw 3 bears and 7 monkeys at the zoo. Luke saw 4 otters and 3 wolves. How many animals did they see altogether?

   __17__ animals

5. Wyatt donated 4 cans of food. Gavin donated 9 + 6 cans. Lyla donated 11 cans. How many cans did they donate in all?

   __30__ cans

BL

Name _____

Lesson 7   Enrich

Problem Solving
STRATEGY: Make a Model

Apply the strategy to solve.

1. Amelia scored 10 goals. Leah scored half as many goals as Amelia. Owen scored 2 more goals than Leah. How many goals did they score altogether?

   __22__ goals

2. Madison, Caden, and Lucas each walked 3 miles. Isaac and Alexis each walked 4 miles. How many miles did they walk in all?

   __17__ miles

3. Bella read 12 chapters. Eli read 5 more chapters than Bella. Austin and Sarah each read 1 less chapter than Bella. How many chapters did they read in all?

   __51__ chapters

4. Allison saw 3 bears and 7 monkeys at the zoo. Colton saw 13 snakes. Luke saw 4 otters and 3 wolves. How many animals did they see altogether?

   __30__ animals

5. Wyatt donated 4 + 4 cans of food. Gavin donated 9 + 6 cans. Lyla donated 11 − 2 cans. How many cans did they donate in all?

   __32__ cans

My Homework

Name _____

My Homework

> Lesson 7
> Problem Solving:
> Make a Model

eHelp

Karen and Jake are counting ribbons. Jake counts 20 blue ribbons. Karen counts 16 red ribbons. How many ribbons did they count in all?

First prize in ribbon counting goes to...

1ST PLACE

1 Understand Underline what you know. Circle what you need to find.

2 Plan How will I solve the problem?

3 Solve Make a model.

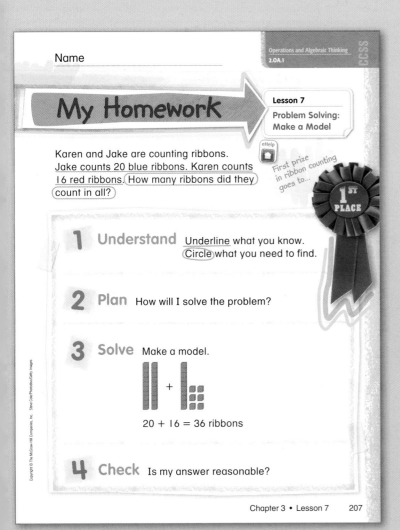

20 + 16 = 36 ribbons

4 Check Is my answer reasonable?

Chapter 3 • Lesson 7   207

Underline what you know. Circle what you need to find. Make a model to solve.

1. Angela and Brittany count 8 windows in the first building, 5 in the next building, and 13 in the last building. How many windows did they count in all?

   26 windows

2. Eric found 14 pennies in the couch, 6 pennies in his mom's car, and 2 pennies under his bed. How many pennies did he find in all?

   22 pennies

3. The girls collected 57 bottle caps. The boys collected 42 caps. How many bottle caps did they collect in all?

   LEMON SODA

   99 caps

My Homework

Assign homework after successful completion of the lesson. Students who understand the concepts may skip the **Homework Helper** section.

Formative Assessment

Ask students to make a model on paper or using base-ten blocks to solve.

Sandy has 19 bean bag animals. Karen has 17 bean bag animals. How many do the girls have in all? $19 + 17 = 36$ bean bag animals

Fluency Practice

Mathematical PRACTICE 6
Mathematical PRACTICE 6 These pages help the students look for and express regularity in repeated reasoning.

These pages encourage students to become proficient in their calculation abilities. You can use these as a timed or untimed exercise.

Pages 209–210 Practice the addition of whole numbers.

Teaching Tip One approach to build student confidence is to use these pages repeatedly. Strive for students to complete a portion of these pages correctly in an untimed situation. Then use the rest of the page as a timed test.

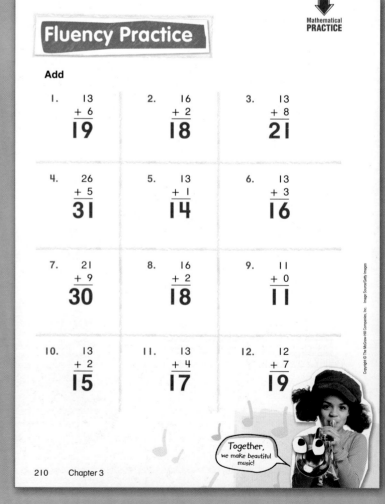

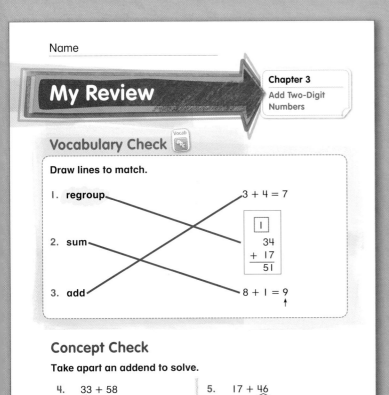

Name _____

My Review

Chapter 3
Add Two-Digit Numbers

Vocabulary Check

Draw lines to match.

1. regroup
2. sum
3. add

3 + 4 = 7

```
  1
 34
+17
 51
```

8 + 1 = 9

Concept Check

Take apart an addend to solve.

4. 33 + 58

$$31 + 2 + 58$$
$$31 + 60 = 91$$
$$91$$
So, 33 + 58 = __91__.

5. 17 + 46

$$17 + 3 + 43$$
$$20 + 43 = 63$$
$$63$$
So, 17 + 46 = __63__.

Chapter 3   211

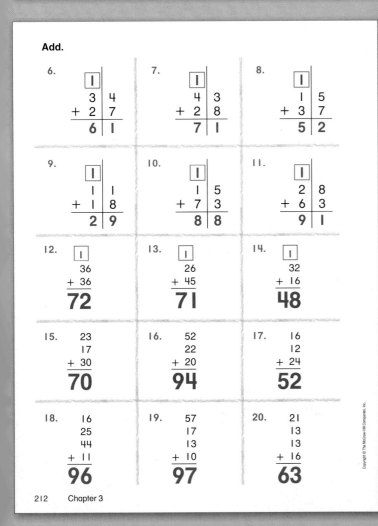

Add.

6.
```
  1
  3 | 4
+ 2 | 7
  6 | 1
```

7.
```
  1
  4 | 3
+ 2 | 8
  7 | 1
```

8.
```
  1
  1 | 5
+ 3 | 7
  5 | 2
```

9.
```
  1
  1 | 1
+ 1 | 8
  2 | 9
```

10.
```
  1
  1 | 5
+ 7 | 3
  8 | 8
```

11.
```
  1
  2 | 8
+ 6 | 3
  9 | 1
```

12.
```
   1
  36
+ 36
  72
```

13.
```
   1
  26
+ 45
  71
```

14.
```
   1
  32
+ 16
  48
```

15.
```
  23
  17
+ 30
  70
```

16.
```
  52
  22
+ 20
  94
```

17.
```
  16
  12
+ 24
  52
```

18.
```
  16
  25
  44
+ 11
  96
```

19.
```
  57
  17
  13
+ 10
  97
```

20.
```
  21
  13
  13
+ 16
  63
```

212   Chapter 3

My Review

Use these pages to assess your students' understanding of the vocabulary and key concepts in this chapter.

Vocabulary Check

Have students point to the new vocabulary word. Ask them how they know it is a new word. I know *regroup* is a new word because it is highlighted.

ELL **ELL Support Strategy** Use this information to participate in purposeful, cooperative learning activities.

Concept Check

If students need reinforcement of skills after completing this section, use the Reteach worksheet to review the concepts again.

Exercises	Concept	Review Lesson
4–5	Take apart addends	1
6–14	Add two-digit numbers	4
15–19	Add three or four two-digit numbers	6

Problem Solving

Remind students of the four-step plan for problem solving. For students who need help in reading comprehension, have them work with another student to read the problem aloud before attempting the four-step plan.

Test Practice

Diagnose Student Errors

Class trends in wrong answers may indicate common errors or misconceptions.

80   added 20 four times
78   correct
59   did not add the second 19
58   did not add the second 20

Reflect

Have students show the ways they can add three-digit numbers.

You may choose to have your students use a different graphic organizer for review.

Summative Assessment

Use these alternate leveled chapter tests from the Assessment Masters to differentiate assessment for the specific needs of your students.

Chapter Tests		
Level	**Type**	**Form**
AL	Multiple Choice	1A
AL	Multiple Choice	1B
OL	Multiple Choice / Free Choice	2A
OL	Multiple Choice / Free Choice	2B
BL	Free Choice	3A
BL	Free Choice	3B
Additional Chapter Resource Masters		
OL	Vocabulary Test	
OL	Listening Assessment	
OL	Oral Assessment	

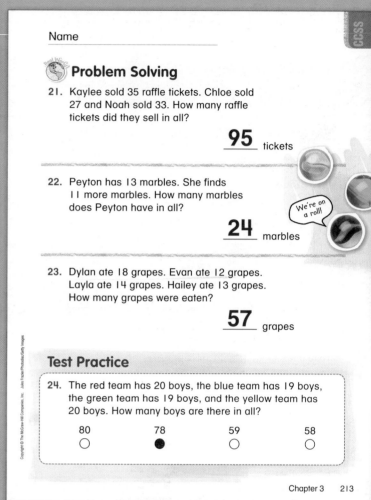

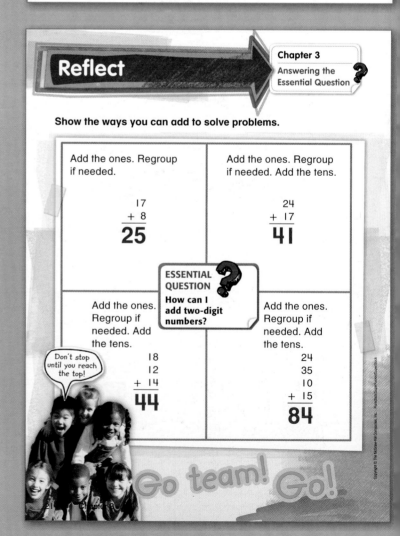

Notes

CHAPTER 4

Subtract Two-Digit Numbers

Suggested Pacing		
Instruction*	Review & Assessment	TOTAL
12 days	2 days	14 days

*Includes additional time for remediation and differentiation.

Chapter at a Glance

Lesson	Objective	Materials & Manipulatives	Vocabulary	CCSS Standard
Lesson 1 *pp. 223–228* **Two-Digit Fact Families**	Use related facts to make two-digit number families.	• base-ten blocks • red and yellow connecting cubes		2.OA.1 2.NBT.5
Lesson 2 *pp. 229–234* **Take Apart Tens to Subtract**	Take apart numbers to make a ten to subtract.	• base-ten blocks • Work Mat 6		2.OA.1
Lesson 3 *pp. 235–240* **Regroup a Ten as Ones**	Use models to regroup and find differences.	• base-ten blocks • Work Mat 6		2.OA.1 2.NBT.5 2.NBT.9
Lesson 4 *pp. 241–246* **Subtract From a Two-Digit Number**	Subtract one-digit numbers from two-digit numbers.	• base-ten blocks • Work Mat 6		2.OA.1 2.NBT.5 2.NBT.9
Check My Progress				
Lesson 5 *pp. 249–254* **Subtract Two-Digit Numbers**	Subtract two-digit numbers.	• base-ten blocks • Work Mat 6		2.OA.1 2.NBT.5 2.NBT.9
Lesson 6 *pp. 255–260* **Rewrite Two-Digit Subtraction**	Rewrite a horizontal two-digit subtraction problem vertically before subtracting.	• number cubes • Work Mat 6 (opt.) • base-ten blocks (opt.)		2.OA.1 2.NBT.5

Lesson	Objective	Materials & Manipulatives	Vocabulary	CCSS Standard
Lesson 7 *pp. 261–266* **Check Subtraction**	Use addition to check subtraction.	• connecting cubes		2.OA.1 2.NBT.5
Lesson 8 *pp. 267–272* **Problem-Solving Strategy: Write a Number Sentence**	Write a number sentence to solve problems.	• connecting cubes		2.OA.1
Lesson 9 *pp. 273–278* **Two-Step Word Problems**	Read and solve two-step word problems.			2.OA.1

Fluency Practice

My Review and Reflect

For customizable online assessment, go to **eAssessment** at connectED.mcgraw-hill.com.

Planning for Differentiated Instruction

Use these differentiated instruction activity suggestions, along with the ongoing support provided in each lesson of this chapter, to meet individual learning needs.

AL APPROACHING LEVEL

Use with Lesson 3

Materials: base-ten blocks

- Write 47 − 9 on the board. Tell students they will need to regroup to subtract 9.
- Have students use base-ten blocks to model the regrouping. Then have them find the difference.
- Have students write a rule that tells when you need to regroup. Sample answer: Regroup if the number you are subtracting has more ones than the number from which you are subtracting.

AL APPROACHING LEVEL

Use with Lesson 5

Materials: number spinner, paper, pencil, Work Mat 6, base-ten blocks

- Students work in small groups and take turns spinning the number spinner two times to make a two-digit number.
- Have students subtract the number they made from 90.
- Have students work together to use mental math to break apart the numbers to make subtracting across zero a little easier. Ask them to record their work on paper.
- When they are finished, students can check their answers with base-ten blocks and Work Mat 6.

AL APPROACHING LEVEL

Use with Lesson 6

Materials: whiteboard, marker, index cards labeled with three numbers that are part of a two-digit number family (For example, 10, 12, 22)

- Give each group of students a whiteboard, marker, and index cards.
- Have students pick an index card with a set of 3 two-digit numbers.
- Students work together to create two addition number sentences and two subtraction number sentences in the two-digit number family.
- Students record their number sentences on the whiteboard and continue with new sets of cards.

OL ON LEVEL

Use with Lesson 6

Materials: various manipulatives, number line with two-digit numbers

- One student writes a two-digit subtraction problem. The partner models it, solves it, and explains why the answer is reasonable.
- The first student uses a number line to demonstrate that the solution is correct or incorrect.

OL ON LEVEL

Use with Lesson 4

Materials: sports pages from a newspaper, base-ten blocks

- Have students find the final scores for a current sport, then write subtraction sentences to find the difference between the scores.
- Students can use base-ten blocks to model the number sentences.

BL BEYOND LEVEL

Use with Lesson 4

Materials: hundred chart, index cards with numbers

- Have students work in groups of three.
- The first student draws a card and locates the number on the hundred chart. Then he or she rounds the number by finding the nearest ten.
- The second student repeats the process.
- The third student subtracts the smaller of the two rounded numbers from the larger number.
- Students continue, switching roles.

BL BEYOND LEVEL

Use with Lesson 8

Write the following story on the board:

Three girls went to the beach with their family. Mary found 21 shells. Joann found 9 shells. Liz found 1 more shell than Joann.

- Have each student write two different questions about the story. One question should involve a joining situation. The other question should involve a comparative situation.
- Have students exchange papers.
- Tell them to write a number sentence for each question, and then answer the question in a complete sentence.

ELL ENGLISH LANGUAGE LEARNERS

Support for English Language Learners is found throughout the chapter and includes:

- ELL strategies at point-of-use in each Teacher Edition lesson
- ELL tiered instruction suggestions for each lesson at connectED.mcgraw-hill.com
- Comprehensive ELL lessons and worksheets for additional instruction at connectED.mcgraw-hill.com
- Non-linguistic representations of concepts on My Math Words, My Vocabulary Cards, and My Foldables

Additional online resources at connectED.mcgraw-hill.com include:

- Visual Vocabulary Cards
- Multilingual eGlossary
- Professional Development support

Looking for more DIFFERENTIATED INSTRUCTION?
Find additional support in each lesson of this chapter and online at connectED.mcgraw-hill.com

AL Approaching Level
OL On Level
BL Beyond Level
ELL English Language Learners

What's the Math in This Chapter?

Points of Intersection

Where
CONTENT STANDARDS

Meet
Mathematical **PRACTICE** ➡ 8

NBT Number and Operations in Base Ten

Look for and express regularity in repeated reasoning.

Most of this chapter concentrates on the **Number and Operations in Base Ten (NBT)** domain. However, aspects of the **Operations and Algebraic Thinking (OA)** domain are also used in the study of **subtraction.**

As you teach subtraction of two-digit numbers, point out to students that the subtraction process involves repeated calculation. Students can use the same algorithm repeatedly with any subtraction problem they encounter. The algorithm consists of subtracting each place-value, starting with the ones place, and regrouping when needed.

What should my students already know?

In the previous grade, students used **Operations and Algebraic Thinking (OA)** in their study of subtraction:

- Use subtraction within 20 to solve word problems.
  1.OA.1

- Subtract within 20, demonstrating fluency for subtraction within 10.
  1.OA.6

Students used **Number and Operations in Base Ten (NBT)** in their study of place-value and subtraction:

- Understand that the two digits of a two-digit number represent amounts of tens and ones.
  1.NBT.2

- Given a two-digit number, mentally find 10 less than the number, without having to count.
  1.NBT.5

- Subtract multiples of 10 in the range 10-90 from multiples of 10 in the range 10-90.
  1.NBT.6

WHAT STUDENTS SHOULD UNDERSTAND

Two-Digit Fact Families
 2.NBT.5, 2.NBT.9

How to write a two-digit fact family when given the three numbers in the fact family.

- A fact family is made up of addition and subtraction sentences that use the same numbers.

Subtract Two Two-Digit Numbers
 2.OA.1, 2.NBT.5, 2.NBT.9

How to take apart a number to make a ten to subtract.

- You can make the subtraction easier by taking apart the subtrahend to make a number that ends in zero.

WHAT STUDENTS SHOULD BE ABLE TO DO

Complete the fact family for the numbers shown below.

$6 + 18 = 24$ $24 - 6 = 18$
$18 + 6 = 24$ $24 - 18 = 6$

Jocelyn has 67 pennies. She gives 32 of them to Evan. How many does she have left?

Find $67 - 32$.

$67 - 30 = 37$
$37 - 2 = 35$

So, she has 35 pennies left.

Take apart 32 as 30 and 2.

Next find $67 - 30$.

Then find $37 - 2$.

WHAT STUDENTS SHOULD UNDERSTAND	WHAT STUDENTS SHOULD BE ABLE TO DO

Regroup When Subtracting Two-Digit Numbers

 2.OA.1, 2.NBT.5, 2.NBT.9

How to regroup 1 ten as 10 ones when subtracting with a two-digit number.

- Subtract the ones and then the tens when you subtract with two-digit numbers.

- If there are not enough ones to subtract from, regroup 1 ten as 10 ones.

Find 53 − 17.

Step 1 Can you subtract 7 ones from 3 ones?

Step 2 Regroup 1 ten as 10 ones.
3 ones + 10 ones = 13 ones

Step 3 Subtract the ones. 13 − 7 = 6

Step 4 Subtract the tens. 4 − 1 = 3

tens	ones
4̶ 5̶	1̶3̶ 3̶
− 1	7
3	6

Check Subtraction

 2.NBT.5, 2.NBT.9

How to check subtraction with addition.

- You can check the answer to a subtraction problem by using addition.

- Add the bottom number and the difference. If the sum equals the top number, the subtraction was done correctly.

Subtract

$$\begin{array}{r} 75 \\ -\ 38 \\ \hline 37 \end{array}$$ Add these numbers to check.

Check by adding

$$\begin{array}{r} 37 \\ +\ 38 \\ \hline 75 \end{array}$$ If this is the number you subtracted from, your answer is correct.

What will my students do next with these skills?

After this chapter, students will learn to:

- subtract three-digit numbers.
2.NBT.7

In the next grade, students will learn to:

- subtract multi-digit numbers.
3.NBT.2

Reading Connections

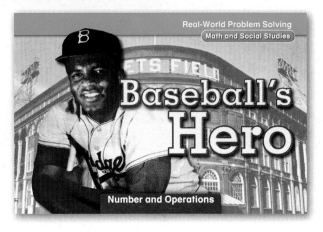

Real-World Problem Solving Library

Math and Social Studies: Baseball's Hero

Use these leveled books to reinforce and extend problem-solving skills and strategies.

Leveled for:

AL Approaching Level

OL On Level Also available in Spanish

BL Beyond Level

For additional support, see the *Real-World Problem Solving Readers Teacher Guide.*

Leveled Reader Database

Available at leveledreaderdatabase.macmillanmh.com
Search by:

- Content Area
- Guided Reading Level
- Lexile Score
- Benchmark Level

Looking for more
Reading and Language Arts Support?
go online to
connectED.mcgraw-hill.com

Library Books

Check with your school library or your local public library for these titles.

Alexander, Who Used to be Rich Last Sunday
Judith Viorst

Elevator Magic
Stuart J. Murphy

Domino Addition
Lynette Long, Ph.D

Monster Musical Chairs
Stuart J. Murphy

Panda Math: Learning About Subtraction from Hua Mei and Mei Sheng
Ann Whitehead Nagda

Reading and Language Arts Support

Math in Our World

Distribute copies of the classified ads from a newspaper. Have students search for two-digit numbers. When a number is found, students should raise their hands, announce the number, and explain to what it is referring. Create a list on the whiteboard of what they find. Discuss the different items and events that students see listed in the paper.

Have each student choose four pairs of numbers from the board to use to create four subtraction problems. Students will solve their subtraction problems and use addition to check their answers.

Chapter 4 Subtract Two-Digit Numbers

ESSENTIAL QUESTION
How can I subtract two-digit numbers?

Let's Explore the Seasons!

Watch a video!

215

LAUNCH THE CHAPTER

Theme:
Let's Explore the Seasons!

All of the lessons in Chapter 4 will connect with the theme of Let's Explore the Seasons, which center around activities kids do in different seasons. This is reflected in the problem-solving exercises and the visuals used throughout the chapter.

▶ Video

Have students watch the video about the seasons. You may want to spark a discussion about how math is used in studying seasons.

❓ Building on the Essential Question

Once students have completed this chapter they should be able to answer the question "How can I subtract two-digit numbers?" In each lesson, students build on their understanding of this question by answering a simpler question. These are indicated in the exercises as Building on the Essential Question. At the end of the chapter, students use a graphic organizer to help them answer the Essential Question.

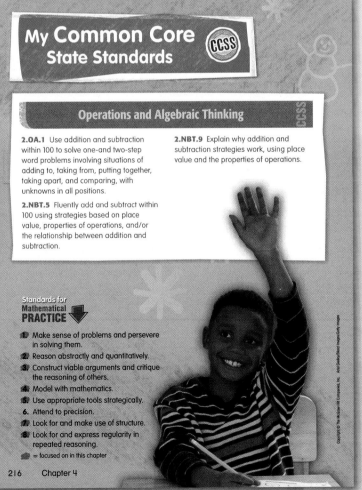

My Common Core State Standards

Operations and Algebraic Thinking

2.OA.1 Use addition and subtraction within 100 to solve one-and two-step word problems involving situations of adding to, taking from, putting together, taking apart, and comparing, with unknowns in all positions.

2.NBT.5 Fluently add and subtract within 100 using strategies based on place value, properties of operations, and/or the relationship between addition and subtraction.

2.NBT.9 Explain why addition and subtraction strategies work, using place value and the properties of operations.

Standards for Mathematical PRACTICE ▼

1. Make sense of problems and persevere in solving them.
2. Reason abstractly and quantitatively.
3. Construct viable arguments and critique the reasoning of others.
4. Model with mathematics.
5. Use appropriate tools strategically.
6. Attend to precision.
7. Look for and make use of structure.
8. Look for and express regularity in repeated reasoning.

= focused on in this chapter

216 Chapter 4

Professional Development

(CCSS) Common Core State Standards

Learn more about how the Common Core State Standards can be implemented in your classroom at mhpdonline.com.

Look for
- eImplementation
- eVideo Clip Libraries
- eTech Training
- ePD Webinars

Feature video for mathematical content in this chapter:
Subtract One- and Two-Digit Numbers

1 Assess

You have two options for assessing student readiness for this chapter. Use student results to determine which level of instruction is needed to help students get ready for the chapter and to determine what ongoing support they will need during the chapter.

Option 1: Am I Ready?

Have students complete the **Am I Ready?** page in their student books.

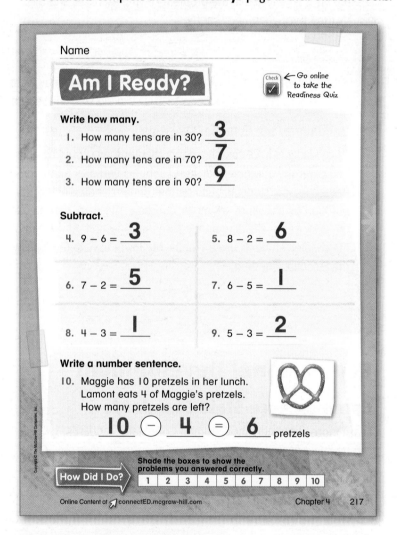

Name

Am I Ready?

Check → Go online to take the Readiness Quiz

Write how many.

1. How many tens are in 30? __3__

2. How many tens are in 70? __7__

3. How many tens are in 90? __9__

Subtract.

4. $9 - 6 =$ __3__   5. $8 - 2 =$ __6__

6. $7 - 2 =$ __5__   7. $6 - 5 =$ __1__

8. $4 - 3 =$ __1__   9. $5 - 3 =$ __2__

Write a number sentence.

10. Maggie has 10 pretzels in her lunch. Lamont eats 4 of Maggie's pretzels. How many pretzels are left?

__10__ ⊖ __4__ ⊜ __6__ pretzels

How Did I Do? → Shade the boxes to show the problems you answered correctly.

| 1 | 2 | 3 | 4 | 5 | 6 | 7 | 8 | 9 | 10 |

Online Content at connectED.mcgraw-hill.com   Chapter 4   217

Option 2: Online Readiness Quiz

 Check ✓

Have students take the **Online Readiness Quiz.**

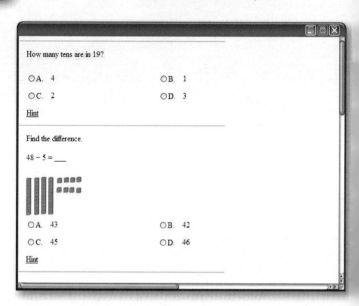

How many tens are in 19?

○ A. 4   ○ B. 1

○ C. 2   ○ D. 3

Hint

Find the difference.

$48 - 5 =$ ____

○ A. 43   ○ B. 42

○ C. 45   ○ D. 46

Hint

OPTION 2

CCSS Common Core Review

Exercises	Skill	Standard
1–10*	Identify Tens	2.OA.1
	Subtraction	2.OA.1

*These questions are randomly generated from a bank of 15 questions.

OPTION 1

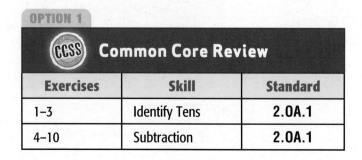

CCSS Common Core Review

Exercises	Skill	Standard
1–3	Identify Tens	2.OA.1
4–10	Subtraction	2.OA.1

2 Diagnose and Prescribe

...ased on the results of the Am I Ready? in the student edition, use the charts below ...o address individual needs **before** beginning the chapter.

...se the **ONGOING** resources to support differentiated instruction as new skills and ...oncepts are presented in the chapter.

TIER 1

OL — ON LEVEL

IF students miss 2–3 in Exercises 1–10,

THEN choose a resource:

→ Am I Ready? Practice

→ Online Readiness Quiz

ONGOING Self-Check Quizzes • Chapter Project • Differentiated Assignments • My Learning Stations • Differentiated Instruction activities

TIER 2

AL — STRATEGIC INTERVENTION

(Approaching Grade Level)

IF students miss 4 in Exercises 1–10,

THEN choose a resource:

→ Online Strategic Intervention activity

→ Am I Ready? Review

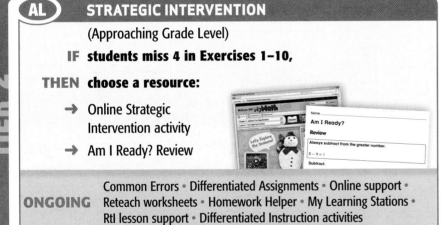

ONGOING Common Errors • Differentiated Assignments • Online support • Reteach worksheets • Homework Helper • My Learning Stations • RtI lesson support • Differentiated Instruction activities

TIER 3

INTENSIVE INTERVENTION

(2 or more years below grade level)

IF students miss 5 or more in Exercises 1–10,

THEN use *Math Triumphs,* an intensive math intervention program from McGraw-Hill.

BL — BEYOND LEVEL

IF students miss 1 or less in Exercises 1–10,

THEN choose a resource:

→ Online Games

→ Am I Ready? Apply

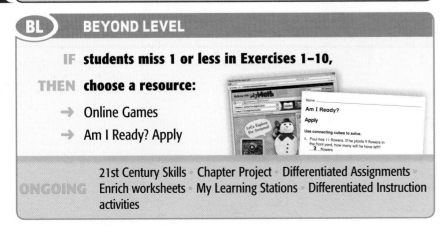

ONGOING 21st Century Skills • Chapter Project • Differentiated Assignments Enrich worksheets • My Learning Stations • Differentiated Instruction activities

3 Reassess

If reassessment is necessary, administer the chapter Diagnostic Test in the **Assessment Masters** or go online for eAssessment.

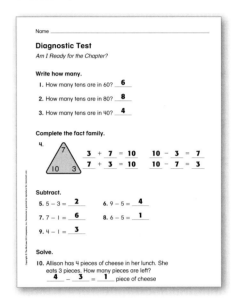

 For additional chapter readiness assessment, go to eAssessment at connectED.mcgraw-hill.com.

DEVELOP VOCABULARY

My Math Words

Review Vocabulary

Where did they learn it?

- difference   (Lesson 1–7)
- fact family   (Lesson 1–12)
- sum   (Lesson 1–1)

Making Connections

Ask students to explain or show what they know about the review vocabulary. For example, they might write an example of a fact family.

Ask a student to read aloud the number sentences in the middle of the graphic organizer. Then discuss with students what the arrows pointing from each of the three boxes to the box with the four number sentences indicate. Sample answer: The sentences in each box describe different parts of the four number sentences.

My Vocabulary Cards

There is no new vocabulary in this chapter. Encourage students to use the blank cards to review vocabulary words, draw examples of important concepts, or write questions they have about what they have learned.

See the Develop Vocabulary column in each lesson for specific suggestions.

Students should clip and store their cards in one place, such as a small envelope, where they can access them as needed throughout the chapter.

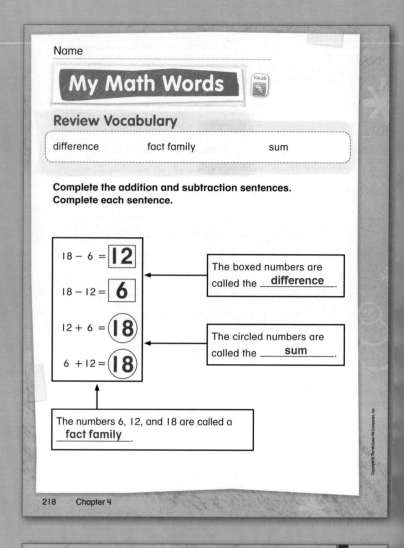

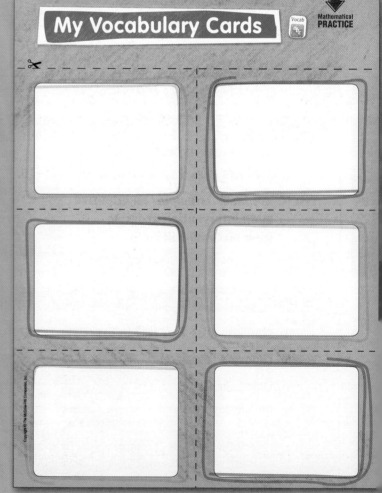

Copyright © The McGraw-Hill Companies, Inc.

Mathematical PRACTICE 3 **My Vocabulary Card Activities**

Suggestions for using blank cards appear in some Developing Vocabulary Activities.

STUDY ORGANIZER

My Foldable

What's the Math?

Content Standard: 2.NBT.5

Mathematical PRACTICE **Use appropriate tools strategically.**

This Foldable provides practice for students in creating fact families with two-digit numbers. In each fact family, the same three numbers are used to create four number sentences.

How Do I Make It?

- Tear out the page and cut off the top banner.
- Fold along green dotted lines so points meet in the center.
- On each triangle, three numbers make up a fact family. Lift each triangle to show the related fact family underneath.

When Do I Use It?

Use after Lesson 1 and at end of the chapter as a review tool.

How Could I Use It?

- Start with all the triangles folded in. Have students look at the green triangle. Have them complete the fact family on the inside using the numbers on the outside of the flap.
- Repeat for the orange and purple triangles.
- Have students create their own fact family on the blue triangle and complete the number sentences on the inside.

ELL **ELL Support Strategy** Use this Foldable to practice 2-digit subtraction.

My Foldable

FOLDABLES Follow the steps on the back to make your Foldable.

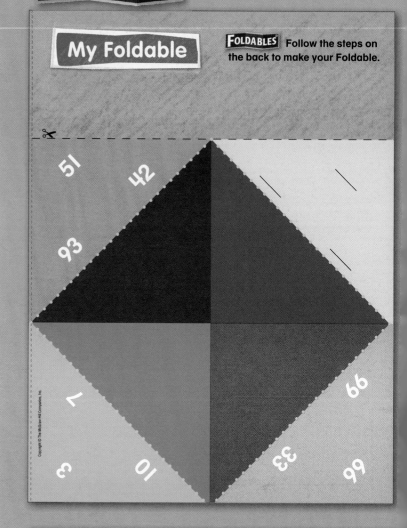

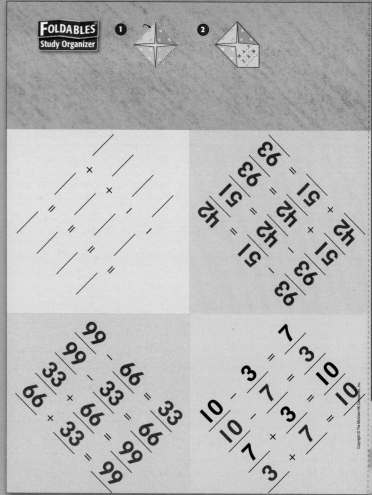

Lunchroom Chat

Building a Learning Community

Sometimes, it may be difficult to relate the mathematical concepts students are studying in the classroom to the real world. In this chapter, you can relate mathematics to social studies topics by talking about significant ages. For example, students will be able to vote when they are 18. Ask students how many years will pass before they turn 18. Another example might be to ask students how old their parents or grandparents are. Have them find the difference between their age and their parents/grandparents ages. Talk with your colleagues about other significant numbers that you could use with two-digit subtraction.

MY Learning Stations

Use the following learning stations to differentiate the instruction for Chapter 4. Includes Spanish!

Learning Station	Title	Use after Lesson(s)
Game	*Hit the Target*	5
Graphic Novel	*Swimming Fun*	5
RWPS Reader	*Baseball's Hero*	5
Activity Card	*Clay Sentences*	5

RWPS = Real-World Problem-Solving Reader

Chapter Project

Teach a Review Lesson

In this project, you will assign a pair of students or small groups a concept from the chapter to teach.

- They will teach a short, 5-minute review lesson to the class.
- Encourage students to use manipulatives, visuals, posters, or props to teach the lesson.
- Have students plan their lesson and practice it several times before presenting it to the class.
- Have students present all lessons on the same day as a review for the chapter test or over several days leading up to the end of the chapter.

 CALENDAR TIME

How Long Until the End of the Month?

- Write the name of the current month on the calendar poster. Fill in the numbers for the days of the month.
- Students should work with a partner. One student should draw a number from a stack of number cards 1–31.
- Have students work together to subtract to find how many days there are from their number to the end of the month.

LESSON 1
Two-Digit Fact Families

OBJECTIVE   Use related facts to make two-digit number families.

What's the Math?

 Common Core State Standards
DOMAIN: Operations and Algebraic Thinking

Standards: 2.OA.1, 2.NBT.5
The wording of these standards can be found on page 216.

CCSS

What Students Should Understand
- A fact family is made up of addition and subtraction sentences that use the same numbers.
- There can be one addition and one subtraction sentence, or two addition and two subtraction sentences in a fact family.

What Students Should be Able to Do
Write the fact family for the numbers shown below.

$7 + 14 = 21$ $21 - 7 = 14$
$14 + 7 = 21$ $21 - 14 = 7$

$12 + 12 = 24$ $24 - 12 = 12$

 Building on the Essential Question

In this lesson, students will build upon the skills and concepts needed to answer the chapter's Essential Question "How can I subtract two-digit numbers?"

Developing Vocabulary

 Review Vocabulary
fact family

Review Activity
- Write the word *fact family* on the board. Ask students what they recall about fact families from previous chapters or grades. For example, they might remember that a fact family can help them identify patterns between addition and subtraction.

- Have students skim the lesson. Direct their attention to the triangles. Ask students why each triangle contains a number in each of its corners. Each number is one of the three numbers in the fact family.

- Discuss with students why a shape such as a rectangle is not used to show fact families. A rectangle has four corners, not three and a fact family has three members.

ELL **ELL Support Strategy** Use this vocabulary activity to visualize what is being taught.

My Vocabulary Cards
Have students write a fact family on a blank card. Then have them work in small groups to write the facts for each family.

IWB **Virtual Word Wall**
You may wish to add this review vocabulary word to the Virtual Word Wall.

ELL Refer to the Multilingual eGlossary for interactive definitions in 13 languages.

Plan Online

Plan for your lesson by using the resources at
connectED.mcgraw-hill.com

Digital Dashboard

Interactive Whiteboard Ready

 Vocab

The eBook **Glossary** shows the definition of the word and has audio for each definition. The **eGlossary** provides definitions in 13 languages.

 Watch

Watch as concepts are brought to life through **animations**, **songs**, and a variety of visual instruction.

 Tools

Virtual Manipulatives with work mats allow teachers and students to model the lesson.

 Check

Use **eAssessment** for online assignments and customized assessments.

Use the **Common Core Quick Check** before the lesson to assess students' retention of previously learned concepts.

Use the interactive **Self-Check Quiz** after the lesson to provide immediate feedback on lesson concepts.

 eHelp

Digital and print resources assist students and parents in completing My Homework.

 Games

Online games and **apps** provide extra practice for lesson concepts.

 PD

Professional development videos help teachers gain a deeper understanding of the lesson concepts and strategies.

 RtI

Support for **approaching**, **on-** and **beyond-level** students as well as **English Language Learners**.

Masters

Reteach and **Enrich** worksheets, **Manipulative Masters**, the **Problem of the Day**, and other blackline masters are available for each lesson.

 # LAUNCH THE LESSON

 If your students are well-versed in two-digit fact families, you may choose to begin instruction with Step 2, **TEACH**.

You will need

☐ red and yellow connecting cubes

Mathematical PRACTICE  **Modeling the Math**

Write the numbers 29, 13, and 16 on the board. Connect 13 red connecting cubes and 16 yellow connecting cubes.

If I add these together, what is the sum? 29 *How would you write this as an addition sentence?* 13 + 16 = 29

Turn the cubes around to model the second addition fact.

How would you write this as an addition sentence?
16 + 13 = 29

Repeat the activity modeling the related subtraction sentences.
29 − 16 = 13 and 29 − 13 = 16

Begin core instruction here.

You will need
☐ base-ten blocks

Explore and Explain

Read the directions at the bottom of the student page.

To find the number of snowballs that Lindsay has left, you can use base-ten blocks to find 16 − 7.

Guide students in using base-ten blocks to model 16.

There are not enough ones in 16 to take away 7 ones. When there are not enough ones, you must regroup 1 ten as 10 ones.

Lead the students in trading 1 ten for 10 ones.

Explain to students that there are now ~~

Now there are enough~~

Guide students in re~~

How many snowb~~

Discuss what numbers ~~

*What numbers mak~~
family has addition a~~
same numbers. 16, 9, ~~
the triangle.*

*You know that 16 − 7 = ~~
sentences in this fact fami~~
sentences that are in this fo~~
9 + 7 = 16, and 7 + 9 = 1~~*

Write the related number sen~~ ~~ jic.~~

Handwritten note:
Olivia
Math - Chpt 4 + 5
- 2 digit #s add + sub.
- regroup + carrying
- place value

See and Show

Help students work through the example at the top of the page. As a group, look at the triangle in the blue box. Ask students to identify the numbers. Discuss what students notice about these three numbers. Guide students to notice that the numbers form a fact family. That is, 15 + 3 = 18; 3 + 15 = 18; 18 − 15 = 3; 18 − 3 = 15. Have students trace the dashed numbers as they work the problems.

Work through Exercises 1–3 as a class.

Mathematical PRACTICE 3 Talk Math

Discuss with students "How are these exercises like fact families that you have learned earlier?" Sample answer: You use the same numbers and addition and subtraction to solve.

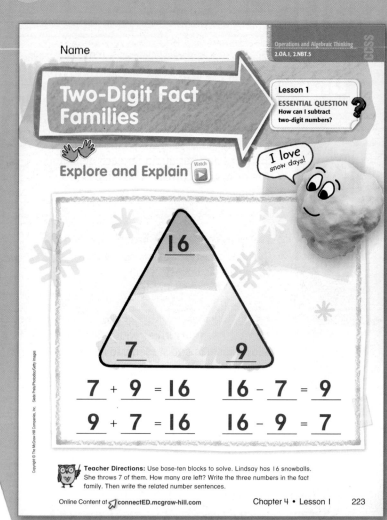

Name _____

Operations and Algebraic Thinking
2.OA.1, 2.NBT.5

Two-Digit Fact Families

Lesson 1
ESSENTIAL QUESTION
How can I subtract two-digit numbers?

Explore and Explain ▶

I love snow days!

Triangle: 16 at top, 7 and 9 at bottom

$7 + 9 = 16$ $16 - 7 = 9$
$9 + 7 = 16$ $16 - 9 = 7$

Teacher Directions: Use base-ten blocks to solve. Lindsay has 16 snowballs. She throws 7 of them. How many are left? Write the three numbers in the fact family. Then write the related number sentences.

Online Content at ✐ connectED.mcgraw-hill.com   Chapter 4 • Lesson 1   223

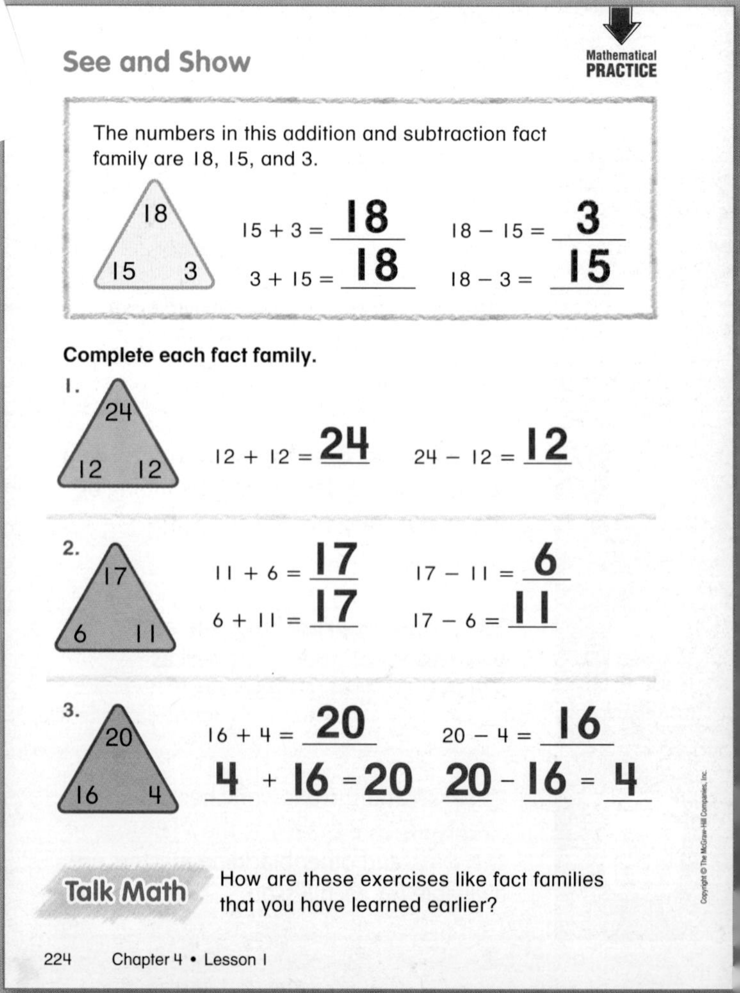

See and Show

Mathematical PRACTICE

The numbers in this addition and subtraction fact family are 18, 15, and 3.

Triangle: 18, 15, 3

$15 + 3 = 18$ $18 - 15 = 3$
$3 + 15 = 18$ $18 - 3 = 15$

Complete each fact family.

1. Triangle: 24, 12, 12
$12 + 12 = 24$ $24 - 12 = 12$

2. Triangle: 17, 6, 11
$11 + 6 = 17$ $17 - 11 = 6$
$6 + 11 = 17$ $17 - 6 = 11$

3. Triangle: 20, 16, 4
$16 + 4 = 20$ $20 - 4 = 16$
$4 + 16 = 20$ $20 - 16 = 4$

Talk Math How are these exercises like fact families that you have learned earlier?

Name _____

On My Own

Complete each fact family.

4.

$8 + 11 = 19$ $19 - 11 = 8$
$11 + 8 = 19$ $19 - 8 = 11$

5.

$23 + 3 = 26$ $26 - 23 = 3$
$3 + 23 = 26$ $26 - 3 = 23$

6.

$22 + 3 = 25$ $25 - 3 = 22$
$3 + 22 = 25$ $25 - 22 = 3$

7.

$14 + 7 = 21$ $21 - 7 = 14$
$7 + 14 = 21$ $21 - 14 = 7$

8.

$32 + 5 = 37$ $37 - 5 = 32$
$5 + 32 = 37$ $37 - 32 = 5$

Chapter 4 • Lesson 1   225

🌐 **Problem Solving**

Mathematical **PRACTICE**

9. Lizzie has 34 necklaces. 22 of the necklaces have beads on them. How many of the necklaces do not have beads? Write the fact family that can be made from these numbers.

12 necklaces

$22 + 12 = 34$ $34 - 12 = 22$
$12 + 22 = 34$ $34 - 22 = 12$

10. How many parking spaces are open in the parking lot?

26 Parking Spaces
14 Filled _____ Open

12 parking spaces

HOT Problem Sophia wrote this fact family. Tell why Sophia is wrong. Make it right.

$76 + 12 = 88$ $76 - 12 = 88$
$12 + 76 = 88$ $12 - 76 = 88$

Sample answer: Sophia is wrong because

she did not subtract the right numbers;

$88 - 76 = 12$ and $88 - 12 = 76$.

226   Chapter 4 • Lesson 1

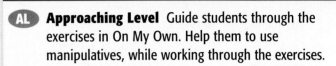
On My Own

Have students work through the exercises on this page independently. You may choose to assign exercises based on the chart below.

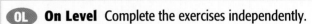

DIFFERENTIATED ASSIGNMENTS

AL **Approaching Level** Guide students through the exercises in On My Own. Help them to use manipulatives, while working through the exercises.

OL **On Level** Complete the exercises independently.

BL **Beyond Level** Complete the exercises independently without manipulatives.

Common Error!

Students may have difficulty writing the correct four sentences related to the two-digit number family. Remind them that they cannot rearrange the numbers in any order. Have them be sure that the sum or difference of the sentence holds true.

Problem Solving

Have students work through the problem-solving exercises on this page independently.

Mathematical **PRACTICE** **2**   In Exercise 10, students **reason abstractly and quantitatively.**

HOT Problem This exercise asks students to build upon their understanding of concepts needed to answer the chapter's Essential Question.

RESPONSE TO INTERVENTION
DIFFERENTIATED INSTRUCTION

AL **APPROACHING LEVEL**

IF my students struggle with two-digit fact families,

THEN choose a resource:

→ Use the Reteach worksheet with small groups.

→ Go online for a Differentiated Instruction activity.

→ **Make a Model** Provide students with a sheet of paper that contains four rows of 23 circles. Have students use two different color of crayons to illustrate two related addition sentences and two related subtraction sentences to make a two-digit addition and subtraction fact family.

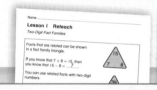 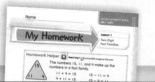

OL **ON LEVEL**

IF my students seem to know two-digit fact families, but need more practice,

THEN choose a resource:

→ Assign My Homework.

→ Go online for a Differentiated Instruction activity.

BL **BEYOND LEVEL**

IF my students have mastered two-digit fact families,

THEN choose a resource:

→ Use the Enrich worksheet in cooperative groups.

→ Assign My Homework.

→ Go online for a Differentiated Instruction activity.

 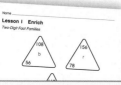

 AL

Name _____

Lesson 1 Reteach

Two-Digit Fact Families

Facts that are related can be shown in a fact family triangle.

If you know that $7 + 8 = 15$, then you know that $15 - 8 = \underline{7}$.

You can use related facts with two-digit numbers.

If you know that $12 + 22 = 34$, then you know the related fact $34 - 22 = \underline{12}$.

Complete each number family.

1.
$$20 + 30 = 50$$
$$30 + 20 = 50$$
$$50 - 20 = \mathbf{30}$$
$$50 - 30 = \mathbf{20}$$

2.
$$15 + \mathbf{18} = 33$$
$$\mathbf{18} + \mathbf{15} = 33$$
$$33 - \mathbf{18} = \mathbf{15}$$
$$33 - \mathbf{15} = \mathbf{18}$$

BL Name _____

Lesson 1 Enrich

Two-Digit Fact Families

Each fact family triangle is missing a number.
Color the triangle that is missing 78 **red**.
Color the triangle that is missing 52 **blue**.
Color the triangle that is missing 90 **yellow**.

___

Make a fact family triangle with 137 at the top.
Write 4 related facts your triangle shows.

_____ + _____ = 137   137 − _____ = _____

_____ + _____ = 137   137 − _____ = _____

See students' work.

Name _____

My Homework

Lesson 1
Two-Digit
Fact Families

Homework Helper **Need help?** connectED.mcgraw-hill.com

The numbers 15, 11, and 4 make up the numbers in a fact family.

△ 15 / 11 4

$11 + 4 = 15$ $15 - 11 = 4$
$4 + 11 = 15$ $15 - 4 = 11$

Practice

Complete each fact family.

1. △ 22 / 9 13

$9 + 13 = 22$ $22 - 9 = 13$
$13 + 9 = 22$ $22 - 13 = 9$

2. △ 21 / 8 13

$8 + 13 = 21$ $21 - 13 = 8$
$13 + 8 = 21$ $21 - 8 = 13$

3. △ 24 / 18 6

$18 + 6 = 24$ $24 - 6 = 18$
$6 + 18 = 24$ $24 - 18 = 6$

Chapter 4 • Lesson 1   227

Complete the fact family.

4. △ 26 / 13 13

$26 - 13 = 13$ $13 + 13 = 26$

Use what you know about fact families to solve.

5. Marcus counts 24 children playing. 11 of the children are boys. How many girls are playing?

   Catch me if you can!

   __13__ girls

6. There are 49 second graders. 26 of them are in Miss Johnson's class. How many students are in Mrs. Stewart's class?

   __23__ students

Test Practice

7. Which number sentence does not belong in the fact family for the numbers 7, 18, and 25?

   ○ $18 + 7 = 25$ ● $18 - 25 = 7$

   ○ $7 + 18 = 25$ ○ $25 - 7 = 18$

 Math at Home Have your child write the fact family for the numbers 22, 13, and 35.

228   Chapter 4 • Lesson 1

---

4 WRAP IT UP

CCSS

My Homework

Assign homework after successful completion of the lesson. Students who understand the concepts may skip the **Homework Helper** section.

Test Practice

Diagnose Student Errors

Class trends in wrong answers may indicate common errors or misconceptions.

$18 + 7 = 25$ part of the fact family
$18 - 25 = 7$ correct
$7 + 18 = 25$ part of the fact family
$25 - 7 = 18$ part of the fact family

Formative Assessment

Have students fill in the missing parts of the number family.

$16 + 12 = 28$ $12 + 16 = 28$
$28 - 12 = 16$ $28 - 16 = 12$

Line Up!

When one student lines up, have him or her say a two-digit addition sentence. Have the next student state the related addition fact. Have the next student state a related subtraction fact, and so on.

LESSON 2
Take Apart Tens to Subtract

OBJECTIVE Take apart numbers to make a ten to subtract.

What's the Math?

 Common Core State Standards
DOMAIN: Operations and Algebraic Thinking

Standard: 2.OA.1
The wording of this standard can be found on page 216.

What Students Should Understand
• You can take apart the second number in a subtraction problem to make a ten so that it is easier to subtract.

What Students Should be Able to Do
Find 58 − 23. Take apart a number to make a ten. Then subtract.

58 − 23

20   3   First, take apart 23 as 20 and 3.

58 − 20 = 38   Next, find 58 − 20.

38 − 3 = 35   Then subtract 3 from the difference of 58 − 20, or 38.

 Building on the Essential Question
In this lesson, students will build upon the skills and concepts needed to answer the chapter's Essential Question "How can I subtract two-digit numbers?"

Developing Vocabulary

 Review Vocabulary
ten

Review Activity
• Write the word *ten* on the board. Have students explain what they have learned about *ten* in previous chapters or grades. For example, they might recall that 10 is easy to work with because it ends in zero.

• Have students work in small groups. Each group should have 25 counters.

• Have each group take apart the counters to show 2 groups of ten and 5 ones.

• Tell students that numbers in a subtraction sentence can be taken apart into tens to make them easier to work with.

ELL **ELL Support Strategy** Use this vocabulary activity to apply visual cues to understand concepts.

My Vocabulary Cards
Have students use a blank card to review vocabulary, such as *tens*.

ELL Refer to the Multilingual eGlossary for interactive definitions in 13 languages.

Plan Online
Plan for your lesson by using the resources at
connectED.mcgraw-hill.com

Digital Dashboard

Interactive Whiteboard Ready

Vocab

The eBook **Glossary** shows the definition of the word and has audio for each definition. The **eGlossary** provides definitions in 13 languages.

Watch

Watch as concepts are brought to life through **animations**, **songs**, and a variety of visual instruction.

Tools

Virtual Manipulatives with work mats allow teachers and students to model the lesson.

Check

Use **eAssessment** for online assignments and customized assessments.

Use the **Common Core Quick Check** before the lesson to assess students' retention of previously learned concepts.

Use the interactive **Self-Check Quiz** after the lesson to provide immediate feedback on lesson concepts.

eHelp

Digital and print resources assist students and parents in completing My Homework.

Games

Online games and **apps** provide extra practice for lesson concepts.

PD

Professional development videos help teachers gain a deeper understanding of the lesson concepts and strategies.

RtI

Support for **approaching**, **on-** and **beyond-level** students as well as **English Language Learners**.

Masters

Reteach and **Enrich** worksheets, **Manipulative Masters**, the **Problem of the Day**, and other blackline masters are available for each lesson.

---

1 LAUNCH THE LESSON

 If your students are well-versed in taking apart tens to subtract, you may choose to begin instruction with Step 2, **TEACH**.

You will need
☐ Work Mat 6
☐ base-ten blocks

Mathematical PRACTICE 4 Modeling the Math

Write 27 − 12 on the board. Explain that to find 27 − 12, you can first take apart 12 to make a ten so that it is easier to subtract. Have students use Work Mat 6 and base-ten blocks to model the problem.

Let's model 27. Use 2 tens rods and 7 unit cubes. Next, let's model 12. Use 1 tens rod and 2 unit cubes.

Demonstrate the subtraction of 27 − 10 first. Then demonstrate the subtraction of the difference of 27 and 10, and 2.

Now, subtract. Take 10 away from 27. What is 27 − 10? 17 Let's now subtract 2. What is 17 − 2? 15 So, what is 27 − 12? 15

Start with 27   Subtract 10; then subtract 2

27 − 12

10   2

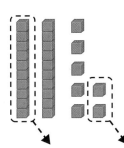

27 − 12 = 15

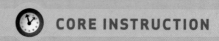

Begin core instruction here.

You will need

☐ base-ten blocks

Explore and Explain

Have students work in small groups. Give each group 7 tens rods and 8 unit cubes.

There are 56 leaves on a tree. 22 leaves fall off of the tree. How many leaves are left? What do you need to find? The number of leaves left on the tree. *How can you do this?* Find 56 – 22.

Read the directions at the bottom of the student page. Guide students in using base-ten blocks to model 56.

Let's subtract the tens. How many tens are in 22? 2 tens *How many ones are in 22?* 2 ones *Since there are 2 tens in 22, take away 2 tens from 56. How many are left?* 36 *Since there are 2 ones in 22, take away 2 ones from 36. How many are left?* 34 *How many leaves are left on the tree?* 34 leaves

Have students record their work on the Explore and Explain mat.

See and Show

Help students work through the example at the top of the page. On the board, show students how they first take apart 13 as 10 and 3. They can then subtract 10 from 35 first to get 25, and then subtract 3 from 25 to get 22. Have them trace the dashed numbers as they work the problems.

Work through Exercises 1 and 2 as a class.

Mathematical PRACTICE ③ Talk Math

Discuss with students "Explain how you decide what to subtract when working these problems." Sample answer: You take apart a number to make a ten and then you subtract.

Name _____

On My Own

**Take apart a number to make a ten.
Then subtract.**

3. 47 − 26

20   6

47 − **20** = **27**

27 − **6** = **21**

So, 47 − 26 = **21**.

4. 77 − 43

40   3

77 − **40** = **37**

37 − **3** = **34**

So, 77 − 43 = **34**.

5. 85 − 32

30   2

85 − **30** = **55**

55 − **2** = **53**

So, 85 − 32 = **53**.

6. 75 − 55

50   5

75 − **50** = **25**

25 − **5** = **20**

So, 75 − 55 = **20**.

Chapter 4 • Lesson 2   231

Problem Solving

7. Cara has 28 sticks of sidewalk chalk.
She lets her friend borrow 11 of them.
How many sticks of chalk does Cara
have now?

17 sticks of chalk

8. Shawna had 37 snowballs. She
threw 23 of them. How many
snowballs does Shawna have left?

Shawna! LOOK OUT!

14 snowballs

HOT Problem There are 22 students in
Ms. Marshall's class. 8 students like science,
2 like art, and 3 like music. The rest of the
students like math. How many students like math?

9 students; If you add 8 + 2 + 3 that equals 13 that like

the other subjects and then you subtract 22 students

minus the 13 and that equals 9 that like math.

232   Chapter 4 • Lesson 2

On My Own

Have students work through the exercises on this page
independently. You may choose to assign exercises based on
the chart below.

DIFFERENTIATED ASSIGNMENTS

AL **Approaching Level** Guide students through the
exercises in On My Own. Help them to use
manipulatives while working through the exercises.

OL **On Level** Complete the exercises independently.

BL **Beyond Level** Complete the exercises independently
without manipulatives.

Common Error!

Students may have a hard time taking apart numbers
to subtract because it is a multi-step problem.
Encourage them to model their problems with
manipulatives.

Problem Solving

Have students work through the problem-solving exercises on
this page independently.

Mathematical **PRACTICE 4** In Exercise 8, students can **model with
mathematics.**

HOT Problem This exercise asks students to build
upon their understanding of concepts needed to answer the
chapter's Essential Question.

AL **APPROACHING LEVEL**

IF my students struggle with taking apart tens to subtract,

THEN choose a resource:

→ Use the Reteach worksheet with small groups.

→ Go online for a Differentiated Instruction activity.

→ **Mental Math** Explore a different strategy for subtracting numbers. Start with 70 — 29. Explain that you are going to add the same number to both 70 and 29 to make it easier to subtract. *What would be that number?* 1 *If you add 1 to both sides, what is the new problem?* 71 — 30. *You no longer need to regroup in this problem. What is the difference?* 41

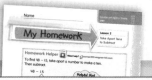

OL **ON LEVEL**

IF my students seem to know how to take apart tens to subtract, but need more practice,

THEN choose a resource:

→ Assign My Homework.

→ Go online for a Differentiated Instruction activity.

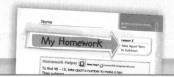

BL **BEYOND LEVEL**

IF my students have mastered taking apart tens to subtract,

THEN choose a resource:

→ Use the Enrich worksheet in cooperative groups.

→ Assign My Homework.

→ Go online for a Differentiated Instruction activity.

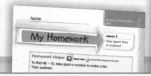

AL Name _____

Lesson 2 Reteach
Take Apart Tens to Subtract

Find 45 — 14.

Sometimes it is easier to take apart one number to make a ten. Then subtract.

45 — 14
  / \
 10 4

 14 can be taken apart as 10 and 4.

Now subtract 10 from 45.
45 — 10 = 35

Then take away 4 from 35.
35 — 4 = 31

Take apart a number to make a ten. Subtract.

1. 62 — 13
    / \
   10 3

   62 — 10 = 52

   52 — 3 = 49

2. 47 — 16
    / \
   10 6

   47 — 10 = 37

   37 — 6 = 31

3. 27 — 11
    / \
   10 1

   27 — 10 = 17

   17 — 1 = 16

BL Name _____

Lesson 2 Enrich
Take Apart Tens to Subtract

These are 3 buildings that are very old. One building is 144 years old, one is 288 years old, and another is 200 years old. Each building is a different color. Use the clues to find out which building is which. Complete the chart below.

• The buildings are named A, B, and C.

• The building that is red is twice as old as the green building.

• Building A is 56 years younger than the blue building.

• C is the oldest building.

Building Name	Age	Color
A	144	green
B	200	blue
C	288	red

My Homework

Name _____

Operations and Algebraic Thinking
2.OA1

CCSS

My Homework

Lesson 2
Take Apart Tens
to Subtract

Homework Helper

eHelp Need help? ⤶ connectED.mcgraw-hill.com

To find 48 − 15, take apart a number to make a ten.
Then subtract.

48 − 15

10   5

48 − 10 = 38
38 − 5 = 33
So, 48 − 15 = 33.

Helpful Hint
Take apart 15 as
10 and 5

Practice

Take apart a number to make a ten. Then subtract.

1. 54 − 13

10   3

54 − 10 = 44
44 − 3 = 41

So, 54 − 13 = 41.

2. 35 − 14

10   4

35 − 10 = 25
25 − 4 = 21

So, 35 − 14 = 21.

3. There are 87 insects in a jar. Someone leaves
the lid off and some crawl away. There are 54
insects left in the jar. How many crawled away?

__33__ insects

4. Emily has 25 onions and 14 peppers
that she grew in her garden. How
many more onions does she have
than peppers?

Come on out,
Caleb!

__11__ onions

5. There were 25 days of rain in April. It rained
16 days in May. If there are 61 days total in
April and May, how many days did it not rain?

__20__ days

Test Practice

6. How would you take apart 14 to solve 28 − 14?

   ○ 7 and 7   ○ 12 and 2

   ● 10 and 4   ○ 20 and 8

 Math at Home Have your child take apart 16 to make a ten to find 87 − 16.

My Homework

Assign homework after successful completion of the lesson.
Students who understand the concepts may skip the
Homework Helper section.

Test Practice
Diagnose Student Errors

Class trends in wrong answers may indicate common errors or
misconceptions.

7 and 7   took apart 14 incorrectly

12 and 2   took apart 14 incorrectly

10 and 4   correct

20 and 8   took apart 20 and 8

Formative Assessment

Model 62 - 12 using base-ten blocks and Work Mat 6.

Demonstrate how to take apart the numbers to make it easier to
subtract and solve.

What answer do you find? 50

LESSON 3
Regroup a Ten as Ones
OBJECTIVE Use models to regroup and find differences.

What's the Math?

 Common Core State Standards
DOMAIN: Operations and Algebraic Thinking
Standards: 2.OA.1, 2.NBT.5, 2.NBT.9
The wording of these standards can be found on page 216.

CCSS

What Students Should Understand
• When subtracting from a two-digit number, you sometimes need to regroup if there are not enough ones to subtract.

What Students Should be Able to Do
Use base-ten blocks to find 26 − 9.

Step 1
Use base-ten blocks to show 26.

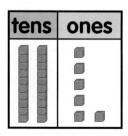

Step 2
Subtract the ones. If there are not enough ones to subtract, regroup.

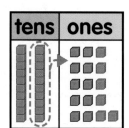

Step 3
Subtract 9 ones.

tens	ones

1 ten 7 ones

So, 26 − 9 = 17

Developing Vocabulary

 Review Vocabulary
regroup   compare

Review Activity
• Ask students when they need to regroup in a subtraction problem. For example, they might recall that sometimes there are not enough ones. Sometimes some need to be taken away from the tens to have enough ones.

• Write 45 − 9 and 45 − 3 on the board. Have students work in small groups to solve each subtraction problem. Tell them they will need to refer to the steps in See and Show to find 45 − 9.

• Afterward, discuss with students why they had to regroup to take 9 away from 45, and why they did not regroup to take 3 away from 45.

ELL **ELL Support Strategy** Use this vocabulary activity to participate in purposeful cooperative learning opportunities.

My Vocabulary Cards
Encourage students to use blank cards to model regrouping using base-ten blocks or place-value charts.

ELL Refer to the Multilingual eGlossary for interactive definitions in 13 languages.

 Building on the Essential Question
In this lesson, students will build upon the skills and concepts needed to answer the chapter's Essential Question "How can I subtract two-digit numbers?"

Plan Online

Plan for your lesson by using the resources at

connectED.mcgraw-hill.com

Digital Dashboard

Interactive Whiteboard Ready

Vocab

The eBook **Glossary** shows the definition of the word and has audio for each definition. The **eGlossary** provides definitions in 13 languages.

Watch

Watch as concepts are brought to life through **animations**, **songs**, and a variety of visual instruction.

Tools

Virtual Manipulatives with work mats allow teachers and students to model the lesson.

Check

Use **eAssessment** for online assignments and customized assessments.

Use the **Common Core Quick Check** before the lesson to assess students' retention of previously learned concepts.

Use the interactive **Self-Check Quiz** after the lesson to provide immediate feedback on lesson concepts.

eHelp

Digital and print resources assist students and parents in completing My Homework.

Games

Online games and **apps** provide extra practice for lesson concepts.

PD

Professional development videos help teachers gain a deeper understanding of the lesson concepts and strategies.

RtI

Support for **approaching**, **on**- and **beyond-level** students as well as **English Language Learners**.

Masters

Reteach and **Enrich** worksheets, **Manipulative Masters**, the **Problem of the Day**, and other blackline masters are available for each lesson.

1 LAUNCH THE LESSON

 If your students are well-versed in regrouping a ten as ones, you may choose to begin instruction with Step 2, **TEACH**.

You will need

☐ base-ten blocks

Mathematical PRACTICE 4 Modeling the Math

Have students work in small groups. Give each group 6 tens rods and 9 unit cubes. Have students model the number 55 by showing five tens rods and 5 unit cubes.

> *Use base-ten blocks to show the number 55. How many tens? How many ones?* 5 tens, 5 ones

Write 55 − 4 on the board. Have students use the base-ten blocks to model the subtraction.

> *Use base-ten blocks to model subtracting 55 − 4. What is the difference?* 51 *How did you find the difference?* Sample answer: I used 5 tens rods and 5 unit cubes to model 55. Then removed 4 of the unit cubes to show subtracting 4. The result was 51.

Ask students to model 21 − 4.

> *Use base-ten blocks to model 21 − 4. How many tens and how many ones are in 21?* 2 tens, 1 one *Can you subtract 4? Why or why no?* You cannot subtract 4 because there are not enough ones.

Explain to students that in this lesson, they will learn to regroup to subtract problems like 21 − 4.

2 TEACH

You will need

☐ base-ten blocks

☐ Work Mat 6

Explore and Explain

Read the directions that are at the bottom of the student page.

What do you need to find? The number of sea shells Adam has left. *To find the number of shells that Adam has left, you can use base-ten blocks to find 23 − 5.*

Guide students in placing base-ten blocks in the chart to model 23.

Are there enough ones in 23 to take away 5 ones? No *You will need to regroup 1 ten as 10 ones.*

Lead the students in trading 1 ten for 10 ones.

How many ones are there now? 13 ones *Are there enough ones to take away 5 ones?* yes *What is 13 ones − 5 ones?* 8 ones *How many tens are left?* 1 ten *You have 1 ten and 8 ones left. What number does this equal?* 18 *So, Adam has 18 sea shells left.*

See and Show

Help students work through the example at the top of the page. You may wish to use virtual base-ten blocks to demonstrate the steps of the example.

Have them trace the dashed number at the end.

Work through Exercises 1 and 2 as a class.

Mathematical PRACTICE ③ **Talk Math**

Discuss with students " How do you know when you need to regroup? Explain." Sample answer: You will know to regroup if you do not have enough ones. You will have to take some away from ten to have enough ones.

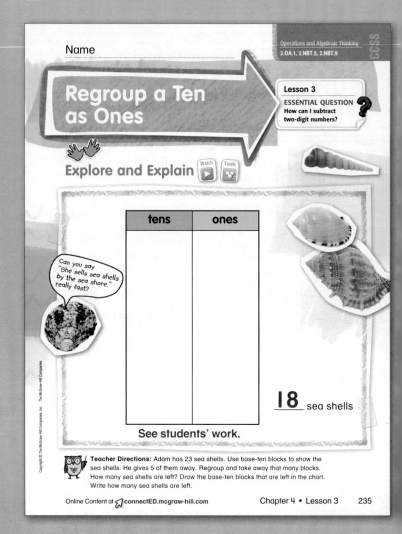

Name _____

Regroup a Ten as Ones

Operations and Algebraic Thinking
2.OA.1, 2.NBT.5, 2.NBT.9

Lesson 3

ESSENTIAL QUESTION
How can I subtract two-digit numbers?

Explore and Explain Watch ▶ Tools

tens	ones

Can you say "She sells sea shells by the sea shore." really fast?

18 sea shells

See students' work.

🦉 **Teacher Directions:** Adam has 23 sea shells. Use base-ten blocks to show the sea shells. He gives 5 of them away. Regroup and take away that many blocks. How many sea shells are left? Draw the base-ten blocks that are left in the chart. Write how many sea shells are left.

Online Content at ✏️ connectED.mcgraw-hill.com   Chapter 4 • Lesson 3   235

See and Show

Find 24 − 8.

Step 1
Use base-ten blocks to show 24.

tens	ones

2 tens 4 ones

Step 2
Subtract the ones. There are not enough ones to subtract. Regroup.

tens	ones

1 ten 14 ones

Step 3
Subtract 8 ones.

tens	ones

1 ten 6 ones

24 − 8 = **16**

Use Work Mat 6 and base-ten blocks to subtract.

	Subtract the ones. Do you need to regroup?	Write the difference.
1. 31 − 4	no (yes)	31 − 4 = **27**
2. 27 − 5	(no) yes	27 − 5 = **22**

Talk Math How do you know when you need to regroup? Explain.

236   Chapter 4 • Lesson 3

Name _____

On My Own

Use Work Mat 6 and base-ten blocks to subtract.

	Subtract the ones. Do you need to regroup?	Write the difference.
3. 46 − 2	(no) yes	46 − 2 = **44**
4. 35 − 9	no (yes)	35 − 9 = **26**
5. 56 − 5	(no) yes	56 − 5 = **51**
6. 22 − 6	no (yes)	22 − 6 = **16**
7. 30 − 4	no (yes)	30 − 4 = **26**
8. 43 − 3	(no) yes	43 − 3 = **40**
9. 76 − 8	no (yes)	76 − 8 = **68**
10. 67 − 8	no (yes)	67 − 8 = **59**

Chapter 4 • Lesson 3   237

Problem Solving

Mathematical **PRACTICE**

Use Work Mat 6 and base-ten blocks to subtract.

11. Logan draws 23 red flowers. He draws 14 yellow flowers. How many more red flowers than yellow flowers does he draw?

9 red flowers

12. There are 25 flower bulbs in a bag. Karen gives 7 bulbs to Ava. How many bulbs are left?

I may not be pretty, but Mom says I'm a late bloomer.

18 bulbs

13. Candice has played in 8 soccer games. There are 14 games in all. How many games does she have left?

6 games

Write Math Liam subtracts 5 from 23. Is the difference less than 20 or greater than 20? Explain.

Sample answer: The difference is less than 20. When you subtract 23 − 3, the difference is 20. You are subtracting more than 3 because 5 is greater than 3.

On My Own

Have students work through the exercises on this page independently. You may choose to assign exercises based on the chart below.

DIFFERENTIATED ASSIGNMENTS

AL **Approaching Level** Guide students through the exercises in On My Own. Help them to use manipulatives while working through the exercises.

OL **On Level** Complete the exercises independently.

BL **Beyond Level** Complete the exercises independently without manipulatives.

Common Error!

Students may have trouble distinguishing between modeling addition and subtraction. Help them see the logic in showing only the greater number because the lesser number is being subtracted or taken away from the greater number.

Problem Solving

Have students work through the problem-solving exercises on this page independently.

Mathematical **PRACTICE** **4** In Exercise 11, students can **model with mathematics.**

Write Math

This exercise asks students to build upon their understanding of concepts needed to answer the chapter's Essential Question.

AL APPROACHING LEVEL

IF my students struggle with regrouping a ten as ones,

THEN choose a resource:

→ Use the Differentiated Instruction activity on p. 215E.

→ Use the Reteach worksheet with small groups.

→ Go online for a Differentiated Instruction activity.

→ **Finger Math** Have students clasp their hands together to make a ball. Point out there are ten fingers in the ball. Have them separate their hands to show 10 fingers. Tell them they have regrouped a group of ten into ten ones.

OL ON LEVEL

IF my students seem to know how to regroup a ten as ones, but need more practice,

THEN choose a resource:

→ Assign My Homework.

→ Go online for a Differentiated Instruction activity.

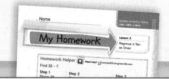

BL BEYOND LEVEL

IF my students have mastered regrouping a ten as ones,

THEN choose a resource:

→ Use the Enrich worksheet in cooperative groups.

→ Assign My Homework.

→ Go online for a Differentiated Instruction activity.

AL Name _____

Lesson 3   Reteach
Regroup a Ten as Ones

Candy has 32 markers. She gives 6 to Ray.
How many markers does she have left?

$$\begin{array}{r} 32 \\ -\ 6 \\ \hline ? \end{array}$$

To help solve this problem, you can regroup one box of markers as ten markers.

 =

Now there are enough markers. Subtract.

$32 - 6 = $ __26__ . Candy has 26 markers left.

Write the number sentences. Use .
Regroup if needed. Then solve.

1. Jim had 52 posters. He sold 18 of them.
   How many posters does he have now?
   __52__ − __18__ = __34__ posters

2. Ellen had 34 crayons. She gives 5 to her friends.
   How many does she have left?
   __34__ − __5__ = __29__ crayons

3. John had 41 pennies. He spent 15 of them.
   How many pennies does he have now?
   __41__ − __15__ = __26__ pennies

BL Name _____

Lesson 3   Enrich
Regroup a Ten as Ones

Draw Xs to show tens. Draw Os to show ones.
Write the numbers.

Draw	Regroup
3 tens 6 ones X X X O O O O O O	2 tens 16 ones X X O O O O O O O O O O O O O O O O
Write the number. __36__	Write the number. __36__

Draw	Regroup
4 tens 5 ones X X X X O O O O O	3 tens 15 ones X X X O O O O O O O O O O O O O O O
Write the number. __45__	Write the number. __45__

Draw	Regroup
2 tens X X	1 ten 10 ones X O O O O O O O O O O
Write the number. __20__	Write the number. __20__

Name

My Homework

Lesson 3
Regroup a Ten
as Ones

Homework Helper   Need help? connectED.mcgraw-hill.com

Find 35 − 7.

Step 1	**Step 2**	**Step 3**
Show 35.	Subtract the ones. There are not enough ones to subtract. Regroup.	Subtract 7 ones.

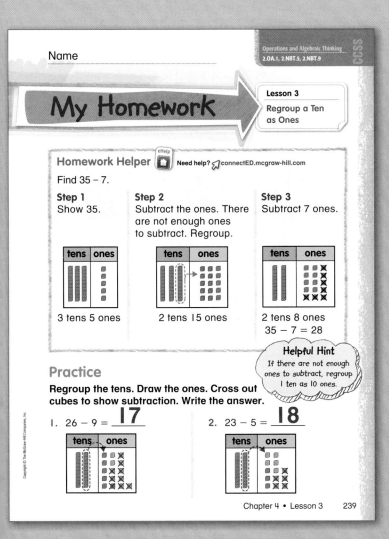

3 tens 5 ones

2 tens 15 ones

2 tens 8 ones
35 − 7 = 28

Helpful Hint
If there are not enough ones to subtract, regroup 1 ten as 10 ones.

Practice

Regroup the tens. Draw the ones. Cross out cubes to show subtraction. Write the answer.

1. 26 − 9 = **17**

2. 23 − 5 = **18**

Chapter 4 • Lesson 3   239

Regroup the tens. Draw the ones. Cross out cubes to show subtraction. Write the answer.

3. 21 − 7 = **14**

4. 30 − 6 = **24**

5. There are 42 icicles. 9 of them melt. How many icicles are left?

33 icicles

Hey! I'm melting!

6. 31 people are at the skating rink. 8 people go home. How many people are left at the skating rink?

23 people

Test Practice

7. 23 − 6 = _____

tens	ones

29 ○   17 ●   13 ○   10 ○

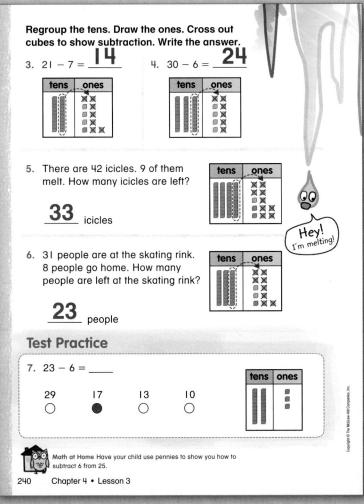

Math at Home Have your child use pennies to show you how to subtract 6 from 25.

---

4 WRAP IT UP

My Homework

Assign homework after successful completion of the lesson. Students who understand the concepts may skip the **Homework Helper** section.

Test Practice
Diagnose Student Errors

Class trends in wrong answers may indicate common errors or misconceptions.

29 added

17 correct

13 subtracted wrong

10 subtracted wrong

Formative Assessment

Why do we sometimes have to regroup to subtract? There are not enough ones to subtract from.

Line Up!

When students line up, have 12 of them count off. Then have them separate into two groups with one group of 2 students and the other group of 10 students. Subtract 4 students, regrouping the tens group.

LESSON 4
Subtract From a Two-Digit Number
OBJECTIVE Subtract one-digit numbers from two-digit numbers.

What's the Math?

 Common Core State Standards
DOMAIN: Operations and Algebraic Thinking

Standards: 2.OA.1, 2.NBT.5, 2.NBT.9
The wording of these standards can be found on page 216.

What Students Should Understand

• When subtracting with two-digit numbers, subtract the ones and then the tens. Regroup 1 ten as 10 ones as needed.

What Students Should be Able to Do

Find 23 − 7.

Step 1
Use base-ten blocks to show 23.
Can you subtract 7 ones?

tens	ones
2	3
−	7

Step 2
Regroup 1 ten as 10 ones.
3 ones + 10 ones = 13 ones

tens	ones
1	13
2̶	3̶
−	7

Step 3
Subtract the ones.

tens	ones
1	13
2̶	3̶
−	7
	6

Step 4
Subtract the tens.

tens	ones
1	13
2̶	3̶
−	7
1	6

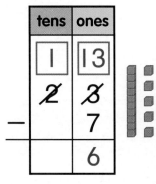

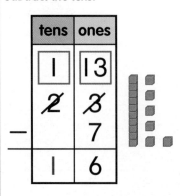

So, 23 − 7 = <u>16</u>

Developing Vocabulary

 **Review Vocabulary**

tens   ones   regroup

Review Activity

• Draw the number line shown below on the board. Show students the number line. Remind them that they have already learned to subtract on a number line. Ask them how they would use the number line to find 32 − 3. Students should explain that they would start at 32 and count back three to find that 32 − 3 is 29.

25 26 27 28 29 30 31 32 33

• Erase the number line. Write 32 − 3 on the board. Ask students what they know about using ones and tens when subtracting. Use the subtraction problem 32 − 3 to prompt discussion. Students might explain that regrouping one ten as ten ones is needed since there are not enough ones.

ELL **ELL Support Strategy** Use this vocabulary activity to use non-linguistic representations to support student work.

My Vocabulary Cards

Have students use a blank card to summarize the steps used to regroup.

ELL Refer to the Multilingual eGlossary for interactive definitions in 13 languages.

❓ Building on the Essential Question

In this lesson, students will build upon the skills and concepts needed to answer the chapter's Essential Question "How can I subtract two-digit numbers?"

Plan Online
Plan for your lesson by using the resources at
 connectED.mcgraw-hill.com

Digital Dashboard

Interactive Whiteboard Ready

 Vocab

The eBook **Glossary** shows the definition of the word and has audio for each definition. The **eGlossary** provides definitions in 13 languages.

 Watch

Watch as concepts are brought to life through **animations**, **songs**, and a variety of visual instruction.

 Tools

Virtual Manipulatives with work mats allow teachers and students to model the lesson.

 Check

Use **eAssessment** for online assignments and customized assessments.

Use the **Common Core Quick Check** before the lesson to assess students' retention of previously learned concepts.

Use the interactive **Self-Check Quiz** after the lesson to provide immediate feedback on lesson concepts.

 eHelp

Digital and print resources assist students and parents in completing My Homework.

 Games

Online games and **apps** provide extra practice for lesson concepts.

 PD

Professional development videos help teachers gain a deeper understanding of the lesson concepts and strategies.

 RtI

Support for **approaching**, **on-** and **beyond-level** students as well as **English Language Learners**.

 Masters

Reteach and **Enrich** worksheets, **Manipulative Masters**, the **Problem of the Day**, and other blackline masters are available for each lesson.

1 LAUNCH THE LESSON

 If your students are well-versed in subtracting from a two-digit number, you may choose to begin instruction with Step 2, **TEACH**.

You will need
☐ base-ten blocks
☐ Work Mat 6

Mathematical PRACTICE 4 Modeling the Math

Prepare subtraction problems, some of which require regrouping and some that do not. Sample problems: $63 - 7$, $75 - 4$, $42 - 9$, and $90 - 4$.

Point to each problem, one at a time. Have students stand up if it is necessary to regroup. Have them raise their right hand if it is not necessary to regroup.

Have students use base-ten blocks to prove their responses. Some students may benefit from using the Work Mat.

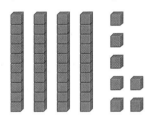

 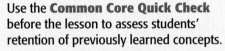

2 TEACH

🕐 **Begin core instruction here.**

You will need
☐ base-ten blocks

Explore and Explain

Read the directions that are at the bottom of the student page.

What do you need to find? The number of crabs left on the beach. *How can you find this?* Find 34 – 8.

Explain to students that they will use the place-value chart to model the subtraction.

Place base-ten blocks on the place-value chart to show the number you are subtracting from. How many tens are you going to place on the chart? 3 tens *How many ones?* 4 ones

Write 34 on the board.

How can you show the subtraction of 8 from 34 using base-ten blocks? Sample answer: Take away 8 of the base-ten blocks from the 34 base-ten blocks.

Write the rest of the subtraction problem on the board.

Subtract the ones first. Can you take away 8 ones from 4 ones? no *What do you do when there are not enough ones to subtract from?* Regroup 1 ten as 10 ones

Cross out the 3 on the board and write 2 above it.

After regrouping, how many ones are there? 14 ones

Cross out the 4 on the board and write 14 above it.

Are there enough ones to take away 8 ones? yes
What is 14 ones – 8 ones? 6 ones

Write 6 in the ones place of the difference on the board.

Subtract the tens next. How many tens are left? 2 tens

Write 2 in the tens place of the difference on the board.

You have 2 tens and 6 ones left. What number does this equal? 26 *So, 26 crabs were left on the beach.*

See and Show

Help students work through the example at the top of the page. You may wish to use virtual manipulatives or Work Mat 6 and base-ten blocks to demonstrate the steps. Have them trace the dashed number as they work the problems.

Work through Exercises 1 and 2 as a class.

Mathematical PRACTICE 3 **Talk Math**

Discuss with students "How do you regroup 1 ten?" Sample answer: You make 10 ones out of 1 ten.

Name _____

Operations and Algebraic Thinking
2.OA.1, 2.NBT.5, 2.NBT.9

Subtract From a Two-Digit Number

Lesson 4
ESSENTIAL QUESTION
How can I subtract two-digit numbers?

Explore and Explain (Watch) (Tools)

See students' work.

tens	ones

The water's perfect today!

26 crabs

🦉 **Teacher Directions:** Jack saw 34 crabs on the beach. Use base-ten blocks to show that number. 8 crabs ran into the water. Regroup and take away that many cubes. Draw the cubes that are left. Write how many crabs were left on the beach.

Online Content at 🔗 connectED.mcgraw-hill.com   Chapter 4 • Lesson 4   241

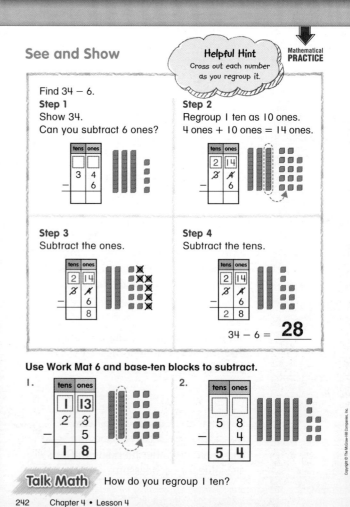

See and Show

Helpful Hint
Cross out each number as you regroup it.

Mathematical PRACTICE

Find 34 – 6.
Step 1
Show 34.
Can you subtract 6 ones?

tens	ones
3	4
–	6

Step 2
Regroup 1 ten as 10 ones.
4 ones + 10 ones = 14 ones.

tens	ones
2	14
3	4
–	6

Step 3
Subtract the ones.

tens	ones
2	14
3	4
–	6
	8

Step 4
Subtract the tens.

tens	ones
2	14
3	4
–	6
2	8

34 – 6 = **28**

Use Work Mat 6 and base-ten blocks to subtract.

1.
tens	ones
1	13
2	3
–	5
1	8

2.
tens	ones
5	8
–	4
5	4

Talk Math How do you regroup 1 ten?

242   Chapter 4 • Lesson 4

3 PRACTICE & APPLY

On My Own

Name _____

Use Work Mat 6 and base-ten blocks to subtract.

3.

tens	ones
2̶	1̶4̶
3̶	4̶
−	7
2	7

4.
tens	ones
7	3
−	3
7	0

5.
tens	ones
5	9
−	4
5	5

6.
8	8
−	2
8	6

7.
	1̶5̶
X̶	5̶
−	9
	6

8.
2̶	1̶1̶
3̶	X̶
−	6
2	5

9.

4̶	1̶8̶
5̶	8̶
−	9
4	9

10.
5̶	1̶6̶
6̶	6̶
−	7
5	9

11.
9	5
−	5
9	0

12.
$$\begin{array}{r} 14 \\ -\ 7 \\ \hline \mathbf{7} \end{array}$$

13.
$$\begin{array}{r} 28 \\ -\ 9 \\ \hline \mathbf{19} \end{array}$$

14.
$$\begin{array}{r} 34 \\ -\ 6 \\ \hline \mathbf{28} \end{array}$$

Problem Solving

Mathematical PRACTICE

15. Tina puts 12 coins in a machine. The machine keeps 4 of the coins. How many coins does she get back?

8 coins

16. There are 38 apples in the cafeteria. Students buy 9 apples for their lunches. How many apples are left?

29 apples

17. A store has 76 shirts on display. The store sells 8 of the shirts. How many shirts are left?

68 shirts

HOT Problem There are 23 boys and 33 girls at a beach. 7 boys and 4 girls leave the beach, how many boys and girls are left altogether? Explain.

There will be 45 left altogether. You

add 23 and 33 for a total of 56 at the

beach. 11 leave the beach and that

leaves 45 at the beach.

On My Own

Have students work through the exercises on this page independently. You may choose to assign exercises based on the chart below.

DIFFERENTIATED ASSIGNMENTS

AL **Approaching Level** Guide students through the exercises in On My Own. Help them to use manipulatives while working through the exercises.

OL **On Level** Complete the exercises independently.

BL **Beyond Level** Complete the exercises independently without manipulatives.

Common Error!
Help students understand that regrouping is necessary when there are not enough ones to subtract the bottom number from the top number.

Problem Solving

Have students work through the problem-solving exercises on this page independently.

Mathematical PRACTICE 1 In Exercise 17, students **make sense of problems and persevere in solving them.**

HOT Problem This exercise asks students to build upon their understanding of concepts needed to answer the chapter's Essential Question.

RtI RESPONSE TO INTERVENTION

DIFFERENTIATED INSTRUCTION

AL) APPROACHING LEVEL

IF my students struggle with subtracting from a two-digit number,

THEN choose a resource:

→ Use the Reteach worksheet with small groups.

→ Go online for a Differentiated Instruction activity.

→ **Use Manipulatives** If students have difficulty grasping the concept using base-ten blocks, try using connecting cubes of 2 colors.

OL) ON LEVEL

IF my students seem to know how to subtract from a two-digit number, but need more practice,

THEN choose a resource:

→ Use the Differentiated Instruction activity on p. 215D.

→ Assign My Homework.

→ Go online for a Differentiated Instruction activity.

BL) BEYOND LEVEL

IF my students have mastered subtracting from a two-digit number,

THEN choose a resource:

→ Use the Differentiated Instruction activity on p. 215D.

→ Use the Enrich worksheet in cooperative groups.

→ Assign My Homework.

→ Go online for a Differentiated Instruction activity.

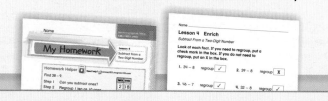

245A **Chapter 4** Subtract Two-Digit Numbers

AL Name _____

Lesson 4 Reteach

Subtract from a Two-Digit Number

Find 42 − 8.

tens	ones

Show 42.
Can you subtract 8 ones?
Regroup 1 ten as 10 ones.
Now there are 3 tens and 12 ones.

$$\begin{array}{r} {}^{3}\!\!\!\!\!\!{}^{12} \\ \cancel{4}2 \\ -8 \\ \hline 34 \end{array}$$

Use Work Mat 6 and ▭▭▭▭ and ▢ to subtract.

1.	tens	ones
	4	**13**
	5	3
	−	9
	4	**4**

2.	tens	ones
	2	**14**
	3	4
	−	6
	2	**8**

3.	tens	ones
	3	**17**
	4	7
	−	8
	3	**9**

4. ☐1☐15
   25
   − 7
   18

5. ☐7☐11
   81
   − 8
   73

6. ☐4☐14
   54
   − 9
   45

7. ☐5☐12
   62
   − 3
   59

8. ☐☐
   76
   − 4
   72

9. ☐2☐13
   33
   − 6
   27

BL Name _____

Lesson 4 Enrich

Subtract From a Two-Digit Number

Look at each fact. If you need to regroup, put a check mark in the box. If you do not need to regroup, put an X in the box.

1. 34 − 8   regroup [✓]   2. 39 − 8   regroup [X]

3. 46 − 7   regroup [✓]   4. 32 − 8   regroup [✓]

5. 50 − 36   regroup [✓]   6. 27 − 15   regroup [X]

7. 61 − 33   regroup [✓]   8. 52 − 29   regroup [✓]

9. 35 − 14   regroup [X]   10. 73 − 52   regroup [X]

11. 24 − 16   regroup [✓]   12. 41 − 25   regroup [✓]

13. 82 − 39   regroup [✓]   14. 70 − 18   regroup [✓]

15. 43 − 38   regroup [✓]   16. 66 − 45   regroup [X]

Name _____

My Homework

Lesson 4
Subtract From a
Two-Digit Number

Homework Helper eHelp Need help? ∑ connectED.mcgraw-hill.com

Find 38 − 9.

	tens	ones
	2	18
	3̶	8̶
−		9
	2	9

Step 1 Can you subtract ones?
Step 2 Regroup 1 ten as 10 ones.
Step 3 Subtract the ones.
Step 4 Subtract the tens.

Practice

Subtract.

1.

tens	ones
1	16
2̶	6̶
	9
1	7

2.

tens	ones
☐	☐
4	7
	6
4	1

3.

tens	ones
5	12
6̶	2̶
	5
5	7

4.

6	13
7̶	3̶
	6
6	7

5.

7	16
8̶	6̶
	8
7	8

6.

☐	☐
4	9
	6
4	3

Chapter 4 • Lesson 4   245

Subtract.

7.
```
  44
−  4
  40
```

8.
```
  51
−  8
  43
```

9.
```
  22
−  3
  19
```

10. There are 27 children playing outside. 13 children go inside. How many are left?

    14 children

11. There are 55 mice in the barn. A cat chases 9 of them away. How many mice are left?

    46 mice

I like barns!

Test Practice

12. Find the difference.
    43 − 9 = _____

    52 ○   44 ○   33 ○   34 ●

I do too!

246   Chapter 4 • Lesson 4

My Homework

Assign homework after successful completion of the lesson. Students who understand the concepts may skip the **Homework Helper** section.

Test Practice

Diagnose Student Errors

Class trends in wrong answers may indicate common errors or misconceptions.

52 added

44 did not regroup

33 subtracted incorrectly

34 correct

Formative Assessment

Ask students to model subtracting a one-digit number from a two-digit number, using base-ten blocks and Work Mat 6.

Line Up!

When students line up for recess, lunch, or dismissal, count off 11 students. Subtract 7 students and have them take one step out of the line.

• *How many students are left?* 4 students
• Write the subtraction sentence on the board.
  11 − 7 = 4

Check My Progress

Use this as a formative assessment to determine if your students are struggling, and if so, with which topics they struggle. The criteria for differentiation are on the next page.

Vocabulary Check

Have students use each vocabulary word in a sentence.

ELL ELL Support Strategy Use this information to participate in purposeful, cooperative learning activities.

Concept Check

These concepts are covered in Lessons 1–4.

Exercise(s)	Concept	Review Lesson(s)
2	Two-digit fact families	1
3–4	Take apart tens to subtract	2
5–10	Subtract two-digit numbers	3–4

Problem Solving

Exercise 11 uses a word problem to check for understanding of the same concepts.

Test Practice

Diagnose Student Errors

Class trends in wrong answers may indicate common errors or misconceptions.

69 correct
78 subtracted the ones incorrectly
79 did not regroup correctly
85 added numbers instead of subtracting

Name

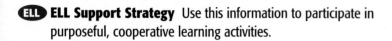

Check My Progress

Vocabulary Check

Complete the sentence.

fact family   regroup

1. The numbers 3, 5, and 8 make up a ___fact family___

Concept Check

Complete the fact family.

2.

$7 + 12 = 19$ $19 - 12 = 7$
$12 + 7 = 19$ $19 - 7 = 12$

Take apart a number to make a ten. Then subtract.

3. $83 - 52$

$83 - 50 = 33$
$33 - 2 = 31$

So, $83 - 52 = 31$.

4. $67 - 45$

$67 - 40 = 27$
$27 - 5 = 22$

So, $67 - 45 = 22$.

Chapter 4   247

Subtract.

5.
tens	ones
5	12
6	2
−	8
5	4

6.
tens	ones
3	13
4	3
−	7
3	6

7.
tens	ones
5	5
−	4
5	1

8.
1	15
2	5
−	6
1	9

9.
4	14
5	4
−	8
4	6

10.
6	13
7	3
−	6
6	7

11. There are 35 robins in a park. 14 of them fly away. How many robins are left in the park?

___21___ robins

Test Practice

12. Yesterday, there were 77 tulips blooming in the garden. Today, 8 of them have wilted. How many tulips are still blooming?

69 ●   78 ○   79 ○   85 ○

248   Chapter 4

Name _____

Check My Progress *(Lessons 1 through 4)*

Complete each fact family.

1.
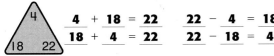

$4 + 18 = 22$ $22 - 4 = 18$
$18 + 4 = 22$ $22 - 18 = 4$

2.
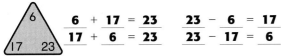

$6 + 17 = 23$ $23 - 6 = 17$
$17 + 6 = 23$ $23 - 17 = 6$

Take apart a number to subtract.

3. $54 - 36 = $ **18**
   30   6
   $54 - 30 = 24$
   $24 - 6 = 18$

4. $86 - 42 = $ **44**
   40   2
   $86 - 40 = 46$
   $46 - 2 = 44$

Subtract.

5. $56 - 6$ **50**   6. $39 - 8$ **31**

7. $74 - 9$ **65**   8. $63 - 7$ **56**

Copyright © The McGraw-Hill Companies, Inc. Permission is granted to reproduce for classroom use.

IF students miss 5 or more,

THEN choose a resource:

→ Check My Progress
→ Self-Check Quiz
→ Use the Reteach worksheets.

IF students miss 3 to 4,

THEN choose a resource:

→ Chapter Project
→ Proceed to the next lesson.

IF students miss 2 or less,

THEN choose a resource:

→ Chapter Project
→ Use the Enrich worksheets.
→ Proceed to the next lesson.

Subtract Two-Digit Numbers

OBJECTIVE Subtract two-digit numbers.

What's the Math?

 Common Core State Standards
DOMAIN: Operations and Algebraic Thinking

Standards: 2.OA.1, 2.NBT.5, 2.NBT.9
The wording of these standards can be found on page 216.

CCSS

What Students Should Understand
- When subtracting two two-digit numbers, subtract the ones and then the tens. Regroup 1 ten as 10 ones as needed.

What Students Should be Able to Do
Find 45 − 28.

Step 1

Can you subtract 8 ones?

tens	ones
4	5
− 2	8

Step 2

Regroup 1 ten as 10 ones.
5 ones + 10 ones = 15 ones.

tens	ones
3	15
4̶	5̶
− 2	8

Step 3

Subtract the ones.

tens	ones
3	15
4̶	5̶
− 2	8
	7

Step 4

Subtract the tens.

tens	ones
3	15
4̶	5̶
− 2	8
1	7

So, 45 − 28 = 17.

Developing Vocabulary

 Review Vocabulary
subtraction

Review Activity
- Write *subtraction* on the board. Have students skim the chapter and identify different examples of subtraction problems. For example, they might notice some problems are written for them, and others are embedded within word problems.
- Have students work in small groups to analyze the problem-solving questions in this chapter. Ask them to compile a list of signal words that tell them they should subtract to solve.
- Have students compare their results with other groups.
- Have students add these words to a word wall for reference.

ELL **ELL Support Strategy** Use this vocabulary activity to recognize text features, such as signal words that tell them to subtract.

My Vocabulary Cards
Have students use blank cards to write review vocabulary cards for words such as *regroup*.

ELL Refer to the Multilingual eGlossary for interactive definitions in 13 languages.

 Building on the Essential Question
In this lesson, students will build upon the skills and concepts needed to answer the chapter's Essential Question "How can I subtract two-digit numbers?"

Digital Dashboard

Interactive Whiteboard Ready

Vocab

The eBook **Glossary** shows the definition of the word and has audio for each definition. The **eGlossary** provides definitions in 13 languages.

Watch

Watch as concepts are brought to life through **animations**, **songs**, and a variety of visual instruction.

Tools

Virtual Manipulatives with work mats allow teachers and students to model the lesson.

Check

Use **eAssessment** for online assignments and customized assessments.

Use the **Common Core Quick Check** before the lesson to assess students' retention of previously learned concepts.

Use the interactive **Self-Check Quiz** after the lesson to provide immediate feedback on lesson concepts.

eHelp

Digital and print resources assist students and parents in completing My Homework.

Games

Online games and **apps** provide extra practice for lesson concepts.

PD

Professional development videos help teachers gain a deeper understanding of the lesson concepts and strategies.

RtI

Support for **approaching**, **on-** and **beyond-level** students as well as **English Language Learners**.

Masters

Reteach and **Enrich** worksheets, **Manipulative Masters**, the **Problem of the Day**, and other blackline masters are available for each lesson.

LAUNCH THE LESSON

 If your students are well-versed in subtracting two-digit numbers, you may choose to begin instruction with Step 2, **TEACH**.

You will need
☐ Work Mat 6
☐ base-ten blocks

Mathematical PRACTICE 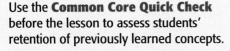 Modeling the Math

Write 37 − 18 on the board. Lead the class in using base-ten blocks and Work Mat 6 to model the subtraction.

Use base-ten blocks and your work mat. Model 37. How many tens and how many ones? 3 tens and 7 ones *In order to subtract the ones, what must you do?* regroup *How do you regroup?* Take 1 ten from 37 and trade it for 10 ones so that you have 2 tens and 17 ones.

As students model the math, show the algorithm on the board.

To regroup, cross out the 3 in the tens place. Write 2 above it to show that you have 2 tens after regrouping. Cross out the 7 and write 17 above it to show that you have 17 ones.

Have students use the base-ten blocks to model subtracting 8 ones from 17 ones.

What is 17 ones − 8 ones? 9 ones

Explain to students that, after subtracting the ones, they will next need to subtract the tens.

Next, you need to subtract the tens. What is 2 tens − 1 ten? 1 ten *So, how many tens and ones are left?* 1 ten and 9 ones *What is 37 − 18?* 19

Step 1   **Step 2**

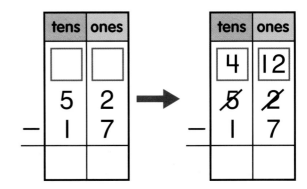

 Begin core instruction here.

You will need
 base-ten blocks

Explore and Explain

Read the directions that are at the bottom of the student page.

You need to find how many people are left at the pool. How can you find this? Find 42 − 13.

Write 42 − 13 on the board in a place-value chart. Point to the number 42 on the board as you ask students the following question.

Which base-ten blocks are you going to place in the chart to show the number you are subtracting from? 4 tens and two ones

Lead students in subtracting.

Subtract the ones first. Can you take away 3 ones from 2 ones? no *What do you do when there are not enough ones to subtract from?* Regroup 1 ten as 10 ones

Cross out the 4 on the board and write 3 above it.

After regrouping 1 ten as 10 ones, how many ones are there? 12 ones

Cross out the 2 on the board and write 12 above it.

Are there enough ones to take away 3 ones? yes *What is 12 ones − 3 ones?* 9 ones

Write 9 in the ones place of the difference on the board.

After regrouping, there are 3 tens. What is 3 tens − 1 ten? 2 tens

Write a 2 in the tens place of the difference on the board.

You have 2 tens and 9 ones left. What number does this equal? 29 *So, there are* 29 *people left at the pool.*

See and Show

Help students work through the example at the top of the page.

Have them trace the dashed number at the end.

Work through Exercises 1 and 2 as a class.

Mathematical PRACTICE 3 ➤ **Talk Math**

Discuss with students "How is subtracting 41 − 16 different than 41 − 6?" Sample answer: 41 − 16 is subtracting a two-digit number from a two-digit number and 41 − 6 is subtracting a one-digit number from a two-digit number.

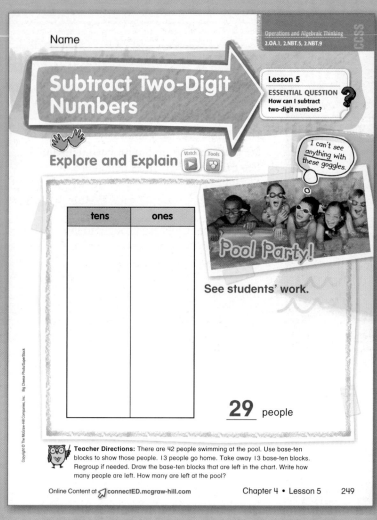

Name _____

Operations and Algebraic Thinking
2.OA.1, 2.NBT.5, 2.NBT.9

Subtract Two-Digit Numbers

Lesson 5

ESSENTIAL QUESTION
How can I subtract two-digit numbers?

Explore and Explain

I can't see anything with these goggles.

Pool Party!

See students' work.

29 people

Teacher Directions: There are 42 people swimming at the pool. Use base-ten blocks to show those people. 13 people go home. Take away 13 base-ten blocks. Regroup if needed. Draw the base-ten blocks that are left in the chart. Write how many people are left. How many are left at the pool?

Online Content at connectED.mcgraw-hill.com   Chapter 4 • Lesson 5   249

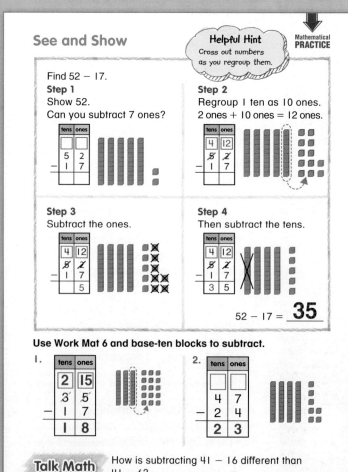

See and Show

Helpful Hint
Cross out numbers as you regroup them.

Mathematical PRACTICE

Find 52 − 17.
Step 1
Show 52.
Can you subtract 7 ones?

Step 2
Regroup 1 ten as 10 ones.
2 ones + 10 ones = 12 ones.

Step 3
Subtract the ones.

Step 4
Then subtract the tens.

52 − 17 = **35**

Use Work Mat 6 and base-ten blocks to subtract.

1.
tens	ones
2	15
3	5
− 1	7
1	8

2.
tens	ones
4	7
− 2	4
2	3

Talk Math How is subtracting 41 − 16 different than 41 − 6?

250   Chapter 4 • Lesson 5

On My Own

Name _____

On My Own

Use Work Mat 6 and base-ten blocks to subtract.

3.
tens	ones
1̶	1̶6̶
2̶	6̶
− 1	9
	7

4.
tens	ones
6̶	1̶4̶
7̶	4̶
− 1	8
	5 6

5.
tens	ones
☐	☐
4	6
− 2	3
2	3

6.
6̶	1̶5̶
7̶	5̶
− 1	6
5	9

7.
4̶	1̶4̶
5̶	4̶
− 2	8
2	6

8.
6̶	1̶2̶
7̶	2̶
− 3	5
3	7

9.
4̶	1̶0̶
5	0
− 2	4
2	6

10.
7̶	1̶2̶
8	2
− 3	7
4	5

11.
☐	☐
3	9
− 2	9
1	0

12.
```
  85
− 46
─────
  39
```

13.
```
  41
− 15
─────
  26
```

14.
```
  37
− 11
─────
  26
```

Problem Solving

  Mathematical **PRACTICE**

15. 35 people are in line for the diving board at the pool. 16 people jump off the diving board. How many people are still in line?

19 people

16. Jason bought a pool pass for 45 trips to the pool. He has gone to the pool 28 times. How many more times can Jason go to the pool with his pass?

17 times

HOT Problem Ella, May, and Sue each pour 24 cups of lemonade for their lemonade stand. They sell 23 of the cups of lemonade to their friends. How many cups are left? Explain.

Sample answer: 49 cups; Each girl pours

24 cups of lemonade. 24 + 24 + 24 is 72. 72 − 23 = 49.

---

3 PRACTICE & APPLY

On My Own

Have students work through the exercises on this page independently. You may choose to assign exercises based on the chart below.

DIFFERENTIATED ASSIGNMENTS

AL **Approaching Level** Guide students through the exercises in On My Own. Help them to use manipulatives while working through the exercises.

OL **On Level** Complete the exercises independently.

BL **Beyond Level** Complete the exercises independently without manipulatives.

Common Error!
If students struggle with regrouping zero, as in 50 − 24, remind them that there are 0 ones. Regroup 1 ten as 10 ones so there are 4 tens and 10 ones.

Problem Solving

Have students work through the problem-solving exercises on this page independently.

Mathematical **PRACTICE** 2   In Exercise 16, students **reason abstractly and quantitatively.**

HOT Problem This exercise asks students to build upon their understanding of concepts needed to answer the chapter's Essential Question.

AL APPROACHING LEVEL

IF my students struggle with subtracting two-digit numbers,

THEN choose a resource:

→ Use the Differentiated Instruction activity on p. 215C.

→ Use the Reteach worksheet with small groups.

→ Go online for a Differentiated Instruction activity.

→ **Use Manipulatives** If base-ten blocks are not helping the students understand regrouping to subtract, try connecting cubes. For example, build 50 (5 groups of ten) and take away 22. They will have to "take apart a ten" to get the 2 ones that they need.

OL ON LEVEL

IF my students seem to know how to subtract two-digit numbers, but need more practice,

THEN choose a resource:

→ Assign My Homework.

→ Go online for a Differentiated Instruction activity.

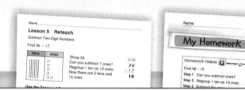

BL BEYOND LEVEL

IF my students have mastered subtracting two-digit numbers,

THEN choose a resource:

→ Use the Enrich worksheet in cooperative groups.

→ Assign My Homework.

→ Go online for a Differentiated Instruction activity.

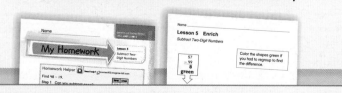

Name _____

AL

Lesson 5   Reteach
Subtract Two-Digit Numbers

Find 36 − 17.

tens	ones

Show 36.
Can you subtract 7 ones?
Regroup 1 ten as 10 ones.
Now there are 2 tens and 16 ones.

```
  2  16
  3  6
- 1  7
─────
  1  9
```

Use the Tens and Ones Workmat and ▭▭▭▭▭▭ **and** ▢ **to subtract.**

1.	tens	ones
	7	10
	8	0
	− 3	6
	4	**4**

2.	tens	ones
	5	15
	6	5
	− 2	7
	3	**8**

3.	tens	ones
	3	17
	4	7
	− 1	9
	2	**8**

4. ▢▢
```
  29
− 15
────
  14
```

5. ³11
```
  41
− 18
────
  23
```

6. ⁵13
```
  63
− 38
────
  25
```

7. ⁶16
```
  76
− 49
────
  27
```

8. ⁴14
```
  54
− 25
────
  29
```

9. ²12
```
  32
− 16
────
  16
```

Name _____

BL

Lesson 5   Enrich
Subtract Two-Digit Numbers

Color the shapes green if you had to regroup to find the difference.

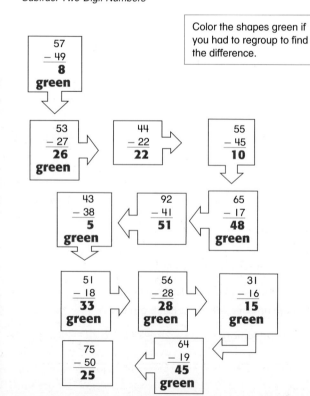

```
  57
− 49
────
   8
green
```

```
  53
− 27
────
  26
green
```

```
  44
− 22
────
  22
```

```
  55
− 45
────
  10
```

```
  43
− 38
────
   5
green
```

```
  92
− 41
────
  51
```

```
  65
− 17
────
  48
green
```

```
  51
− 18
────
  33
green
```

```
  56
− 28
────
  28
green
```

```
  31
− 16
────
  15
green
```

```
  75
− 50
────
  25
```

```
  64
− 19
────
  45
green
```

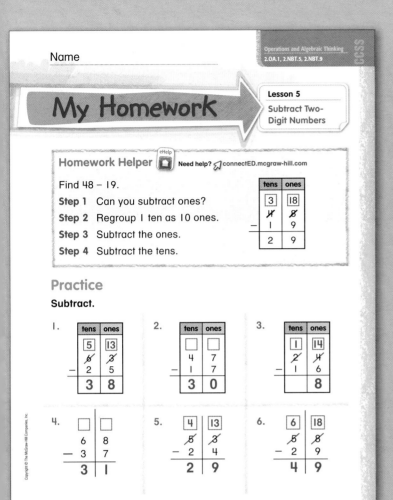

Name _____

Operations and Algebraic Thinking
2.OA.1, 2.NBT.5, 2.NBT.9

CCSS

My Homework

Lesson 5
Subtract Two-Digit Numbers

Homework Helper
Need help? connectED.mcgraw-hill.com

Find 48 – 19.

Step 1 Can you subtract ones?
Step 2 Regroup 1 ten as 10 ones.
Step 3 Subtract the ones.
Step 4 Subtract the tens.

tens	ones
3 18	
4̶	8̶
– 1	9
2	9

Practice

Subtract.

1.
tens	ones
5 13	
6̶	3̶
– 2	5
3	8

2.
tens	ones
□	□
4	7
– 1	7
3	0

3.
tens	ones
1 14	
2̶	4̶
– 1	6
	8

4.
	□	□
	6	8
–	3	7
	3	1

5.
	4	13
	5̶	3̶
–	2	4
	2	9

6.
	6	18
	5̶	8̶
–	2	9
	4	9

Chapter 4 • Lesson 5   253

Subtract.

7.
```
   54
 – 45
 ───
    9
```

8.
```
   27
 –  9
 ───
   18
```

9.
```
   63
 – 11
 ───
   52
```

10.
```
   91
 – 59
 ───
   32
```

11.
```
   35
 – 26
 ───
    9
```

12.
```
   87
 – 42
 ───
   45
```

13. 83 people were at the water park. 29 people left. How many people were left at the water park?

Which way to the water?

54 people

Test Practice

14. 25 people brought dogs to the picnic. 18 of them were large dogs. How many small dogs were at the picnic?

   ○ 6   ● 7   ○ 13   ○ 17

Math at Home Ask your child to show you how to subtract 24 from 41.

254   Chapter 4 • Lesson 5

---

4 WRAP IT UP

CCSS

My Homework

Assign homework after successful completion of the lesson. Students who understand the concepts may skip the **Homework Helper** section.

Test Practice
Diagnose Student Errors

Class trends in wrong answers may indicate common errors or misconceptions.

6   subtracted incorrectly

7   correct

13 regrouped and subtracted

17 regrouped incorrectly

Formative Assessment

Ask students to model 62 – 18 and solve, using base-ten blocks and WorkMat 6.

MY Learning Stations

Use the game **Hit the Target**, the graphic novel **Swimming Fun**, the real-world problem-solving reader **Baseball's Hero**, and the activity card **Clay Sentences** after this lesson. The Teacher Guide provides suggestions for differentiated instruction.

Line Up!

When students line up, say subtraction problems. Have students give thumbs up if regrouping is needed and thumbs down if not needed.

Rewrite Two-Digit Subtraction

OBJECTIVE Take two-digit subtraction and write it in a different way.
Rewrite a horizontal two-digit subtraction problem vertically before subtracting.

What's the Math?

 Common Core State Standards
DOMAIN: Operations and Algebraic Thinking
Standards: 2.OA.1, 2.NBT.5
The wording of these standards can be found on page 216.

What Students Should Understand

- You can rewrite a horizontal subtraction problem vertically before finding the difference.
- When rewriting the subtraction problem, write the greater number on top. Line up the ones digits and tens digits.
- After rewriting the problem, subtract the ones, regroup if needed, and then subtract the tens.

What Students Should be Able to Do

Find $74 - 36$.

Step 1
Rewrite the problem.

Step 2
Subtract.

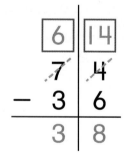

Building on the Essential Question

In this lesson, students will build upon the skills and concepts needed to answer the chapter's Essential Question "How can I subtract two-digit numbers?"

Developing Vocabulary

 Review Vocabulary
greater

Review Activity

- Write *greater* on the board. Ask students what is meant by a greater number. Prompt them by comparing 2 numbers, such as 57 and 22.
- Next, write $57 - 22$ horizontally. Explain to students that this subtraction problem can be solved when one number is stacked atop the other, or *vertically*. Explain that the greater number should be the top number.
- Tell students that they should determine greater numbers when rewriting subtraction sentences.

ELL **ELL Support Strategy** Use this vocabulary activity to apply visual cues to understand concepts.

My Vocabulary Cards

Have students use blank cards to review basic subtraction facts.

ELL Refer to the Multilingual eGlossary for interactive definitions in 13 languages.

Plan Online

Plan for your lesson by using the resources at

connectED.mcgraw-hill.com

Digital Dashboard

Interactive Whiteboard Ready

Vocab
abc

The eBook **Glossary** shows the definition of the word and has audio for each definition. The **eGlossary** provides definitions in 13 languages.

Watch

Watch as concepts are brought to life through **animations**, **songs**, and a variety of visual instruction.

Tools

Virtual Manipulatives with work mats allow teachers and students to model the lesson.

Check

Use **eAssessment** for online assignments and customized assessments.

Use the **Common Core Quick Check** before the lesson to assess students' retention of previously learned concepts.

Use the interactive **Self-Check Quiz** after the lesson to provide immediate feedback on lesson concepts.

eHelp

Digital and print resources assist students and parents in completing My Homework.

Games

Online games and **apps** provide extra practice for lesson concepts.

PD

Professional development videos help teachers gain a deeper understanding of the lesson concepts and strategies.

RtI

Support for **approaching**, **on-** and **beyond-level** students as well as **English Language Learners**.

Masters

Reteach and **Enrich** worksheets, **Manipulative Masters**, the **Problem of the Day**, and other blackline masters are available for each lesson.

 If your students are well-versed in rewriting subtraction, you may choose to begin instruction with Step 2, **TEACH**.

You will need

☐ number cubes

☐ Work Mat 6 (optional)

☐ base-ten blocks (optional)

Mathematical PRACTICE 4 Modeling the Math

Have students work in pairs. Have them roll two number cubes twice to make two two-digit numbers.

Roll the number cubes once to make a two-digit number. Write down the number. Roll the number cubes again to make another two-digit number. Write down the number.

Write _____ − _____ on the board. Ask students to write a horizontal subtraction problem with the larger number first and the smaller number second.

Using the two numbers you made, write a horizontal subtraction problem.

As a class, discuss whether it is easy to subtract ones and tens and regroup as needed when the problem is written horizontally. Next, show a tens and ones chart on the board. Ask students to write the problem vertically with the greater number on top and the smaller number on the bottom.

Using the same two numbers, write the subtraction problem in the tens and ones chart.

Lead a discussion that when given a problem horizontally, it is easier to write the problem vertically before subtracting. Have students work together to subtract the two numbers. Use base-ten blocks and Work Mat 6 if needed.

Begin core instruction here.

Explore and Explain

Read the directions that are at the bottom of the student page.

You need to find how many flowers still need to bloom. How can you do that? Find 54 − 36.

Write 54 − 36 on the board horizontally.

You can rewrite this subtraction problem in the place-value chart with the greater number on top of the smaller number.

Guide students in writing 54 − 36 vertically in a place-value chart.

Which place value do you subtract first, ones or tens? **ones**
Do you need to regroup 1 ten as 10 ones? **yes** *Why?*
Sample answer: There are not enough ones in the top number to subtract from.

Lead students to regroup 1 ten as 10 ones both with the base-ten blocks and in the written problem.

After regrouping 1 ten as 10 ones, how many ones are there in the top number? **14 ones** *What is 14 ones − 6 ones?* **8 ones** *Write an 8 in the ones place in the difference. Since you regrouped 1 ten as 10 ones, there are 4 tens in the top number. How many tens are left after you subtract?* **1 ten** *Write a 1 in the tens place in the difference. How many flowers still need to bloom?* **18 flowers**

See and Show

Help students work through the example at the top of the page. They need to rewrite the problem vertically with the greater number on top. Have them trace the dashed numbers as they work the problems.

Work through Exercises 1 − 6 as a class.

ELL Use tiered questions to informally assess student's progress.
Beginning: Point to See and Show.
Intermediate: What are the two steps shown in See and Show?
Advanced: When is it necessary to rewrite a subtraction problem?

Mathematical PRACTICE ③ **Talk Math**

Discuss with students "Why is it helpful to rewrite subtraction?" Sample answer: You can rewrite it so the numbers line up it is easier when you regroup tens and ones.

255-256   Chapter 4 Subtract Two-Digit Numbers

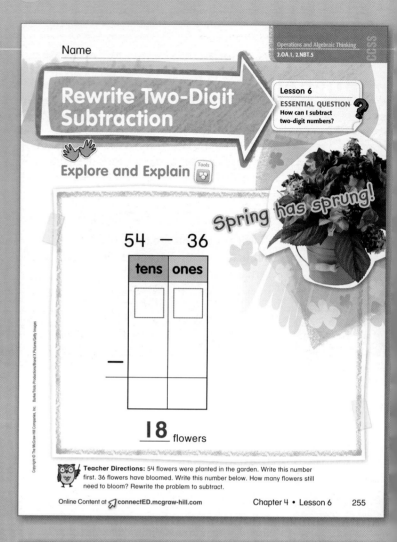

Name _____

Operations and Algebraic Thinking
2.OA.1, 2.NBT.5

Rewrite Two-Digit Subtraction

Lesson 6
ESSENTIAL QUESTION
How can I subtract two-digit numbers?

Explore and Explain

Spring has sprung!

$$54 - 36$$

tens	ones

−

____18____ flowers

Teacher Directions: 54 flowers were planted in the garden. Write this number first. 36 flowers have bloomed. Write this number below. How many flowers still need to bloom? Rewrite the problem to subtract.

Online Content at connectED.mcgraw-hill.com   Chapter 4 • Lesson 6   255

See and Show

Mathematical **PRACTICE**

You can rewrite a problem to subtract.
Find 83 − 28.

Step 1 Rewrite.

Step 2 Subtract.

Helpful Hint
Write the greater number on top. Write the other number below it.

```
  8 | 3        7 |13
     |          8 | 3
−  2 | 8      − 2 | 8
              ────────
                5 | 5
```

Line up the ones and the tens.

Rewrite the problem. Subtract.

1. 38 − 19
```
  2 |18
  3 | 8
− 1 | 9
─────────
  1 | 9
```

2. 42 − 27
```
  3 |12
  4 | 2
− 2 | 7
─────────
  1 | 5
```

3. 53 − 38
```
  4 |13
  5 | 3
− 3 | 8
─────────
  1 | 5
```

4. 82 − 46
```
  7 |12
  8 | 2
− 4 | 6
─────────
  3 | 6
```

5. 74 − 38
```
  6 |14
  7 | 4
− 3 | 8
─────────
  3 | 6
```

6. 60 − 48
```
  5 |10
  6 | 0
− 4 | 8
─────────
  1 | 2
```

Talk Math   Why is it helpful to rewrite subtraction?

256   Chapter 4 • Lesson 6

Name _____

On My Own

Rewrite the problems. Subtract.

7. 62 − 38

$$\begin{array}{r} 5\ |\ 12 \\ \not{6}\ \ \not{2} \\ -\ 3\ \ \ 8 \\ \hline 2\ \ \ 4 \end{array}$$

8. 74 − 39

$$\begin{array}{r} 6\ |\ 14 \\ \not{7}\ \ \not{4} \\ -\ 3\ \ \ 9 \\ \hline 3\ \ \ 5 \end{array}$$

9. 57 − 39

$$\begin{array}{r} 4\ |\ 17 \\ \not{5}\ \ \not{7} \\ -\ 3\ \ \ 9 \\ \hline 1\ \ \ 8 \end{array}$$

10. 88 − 49

$$\begin{array}{r} 7\ 18 \\ \not{8}\not{8} \\ -\ 49 \\ \hline 39 \end{array}$$

11. 35 − 25

$$\begin{array}{r} 35 \\ -\ 25 \\ \hline 10 \end{array}$$

12. 62 − 38

$$\begin{array}{r} 5\ 12 \\ \not{6}\not{2} \\ -\ 38 \\ \hline 24 \end{array}$$

13. 67 − 19

$$\begin{array}{r} 5\ 17 \\ \not{6}\not{7} \\ -\ 29 \\ \hline 38 \end{array}$$

14. 83 − 39

$$\begin{array}{r} 7\ 12 \\ \not{8}\not{3} \\ -\ 39 \\ \hline 44 \end{array}$$

15. 90 − 36

$$\begin{array}{r} 8\ 10 \\ \not{9}\not{0} \\ -\ 36 \\ \hline 54 \end{array}$$

Problem Solving

16. There are 64 flowers growing in Kyla's garden. She picks 18 flowers. How many flowers are left in the garden?

46 flowers

Mathematical PRACTICE

Hooray for rain!

17. Tyler kept track of the weather for 73 days. It was sunny 59 days. How many days were not sunny?

14 days

Hooray!

18. Jackie has 32 houses on her street. She counted 17 that are brick. How many houses are not brick?

15 houses

HOT Problem There are 91 children. 32 children play baseball. 21 children play soccer. How many children do not play baseball or soccer? Explain.

Sample answer: 32 + 21 is 53. 53 children play baseball

and soccer. Subtract 53 from 91 to find how many

children do not play either sport. 91 − 53 is 38.

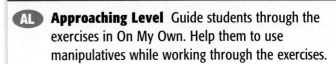
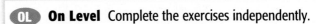

3 PRACTICE & APPLY

CCSS

On My Own

Have students work through the exercises on this page independently. You may choose to assign exercises based on the chart below.

DIFFERENTIATED ASSIGNMENTS
AL **Approaching Level** Guide students through the exercises in On My Own. Help them to use manipulatives while working through the exercises.
OL **On Level** Complete the exercises independently.
BL **Beyond Level** Complete the exercises independently without manipulatives.

Problem Solving

Have students work through the problem-solving exercises on this page independently.

Mathematical PRACTICE ① In Exercise 17, students **make sense of problems and persevere in solving them.**

HOT Problem This exercise asks students to build upon their understanding of concepts needed to answer the chapter's Essential Question.

RtI RESPONSE TO INTERVENTION

DIFFERENTIATED INSTRUCTION

AL **APPROACHING LEVEL**

IF my students struggle with rewriting subtraction,

THEN choose a resource:

→ Use the Reteach worksheet with small groups.

→ Go online for a Differentiated Instruction activity.

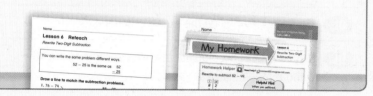

OL **ON LEVEL**

IF my students seem to know how to rewrite subtraction, but need more practice,

THEN choose a resource:

→ Use the Differentiated Instruction activity from p. 215C.

→ Assign My Homework.

→ Go online for a Differentiated Instruction activity.

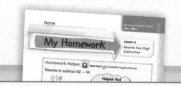

BL **BEYOND LEVEL**

IF my students have mastered rewriting subtraction,

THEN choose a resource:

→ Use the Enrich worksheet in cooperative groups.

→ Assign My Homework.

→ Go online for a Differentiated Instruction activity.

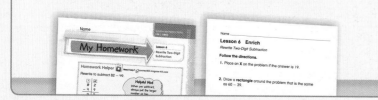

259A **Chapter 4** Subtract Two-Digit Numbers

AL Name _____

Lesson 6 Reteach

Rewrite Two-Digit Subtraction

You can write the same problem different ways.

52 − 25 is the same as
$$\begin{array}{r} 52 \\ -\ 25 \\ \hline \end{array}$$

Draw a line to match the subtraction problems.

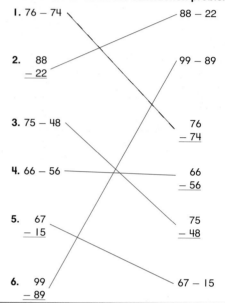

1. 76 − 74   88 − 22

2. $\begin{array}{r} 88 \\ -\ 22 \\ \hline \end{array}$ 99 − 89

3. 75 − 48 $\begin{array}{r} 76 \\ -\ 74 \\ \hline \end{array}$

4. 66 − 56 $\begin{array}{r} 66 \\ -\ 56 \\ \hline \end{array}$

5. $\begin{array}{r} 67 \\ -\ 15 \\ \hline \end{array}$ $\begin{array}{r} 75 \\ -\ 48 \\ \hline \end{array}$

6. $\begin{array}{r} 99 \\ -\ 89 \\ \hline \end{array}$ 67 − 15

Copyright © The McGraw-Hill Companies, Inc. Permission is granted to reproduce for classroom use.

BL Name _____

Lesson 6 Enrich

Rewrite Two-Digit Subtraction

Follow the directions.

1. Place an **X** on the problem if the answer is 19.

2. Draw a **rectangle** around the problem that is the same as 60 − 39.

3. Draw a **trapezoid** around the problems with a difference of 20.

4. Draw a **triangle** around the problem that is equal to $\begin{array}{r} 55 \\ +\ 33 \\ \hline \end{array}$

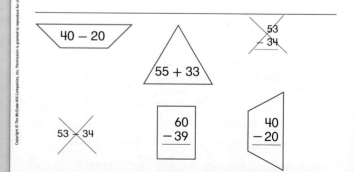

Copyright © The McGraw-Hill Companies, Inc. Permission is granted to reproduce for classroom use.

My Homework (student page)

Name _____

Operations and Algebraic Thinking
2.OA.1, 2.NBT.5

CCSS

My Homework →

Lesson 6
Rewrite Two-Digit
Subtraction

Homework Helper   Need help? connectED.mcgraw-hill.com

Rewrite to subtract 82 − 49.

	7	12
	8̶	2
−	4	9
	3	3

Helpful Hint
When you subtract, always put the larger number on top.

Practice

Rewrite the problems. Subtract.

1. 74 − 25

	6	14
	7̶	4̶
−	2	5
	4	9

2. 60 − 37

	5	10
	6̶	0̶
−	3	7
	2	3

3. 86 − 48

	7	16
	8̶	6̶
−	4	8
	3	8

4. 45 − 28

    315
    4̶5̶
  − 28
   17

5. 84 − 38

    814
    8̶4̶
  − 38
   46

6. 37 − 18

    217
    3̶7̶
  − 18
   19

Rewrite the problems. Subtract.

7. 72 − 37

    612
    7̶2̶
  − 37
   35

8. 27 − 18

    117
    2̶7̶
  − 18
    9

9. 68 − 39

    518
    6̶8̶
  − 39
   29

10. 45 birds are flying. 17 birds land on the water. How many birds are still flying?

28 birds

I would never swim anywhere else!

SWIM AT BEACH ONLY

Test Practice

11. Mark the answer that shows how to rewrite and solve 83 − 46.

7 13	7 13	3 16	3 16
8̶3̶	8̶3̶	4̶6̶	4̶6̶
−46	−46	−83	−83
36	37	37	43
○	●	○	○

🦉 **Math at Home** Together with your child think of a 2-digit subtraction problem in your lives. Have them solve it.

My Homework (teacher page)

Assign homework after successful completion of the lesson. Students who understand the concepts may skip the **Homework Helper** section.

Test Practice

Diagnose Student Errors

Class trends in wrong answers may indicate common errors or misconceptions.

    7 13
    8̶3̶
  − 46   subtracted incorrectly
    36

    7 13
    8̶3̶
  − 46   correct
    37

    3 16
    4̶6̶
  − 83   set up wrong
    37

    3 16
    4̶6̶
  − 83   set up wrong
    43

Formative Assessment

Katy had 36 red and blue balloons for the party. She had 17 blue balloons.

How many red balloons did she have?

Ask students to demonstrate how to re-write a subtraction problem in vertical form and solve this problem. 19 red balloons

LESSON 7
Check Subtraction
OBJECTIVE Use addition to check subtraction.

What's the Math?

 Common Core State Standards
DOMAIN: Operations and Algebraic Thinking

Standards: 2.OA.1, 2.NBT.5
The wording of these standards can be found on page 216.

What Students Should Understand
- You can check the answer to a subtraction problem with addition.
- Add the bottom number and the difference. If the sum is the same number as the top number, the subtraction was done correctly.

What Students Should be Able to Do
Subtract 62 − 21. Check by adding.

Subtract

```
  62      Add these
− 21      numbers to
  41      check.
```

Check by adding

```
  41      If this is the number you
+ 21      subtracted from,
  62      your answer is correct.
```

? Building on the Essential Question
In this lesson, students will build upon the skills and concepts needed to answer the chapter's Essential Question "How can I subtract two-digit numbers?"

Developing Vocabulary

 Review Vocabulary
fact family

Review Activity
- Write *fact family* on the board, and the numbers 10, 12, and 22 within a triangle.
- Ask a volunteer to write the related number sentences. $12 + 10 = 22$, $10 + 12 = 22$, $22 − 10 = 12$, $22 − 12 = 10$
- Use this example to model for students how they can use the addition sentences to check the math in the subtraction sentences.

ELL **ELL Support Strategy** Use this vocabulary activity to demonstrate understanding by modeling.

My Vocabulary Cards
Have students use blank cards to review basic subtraction facts.

ELL Refer to the Multilingual eGlossary for interactive definitions in 13 languages.

Plan Online

Plan for your lesson by using the resources at

↗ connectED.mcgraw-hill.com

Digital Dashboard

Interactive Whiteboard Ready

Vocab

The eBook **Glossary** shows the definition of the word and has audio for each definition. The **eGlossary** provides definitions in 13 languages.

Watch

Watch as concepts are brought to life through **animations**, **songs**, and a variety of visual instruction.

Tools

Virtual Manipulatives with work mats allow teachers and students to model the lesson.

Check

Use **eAssessment** for online assignments and customized assessments.

Use the **Common Core Quick Check** before the lesson to assess students' retention of previously learned concepts.

Use the interactive **Self-Check Quiz** after the lesson to provide immediate feedback on lesson concepts.

eHelp

Digital and print resources assist students and parents in completing My Homework.

Games

Online games and **apps** provide extra practice for lesson concepts.

PD

Professional development videos help teachers gain a deeper understanding of the lesson concepts and strategies.

RtI

Support for **approaching**, **on**- and **beyond-level** students as well as **English Language Learners**.

Masters

Reteach and **Enrich** worksheets, **Manipulative Masters**, the **Problem of the Day**, and other blackline masters are available for each lesson.

---

1 LAUNCH THE LESSON

 If your students are well-versed in checking subtraction, you may choose to begin instruction with Step 2, **TEACH**.

You will need

☐ connecting cubes

Mathematical PRACTICE 4 Modeling the Math

Write 5 — 2 on the board. Ask students how they might use connecting cubes to model the subtraction.

How can you model 5 — 2 using connecting cubes? Begin with 5 cubes and remove 2 of the cubes.

Ask students to find the difference.

Remove two of the connecting cubes. What is the difference? 3

Ask students how they can check that their answer is correct. Have them replace the two connecting cubes and count.

How can you check that your answer is correct? You had 5 connecting cubes. You removed two of the connecting cubes and then you had 3 connecting cubes. Let's replace the 2 connecting cubes; count on 3, 4, 5. How many connecting cubes do you have? 5

Lead a classroom discussion that addition can be used to check subtraction. Continue modeling with connecting cubes. Subtract and then check the subtraction using addition for the following problems:

13 — 8   23 — 9   25 — 12   45 — 37

Explore and Explain

Read the directions that are at the bottom of the student page.

How will you find how many vegetables are left in the garden? Find 38 – 12.

Guide students in writing 38 – 12 vertically on the left side of the page.

When you subtract the ones, do you need to regroup? no *Why not?* Sample answer: There are enough ones in the top number to subtract from. *What is 8 ones – 2 ones?* 6 ones *Write a 6 in the ones place in the difference. What is 3 tens – 1 ten?* 2 tens *Write a 2 in the tens place in the difference.*

There are 26 vegetables left in the garden.

Explain to students that they can use addition to check their subtraction.

You can use addition to check subtraction.

Work together as a class to check the subtraction. The exercise is color coded to help students see the inverse operation.

Subtraction involves taking the whole and subtracting a part. The whole is 38 vegetables. One part is 12 vegetables. When you subtracted, you find the other part, 26. To check the subtraction, add the parts, 26 and 12 to see if you get the whole, 38. If you get the whole, then you know that the answer is correct.

Have students add the parts to see if they get the whole.

Add 26 and 12. Do you get 38? yes *If so, then the answer is correct.*

See and Show

Help students work through the example at the top of the page. Be sure that students see and understand the inverse operation. The example uses a similar color coding as used on the Explore and Explain activity. Have them trace the dashed numbers as they work the problems.

Work through Exercises 1–4 as a class.

Mathematical PRACTICE 3 — Talk Math

Discuss with students "Why does addition work as a check for subtraction?" Sample answer: Because addition and subtraction are inverse operations.

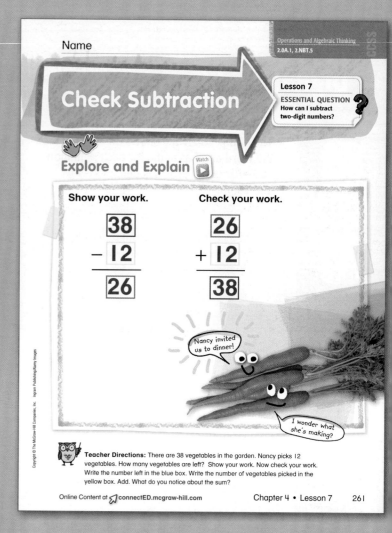

Name _____

Operations and Algebraic Thinking
2.OA.1, 2.NBT.5

Check Subtraction

Lesson 7

ESSENTIAL QUESTION
How can I subtract two-digit numbers?

Explore and Explain

Show your work.

$$\begin{array}{r} 38 \\ -12 \\ \hline 26 \end{array}$$

Check your work.

$$\begin{array}{r} 26 \\ +12 \\ \hline 38 \end{array}$$

"Nancy invited us to dinner!"

"I wonder what she's making?"

Teacher Directions: There are 38 vegetables in the garden. Nancy picks 12 vegetables. How many vegetables are left? Show your work. Now check your work. Write the number left in the blue box. Write the number of vegetables picked in the yellow box. Add. What do you notice about the sum?

Online Content at ⌐connectED.mcgraw-hill.com   Chapter 4 • Lesson 7   261

See and Show

Mathematical PRACTICE

Helpful Hint
Add the number you subtracted to the difference. The sum should match the number you subtracted from.

You can check the answer to a subtraction problem.
Check 25 – 10 = 15.

Subtract

$$\begin{array}{r} 25 \\ -10 \\ \hline 15 \end{array}$$ Add these numbers to check.

Check by Adding

$$\begin{array}{r} 15 \\ +10 \\ \hline 25 \end{array}$$ If this is the number you subtracted from, your answer is correct.

Subtract. Check by adding.

1. $$\begin{array}{r} 36 \\ -20 \\ \hline 16 \end{array}$$ $$\begin{array}{r} 16 \\ +20 \\ \hline 36 \end{array}$$

2. $$\begin{array}{r} 50 \\ -12 \\ \hline 38 \end{array}$$ $$\begin{array}{r} 38 \\ +12 \\ \hline 50 \end{array}$$

3. $$\begin{array}{r} 21 \\ -3 \\ \hline 18 \end{array}$$ $$\begin{array}{r} 18 \\ +3 \\ \hline 21 \end{array}$$

4. $$\begin{array}{r} 32 \\ -14 \\ \hline 18 \end{array}$$ $$\begin{array}{r} 18 \\ +14 \\ \hline 32 \end{array}$$

Talk Math Why does addition work as a check for subtraction?

CORE INSTRUCTION

Name _____

On My Own

Subtract. Check by adding.

> **Helpful Hint**
> To check subtraction, add the number you subtracted and the difference.

5.
```
   57        27
 – 30      +30
 ────      ────
   27        57
```

6.
```
   60        50
 – 10      +10
 ────      ────
   50        60
```

7.
```
   42        37
 –  5      + 5
 ────      ────
   37        42
```

8.
```
   75        34
 – 41      +41
 ────      ────
   34        75
```

9.
```
   67        35
 – 32      +35
 ────      ────
   35        67
```

10.
```
   40        14
 – 26      +26
 ────      ────
   14        40
```

11.
```
   76        48
 – 28      +28
 ────      ────
   48        76
```

12.
```
   56        26
 – 28      +46
 ────      ────
   28        56
```

Problem Solving

Mathematical PRACTICE

13. Ima went to the apple orchard with her class. The class picked 48 apples. They ate 17 of them. How many apples are left?

   __31__ apples

> I was once a seed just like you!

14. The second grade classes are planting seeds. Roy's class plants 81 seeds. Jessica's class plants 66 seeds. How many more seeds does Roy's class plant than Jessica's class?

   __15__ seeds

15. 97 people went sailing yesterday. 38 people went sailing today. How many more people went sailing yesterday than today?

   __59__ people

Write Math How do you check a subtraction problem?

Sample answer: Add the difference from the
subtraction problem to the number you subtracted. The
sum should equal the number you subtracted from.

---

3 PRACTICE & APPLY

CCSS

On My Own

Have students work through the exercises on this page independently. You may choose to assign exercises based on the chart below.

DIFFERENTIATED ASSIGNMENTS

AL **Approaching Level** Guide students through the exercises in On My Own. Help them to use manipulatives or a number line while they work through the exercises.

OL **On Level** Complete the exercises independently.

BL **Beyond Level** Complete the exercises independently without manipulatives.

Common Error!
Students will struggle using addition to check subtraction if they have not mastered number facts. Have them practice facts with flash cards.

Problem Solving

Have students work through the problem-solving exercises on this page independently.

Mathematical PRACTICE 5 In Exercise 14, students **use appropriate tools strategically.**

Write Math

This exercise asks students to build upon their understanding of concepts needed to answer the chapter's Essential Question.

Online Content at connectED.mcgraw-hill.com

RESPONSE TO INTERVENTION

DIFFERENTIATED INSTRUCTION

AL **APPROACHING LEVEL**

IF my students struggle with checking subtraction,

THEN choose a resource:

→ Use the Reteach worksheet with small groups.

→ Go online for a Differentiated Instruction activity.

→ **Show a Model** Model a fact family with two-color counters. Add and subtract the counters.

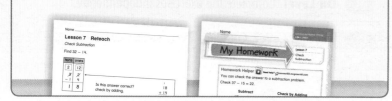

OL **ON LEVEL**

IF my students seem to know how to check subtraction, but need more practice,

THEN choose a resource:

→ Assign My Homework.

→ Go online for a Differentiated Instruction activity.

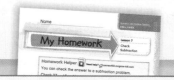

BL **BEYOND LEVEL**

IF my students have mastered checking subtraction,

THEN choose a resource:

→ Use the Enrich worksheet in cooperative groups.

→ Assign My Homework.

→ Go online for a Differentiated Instruction activity.

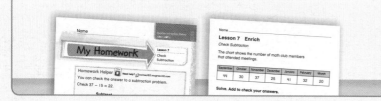

AL

Name _____

Lesson 7 Reteach

Check Subtraction

Find 32 − 14.

tens	ones
2	12
~~3~~	~~2~~
− 1	4
1	8

Is this answer correct?
check by adding.

```
  1
  18
+ 14
  32
```

Subtract. Then check by adding.

1.
```
  16      11
 − 5     + 5
  11      16
```

2.
```
  53      35
 − 18    + 18
  35      53
```

3.
```
  93      55
 − 38    + 38
  55      93
```

4.
```
  46      23
 − 23    + 23
  23      46
```

5.
```
  84      27
 − 57    + 57
  27      84
```

6.
```
  75      26
 − 49    + 49
  26      75
```

Copyright © The McGraw-Hill Companies, Inc. Permission is granted to reproduce for classroom use.

BL

Name _____

Lesson 7 Enrich

Check Subtraction

The chart shows the number of math club members that attended meetings.

September	October	November	December	January	February	March
44	30	37	25	41	32	20

Solve. Add to check your answers.

1. How many more members attended in November than in February?

```
  37        5
 − 32    + 32
   5       37
```

2. How many more members attended in September than in October?

```
  44       14
 − 30    + 30
  14       44
```

3. How many more members attended in January than in March?

```
  41       21
 − 20    + 20
  21       41
```

Copyright © The McGraw-Hill Companies, Inc. Permission is granted to reproduce for classroom use.

265A Chapter 4 Subtract Two-Digit Numbers

My Homework

Name _____

Operations and Algebraic Thinking
2.OA.1, 2.NBT.5

My Homework →

Lesson 7
Check Subtraction

Homework Helper Need help? connectED.mcgraw-hill.com

You can check the answer to a subtraction problem.

Check $37 - 15 = 22$.

Subtract

$\begin{array}{r} 37 \\ -\ 15 \\ \hline 22 \end{array}$ Add these numbers to check.

Check by Adding

$\begin{array}{r} 22 \\ +\ 15 \\ \hline 37 \end{array}$ If this is the number you subtracted from, you are correct.

Practice

Subtract. Check by adding.

1. $\begin{array}{r} 67 \\ -\ 48 \\ \hline 19 \end{array}$ $\begin{array}{r} 19 \\ +\ 48 \\ \hline 67 \end{array}$

2. $\begin{array}{r} 52 \\ -\ 36 \\ \hline 16 \end{array}$ $\begin{array}{r} 16 \\ +\ 36 \\ \hline 52 \end{array}$

3. $\begin{array}{r} 80 \\ -\ 68 \\ \hline 12 \end{array}$ $\begin{array}{r} 12 \\ +\ 62 \\ \hline 80 \end{array}$

4. $\begin{array}{r} 91 \\ -\ 45 \\ \hline 46 \end{array}$ $\begin{array}{r} 46 \\ +\ 45 \\ \hline 91 \end{array}$

Chapter 4 • Lesson 7   265

Solve. Check by adding.

Ice is nice!

5. There are 46 girls skating. There are 67 boys skating. How many more boys than girls are skating?

    21 boys

6. Molly checks out 21 books from the library. She returns 12. How many books does Molly still have?

    9 books

7. Reid kicked the football 20 times. He missed a field goal 6 times. How many times did he make a field goal?

    14 times

Test Practice

8. Mrs. Levine is 83 years old. Mrs. Smith is 67 years old. How many years older is Mrs. Levine than Mrs. Smith?

    ● 16 years   ○ 20 years   ○ 26 years   ○ 17 years

Math at Home Ask your child to find $43 - 16$. Then have your child show you how to check the answer.

266   Chapter 4 • Lesson 7

My Homework

Assign homework after successful completion of the lesson. Students who understand the concepts may skip the **Homework Helper** section.

Test Practice

Diagnose Student Errors

Class trends in wrong answers may indicate common errors or misconceptions.

16 years correct

20 years incorrect answer

26 years did not regroup

17 years subtracted incorrectly

Formative Assessment

Ask students to model and solve $29 - 23$ by checking subtraction with addition, using connecting cubes and Work Mat 6. $29 - 23 = 6$, $23 + 6 = 29$

Problem Solving
STRATEGY: Write a Number Sentence

OBJECTIVE   Write a number sentence strategy to solve problems.

What's the Math?

 Common Core State Standards
DOMAIN: Operations and Algebraic Thinking

Standard: 2.OA.1

The wording of this standard can be found on page 216.

 Model with mathematics.

What Students Should Understand

- You can write a number sentence to solve a real-world problem.
- First, make sure you understand the meaning of the problem. Determine what facts are important and the question being asked.
- Make a plan and follow through to solve the problem.
- Justify your conclusion by checking your answer to determine whether it is correct and makes sense.

What Students Should be Able to Do

There are 56 tomatoes in a garden. 29 of the tomatoes are picked. How many tomatoes are left in the garden?

1 Understand

Underline what you know. Circle what you need to find.

2 Plan

How will I solve this problem?

I can write a number sentence.

3 Solve

I will… find $56 - 29$.

$$\begin{array}{r} \overset{4\ 16}{\cancel{56}} \\ -\ 29 \\ \hline 27 \end{array}$$

So, there are 27 tomatoes left in the garden.

4 Check

Is my answer reasonable? Explain.
Sample answer: yes, $27 + 29 = 56$, so my answer is correct.

Developing the Strategy

What's the Strategy

Write a Number Sentence   Students use language in their everyday life. By translating English phrases/sentences into "Math" phrases/sentences which are called expressions, and sentences that are called equations, the answers become more apparent. Students will translate the word problems in this lesson and write number sentences to solve them.

Example:

Kate saw 16 rabbits at the pet shop.

12 of the rabbits were brown.

How many of the rabbits were not brown?

This word problem translates into $16 - 12 = ?$

Students then solve the number sentence to find:

$16 - 12 = 4$

Other Strategies

Other strategies that have been taught and that can be used are:

- *Find a pattern*
- *Act it out*

ELL **Signal Words**   Encourage English-language learners to identify signal phrases, such as *have left*, as they read word problems.

Mathematical PRACTICE

The Mathematical Practices are especially evident in problem-solving situations, in which students connect procedures and processes with mathematical understanding. In this lesson, the following Mathematical Practices are addressed.

 Make sense of problems and persevere in solving them.

 Model with mathematics.

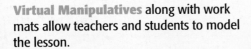

Interactive Whiteboard Ready

| | The eBook **Glossary** shows the definition of the word and has audio for each definition. The **eGlossary** provides definitions in 13 languages. |

Virtual Manipulatives along with work mats allow teachers and students to model the lesson.

Use **eAssessment** for online assignments and customized assessments.

Use the **Common Core Quick Check** before the lesson to assess students' retention of previously learned concepts.

Digital and print resources assist students and parents in completing My Homework.

Professional development videos help teachers gain a deeper understanding of the lesson concepts and strategies.

Support for **approaching**, **on**- and **beyond-level** students as well as **English Language Learners**.

Reteach and **Enrich** worksheets, **Manipulative Masters**, the **Problem of the Day**, and other blackline masters are available for each lesson.

1 LAUNCH THE LESSON

 If your students are well-versed in writing a number sentence, you may choose to begin instruction with Step 2, **TEACH**.

You will need

☐ connecting cubes

Review

Write 31 − 8. Put students in small groups. Have students use connecting cubes to solve 31 − 8. Ask students to connect 3 ten-cube trains and lay them next to a single cube.

How many cubes are there? 31 cubes

Have students remove eight cubes from the left.

How can we use regrouping to solve this problem? Regroup 1 ten for 10 ones. *What is 31 − 8?* 23

Lunchroom Chat
Building a Learning Community

In this lesson, students learn to look for key words that enable them to write a number sentence to solve the problem. Talk with your fellow teachers to make lists of words that indicate addition or subtraction in the context of the problem. You may wish to add these to your word wall in groups to remind students to look for key words.

🕐 **Begin core instruction here.**

Problem Solving

1 Understand

Reread the problem with the students. Point out information as you read it.

2 Plan

Discuss several ideas. Lead the students towards the number sentence needed to solve the problem.

3 Solve

Work through the problem using the student page with the students. Show step-by-step how to find and write the number sentence needed to solve the problem.

4 Check

Discuss why the answer makes sense. Try to develop a sense of reasoning.

Practice the Strategy

1 Understand

Reread the problem with the students. Ask students to point out information that is important as you read it.

2 Plan

Lead the students in discussing several ideas. Direct the students toward the correct plan to solve the problem.

3 Solve

Work through the problem using the student page with the class. Have the class show how to solve it using a number sentence and working through it step-by-step.

4 Check

Discuss why the answer makes sense. Try to develop a sense of reasoning.

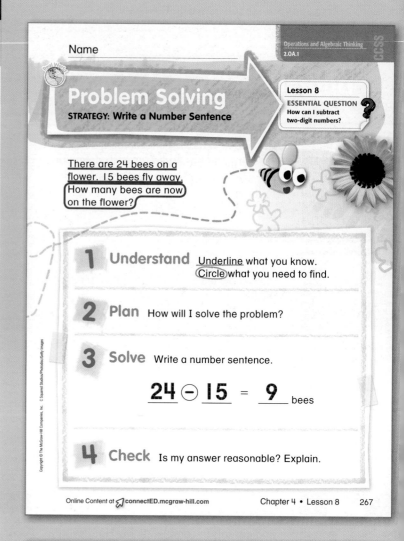

Name _____

Operations and Algebraic Thinking
2.OA.1

Problem Solving
STRATEGY: Write a Number Sentence

Lesson 8
ESSENTIAL QUESTION
How can I subtract two-digit numbers?

There are 24 bees on a flower. 15 bees fly away. How many bees are now on the flower?

1 Understand Underline what you know. Circle what you need to find.

2 Plan How will I solve the problem?

3 Solve Write a number sentence.

$$24 - 15 = 9 \text{ bees}$$

4 Check Is my answer reasonable? Explain.

Online Content at connectED.mcgraw-hill.com   Chapter 4 • Lesson 8   267

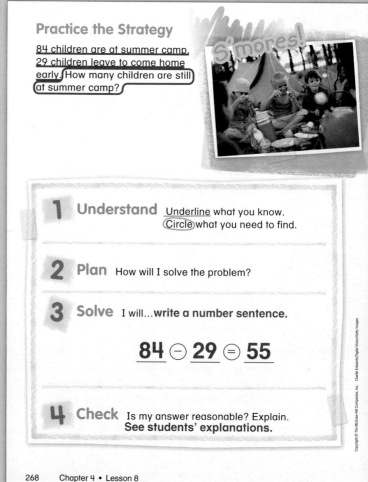

Practice the Strategy

84 children are at summer camp. 29 children leave to come home early. How many children are still at summer camp?

1 Understand Underline what you know. Circle what you need to find.

2 Plan How will I solve the problem?

3 Solve I will...write a number sentence.

$$84 - 29 = 55$$

4 Check Is my answer reasonable? Explain.
See students' explanations.

268   Chapter 4 • Lesson 8

Apply the Strategy

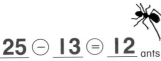

Write a number sentence to solve.

1. There are 25 ants in an ant hill. 13 ants leave. How many ants are there now?

$$\underline{25} \ominus \underline{13} = \underline{12} \text{ ants}$$

2. There are 18 lions in the yard at the zoo. 7 lions run into the lion house. How many lions are left in the yard?

$$\underline{18} \ominus \underline{7} = \underline{11} \text{ lions}$$

3. Jay planted 12 daisies. His sister, Sarah, planted 29 daisies. How many more daisies did Sarah plant than Jay?

$$\underline{29} \ominus \underline{12} = \underline{17} \text{ daisies}$$

Chapter 4 • Lesson 8   269

Mathematical PRACTICE 1 Apply the Strategy

Have students work through the exercises on these pages independently. You may choose to assign exercises based on the chart below.

DIFFERENTIATED ASSIGNMENTS

AL	**Approaching Level** Guide students through the exercises. Help them to use manipulatives.
OL	**On Level** Complete the exercises independently.
BL	**Beyond Level** Complete the exercises independently without manipulatives.

Review the Strategies

Students may use other strategies to solve these exercises.

• *Find a pattern*

• *Act it out*

Review the Strategies

Choose a strategy
• Find a pattern.
• Write a number sentence.
• Act it out.

4. Brenda collects 39 leaves. Janet collects 45 leaves. How many more leaves did Janet collect than Brenda?

$$\underline{6} \text{ leaves}$$

5. Anna is picking vegetables. She picks 12 tomatoes, 15 peppers, and 5 cucumbers. How many vegetables does she pick?

$$\underline{32} \text{ vegetables}$$

6. Scott has 63 blueberries to put in a pie. He eats 21 of the blueberries. How many blueberries are in the pie?

$$\underline{42} \text{ blueberries}$$

HOT Problem Trey's dog likes dog treats. There are 60 treats in a box. He is allowed 2 treats a day. How many treats will he have left after 10 days? Explain.

Sample answer: Two treats for ten days is 2 + 2 + 2 +

2 + 2 + 2 + 2 + 2 + 2 + 2 or 20 treats. Subtract 20 from

60. 40 treats will be left in the box.

RESPONSE TO INTERVENTION

DIFFERENTIATED INSTRUCTION

AL **APPROACHING LEVEL**

IF my students struggle with writing a number sentence,

THEN choose a resource:

→ Use the Reteach worksheet with small groups.

→ Go online for a Differentiated Instruction activity.

OL **ON LEVEL**

IF my students seem to know how to write a number sentence, but need more practice,

THEN choose a resource:

→ Assign My Homework.

→ Go online for a Differentiated Instruction activity.

BL **BEYOND LEVEL**

IF my students have mastered writing a number sentence,

THEN choose a resource:

→ Use the Differentiated Instruction activity on p. 215D.

→ Use the Enrich worksheet in cooperative groups.

→ Assign My Homework.

→ Go online for a Differentiated Instruction activity.

271A **Chapter 4** Subtract Two-Digit Numbers

AL

Name _____

Lesson 8   Reteach (1)

Problem Solving
STRATEGY: Write a Number Sentence

There are eight bats in a tower.
Three bats fly away.
How many bats are now in the tower?

Step 1 Understand	**What do I know?** There are eleven bats. Three bats fly away. **What do I need to find out?** The number of bats there are now.
Step 2 Plan	**How will I find out how many bats there are in all?** A number sentence would tell me how many there are left. I would add if some bats flew to the tower, but bats flew away from the tower. I will write a number sentence and **subtract**
Step 3 Solve	**Write subtraction sentence.** $11 - 3 = 8$ bats
Step 4 Check	Is my answer reasonable? Explain. _____ **See students' work.**

AL

Name _____

Lesson 8   Reteach (2)

Problem Solving
STRATEGY: Write a Number Sentence

Write a number sentence to solve.

1. Spot has 13 bones in his doghouse. He found 4 more in the yard. How many bones does Spot have?

   $13 + 4 = 17$ bones

2. Lu sees 17 rabbits in a field. She sees 6 more in the woods. How many rabbits does she see in all?

   $17 + 6 = 23$ rabbits

3. Twenty-one monkeys are in the tree. Five monkeys swing away. How many monkeys are left?

   $21 - 5 = 16$ monkeys

4. Thirteen crows are in a cornfield. Six fly away. How many crows are left?

   $13 - 6 = 7$ crows

BL

Name _____

Lesson 8   Enrich

Problem Solving
STRATEGY: Write a Number Sentence

Subtract the numbers next to each other in the chart. Write the number sentences with a difference of 26. Can you find all six?

The target number is 26.

71	78	52	15
75	49	96	79
42	63	37	53
16	37	41	15

Write the subtraction sentences on the lines.

$78 - 52 = 26$

$75 - 49 = 26$

$63 - 37 = 26$

$41 - 15 = 26$

$79 - 53 = 26$

$42 - 16 = 26$

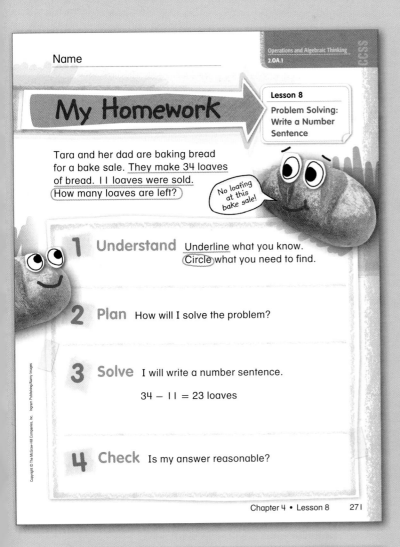

Name _____

Operations and Algebraic Thinking
2.0A.1

My Homework ➔

Lesson 8
Problem Solving:
Write a Number
Sentence

Tara and her dad are baking bread for a bake sale. They make 34 loaves of bread. 11 loaves were sold. How many loaves are left?

No loafing at this bake sale!

1 Understand Underline what you know.
Circle what you need to find.

2 Plan How will I solve the problem?

3 Solve I will write a number sentence.
34 − 11 = 23 loaves

4 Check Is my answer reasonable?

Chapter 4 • Lesson 8   271

Practice

Write a number sentence to solve.

1. Emma has 31 ribbons for her hair. She loses 12 ribbons. How many does she have left?

   __31__ ⊖ __12__ ⊜ __19__ ribbons

   Living on a pond isn't what it's quacked up to be.

2. Mason's soccer team has 24 games this season. He has already played 18 games. How many games are left?

   __24__ ⊖ __18__ ⊜ __6__ games

3. There are 18 ducks in the pond. 11 ducks get out of the pond. How many are still in the pond?

   __18__ ⊖ __11__ ⊜ __7__ ducks

Test Practice

4. Karen took a walk on the beach and counted 25 sandcastles. On the way back she counted again but some were gone. There were only 16 left. How many had disappeared while she walked?

   11   9   19   41
   ○   ●   ○   ○

Math at Home Ask your child to subtract 52 − 17. Then have your child show you how to check the answer.

My Homework

Assign homework after successful completion of the lesson. Students who understand the concepts may skip the **Homework Helper** section.

Test Practice

Diagnose Student Errors

Class trends in wrong answers may indicate common errors or misconceptions.

11 subtracted incorrectly

9 correct

19 only subtracted 6

41 added instead of subtracted

Formative Assessment

How do number sentences help us find what we need to know? Sample answer: They put together what we know and what we need to know.

LESSON 9
Two-Step Word Problems
OBJECTIVE Read and solve two-step word problems.

What's the Math?

 Common Core State Standards
DOMAIN: Operations and Algebraic Thinking

Standard: 2.OA.1
The wording of this standard can be found on page 216.

What Students Should Understand
- You can solve two-step word problems by reading the problem very carefully and determining what information is important and what is being asked.
- Since two steps are involved, you must figure out what to do first to get the information you need for the second step.

What Students Should be Able to Do

Emerson's book has 76 pages. She read 18 pages one day. Then she read 24 pages another day. How many pages does she have left to read?

First, find the number of pages Emerson had left to read after the first day. Then find the number of pages she had left to read after the second day.

$$
\begin{array}{r}
{}^{6\ 16} \\
\cancel{7\,6} \\
-\ 18 \\
\hline
58
\end{array}
\qquad
\begin{array}{r}
58 \\
-\ 24 \\
\hline
34
\end{array}
$$

So, Emerson has 34 pages left to read.

 Building on the Essential Question

In this lesson, students will build upon the skills and concepts needed to answer the chapter's Essential Question "How can I subtract two-digit numbers?"

Developing Vocabulary

Review Vocabulary
difference

Review Activity
- Have students skim the lesson. Have a volunteer tell what the lesson is about. two-step word problems
- Explain that when solving two-step word problems using subtraction, students will need to use the difference from one problem as part of the next problem.
- Review the example in the text box on the second page of the lesson. Tell students if they visualize and think aloud as they read problems, this might help them solve.

ELL **ELL Support Strategy** Use this vocabulary activity to provide oral summaries of information.

My Vocabulary Cards

Have students use a blank card to write a question about the chapter that they cannot answer. Collect the cards. Read the questions aloud, and work with the class to provide answers.

ELL Refer to the Multilingual eGlossary for interactive definitions in 13 languages.

Plan Online

Plan for your lesson by using the resources at

connectED.mcgraw-hill.com

Digital Dashboard

Interactive Whiteboard Ready

Vocab

The eBook **Glossary** shows the definition of the word and has audio for each definition. The **eGlossary** provides definitions in 13 languages.

Watch

Watch as concepts are brought to life through **animations**, **songs**, and a variety of visual instruction.

Tools

Virtual Manipulatives with work mats allow teachers and students to model the lesson.

Check

Use **eAssessment** for online assignments and customized assessments.

Use the **Common Core Quick Check** before the lesson to assess students' retention of previously learned concepts.

Use the interactive **Self-Check Quiz** after the lesson to provide immediate feedback on lesson concepts.

eHelp

Digital and print resources assist students and parents in completing My Homework.

Games

Online games and **apps** provide extra practice for lesson concepts.

PD

Professional development videos help teachers gain a deeper understanding of the lesson concepts and strategies.

RtI

Support for **approaching**, **on-** and **beyond-level** students as well as **English Language Learners**.

Masters

Reteach and **Enrich** worksheets, **Manipulative Masters**, the **Problem of the Day**, and other blackline masters are available for each lesson.

---

1 LAUNCH THE LESSON

CCSS

If your students are well-versed in two-step word problems, you may choose to begin instruction with Step 2, **TEACH**.

Mathematical PRACTICE 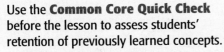 **4 Modeling the Math**

As a class, guide students to create a two-step word problem without them knowing in advance that the problem will be a two-step problem. Use base-ten blocks or connecting cubes to model the math if needed.

Create an addition or subtraction word problem, and solve the problem. Sample answer: There are 26 students in a classroom. 14 of the students are wearing blue shirts. How many students are not wearing blue shirts? $26 - 14 = 12$, so 12 students are not wearing blue shirts.

Extend the problem by asking another question. For example,

Six students are wearing red shirts. How can we find the number of students not wearing a blue or a red shirt? Subtract 6 from 12.

Explain to students that some word problems can be solved using two steps. Pose the situation below. As a class, discuss how the problem can be solved.

There are 34 library books on a shelf. Carly takes 16 of the books off of the shelf. She then puts five books back on the shelf. How many books are on the shelf? First, find $34 - 16$ to get 18. Then find $18 + 5$ to get 23. So, there are 23 books on the shelf.

TEACH

 Begin core instruction here.

You will need

☐ base-ten blocks (optional)

Explore and Explain

Read the directions that are at the bottom of the student page.

This problem will have to be solved in two steps. This may make this problem seem challenging. When a problem seems challenging, you can read it more than once, focus on solving it one step at a time, and model it with objects such as base-ten blocks to make the problem easier to understand.

Read the directions again. Use base-ten blocks to model what is taking place in the problem.

What question is being asked? How many people are still sledding? *What information do you need to solve the first step?* There are 62 people sledding. 13 people leave to go home. *What is the first step you will take to solve this problem?* Find 62 – 13. *What is 62 – 13?* 49 *There are 49 people still sledding. You will need this difference to do the next step in this problem. What information do you need to solve the second step?* There are 49 people sledding. 12 people go inside for hot cocoa.

What is the next step you will take to solve this problem? Find 49 – 12. *What is 49 – 12?* 37 *So, 37 people are still sledding.*

See and Show

Help students work through the example at the top of the page. Read the word problem together as a class. Discuss what you are trying to find. Have one student write the problem on the board. Have another student volunteer to solve it while the rest of the class follows along in their book.

Work through Exercises 1 and 2 as a class.

 **Talk Math**

Discuss with students "How do you solve a two-step problem?" Sample answer: You subtract one number from the whole. Then you subtract the other number from that difference.

273-274 Chapter 4 Subtract Two-Digit Numbers

Name _____

Operations and Algebraic Thinking
2.OA.1

Two-Step Word Problems

Lesson 9

ESSENTIAL QUESTION
How can I subtract two-digit numbers?

Explore and Explain

Wipe out!

37 people

 Teacher Directions: Use base-ten blocks to solve the problem. Draw the blocks to show your work. There are 62 people sledding. 13 people leave to go home. 12 people go inside for hot cocoa. How many people are still sledding?

Online Content at connectED.mcgraw-hill.com   Chapter 4 • Lesson 9   273

See and Show

 Mathematical **PRACTICE**

Some word problems take two-steps to solve.
There are 87 books at the library. 23 of the books are checked out. 4 of those books are returned. How many books are at the library now?

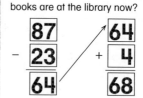

$$87 - 23 = 64$$ $$64 + 4 = 68$$ **68** books

Solve each two-step word problem.

1. Hailey has 33 books. She gives 14 books to her cousin. She gives 5 books to her sister. How many books does Hailey have left?

$$33 - 14 = 19$$ $$19 - 5 = 14$$ **14** books

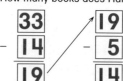 I read books every day. I eat a few too!

2. Dale invites 25 people to his party. 8 people can not come. 5 people come that were not invited. How many people come to the party?

22 people

Talk Math   How do you solve a two-step problem?

274   Chapter 4 • Lesson 9

Name _____

On My Own

Solve each two-step word problem.

3. Maryanne builds a tower out of blocks. She uses 89 blocks. 18 blocks fall off the tower. Her brother knocks 14 more blocks off the tower. How many blocks are still on the tower?

$$\begin{array}{r} 89 \\ -18 \\ \hline 71 \end{array} \qquad \begin{array}{r} 71 \\ -14 \\ \hline 57 \end{array} \quad \underline{57} \text{ blocks}$$

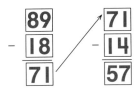

4. Ray has 56 comics. He gives 12 to his friend. He borrows 14 from his little brother. How many comics does Ray have now?

__58__ comics

I hope Ray lends me that comic!

5. There are 39 penguins on the iceberg. 11 penguins jump into the water. 4 more penguins jump onto another iceberg. How many penguins are left?

__24__ penguins

Chapter 4 • Lesson 9   275

Problem Solving

Solve each two-step word problem.

Mathematical
PRACTICE

6. There are 48 grapes in the bowl. Mia eats 18 grapes. Her mom adds 22 grapes to the bowl. How many grapes are in the bowl now?

__52__ grapes

7. Connor's mom cut 32 apple slices for his two brothers and him to share. Connor ate 5 slices. His brothers ate a total of 18 slices. How many apple slices were left?

Try a kiwi slice next time!

__14__ slices

HOT Problem Write a two-step word problem using the number sentences 23 + 10 = 23 and 23 − 5 = 18.

Sample answer: Jane picks 23 carrots from her garden.

She buys 10 carrots from the grocery store. Her brother

eats 5 carrots. How many carrots does Jane have left?

PRACTICE & APPLY

CCSS

On My Own

Have students work through the exercises on this page independently. You may choose to assign exercises based on the chart below.

DIFFERENTIATED ASSIGNMENTS

AL **Approaching Level** Guide students through the exercises in On My Own. Help them to use manipulatives while they work through the exercises.

OL **On Level** Complete the exercises independently.

BL **Beyond Level** Complete the exercises independently without manipulatives.

Problem Solving

Have students work through the problem-solving exercises on this page independently.

Mathematical
PRACTICE 7   In Exercise 6, students **look for and make use of structure.**

HOT Problem This exercise asks students to build upon their understanding of concepts needed to answer the chapter's Essential Question.

21ST CENTURY SKILLS

Critical Thinking and Problem Solving

This lesson introduces students to the process of having to do more than one step to find the solution to a problem. Teaching students how to think critically can help them not only in this grade, but as they progress through their education and career choices. Asking themselves if what they have done truly answers the question or do they have another step to perform is key in multi-step problems. They also need to look at their final answer and see if it makes sense in the context of the problem.

(AL) APPROACHING LEVEL

IF my students struggle with two-step word problems,

THEN choose a resource:

→ Use the Reteach worksheet with small groups.

→ Go online for a Differentiated Instruction activity.

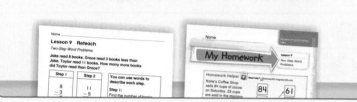

(OL) ON LEVEL

IF my students seem to know how to solve two-step word problems, but need more practice,

THEN choose a resource:

→ Assign My Homework.

→ Go online for a Differentiated Instruction activity.

(BL) BEYOND LEVEL

IF my students have mastered two-step word problems,

THEN choose a resource:

→ Use the Enrich worksheet in cooperative groups.

→ Assign My Homework.

→ Go online for a Differentiated Instruction activity.

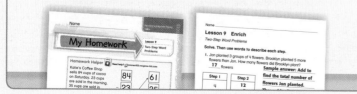

(AL)   Name _____

Lesson 9   Reteach

Two-Step Word Problems

Jake read 8 books. Grace read 3 books less than Jake. Taylor read 11 books. How many more books did Taylor read than Grace?

Step 1	Step 2
8 − 3 ___ 5	11 − 5 ___ 6

You can use words to describe each step.

Step 1: Find the number of books Grace read.

Step 2: Find the difference between the number of books Grace and Taylor each read.

Taylor read ___6___ more books than Grace.

1. Will wrote 9 stories. Sydney wrote 10 stories. Isaac wrote 8 more stories than Will. What is the difference between the number of stories Sydney and Issac each wrote? Explain each step.

___7___ stories

Step 1	Step 2
9 + 8 ___ 17	17 − 10 ___ 7

Sample answer: Add to find the number of stories Isaac wrote. Then, subtract to find difference between the number of stories Sydney and Issac each wrote.

(BL)   Name _____

Lesson 9   Enrich

Two-Step Word Problems

Solve. Then use words to describe each step.

1. Jon planted 3 groups of 4 flowers. Brooklyn planted 5 more flowers than Jon. How many flowers did Brooklyn plant?

___17___ flowers

Step 1	Step 2
4 4 + 4 ___ 12	12 + 5 ___ 17

Sample answer: Add to find the total number of flowers Jon planted. Then add 5 flowers to Jon's total.

2. Will wrote 22 poems. Sydney wrote 10 poems. Isaac wrote 13 more poems than Will. What is the difference between the number of poems Sydney and Isaac each wrote? Explain each step.

___25___ poems

Step 1	Step 2
22 + 13 ___ 35	35 − 10 ___ 25

Sample answer: Add to find the number of poems Isaac wrote. Then, subtract to find difference between the number of poems Sydney and Issac each wrote.

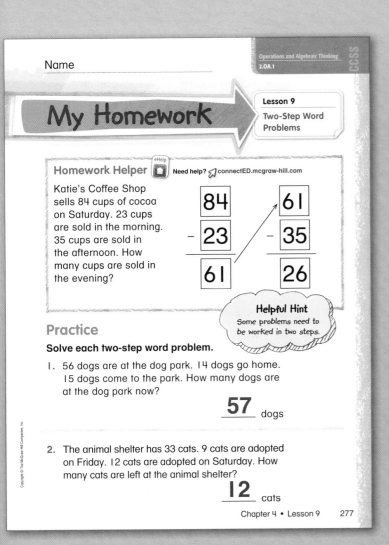

Practice

Solve each two-step word problem.

1. 56 dogs are at the dog park. 14 dogs go home. 15 dogs come to the park. How many dogs are at the dog park now?

   57 dogs

2. The animal shelter has 33 cats. 9 cats are adopted on Friday. 12 cats are adopted on Saturday. How many cats are left at the animal shelter?

   12 cats

Chapter 4 • Lesson 9   277

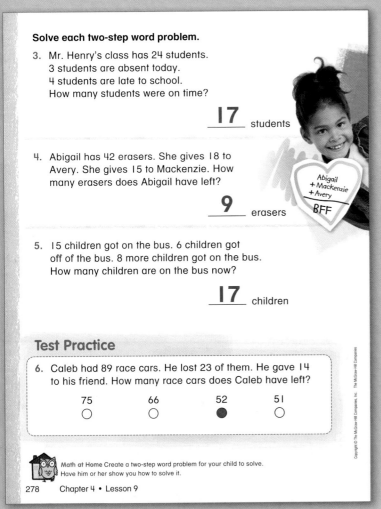

Solve each two-step word problem.

3. Mr. Henry's class has 24 students. 3 students are absent today. 4 students are late to school. How many students were on time?

   17 students

4. Abigail has 42 erasers. She gives 18 to Avery. She gives 15 to Mackenzie. How many erasers does Abigail have left?

   9 erasers

5. 15 children got on the bus. 6 children got off of the bus. 8 more children got on the bus. How many children are on the bus now?

   17 children

Test Practice

6. Caleb had 89 race cars. He lost 23 of them. He gave 14 to his friend. How many race cars does Caleb have left?

   75 ○   66 ○   52 ●   51 ○

Math at Home Create a two-step word problem for your child to solve. Have him or her show you how to solve it.

278   Chapter 4 • Lesson 9

My Homework

Assign homework after successful completion of the lesson. Students who understand the concepts may skip the **Homework Helper** section.

Test Practice

Diagnose Student Errors

Class trends in wrong answers may indicate common errors or misconceptions.

75 subtracted 89 — 14 only

66 did not do the second step

52 correct

51 subtracted incorrectly

Formative Assessment

Janice took 27 cupcakes to school. She shared 19 of them with her class. Four people from the office also wanted one. *How many does she have left?* 4 Write the following on the board. *Which is the correct way to solve this?*

$$
\begin{array}{cc}
27 & 8 \\
-19 & -4 \\
\hline
8 & 8
\end{array}
\quad \text{or} \quad
\boxed{
\begin{array}{cc}
19 & 27 \\
+4 & -23 \\
\hline
23 & 4
\end{array}
}
$$

Fluency Practice

Mathematical PRACTICE 6 These pages encourage students to become proficient in their calculation abilities. You can use this as a timed or untimed exercise.

Pages 279–280 Practice subtraction of whole numbers.

Teaching Tip One approach to build student confidence is to use this page repeatedly. Strive to have students complete a portion of the page correctly in an untimed situation. Then use the rest of the page as a timed test.

Name _____

Fluency Practice

Subtract.

1.	16 − 3 = **13**	2.	26 − 6 = **20**	3.	13 − 8 = **5**
4.	15 − 9 = **6**	5.	12 − 5 = **7**	6.	19 − 5 = **14**
7.	11 − 9 = **2**	8.	12 − 6 = **6**	9.	14 − 8 = **6**
10.	19 − 8 = **11**	11.	18 − 9 = **9**	12.	17 − 3 = **14**
13.	19 − 1 = **18**	14.	15 − 5 = **10**	15.	17 − 4 = **3**

Fluency Practice

Subtract.

1.	13 − 6 = **7**	2.	13 − 7 = **6**	3.	18 − 8 = **10**
4.	15 − 6 = **9**	5.	17 − 5 = **12**	6.	14 − 8 = **6**
7.	20 − 9 = **11**	8.	16 − 7 = **9**	9.	11 − 10 = **1**
10.	12 − 9 = **3**	11.	18 − 7 = **11**	12.	12 − 7 = **5**
13.	16 − 2 = **14**	14.	13 − 3 = **10**	15.	19 − 7 = **12**

My Review

Name _____

Vocabulary Check

Complete each sentence. Use words from the box.

| subtract | fact family | regroup | difference |

1. A ___fact family___ is a group of 3 numbers that work together.

2. You can ___regroup___ a ten into ten ones.

3. When you ___subtract___, you take something away from another number.

4. The answer you get from subtracting is called the ___difference___.

Write an example of a fact family.

5.
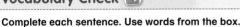

Triangle: 12 (top), 5 and 7 (bottom)

$$5 + 7 = 12 \qquad 12 - 5 = 7$$
$$7 + 5 = 12 \qquad 12 - 7 = 5$$

Sample answer given.

Chapter 4   281

Concept Check

Subtract.

6.	7.	8.	9.
27 − 18 **9**	32 − 17 **15**	26 − 19 **7**	48 − 28 **20**

10.	11.	12.	13.
83 − 37 **46**	80 − 26 **54**	74 − 25 **49**	71 − 37 **34**

Rewrite the numbers. Subtract.

14. 48 − 29

$$\begin{array}{r} 3\,18 \\ \cancel{48} \\ -\ 29 \\ \hline 19 \end{array}$$

15. 26 − 17

$$\begin{array}{r} 1\,16 \\ \cancel{26} \\ -\ 17 \\ \hline 9 \end{array}$$

16. 53 − 37

$$\begin{array}{r} 4\,13 \\ \cancel{26} \\ -\ 37 \\ \hline 16 \end{array}$$

Subtract. Check by adding.

17.
$$\begin{array}{r} 73 \\ -\ 27 \\ \hline 46 \end{array} \qquad \begin{array}{r} 46 \\ +\ 27 \\ \hline 73 \end{array}$$

18.
$$\begin{array}{r} 63 \\ -\ 36 \\ \hline 27 \end{array} \qquad \begin{array}{r} 27 \\ +\ 36 \\ \hline 63 \end{array}$$

Hit the beach!

282   Chapter 4

My Review

Use these pages to assess your students' understanding of the vocabulary and key concepts in this chapter.

Vocabulary Check

Display this chapter's vocabulary on the virtual word wall. Have students refer to these examples as they complete the exercises.

ELL **ELL Support Strategy** Use this information to participate in purposeful, cooperative learning activities.

Concept Check

If students need reinforcement of skills after completing this section, use the Reteach worksheet to review the concepts again.

Exercises	Concept	Review Lesson
6–13	Subtraction	5
14–16	Rewrite two-digit subtraction	6
17–18	Check subtraction	7

Problem Solving

Remind students of the four-step plan for problem solving. For students who need help in reading comprehension, have them work with another student to read the problem aloud before attempting the four-step plan.

Reflect

Display this chapter's vocabulary on the Virtual Word Wall. Ask students to refer to the words as they complete the graphic organizer.

You may choose to have your students use a different graphic organizer for review.

Summative Assessment

Use these alternate leveled chapter tests from the Assessment Masters to differentiate assessment for the specific needs of your students.

Chapter Tests		
Level	**Type**	**Form**
AL	Multiple Choice	1A
AL	Multiple Choice	1B
OL	Multiple Choice / Free Choice	2A
OL	Multiple Choice / Free Choice	2B
BL	Free Choice	3A
BL	Free Choice	3B
Additional Chapter Resource Masters		
OL	Vocabulary Test	
OL	Listening Assessment	
OL	Oral Assessment	

Name _____

 Problem Solving

19. Max has 34 marbles. He gives 19 marbles away. How many marbles does Max have left?

 15 marbles

20. There are 18 alligators around a pond. 10 alligators slide into the water. 2 come back out. How many alligators are around the pond now?

 10 alligators

21. Matt sees 25 planes at the air show. 6 of the planes are red. 8 are white. The rest are blue. How many planes are blue?

 11 blue planes

22. Jill collects 68 golf balls. She gives 39 of them to her dad. She loses 8 of them. How many golf balls does Jill have left?

 21 golf balls

Chapter 4   283

Reflect

Chapter 4
Answering the Essential Question

Show the ways to subtract. Check your work.

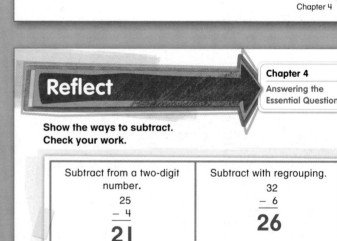

Subtract from a two-digit number.	Subtract with regrouping.
25 − 4 **21**	32 − 6 **26**

ESSENTIAL QUESTION

How can I subtract two-digit numbers?

Subtract without regrouping.	Subtract with regrouping.
48 − 35 **13**	71 − 19 **52**

Have a ball!

Let's get rolling!

284   Chapter 4

Notes

CHAPTER 5

Place Value to 1,000

Chapter at a Glance

Suggested Pacing		
Instruction*	**Review & Assessment**	**TOTAL**
10 days	2 days	**12 days**

*Includes additional time for remediation and differentiation.

Lesson	Objective	Materials & Manipulatives	Vocabulary	CCSS Standard
Lesson 1 *pp. 295–300* **Hundreds**	Relate hundreds, tens and ones.	• ten-frames • thin-line markers • crayons or colored pencils	**hundreds**	2.NBT.1 2.NBT.1a 2.NBT.1b
Lesson 2 *pp. 301–306* **Hundreds, Tens, and Ones**	Read, write, and model numbers to 999.	• base-ten blocks • Work Mat 7		2.NBT.1 2.NBT.1a 2.NBT.1b 2.NBT.3
Lesson 3 *pp. 307–312* **Place Value to 1,000**	Identify and use words, models, and expanded form to represent numbers to 999.	• number cube • Work Mat 7 • base-ten blocks	**place value** **digit** **expanded form**	2.NBT.1 2.NBT.1a 2.NBT.1b 2.NBT.3
✓ **Check My Progress**				
Lesson 4 *pp. 315–320* **Problem-Solving Strategy: Use Logical Reasoning**	Use logical reasoning to solve problems.			2.NBT.1 2.NBT.1a 2.NBT.1b 2.NBT.3
Lesson 5 *pp. 321–326* **Read and Write Numbers to 1,000**	Read and write numbers to 1,000.	• base-ten blocks • crayons or colored pencils	**thousand**	2.NBT.3
Lesson 6 *pp. 327–332* **Count by 5s, 10s, and 100s**	Find counting patterns.	• crayons or colored pencils		2.NBT.2 2.NBT.8
Lesson 7 *pp. 333–338* **Compare Numbers to 1,000**	Compare three-digit numbers using <, >, and =.	• number cards (1 to 10) • blank index cards • base-ten blocks	**compare** **greater than** **less than** **equal to**	2.NBT.4
✓ **My Review and Reflect**				

Planning for Differentiated Instruction

Use these differentiated instruction activity suggestions, along with the ongoing support provided in each lesson of this chapter, to meet individual learning needs.

AL APPROACHING LEVEL

Use with Lesson 2

Materials: base-ten blocks

- Give students varying groups of base-ten blocks.
- Tell them to sort by hundreds, tens, and ones. Then have them count each group and record the three-digit number.
- Students repeat with different groups of base-ten blocks.

BL BEYOND LEVEL

Use with Lesson 4

- Have students work together to use the following clues to find the number 642. Then have students make their own clues for a three-digit number and have classmates find the number.
- It is a three-digit number.
- The digit in the tens place is twice the digit in the ones place.
- The digit in the tens place is less than 5.
- If you start at the digit in the ones place, you can skip count by 2 to find the digits in the tens and hundreds places.

OL ON LEVEL

Use with Lesson 3

Materials: spinners

- Students spin to get three numbers. They write the first number in the ones place, second in the tens place, etc.
- Students read the numbers they wrote.
- Have them trade papers. *How many ones are in your partner's number? How many tens? hundreds?*
- Students write the numbers in expanded form and read them out loud.

ELL ENGLISH LANGUAGE LEARNERS

Support for English Language Learners is found throughout the chapter and includes:

- ELL strategies at point-of-use in each Teacher Edition lesson
- ELL tiered instruction suggestions for each lesson at connectED.mcgraw-hill.com
- Comprehensive ELL lessons and worksheets for additional instruction at connectED.mcgraw-hill.com
- Non-linguistic representations of concepts on My Math Words, My Vocabulary Cards, and My Foldables

Additional online resources at connectED.mcgraw-hill.com include:

- Visual Vocabulary Cards
- Multilingual eGlossary
- Professional Development support

Looking for more DIFFERENTIATED INSTRUCTION?
Find additional support in each lesson of this chapter and online at connectED.mcgraw-hill.com

RtI

AL Approaching Level
OL On Level
BL Beyond Level
ELL English Language Learners

What's the Math in This Chapter?

Where

CONTENT STANDARDS

NBT
Number and Operations in Base Ten

Meet

Mathematical
PRACTICE **5**

Use appropriate tools strategically.

Most of this chapter concentrates on the **Number and Operations in Base Ten (NBT)** domain. However, aspects of the **Operations and Algebraic Thinking (OA)** domain are also used in the study of **place value**.

As you teach place value to 1,000, make students aware of all of the tools available to them that they can use to learn about this concept. They can use pencil and paper, a place-value chart, a hundred chart, and base-ten blocks. When students are aware of the variety of tools available to them, they can choose the tool that will help them to best understand the concept being taught.

What should my students already know?

In the previous grade, students used **Number and Operations in Base Ten (NBT)** in their study of place value:

- Understand that the two digits of a two-digit number represent amounts of tens and ones. **1.NBT.2**

- Understand that 10 can be thought of as a bundle of ten ones – called a "ten." **1.NBT.2a**

- Understand that the numbers from 11–19 are composed of a ten and one, two, three, four, five, six, seven, eight, or nine ones. **1.NBT.2b**

- Understand that the numbers 10, 20, 30, 40, 50, 60, 70, 80, 90 refer to one, two, three, four, five, six, seven, eight, or nine tens (and zero ones). **1.NBT.2c**

- Compare two two-digit numbers based on meanings of the tens and ones digits, recording the results of comparisons with the symbols >, =, and <. **1.NBT.3**

WHAT STUDENTS SHOULD UNDERSTAND

Hundreds
CCSS 2.NBT.1a, 2.NBT.1b

How to write a given amount of hundreds as tens and ones.

- one hundred = 10 tens = 100 ones
- Use this information to tell how many tens and ones are in different amounts of hundreds.

Hundreds, Tens, and Ones
CCSS 2.NBT.3, 2.NBT.1a, 2.NBT.1b

How to represent a three-digit number with base-ten blocks, in a place-value chart, and in standard form.

- A number can be modeled by using base-ten blocks.
- A place-value chart is helpful when writing a number in standard form.

WHAT STUDENTS SHOULD BE ABLE TO DO

Tell how many hundreds, tens, and ones are shown.

4 hundreds = 40 tens = 400 ones

Write how many hundreds, tens, and ones. Then write the number.

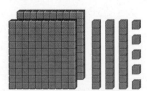

hundreds	tens	ones
2	3	5

two hundred thirty-five

WHAT STUDENTS SHOULD UNDERSTAND	WHAT STUDENTS SHOULD BE ABLE TO DO

Write a Number in Standard Form, Word Form, and Expanded Form

 2.NBT.3

How to use place value to write a number that is 1,000 or less in standard form, word form, and expanded form.

- A number can be written in expanded form, which shows the value of each digit.
- You can read and write numbers with symbols (digits and commas) and words.

Write 5 hundreds, 7 tens, and 2 ones in expanded form. Then write the number.

$$500 + 70 + 2 \qquad = \qquad 572$$
$$\uparrow \qquad\qquad\qquad\qquad \uparrow$$
expanded form   standard form

Write 294 in word form.

two hundred ninety-four

Complete Number Patterns

 2.NBT.2, 2.NBT.8

How to complete a counting pattern that increases by 5s, 10s, or 100s.

- You can skip count by 5s, 10s, and 100s, to help you complete a counting pattern.

Write the missing numbers in this pattern:

530, 540, ____, ____, 570
Then write the counting pattern.

530, 540, 550, 560, 570

The pattern is 10 more.

Compare Numbers

 2.NBT.4

How to compare numbers to 1,000.

- You can compare numbers to 1,000 by writing the numbers in a place-value chart. Compare the digits in each place value, starting with the greatest place value.
- Use the symbols > (greater than), < (less than), and = (equal to).

Compare 643 and 634. Write >, <, r =.

hundreds	tens	ones
6	4	3
6	3	4

In the tens place, 4 is greater than 3.

643 $>$ 634

643 is greater than 634.

What will my students do next with these skills?

After this chapter, students will learn to:

- Add three-digit numbers. 2.NBT.7

In the next grade, students will learn to:

- Add multi-digit numbers. 3.NBT.2

Reading Connections

 Real-World Problem Solving Library

Math and Social Studies: Lady Liberty

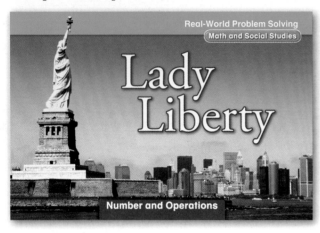

Use these leveled books to reinforce and extend problem solving skills and strategies.

Leveled for:

AL Approaching Level

OL On Level Also available in Spanish

BL Beyond Level

For additional support, see the *Real-World Problem Solving Readers Teacher Guide.*

Leveled Reader Database

Available at leveledreaderdatabase.macmillanmh.com
Search by:

- Content Area
- Lexile Score
- Guided Reading Level
- Benchmark Level

Library Books

Check with your school library or your local public library for these titles.

Just Enough Carrots
Stuart J. Murphy

Less Than Zero
Stuart J. Murphy

Fun with 9umbers
Massin

The History of Counting
Denise Schmandt-Besserat

How Much Is a Million?
David M. Schwartz

How Much, How Many, How Far, How Heavy, How Long, How Tall is 1000?
Helen Nolan

Reading and Language Arts Support

Examining Math

Divide the class into groups of 4. Distribute an index card to each group. Instruct students to discuss what they have learned so far about numbers to 1,000. Have each group write one question about something from this chapter that they are confused or are unsure about and write it on the index card. Collect the cards, and come together again as a class to discuss the questions.

Looking for more Reading and Language Arts Support?
go online to
connectED.mcgraw-hill.com

LAUNCH THE CHAPTER

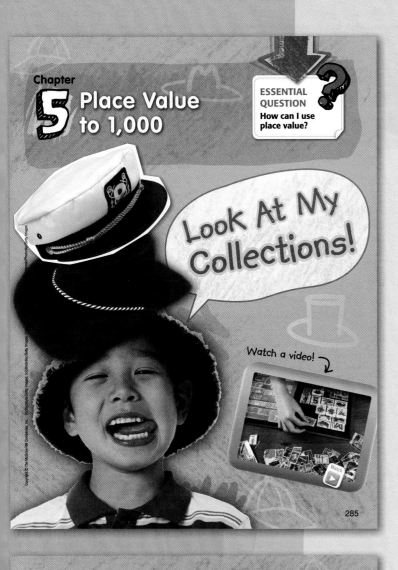

Chapter
5 Place Value to 1,000

ESSENTIAL QUESTION
How can I use place value?

Look At My Collections!

Watch a video!

285

Theme:
Look at My Collections!

All of the lessons in Chapter 5 will connect with the theme of Look at My Collections, which centers on things that kids collect. This is reflected in problem solving and the visuals used throughout the chapter.

 Video

Watch

Have students watch the video about collections. You may want to spark a discussion about how math is used in organizing collections.

 Building on the Essential Question

Once students have completed this chapter, they should be able to answer the question "How can I use place value?" In each lesson, students build upon their understanding by answering a simpler question. These are indicated in the exercises as Building on the Essential Question. At the end of the chapter, students use a graphic organizer to help them answer the Essential Question.

My Common Core State Standards CCSS

Number and Operations in Base Ten

2.NBT.1 Understand that the three digits of a three-digit number represent amounts of hundreds, tens, and ones; e.g., 706 equals 7 hundreds, 0 tens, and 6 ones. Understand the following as special cases:

2.NBT.1a 100 can be thought of as a bundle of ten tens — called a "hundred."

2.NBT.1b The numbers 100, 200, 300, 400, 500, 600, 700, 800, 900 refer to one, two, three, four, five, six, seven, eight, or nine hundreds (and 0 tens and 0 ones).

2.NBT.2 Count within 1000; skip count by 5s, 10s, and 100.

2.NBT.3 Read and write numbers to 1000 using base-ten numerals, number names, and expanded form.

2.NBT.4 Compare two three-digit numbers based on meanings of the hundreds, tens, and ones digits, using >, =, and < symbols to record the results of comparisons.

2.NBT.8 Mentally add 10 or 100 to a given number 100–900, and mentally subtract 10 or 100 from a given number 100–900.

Standards for Mathematical PRACTICE

1. Make sense of problems and persevere in solving them.
2. Reason abstractly and quantitatively.
3. Construct viable arguments and critique the reasoning of others.
4. Model with mathematics.
5. Use appropriate tools strategically.
6. Attend to precision.
7. Look for and make use of structure.
8. Look for and express regularity in repeated reasoning.

= focused on in this chapter

286   Chapter 5

Professional Development

 Common Core State Standards

Learn more about how the Common Core State Standards can be implemented in your classroom at mhpdonline.com.

Look for
- **eImplementation**
- **eVideo Clip Libraries**
- **eTech Training**
- **ePD Webinars**

Watch

Feature video for mathematical content in this chapter:
Place Value Games

1 Assess

You have two options for assessing student readiness for this chapter. Use student results to determine which level of instruction is needed to help students get ready for the chapter and to determine what ongoing support they will need during the chapter.

Option 1: Am I Ready?

Have students complete the Am I Ready? page in their student books.

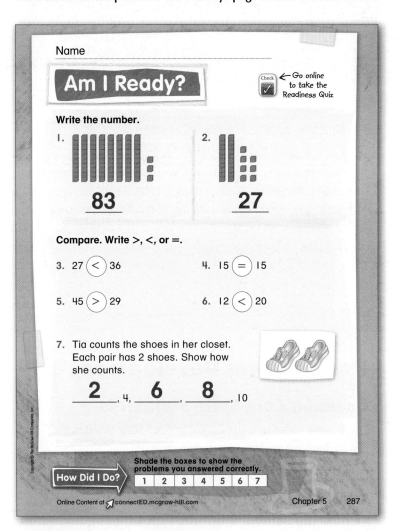

Name

Am I Ready?

Check → Go online to take the Readiness Quiz

Write the number.

1. 83

2. 27

Compare. Write >, <, or =.

3. 27 < 36

4. 15 = 15

5. 45 > 29

6. 12 < 20

7. Tia counts the shoes in her closet. Each pair has 2 shoes. Show how she counts.

2 , 4, 6 , 8 , 10

How Did I Do? Shade the boxes to show the problems you answered correctly. 1 2 3 4 5 6 7

Online Content at connectED.mcgraw-hill.com   Chapter 5   287

Option 2: Online Readiness Quiz

Have students take the **Online Readiness Quiz.**

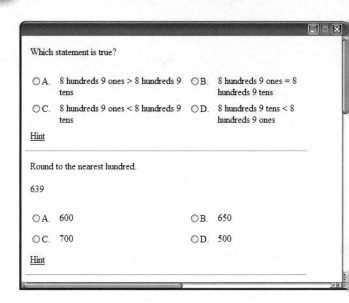

Which statement is true?

○ A. 8 hundreds 9 ones > 8 hundreds 9 tens
○ B. 8 hundreds 9 ones = 8 hundreds 9 tens
○ C. 8 hundreds 9 ones < 8 hundreds 9 tens
○ D. 8 hundreds 9 tens < 8 hundreds 9 ones

Hint

Round to the nearest hundred.

639

○ A. 600
○ B. 650
○ C. 700
○ D. 500

Hint

OPTION 2

Common Core Review

Exercises	Skill	Standard
1–10*	Number sense	2.NBT.1
	Comparing numbers	2.NBT.1
	Skip counting	2.NBT.1

*These questions are randomly generated from a bank of 15 questions.

OPTION 1

Common Core Review

Exercises	Skill	Standard
1–2	Number sense	2.NBT.1
3–6	Comparing numbers	2.NBT.1
7	Skip counting	2.NBT.1

2 Diagnose and Prescribe

3 Reassess

Based on the results of the Am I Ready? in the student edition, use the charts below to address individual needs **before** beginning the chapter.

Use the **ONGOING** resources to support differentiated instruction as new skills and concepts are presented in the chapter.

If reassessment is necessary, administer the chapter Diagnostic Test in the **Assessment Masters** or go online for eAssessment.

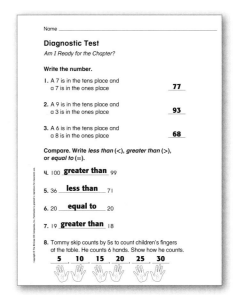

TIER 1

OL ON LEVEL

IF students miss 2 in Exercises 1–7,

THEN choose a resource:

→ Am I Ready? Practice
→ Online Readiness Quiz

ONGOING Self-Check Quizzes • Chapter Project • Differentiated Assignments • My Learning Stations • Differentiated Instruction activities

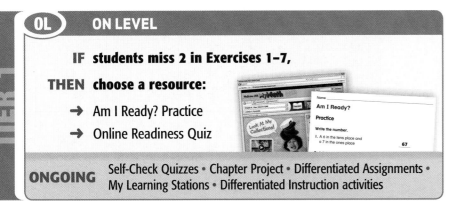

TIER 2

AL STRATEGIC INTERVENTION

(Approaching Grade Level)

IF students miss 3–4 in Exercises 1–7,

THEN choose a resource:

→ Online Strategic Intervention activity
→ Am I Ready? Review

ONGOING Common Errors • Differentiated Assignments • Online support • Reteach worksheets • Homework Helper • My Learning Stations • RtI lesson support • Differentiated Instruction activities

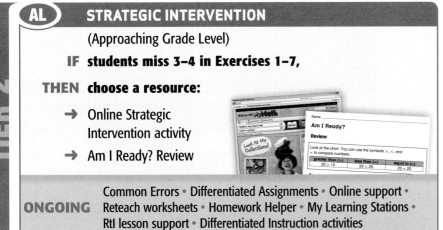

TIER 3

INTENSIVE INTERVENTION

(2 or more years below grade level)

IF students miss 5 or more in Exercises 1–7,

THEN use *Math Triumphs,* an intensive math intervention program from McGraw-Hill.

For additional chapter readiness assessment, go to eAssessment at connectED.mcgraw-hill.com.

BL BEYOND LEVEL

IF students miss 1 or less in Exercises 1–7,

THEN choose a resource:

→ Online Games
→ Am I Ready? Apply

ONGOING 21st Century Skills • Chapter Project • Differentiated Assignments • Enrich worksheets • My Learning Stations • Differentiated Instruction activities

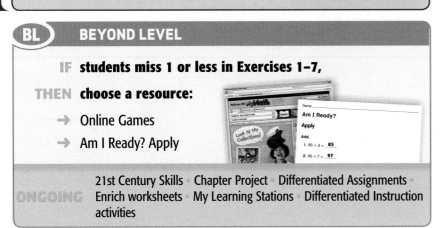

DEVELOP VOCABULARY

My Math Words

Review Vocabulary

Where did they learn it?

- ones   (Grade 1)
- tens   (Grade 1)

Making Connections

Ask students to describe or show what they know about the review vocabulary. Encourage students to describe, draw, act out, or model examples of each word.

Ask students to examine the graphic organizer. Have them identify the headings in the chart. Tens, Ones, Value Ask students to describe how they could read this chart for information. Sample answer: Each blank box shows where the numbers in each row and the categories in each column come together.

Have students share the sentences they wrote at the bottom of the page.

My Vocabulary Cards

Ask students to browse the words and examples on each of this chapter's cards. Discuss with them what they already know about these words or the examples shown on the cards. Note on the board any questions or observations students have about these words.

Students should clip and store their cards in one place, such as a small envelope, where they can access them as needed throughout the chapter.

My Vocabulary Card Activities

The table on the next page lists an activity for each card, as well as the answer or sample answer. The activities will include opportunities for students to hear, say, or write the vocabulary words. When applicable, activities will involve drawing or modeling vocabulary. Students' answers can be recorded using various media, such as Notebook Foldables, IWB, electronic tablets, or computers. Suggestions for using blank cards appear in some Developing Vocabulary activities.

Definitions appear on the back of each card. Discuss the definitions with students.

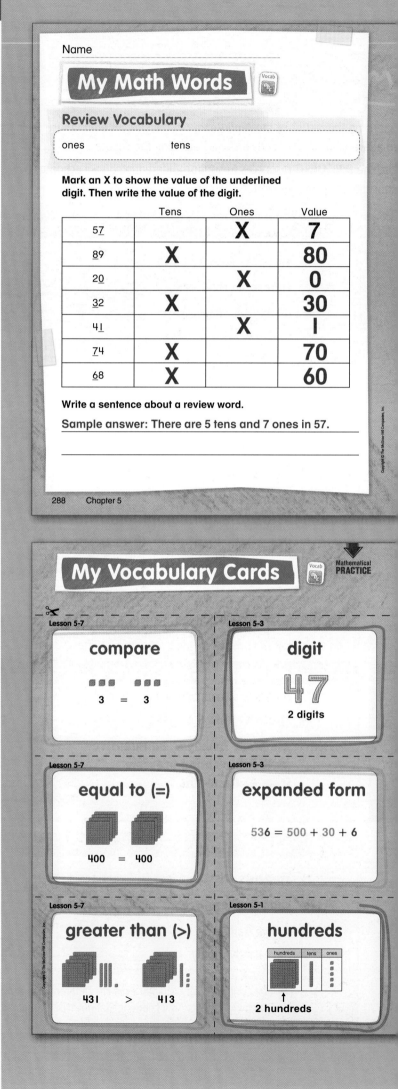

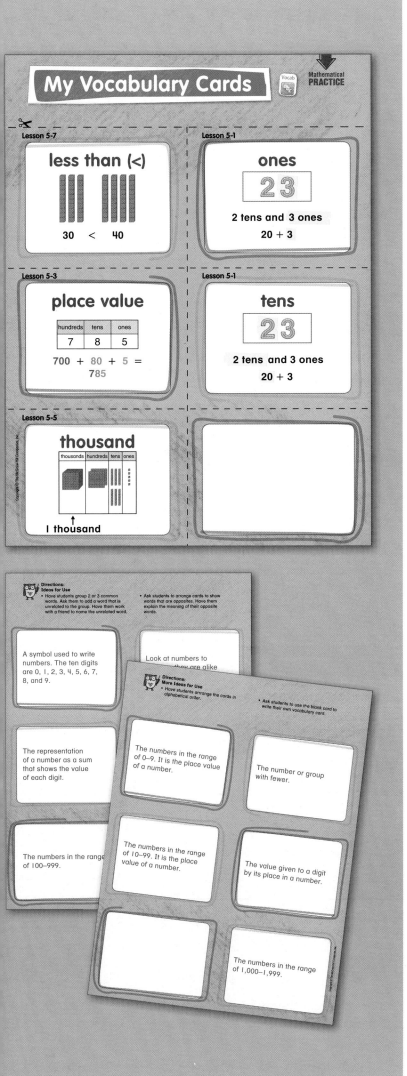

My Vocabulary Cards

Vocab
Mathematical PRACTICE

Lesson 5-7

less than (<)

30 < 40

Lesson 5-1

ones

2 3

2 tens and 3 ones

20 + 3

Lesson 5-3

place value

hundreds	tens	ones
7	8	5

700 + 80 + 5 = 785

Lesson 5-1

tens

2 3

2 tens and 3 ones

20 + 3

Lesson 5-5

thousand

thousands	hundreds	tens	ones

↑ 1 thousand

Copyright © The McGraw-Hill Companies, Inc.

Directions:
Ideas for Use
• Have students group 2 or 3 common words. Ask them to add a word that is unrelated to the group. Have them work with a friend to name the unrelated word.

• Ask students to arrange cards to show words that are opposites. Have them explain the meaning of their opposite words.

A symbol used to write numbers. The ten digits are 0, 1, 2, 3, 4, 5, 6, 7, 8, and 9.

Look at numbers to ... they are alike

Directions:
More Ideas for Use
• Have students arrange the cards in alphabetical order.

• Ask students to use the blank card to write their own vocabulary card.

The representation of a number as a sum that shows the value of each digit.

The numbers in the range of 0–9. It is the place value of a number.

The number or group with fewer.

The numbers in the range of 100–999.

The numbers in the range of 10–99. It is the place value of a number.

The value given to a digit by its place in a number.

The numbers in the range of 1,000–1,999.

Mathematical PRACTICE ③ My Vocabulary Card Activities

On the back of each vocabulary card is the definition of the word or phrase. Students also record their answers to the activities printed on the back of the cards. The table below gives sample answers for each card's activity.

Vocabulary Card	Activity/ Activity Answer
compare	Write a sentence comparing 2 two-digit numbers. Sample answer: 99 is more than 33.
digit	How many digits are in your age? How many digits are in the year you were born? See students' work.
equal to (=)	Write a sentence about the art on the card. Use *is equal to*. Sample answer: One group of balloons is equal to the other.
expanded form	Write *27* in expanded form. 20 + 7
greater than (>)	Draw an example of *is greater than*. See students' work.
hundreds	Write how many hundreds, tens, and ones are shown on the front of this card. 2 hundreds, 1 ten, 5 ones
less than (<)	Tell a friend how the < symbol helps you compare numbers. See students' work.
ones	Show *ones* using classroom objects. Sample answer: Students use pencils to show 6 ones.
place value	Draw how you will remember the meaning of *place value*. See students' work.
tens	Show *tens* using classroom objects. See students' work.
thousand	Write how many thousands, hundreds, tens, and ones are shown on the front of this card. 1 thousand, 2 hundreds, 6 tens, 5 ones

STUDY ORGANIZER

My Foldable

What's the Math?

Content Standard: 2.NBT.1

Mathematical PRACTICE 2 Reason abstractly and quantitively.

This Foldable allows students to identify hundreds, tens, and ones in a three-digit number.

How Do I Make It?

- Tear out the page and cut off the top banner.
- Fold along the green dotted line.
- Cut along the two orange dashed lines to make three tabs.

When Do I Use It?

Use after Lesson 2, and as a review tool at the end of the chapter.

How Could I Use It?

- Begin with the tabs closed on the Foldable. Identify each tab as hundreds, tens, and ones.
- Tell students you are thinking of a number. Tell them the amount of tens in your number. They can open the tens tab and write the number. Next tell them the amount of ones in your number. They can open the ones tab and write the number. Then tell them the amount of hundreds in your number and they can open the hundreds tab and write the number.
- Have students identify your number.
- Have students close the tabs. Repeat with other numbers changing the order.

ELL **ELL Support Strategy** Use this Foldable to demonstrate understanding by identifying the proper tab.

© The McGraw-Hill Companies, Inc.

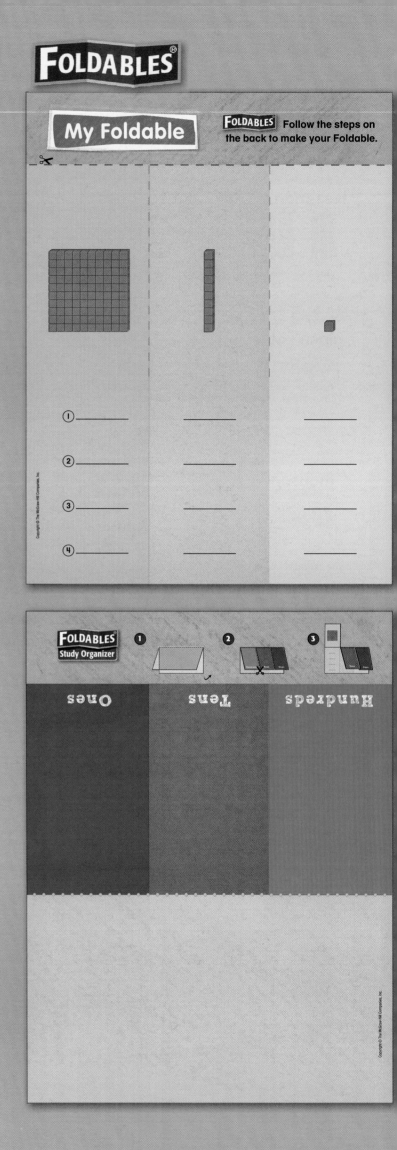

Project *Express*™

From Dinah Zike, creator of Foldables®

This ready-to-make project format comes in eight bright colors and offers the ability to customize your learning center with different content-based Project Packets. These packets include pre-printed, full color stickers, assorted envelopes and pockets, reproducible templates, and materials needed for quick assembly. You can use these materials as illustrated or use them to design your own learning center.

Order with a McGraw-Hill discount at www.dinah.com.

**Place Value II
(Thousands)**

Also available for Chapter 5:

- Project Express Place Value Ones, Tens, and Hundreds

MY Learning Stations

Use the following learning stations to differentiate the instruction for Chapter 5. Includes Spanish!

Learning Station	Title	Use after Lesson(s)
Game	*Butterfly Fun*	3
Activity Card	*Comparing Stories*	5
Graphic Novel	*Home Run Records*	7

Chapter Project

Number Pattern Stories

Small groups work together to write a fiction story that includes a counting pattern using numbers up to 1,000.

- Encourage students to reread some of the books you have shared with them throughout the chapter to help generate ideas for their own stories.
- Have students plan what they will write, using a story map or storyboard and the number pattern they will include in the story.
- Ask students to create illustrations for each page and a cover for their book.
- Invite students to share and read their stories aloud to the class.

CALENDAR TIME

What is the Year?

- Point out today's date on the calendar, including the year.
- Write the date on the board.
- Focus on the year. Show ways to make the current year using four, five, or six addends.
- On the board, show one way to make the year using four addends. For example, for 2010 write $1000 + 1000 + 5 + 5$. **What other addition sentences can you think of?** See students' responses.
- You can use base-ten blocks to check your addition sentences.

Dinah-Might Adventures, LP

LESSON 1
Hundreds
OBJECTIVE   Relate hundreds, tens, and ones.

What's the Math?

 Common Core State Standards
DOMAIN: Number and Operations in Base Ten

Standards: 2.NBT.1, 2.NBT.1a, 2.NBT.1b
The wording of these standards can be found on page 286.

What Students Should Understand
- One hundred equals 10 tens. One hundred also equals 100 ones.
- You can use the fact that 1 hundred = 10 tens = 100 ones to tell how many tens and ones are in different amounts of hundreds.

What Students Should be Able to Do
Write how many hundreds, tens, and ones are shown by the base-ten blocks.

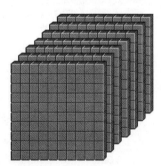

7 hundreds = 70 tens = 700 ones

 Building on the Essential Question

In this lesson, students will build upon the skills and concepts needed to answer the chapter's Essential Question "How can I use place value?"

Developing Vocabulary

 New Vocabulary

hundreds

Activity
- Discuss the word *hundreds* and write it on the board.
- Write the hundreds from 100 through 900. *What do these numbers have in common?* They are hundreds. Explain that any number with a value in the hundreds will appear on the far left in the hundreds place.
- Draw a place-value chart on the board. Write 471 on the place-value chart. *How many hundreds are in this number?* 4
- Repeat with other numbers in the hundreds.

ELL **ELL Support Strategy** Use this vocabulary activity to apply visual cues to understand concepts.

My Vocabulary Cards

Read the activity that matches the activity on the *hundreds* card. Then organize students in pairs or small groups. Have them discuss their answers.

IWB **Virtual Word Wall**

Add the vocabulary cards to the Virtual Word Wall for the chapter.

ELL Refer to the Multilingual eGlossary for interactive definitions in 13 languages.

Plan Online

Plan for your lesson by using the resources at
connectED.mcgraw-hill.com

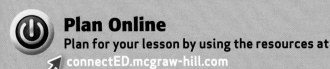

Digital Dashboard

Interactive Whiteboard Ready

Vocab

The eBook **Glossary** shows the definition of the word and has audio for each definition. The **eGlossary** provides definitions in 13 languages.

Watch

Watch as concepts are brought to life through **animations**, **songs**, and a variety of visual instruction.

Tools

Virtual Manipulatives with work mats allow teachers and students to model the lesson.

Check

Use **eAssessment** for online assignments and customized assessments.

Use the **Common Core Quick Check** before the lesson to assess students' retention of previously learned concepts.

Use the interactive **Self-Check Quiz** after the lesson to provide immediate feedback on lesson concepts.

eHelp

Digital and print resources assist students and parents in completing My Homework.

Games

Online games and **apps** provide extra practice for lesson concepts.

PD

Professional development videos help teachers gain a deeper understanding of the lesson concepts and strategies.

RtI

Support for **approaching**, **on-** and **beyond-level** students as well as **English Language Learners**.

Masters

Reteach and **Enrich** worksheets, **Manipulative Masters**, the **Problem of the Day**, and other blackline masters are available for each lesson.

---

1 LAUNCH THE LESSON

 If your students are well-versed in hundreds, you may choose to begin instruction with Step 2, **TEACH**.

You will need

☐ ten-frames
☐ thin line markers

Mathematical PRACTICE Modeling the Math

Distribute ten-frames and one thin-line marker to each student. Write the word *hundred* on the board, and write the number 100 beside it.

Review with students that 100 is a group of 10 tens. Have students fill each section of the ten-frame with 10 circles.

How many circles are in one section? 10 *In two sections?* 20 *How do you know?* There are 2 groups of 10, and that equals 20.

Have students count by 10s as they point to each section of the ten-frame.

How many circles did you draw in the entire ten-frame? 100

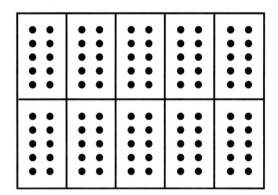

🕐 Begin core instruction here.

You will need

☐ yellow, green, and red crayons or colored pencils

Explore and Explain

Read the directions that are on the bottom of the student page. Have students color each stamp yellow to show ones.

How many ones are there? 100 ones

Have students circle groups of ten in green to show tens. Students may choose to circle rows or columns of 10 ones, or they may choose to circle 10 ones in other ways.

How many tens are there? 10 tens

Have students circle one hundred in red to show hundreds.

How many hundreds are there? 1 hundred

How many ones are in 100? 100 ones

How many tens are in 100? 10 tens

Vocabulary

Direct students' attention to *hundred* in See and Show. Ask them how it differs from the lesson title. It does not end in -s. Explain that a singular noun names one thing, while a plural noun names more than one thing. Tell them they should always write 1 hundred, 1 ten, and 1 one as singular nouns.

ELL **ELL Support Strategy** Use this information to develop oral language with a content-specific vocabulary.

See and Show

Help students work through the example at the top of the page. Look at and discuss the diagram on the page. Use base-ten blocks to demonstrate what is being shown. Have the students trace the dashed numbers as they work the problems.

Work through Exercises 1–4 as a class. In Exercises 1 and 2, students are going from hundreds to ones. In Exercises 3 and 4, students are going from ones to hundreds.

Mathematical PRACTICE ➌ **Talk Math**

Discuss with students "Is 100 the same as ten tens? How do you know?" Sample answer: Yes, because ten tens is 100 ones.

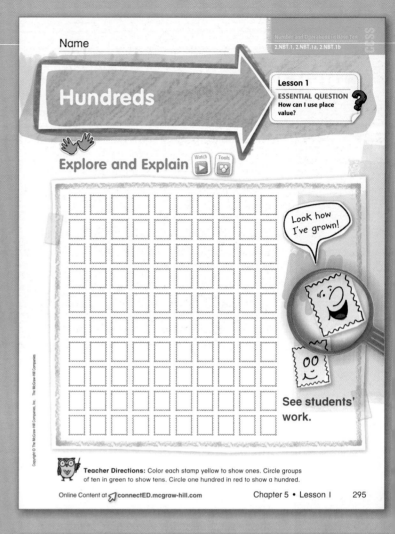

Name _____ Number and Operations in Base Ten
2.NBT.1, 2.NBT.1a, 2.NBT.1b

Hundreds

Lesson 1
ESSENTIAL QUESTION
How can I use place value?

Explore and Explain ▶ 🔧

Look how I've grown!

See students' work.

🦉 **Teacher Directions:** Color each stamp yellow to show ones. Circle groups of ten in green to show tens. Circle one hundred in red to show a hundred.

Online Content at connectED.mcgraw-hill.com   Chapter 5 • Lesson 1   295

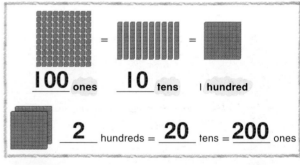

See and Show

Mathematical PRACTICE

100 ones = 10 tens = 1 hundred

_____2_____ hundreds = _____20_____ tens = _____200_____ ones

Write how many hundreds, tens, and ones.

1. _____1_____ hundred = _____10_____ tens = _____100_____ ones

2. _____3_____ hundreds = _____30_____ tens = _____300_____ ones

Write how many tens and hundreds.

3. 500 ones = _____50_____ tens = _____5_____ hundreds

4. 600 ones = _____60_____ tens = _____6_____ hundreds

Talk Math Is 100 the same as ten tens? How do you know?

296   Chapter 5 • Lesson 1

Name _____

On My Own

Write how many hundreds, tens, and ones.

5. __6__ hundreds = __60__ tens = __600__ ones

6. __4__ hundreds = __40__ tens = __400__ ones

7. __5__ hundreds = __50__ tens = __500__ ones

Write how many tens and hundreds.

8. 800 ones = __80__ tens = __8__ hundreds

9. 700 ones = __70__ tens = __7__ hundreds

Write how many hundreds, tens, or ones.

10. 500 = __50__ tens

11. 200 = __200__ ones

12. 400 = __4__ hundreds

13. 300 = __30__ tens

Chapter 5 • Lesson 1   297

Problem Solving

Mathematical
PRACTICE

14. Sara has a collection of coins. She puts them in 30 piles of 10. How many hundreds does she have?

__3__ hundreds

15. Kenny places his rock collection in 20 groups of 10. How many ones does he have?

 Come on rocks. Let's roll!

__200__ ones

16. Andreas counts 300 leaves on a tree. How many tens does he count?

__30__ tens

Write Math   How many ones are in 4 hundreds? How do you know?

Sample answer: There are 100 ones in 1 hundred,

so there are 400 ones in 4 hundreds.

298   Chapter 5 • Lesson 1

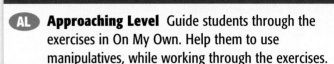

PRACTICE & APPLY

On My Own

Have students work through the exercises on this page independently. You may choose to assign exercises based on the chart below.

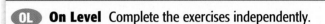

DIFFERENTIATED ASSIGNMENTS

AL Approaching Level Guide students through the exercises in On My Own. Help them to use manipulatives, while working through the exercises.

OL On Level Complete the exercises independently.

BL Beyond Level Complete the exercises independently without manipulatives.

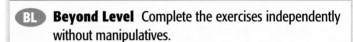
Common Error!

Students may have difficulty remembering how many 10s are in 100. Write 10 + 10 + 10 + 10 + 10 + 10 + 10 + 10 + 10 + 10 = 100. Count by tens together.

Problem Solving

Have students work through the problem-solving exercises on this page independently. If students struggle, have them use base-ten blocks to solve.

Mathematical
PRACTICE 2   In Exercise 15, students **reason abstractly and quantitatively.**

Write Math

This exercise asks students to build upon their understanding of concepts needed to answer the chapter's Essential Question.

AL APPROACHING LEVEL

IF my students struggle with hundreds,

THEN choose a resource:

→ Use the Reteach worksheet with small groups.

→ Go online for a Differentiated Instruction activity.

→ **Show a Model** Display a dime. *How much is this worth?* 10¢ Display a $1 bill. *How many cents is this worth?* 100¢ *How many dimes can I trade this for?* 10 dimes Show two $1 bills. Continue adding $1 bills up to $10. *How many $1 bills can I trade for this?* 10 one-dollar bills

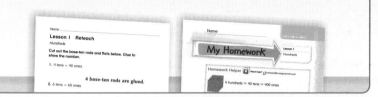

OL ON LEVEL

IF my students seem to know hundreds, but need more practice,

THEN choose a resource:

→ Assign My Homework.

→ Go online for a Differentiated Instruction activity.

BL BEYOND LEVEL

IF my students have mastered hundreds,

THEN choose a resource:

→ Use the Enrich worksheet in cooperative groups.

→ Assign My Homework.

→ Go online for a Differentiated Instruction activity.

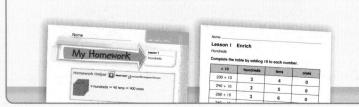

Name _____

AL Lesson I   Reteach
Hundreds

Cut out the base-ten rods and flats below. Glue to show the number.

1. 4 tens = 40 ones

    4 base-ten rods are glued.

2. 6 tens = 60 ones

    6 base-ten rods are glued.

3. 2 hundreds = 20 tens = 200 ones

    2 hundred flats are glued.

4. 3 hundreds = 30 tens = 300 ones

    3 hundred flats are glued.

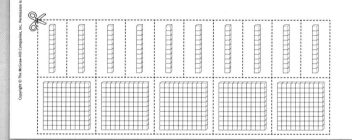

Name _____

BL Lesson I   Enrich
Hundreds

Complete the table by adding 10 to each number.

+ 10	hundreds	tens	ones
230 + 10	2	4	0
240 + 10	2	5	0
250 + 10	2	6	0
260 + 10	2	7	0
270 + 10	2	8	0
280 + 10	2	9	0

Complete this table, adding 100 and 10 to each number.

+100 and 10	hundreds	tens	ones
200 + 110	3	1	0
310 + 110	4	2	0
420 + 110	5	3	0
530 + 110	6	4	0
640 + 110	7	5	0
750 + 110	8	6	0

My Homework

Number and Operations in Base Ten
2.NBT.1, 2.NBT.1a, 2.NBT.1b

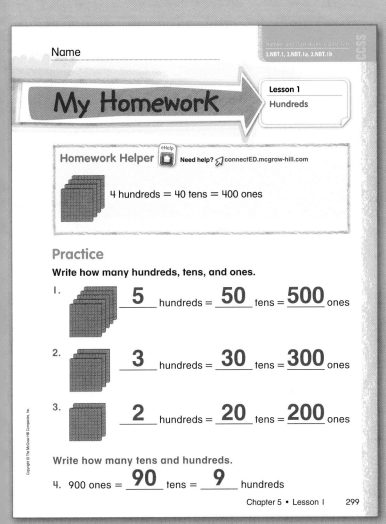

My Homework →

Lesson 1
Hundreds

Homework Helper [eHelp] Need help? connectED.mcgraw-hill.com

4 hundreds = 40 tens = 400 ones

Practice

Write how many hundreds, tens, and ones.

1. __5__ hundreds = __50__ tens = __500__ ones

2. __3__ hundreds = __30__ tens = __300__ ones

3. __2__ hundreds = __20__ tens = __200__ ones

Write how many tens and hundreds.

4. 900 ones = __90__ tens = __9__ hundreds

Chapter 5 • Lesson 1   299

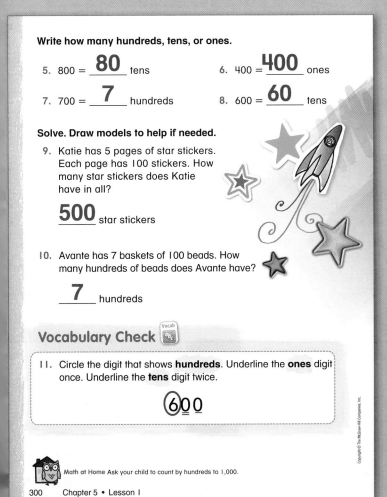

Write how many hundreds, tens, or ones.

5. 800 = __80__ tens

6. 400 = __400__ ones

7. 700 = __7__ hundreds

8. 600 = __60__ tens

Solve. Draw models to help if needed.

9. Katie has 5 pages of star stickers. Each page has 100 stickers. How many star stickers does Katie have in all?

__500__ star stickers

10. Avante has 7 baskets of 100 beads. How many hundreds of beads does Avante have?

__7__ hundreds

Vocabulary Check [Vocab]

11. Circle the digit that shows **hundreds**. Underline the **ones** digit once. Underline the **tens** digit twice.

⑥0̲0̲

Math at Home Ask your child to count by hundreds to 1,000.

---

4 WRAP IT UP

My Homework

Assign homework after successful completion of the lesson. Students who understand the concepts may skip the **Homework Helper** section.

Vocabulary Check [Vocab]

Students will learn *digit* in a later lesson. Explain that a digit is used to represent any of the following numbers: 0, 1, 2, 3, 4, 5, 6, 7, 8, or 9.

Formative Assessment

Ask students to tell you how many hundreds, tens, and ones are in the number 400. 4 hundreds, 40 tens, 400 ones

Line Up!

When students line up have them skip count aloud:

• Start with the first person in line and ending with the last person in line skip count by 10s to 200.

• Have students skip count by 100s up to 1,000.

• Ask students to skip count backwards by 100s from 1,000 down to 0.

When you get to the last one and have remaining students start over or move to the next one.

LESSON 2
Hundreds, Tens, and Ones

OBJECTIVE   Read, write, and model numbers to 999.

What's the Math?

 Common Core State Standards
DOMAIN: Number and Operations in Base Ten

Standards: 2.NBT.1, 2.NBT.1a, 2.NBT.1b, 2.NBT.3

The wording of these standards can be found on page 281–282.

What Students Should Understand
- A number can be represented in many ways. You can use base-ten blocks or a place-value chart. Numbers can also be written in standard form.

What Students Should be Able to Do
Use base-ten blocks to show 346.
Write how many hundreds, tens, and ones. Then write the number.

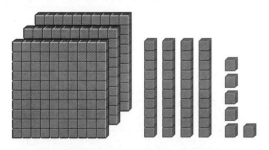

hundreds	tens	ones
3	4	6

 Building on the Essential Question
In this lesson, students will build upon the skills and concepts needed to answer the chapter's Essential Question "How can I use place value?"

Developing Vocabulary

Review Vocabulary
hundreds   tens
ones

Review Activity
- Write the words on the board. Ask students what they have learned about hundreds, tens, and ones in previous lessons.
- Have students preview the lesson by looking at headings, vocabulary words, and charts. Discuss with them how the base-ten blocks and place-value charts represent hundreds, tens, and ones.
- Ask the class what questions they have about the lesson. Encourage students to write any questions they have. Tell them to write signal phrases or signal words they encounter while completing this lesson that might help them answer their questions.

ELL **ELL Support Strategy** Use this vocabulary activity to recognize text features, such as signal words or phrases that help them with the math problems.

My Vocabulary Cards
Have students look at the set of cards for this chapter. Ask them to identify a word that names a number in this lesson's title. Sample answer: tens

IWB **Virtual Word Wall**
You may wish to add these review vocabulary cards to the Virtual Word Wall for the chapter.

ELL Refer to the Multilingual eGlossary for interactive definitions in 13 languages.

Plan Online
Plan for your lesson by using the resources at
connectED.mcgraw-hill.com

Digital Dashboard

Interactive Whiteboard Ready

Vocab
The eBook **Glossary** shows the definition of the word and has audio for each definition. The **eGlossary** provides definitions in 13 languages.

Watch
Watch as concepts are brought to life through **animations**, **songs**, and a variety of visual instruction.

Tools
Virtual Manipulatives with work mats allow teachers and students to model the lesson.

Check
Use **eAssessment** for online assignments and customized assessments.

Use the **Common Core Quick Check** before the lesson to assess students' retention of previously learned concepts.

Use the interactive **Self-Check Quiz** after the lesson to provide immediate feedback on lesson concepts.

eHelp
Digital and print resources assist students and parents in completing My Homework.

Games
Online games and **apps** provide extra practice for lesson concepts.

PD
Professional development videos help teachers gain a deeper understanding of the lesson concepts and strategies.

RtI
Support for **approaching**, **on-** and **beyond-level** students as well as **English Language Learners**.

Masters
Reteach and **Enrich** worksheets, **Manipulative Masters**, the **Problem of the Day**, and other blackline masters are available for each lesson.

1 LAUNCH THE LESSON

 If your students are well-versed in hundreds, tens, and ones, you may choose to begin instruction with Step 2, **TEACH.**

You will need
☐ base-ten blocks

Mathematical PRACTICE 4 Modeling the Math

Divide the class into 5 groups. Give each group base-ten blocks.

Have students use hundreds blocks to show 100. Then have them use tens blocks to show 100. Have them check their work by placing the tens blocks on top of the hundreds block.

How can you tell if your answers are correct? If the tens blocks completely cover the hundreds blocks with no tens left over, the answers are correct.

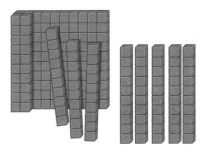

21ST CENTURY SKILLS

Communication

In this lesson, students learn multiple representations of a number. They learn the word(s) to express the number, they write the symbols or digits representing the number, and they present a visualization of the number through models. People relate to information in different ways. Being able to communicate a concept in multiple ways is a skill that can be applied in higher grades as well as in the workplace.

 Begin core instruction here.

You will need
☐ base-ten blocks
☐ WorkMat 7

Explore and Explain

Read the directions that are on the bottom of the student page. Discuss with students how they would model the number.

> *Which base-ten blocks will you use to model the number of cans?* **3 hundreds flats, 6 tens rods, and 7 unit cubes**

Discuss the number of ones, tens, and hundreds used. Have students write the number of ones, tens, and hundreds used.

> *How many ones did you use?* **7 ones** *Write that number in the ones place.*

> *How many tens are in the amount?* **6 tens** *Write that number in the tens place.*

> *What number will you write in the hundreds place?* **3** *Why?* **Sample answer: There are 3 hundreds in the number.**

Have students write the number below the chart.

> *How many cans did Mya collect? Write the number.* **367**

See and Show

Help students work through the example at the top of the page. Discuss the use of the base-ten blocks to show 427, and the placement of each digit. You may wish to provide extra examples if needed. Have them trace the dashed numbers as they work the problems.

Work through Exercises 1 and 2 as a class.

Mathematical PRACTICE 3 **Talk Math**

Discuss with students "What is the value of the 1 in 712, in 165, and in 381?" Sample answer: In 712, the value of the 1 is 10; in 165, the value of the 1 is 100; in 381, the value of the 1 is 1.

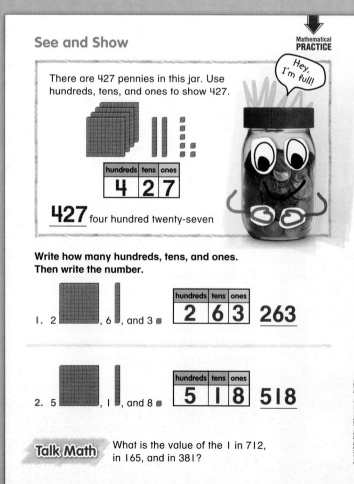

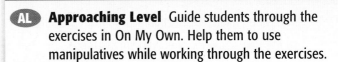
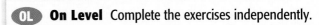
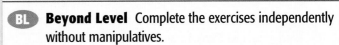

CORE INSTRUCTION

Name _____

On My Own

Write how many hundreds, tens, and ones.
Then write the number.

	hundreds	tens	ones	
3. 3 ▦, 8 ▮, and 2 ▪	3	8	2	**382**
4. 6 ▦, 4 ▮, and 3 ▪	6	4	3	**643**
5. 7 ▦, 0 ▮, and 9 ▪	7	0	9	**709**
6. 7 ▦, 2 ▮, and 1 ▪	7	2	1	**721**

Write how many hundreds, tens, and ones.

7. 684 = __6__ hundreds, __8__ tens, and __4__ ones

8. 805 = __8__ hundreds, __0__ tens, and __5__ ones

9. 290 = __2__ hundreds, __9__ tens, and __0__ ones

Copyright © The McGraw-Hill Companies, Inc.

Chapter 5 • Lesson 2   303

Problem Solving

Mathematical PRACTICE

10. This number has 4 hundreds and 2 ones.
The number of tens is the digit between the
number of ones and the number of hundreds.
What is the number?

    432

You can view the largest, most complete
T. Rex at The Field Museum in Chicago,
Illinois. It has more than 200 bones. Look
at the number 200.

11. What number is in the hundreds place?

    2

12. What number is in the tens place?

    0

13. What number is in the ones place?

    Grrrrr!

    0

Write Math What do hundreds, tens, and ones tell you
about a number?

__Sample answer: If you know the place value of a__

__number, you can tell how large or small a number is.__

---

③ PRACTICE & APPLY

On My Own

Have students work through the exercises on this page
independently. You may choose to assign exercises based on the
chart below.

DIFFERENTIATED ASSIGNMENTS

AL **Approaching Level** Guide students through the
exercises in On My Own. Help them to use
manipulatives while working through the exercises.

OL **On Level** Complete the exercises independently.

BL **Beyond Level** Complete the exercises independently
without manipulatives.

Common Error!
Students may have difficulty remembering the
hundreds, tens, and ones places. Have students use
workmats to assist them.

Problem Solving

Have students work through the problem-solving exercises on
this page independently.

Mathematical PRACTICE 4 In Exercises 11-13, students **model with
mathematics.**

Write Math

This exercise asks students to build upon their understanding of
concepts needed to answer the chapter's Essential Question.

RESPONSE TO INTERVENTION
DIFFERENTIATED INSTRUCTION

AL **APPROACHING LEVEL**

IF my students struggle with hundreds, tens, and ones,

THEN choose a resource:

→ Use a Differentiated Instruction activity from p. 285B.

→ Use the Reteach worksheet with small groups.

→ Go online for a Differentiated Instruction activity.

→ **Place-Value Chart** Draw a place-value chart. Write 7 in the ones place. *Is the 7 in the ones, tens, or hundreds place?* ones Have students make a model on a whiteboard and hold it up. Repeat the procedure, writing a 7 in the tens place and a 0 in the ones place. Then write a 7 in the hundreds place and a 0 in the tens and ones places.

OL **ON LEVEL**

IF my students seem to know hundreds, tens, and ones, but need more practice,

THEN choose a resource:

→ Assign My Homework.

→ Go online for a Differentiated Instruction activity.

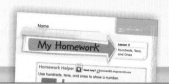

BL **BEYOND LEVEL**

IF my students have mastered hundreds, tens, and ones,

THEN choose a resource:

→ Use the Enrich worksheet in cooperative groups.

→ Assign My Homework.

→ Go online for a Differentiated Instruction activity.

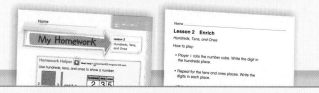

AL Name _____

Lesson 2   Reteach
Hundreds, Tens, and Ones

> You can use pictures to represent hundreds, tens, and ones.
>
> | 126 | __1__ hundred | __2__ tens | __6__ ones |
> |---|---|---|---|

Write and draw how many hundreds, tens, and ones.

1. 192

__1__ hundred(s)	__9__ tens	__2__ ones

2. 267

__2__ hundred(s)	__6__ tens	__7__ ones

Write the number.

3. 3 hundreds 2 tens 5 ones = __325__

4. 2 hundreds 4 tens 9 ones = __249__

5. 8 hundreds 7 tens 0 ones = __870__

BL Name _____

Lesson 2   Enrich
Hundreds, Tens, and Ones

How to play:

• Player 1 rolls the number cube. Write the digit in the hundreds place.

• Repeat for the tens and ones places. Write the digits in each place.

• Write the final number on the line.

• Player 2 takes a turn.

• Compare the numbers. Check the box under the greater number.

• Play three more times. Record the results on a separate piece of paper.

Player 1	Player 2		Player 1	Player 2
Roll	Roll		Roll	Roll
_ _ _	_ _ _		_ _ _	_ _ _
Final	Final		Final	Final
Greater ☐	Greater ☐		Greater ☐	Greater ☐

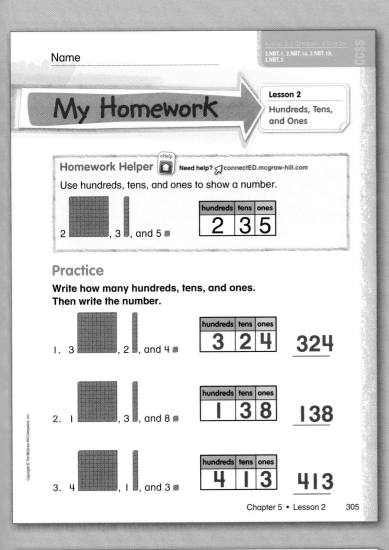

Name _____

2.NBT.1, 2.NBT.1a, 2.NBT.1b, 2.NBT.3

My Homework

Lesson 2
Hundreds, Tens, and Ones

Homework Helper Need help? connectED.mcgraw-hill.com

Use hundreds, tens, and ones to show a number.

2 , 3 , and 5

hundreds	tens	ones
2	3	5

Practice

Write how many hundreds, tens, and ones.
Then write the number.

1. 3 , 2 , and 4

hundreds	tens	ones
3	2	4

324

2. 1 , 3 , and 8

hundreds	tens	ones
1	3	8

138

3. 4 , 1 , and 3

hundreds	tens	ones
4	1	3

413

Chapter 5 • Lesson 2   305

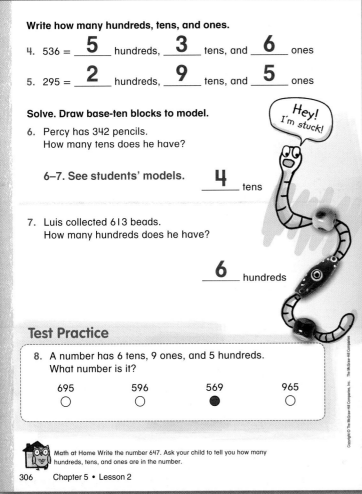

Write how many hundreds, tens, and ones.

4. 536 = **5** hundreds, **3** tens, and **6** ones

5. 295 = **2** hundreds, **9** tens, and **5** ones

Solve. Draw base-ten blocks to model.

6. Percy has 342 pencils.
   How many tens does he have?

   6–7. See students' models.   **4** tens

   Hey! I'm stuck!

7. Luis collected 613 beads.
   How many hundreds does he have?

   6 hundreds

Test Practice

8. A number has 6 tens, 9 ones, and 5 hundreds.
   What number is it?

   695 ○   596 ○   569 ●   965 ○

Math at Home Write the number 647. Ask your child to tell you how many hundreds, tens, and ones are in the number.

306   Chapter 5 • Lesson 2

---

4 WRAP IT UP

CCSS

My Homework

Assign homework after successful completion of the lesson. Students who understand the concepts may skip the **Homework Helper** section.

Test Practice

Diagnose Student Errors

Class trends in wrong answers may indicate common errors or misconceptions.

695 placed digits in order listed in problem

596 tens and ones are incorrect

569 correct

965 hundreds and one are incorrect

Formative Assessment

Have students tell you what number has 2 tens, 5 hundreds, and 0 ones. 520

Line Up!

When students line up, play "before and after."

- Give students the hundreds number 400. Ask a volunteer to tell you what hundred comes before and after 400. 300, 500

- Repeat with other hundreds.

LESSON 3
Place Value to 1,000

OBJECTIVE   Identify and use words, models, and expanded form to represent numbers to 999.

What's the Math?

 Common Core State Standards
DOMAIN: Number and Operations in Base Ten

Standards: 2.NBT.1, 2.NBT.1a, 2.NBT.1b, 2.NBT.3
The wording of these standards can be found on page 286.

What Students Should Understand
• Place value tells the value of a digit in a number.
• A number can be written in expanded form, which shows the value of each digit.

What Students Should be Able to Do
Write 2 hundreds, 3 tens, and 8 ones in expanded form. Then write the number.

$$200 + 30 + 8 \quad = \quad 238$$

expanded form   standard form

 Building on the Essential Question
In this lesson, students will build upon the skills and concepts needed to answer the chapter's Essential Question "How can I use place value?"

Developing Vocabulary

 New Vocabulary

place value   digit
expanded form

Activity
• Discuss the word *expanded form* and write it on the board.
• Write a three-digit number on the board that has significance for students, such as the school's address or the current page number in a textbook.
• Write 319 in expanded form: $300 + 10 + 9$. Explain that this is the expanded form of 319.
• Have a volunteer come to the board and repeat the activity, using a different three-digit number.

ELL **ELL Support Strategy** Use this vocabulary activity to provide multiple exposures to the term *expanded form*.

My Vocabulary Cards
Ask students to skim the lesson. Tell them to identify the three vocabulary words. Then read the activity for each card.

IWB **Virtual Word Wall**
Add the vocabulary cards to the Virtual Word Wall for the chapter.

ELL Refer to the Multilingual eGlossary for interactive definitions in 13 languages.

Plan Online
Plan for your lesson by using the resources at
 connectED.mcgraw-hill.com

Digital Dashboard

Interactive Whiteboard Ready

Vocab

The eBook **Glossary** shows the definition of the word and has audio for each definition. The **eGlossary** provides definitions in 13 languages.

Watch

Watch as concepts are brought to life through **animations**, **songs**, and a variety of visual instruction.

Tools

Virtual Manipulatives with work mats allow teachers and students to model the lesson.

Check

Use **eAssessment** for online assignments and customized assessments.

Use the **Common Core Quick Check** before the lesson to assess students' retention of previously learned concepts.

Use the interactive **Self-Check Quiz** after the lesson to provide immediate feedback on lesson concepts.

eHelp

Digital and print resources assist students and parents in completing My Homework.

Games

Online games and **apps** provide extra practice for lesson concepts.

PD

Professional development videos help teachers gain a deeper understanding of the lesson concepts and strategies.

RtI

Support for **approaching**, **on**- and **beyond-level** students as well as **English Language Learners**.

Masters

Reteach and **Enrich** worksheets, **Manipulative Masters**, the **Problem of the Day**, and other blackline masters are available for each lesson.

---

1 LAUNCH THE LESSON

If your students are well-versed in place value, you may choose to begin instruction with Step 2, **TEACH**.

You will need
☐ base-ten blocks
☐ Work Mat 7

Mathematical PRACTICE  Modeling the Math

Write 100 on the board and have students place one hundred flat in the hundreds section of the place-value chart.

What number did you show? 100

If you add one to the workmat, how will the number shown change? It will be one more.

Write $100 + 1 = 101$ on the board.

Write $1 + 20 + 5$ on the board. As a class, discuss how base-ten blocks can be used to show the number.

 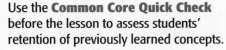

# TEACH

 Begin core instruction here.

You will need

☐ number cube

Explore and Explain

Read the directions that are at the bottom of the student page. Model rolling a number cube 3 times to generate a three-digit number. Have students use their own number cube to generate their own three-digit number at their desks.

Roll the number cube once. Write the number you roll in the hundreds place of the place value chart. Roll the number cube a second time. Write the number you roll in the tens place of the chart. Roll the number a third time. Write the number you rolled in the ones place.

Call on 4–5 students to discuss the number of hundreds, tens, and ones in the number they generated. Next, using the blank number sentence, guide students in writing the value of each number in their place-value chart.

How many hundreds are in your number? Write the hundreds on the first blank. How many tens are in your number? Write the tens on the second blank. How many ones? Write the ones on the third blank.

Ask students to write the number after the equals sign.

See and Show

Help students work through the example at the top of the page. Discuss the vocabulary introduced in this lesson. Make sure you point out what each highlighted terms refers to in the example. Use the illustrations to emphasize that expanded form shows the value of each digit. Have them trace the dashed numbers as they work the problems.

Work through Exercises 1–3 as a class.

Mathematical PRACTICE 3 **Talk Math**

Discuss with students "How are 562 and 265 the same? How are they different?" Sample answer: 562 and 265 have the same digits and the same number of tens. They have different values and a different number of hundreds and ones.

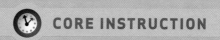
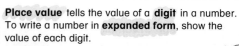

Name _____

2.NBT.1, 2.NBT.1a, 2.NBT1.b, 2.NBT.3

Place Value to 1,000

Lesson 3
ESSENTIAL QUESTION
How can I use place value?

Explore and Explain

hundreds	tens	ones

_____ + _____ + _____ = _____

See students' work.

Teacher Directions: Roll a number cube. Write that number in the hundreds place. Roll again. Write that number in the tens place. Roll again. Write that number in the ones place. Write the value of each number and their sum when added together.

Online Content at ⏵connectED.mcgraw-hill.com   Chapter 5 • Lesson 3   307

See and Show

Mathematical PRACTICE

Place value tells the value of a **digit** in a number. To write a number in **expanded form**, show the value of each digit.

hundreds	tens	ones
2	1	3

Helpful Hint
When you write a number in expanded form, you show the value of each digit.

2 hundreds   I ten   3 ones
$200 + 10 + 3 = 213$

Write each number in expanded form.
Then write the number.

1. I hundred, 4 tens, and 9 ones

$100 + 40 + 9 = 149$

2. 3 hundreds, 2 tens, and 5 ones

$300 + 20 + 5 = 325$

3. 5 hundreds, 7 tens, and I one

$500 + 70 + 1 = 571$

Talk Math   How are 562 and 265 the same? How are they different?

308   Chapter 5 • Lesson 3

307-308 **Chapter 5** Place Value to 1,000

Name _____

On My Own

**Write each number in expanded form.
Then write the number.**

4. 7 hundreds, 0 tens, and 2 ones

$$\underline{700} + \underline{0} + \underline{2} = \underline{702}$$

5. 4 hundreds, 2 tens, and 1 one

$$\underline{400} + \underline{20} + \underline{1} = \underline{421}$$

Circle the value of the green digit.

6. 965

⦿900   90   9

7. 673

300   30   ③

Write the number.

8. $800 + 30 + 3 = \underline{833}$

9. $200 + 90 + 0 = \underline{290}$

10. $700 + 10 + 9 = \underline{719}$

11. $900 + 80 + 9 = \underline{989}$

Write the number in expanded form.

12. $254 = \underline{200} + \underline{50} + \underline{4}$

13. $526 = \underline{500} + \underline{20} + \underline{6}$

Problem Solving

Mathematical **PRACTICE**

14. The number of raisins in a box has 4 in the ones place, 2 in the hundreds place, and 5 in the tens place. How many raisins are in the box?

$\underline{254}$ raisins

15. Sharon has a pile of 100 erasers, a pile of 20 erasers, and a pile of 5 erasers. How many erasers does Sharon have in all?

Erasers make me smile!

$\underline{125}$ erasers

16. Luis wrote a story. The number of pages in his story has 1 hundred, 7 tens, and 9 ones. How many pages are in his story?

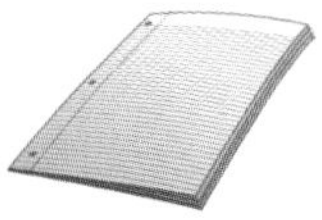

$\underline{179}$ pages

HOT Problem A number has three digits. Which digit has the greatest value and why?

Sample answer: The digit in the hundreds place

will have the greatest value because it represents

hundreds. The other two digits represent tens or ones.

On My Own

Have students work through the exercises on this page independently. You may choose to assign exercises based on the chart below.

DIFFERENTIATED ASSIGNMENTS

AL Approaching Level Guide students through the exercises in On My Own. Help them to use manipulatives while they work through the exercises.

OL On Level Complete the exercises independently.

BL Beyond Level Complete the exercises independently without manipulatives.

Common Error!

Students may have difficulty writing numbers in expanded form. Tell them the digit in the hundreds place is always followed by two zeros. The digit in the tens place is always followed by one zero.

Problem Solving

Have students work through the problem-solving exercises on this page independently.

Mathematical **PRACTICE 7** In Exercise 15, students **look for and make use of structure.**

HOT Problem This exercise asks students to build upon their understanding of concepts needed to answer the chapter's Essential Question.

RtI RESPONSE TO INTERVENTION

DIFFERENTIATED INSTRUCTION

AL APPROACHING LEVEL

IF my students struggle with place value,

THEN choose a resource:

→ Use the Reteach worksheet with small groups.

→ Go online for a Differentiated Instruction activity.

→ **Show a Model** Write 1,000 in a Place-Value Chart. *What number is in the hundreds place?* 0 *thousands place?* 1 Students write their responses on a whiteboard and hold it up. Repeat the procedure with 950.

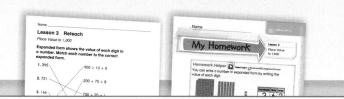

OL ON LEVEL

IF my students seem to know place value, but need more practice,

THEN choose a resource:

→ Use a Differentiated Instruction activity from p. 285B.

→ Assign My Homework.

→ Go online for a Differentiated Instruction activity.

BL BEYOND LEVEL

IF my students have mastered place value,

THEN choose a resource:

→ Use the Enrich worksheet in cooperative groups.

→ Assign My Homework.

→ Go online for a Differentiated Instruction activity.

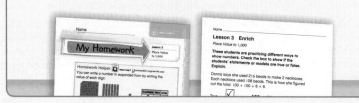

AL Name _____

Lesson 3 Reteach
Place Value to 1,000

Expanded form shows the value of each digit in a number. Match each number to the correct expanded form.

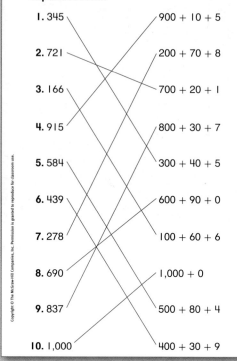

1. 345
2. 721
3. 166
4. 915
5. 584
6. 439
7. 278
8. 690
9. 837
10. 1,000

900 + 10 + 5
200 + 70 + 8
700 + 20 + 1
800 + 30 + 7
300 + 40 + 5
600 + 90 + 0
100 + 60 + 6
1,000 + 0
500 + 80 + 4
400 + 30 + 9

BL Name _____

Lesson 3 Enrich
Place Value to 1,000

These students are practicing different ways to show numbers. Check the box to show if the students' statements or models are true or false. Explain.

Donna says she used 216 beads to make 2 necklaces. Each necklace used 108 beads. This is how she figured out the total: 100 + 100 + 8 + 8.

True ✓ because **108 + 108 = 216**

False ☐ because _____

Patrick wants to show the number of students in his school. There are 643 students in the school. This is how he shows the number: 600 + 4 + 3.

True ☐ because _____

False ✓ because **600 + 40 + 3 = 643**

This is how Diego modeled 253.

True ✓ because **2 hundreds + 5 tens + 3 ones = 253**

False ☐ because _____

Name _____

2.NBT.1, 2.NBT.1a, 2.NBT.1b, 2.NBT.3 CCSS

My Homework

Lesson 3
Place Value
to 1,000

Homework Helper   Need help? connectED.mcgraw-hill.com

You can write a number in expanded form by writing the value of each digit.

hundreds	tens	ones
2	6	3

2 hundreds   6 tens   3 ones

200   +   60   +   3   = 263

Practice

Write each number in expanded form. Then write the number.

1. 2 hundreds, 6 tens, and 8 ones

   $\underline{200} + \underline{60} + \underline{8} = \underline{268}$

2. 3 hundreds, 1 ten, and 5 ones

   $\underline{300} + \underline{10} + \underline{5} = \underline{315}$

3. 6 hundreds, 0 tens, and 2 ones

   $\underline{600} + \underline{0} + \underline{2} = \underline{602}$

Chapter 5 • Lesson 3   311

Write the number in expanded form.

4. $637 = \underline{600} + \underline{30} + \underline{7}$

5. $742 = \underline{700} + \underline{40} + \underline{2}$

6. $295 = \underline{200} + \underline{90} + \underline{5}$

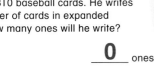
Here's what I'll look like on my baseball card!
14
Joe

7. Joe has 310 baseball cards. He writes the number of cards in expanded form. How many ones will he write?

   $\underline{0}$ ones

8. Trey reads that 482 people went to the baseball game. How can Trey show this number of people in expanded form?

   $\underline{400} + \underline{80} + \underline{2}$

Vocabulary Check

Circle the numbers that show the word below.

9. expanded form   300 + 42   (300 + 40 + 2)   3 + 4 + 2

 Math at Home Have your child tell you a three-digit number. Then ask your child to tell you the value of the first digit.

My Homework

Assign homework after successful completion of the lesson. Students who understand the concepts may skip the **Homework Helper** section.

Vocabulary Check

Have students refer to the My Vocabulary Card for a visual example of *expanded form*.

Formative Assessment

Have students find the value of 800 + 20 + 8. 828

Have students write 567 in expanded form. 500 + 60 + 7

MY Learning Stations

Use the game **Butterfly Fun** after this lesson. The Teacher Guide provides suggestions for differentiated instruction.

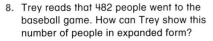

Line Up!

When students line up, give them numbers to write in expanded form.

Check My Progress

Use this as a formative assessment to determine if your students are struggling, and if so, with which topics they struggle. The criteria for differentiation are on the next page.

Vocabulary Check

Ask students to identify the vocabulary word that is plural.
hundreds

ELL **ELL Support Strategy** Use this vocabulary activity to demonstrate understanding by selecting the correct word.

Concept Check

These concepts are covered in Lessons 1–3.

Exercises	Concept	Review Lesson
5–6	Hundreds	1
7–9	Hundreds, tens, and ones	2
10–11	Place value to 1,000	3

Problem Solving

Exercise 12 uses a word problem to check for understanding of the same concepts.

Test Practice

Diagnose Student Errors

Class trends in wrong answers may indicate common errors or misconceptions.

512 5 is in the hundreds place
215 5 is in the ones place
152 correct
125 5 is in the ones place

Name _____

Check My Progress

Vocabulary Check

Draw lines to match.

1. hundreds
2. expanded form
3. place value
4. digit

500 + 60 + 3

hundreds	tens	ones
5	6	3

3

563

Concept Check

Write how many tens and hundreds.

5. 900 ones = **90** tens = **9** hundreds
6. 600 ones = **60** tens = **6** hundreds

Write how many hundreds, tens, or ones.

7. 300 = **300** ones
8. 400 = **4** tens

Chapter 5   313

Write how many hundreds, tens, and ones. Then write the number.

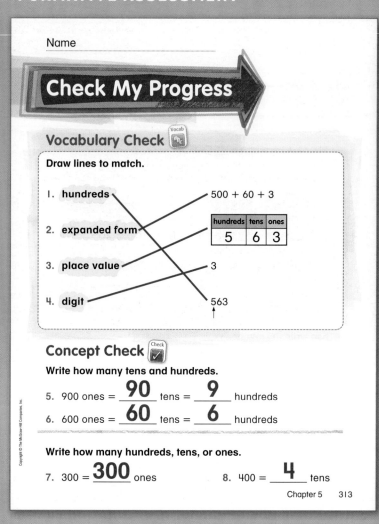

9. 8 _____ , 2 _____ , 1 _____

hundreds	tens	ones
8	2	1

821

Write each number in expanded form. Then write the number.

10. five hundred sixty-six

500 + **60** + **6** = **566**

11. nine hundred ten

900 + **10** + **0** = **910**

12. Janie is thinking of a number. It has 8 ones and 9 tens. It has the same amount of hundreds as tens. What is the number?

998

Test Practice

13. A number has a 5 in the tens place. The number of ones is 3 less than the number of tens. The number of hundreds is 1 less than the number of ones. What is the number?

512	215	152	125
○	○	●	○

314   Chapter 5

Name _____

Check My Progress *(Lessons 1 through 3)*

Write how many hundreds, tens, and ones.
Then write the number.

1.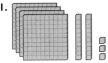

   __4__ hundreds __2__ tens __3__ ones
   __423__

2.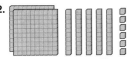

   __2__ hundreds __5__ tens __6__ ones
   __256__

Write each number in expanded form.
Then write the number.

3. 3 hundreds 5 tens 4 ones

   __300__ + __50__ + __4__ = __354__

4. 2 hundreds 9 tens 6 ones

   __200__ + __90__ + __6__ = __296__

5. Makenna is writing that there are 365 days in a year. How can she show this number in expanded form?

   __300__ + __60__ + __5__ = __365__

RESPONSE TO INTERVENTION

Rtl

CCSS

DIFFERENTIATED INSTRUCTION

AL ▸ STRATEGIC INTERVENTION

(Approaching Grade Level)

IF students miss 7 or more in Exercises 1-13,

THEN choose a resource:

→ Check My Progress
→ Self-Check Quiz
→ Use the Reteach worksheets.

OL ▸ ON LEVEL

IF students miss 3 to 4 in Exercises 1-13,

THEN choose a resource:

→ Chapter Project
→ Proceed to the next lesson.

BL ▸ BEYOND LEVEL

IF students miss 2 or less in Exercise 1-13,

THEN choose a resource:

→ Chapter Project
→ Use the Enrich worksheets.
→ Proceed to the next lesson.

LESSON 4

Problem Solving
STRATEGY: Use Logical Reasoning
OBJECTIVE Use logical reasoning to solve problems.

What's the Math?

 Common Core State Standards
DOMAIN: Number and Operations in Base Ten

Standards: 2.NBT.1, 2.NBT.1a, 2.NBT.1b, 2.NBT.3
The wording of these standards can be found on page 286.

Mathematical PRACTICE  **2** Reason abstractly and quantitatively.

What Students Should Understand

• You can use logical reasoning to solve word problems.

• First, make sure you understand the meaning of the problem. Determine what facts are important and what question is being asked. Then make a plan and use it to solve the problem.

What Students Should be Able to Do

Students should be able to implement the following four-step plan for problem-solving.

1 Understand

Underline what you know. Circle what you need to find.

2 Plan

How will I solve this problem?

3 Solve

Use logical reasoning to carry out the plan for a solution.

4 Check

Is the answer reasonable? Explain.

Mathematical PRACTICE

The Mathematical Practices are especially evident in problem-solving situations, in which students connect procedures and processes with mathematical understanding. In this lesson, the following Mathematical Practices are addressed.

1 Make sense of problems and persevere in solving them.

2 Reason abstractly and quantitatively.

Developing the Strategy

What's the Strategy?

Use Logical Reasoning We use logical reasoning in daily living. When we encounter a problem we have to think of the steps needed to come to a solution. In mathematics, we use it as one of many strategies to help us solve problems. Students will use logical reasoning to solve a problem in this lesson. This helps students think through problems and plan how to solve in a logical and efficient manner.

Example:

There are ducks, turtles, and geese in a pond. There are three ducks and five turtles. If there are more geese than ducks and more turtles than geese, how many geese are in the pond?

Logical reasoning can be used to solve this word problem. Students know that there are more geese than ducks, and more turtles than geese. Using the information given, it is logical there are 4 geese.

Other Strategies:

Other strategies that have been taught and that students may choose to use in the Review the Strategies section are:

• Look for a pattern

• Write a number sentence

ELL Signal Words Encourage English-language learners to identify signal words or signal phrases, such as *draw* or *odd number*, as they read word problems.

Plan Online
Plan for your lesson by using the resources at
connectED.mcgraw-hill.com

Digital Dashboard

 Vocab

The eBook **Glossary** shows the definition of the word and has audio for each definition. The **eGlossary** provides definitions in 13 languages.

 Tools

Virtual Manipulatives along with work mats allow teachers and students to model the lesson.

 Check

Use **eAssessment** for online assignments and customized assessments.

Use the **Common Core Quick Check** before the lesson to assess students' retention of previously learned concepts.

 eHelp

Digital and print resources assist students and parents in completing My Homework.

 PD

Professional development videos help teachers gain a deeper understanding of the lesson concepts and strategies.

 RtI

Support for **approaching**, **on-** and **beyond-level** students as well as **English Language Learners**.

 Masters

Reteach and **Enrich** worksheets, **Manipulative Masters**, the **Problem of the Day**, and other blackline masters are available for each lesson.

---

1 LAUNCH THE LESSON

 If your students are well-versed in problem solving, you may choose to begin instruction with Step 2, **TEACH**.

Review

Read the following problem to students. Have them work in pairs to find the missing digits.

Keith thought of a three-digit number. The sum of the digits is 4. Two of the digits are odd. The middle digit is 0. The first digit is less than the last digit. What is the number? 103

$$ \underline{\quad\quad}\ \underline{\quad 0 \quad}\ \underline{\quad\quad} $$

🕐 **Begin core instruction here.**

Problem Solving

1 Understand

Reread the problem with the students. Point out information as you read it.

2 Plan

Discuss several ideas. Lead the students towards the logical reasoning needed to solve the problem.

3 Solve

Work through the problem using the student page with the students. Discuss with them how to solve the problem using logical reasoning step-by-step.

4 Check

Discuss why the answer makes sense. Try to develop a sense of reasoning.

Practice the Strategy

1 Understand

Reread the problem with the students. Ask students to point out information that is important as you read it.

2 Plan

Lead the students in discussing several ideas. Direct the students toward the correct plan using logical reasoning to solve the problem.

3 Solve

Work through the problem step-by-step using the student page with the class. Show how to solve it using logical reasoning.

4 Check

Discuss why the answer makes sense. Try to develop a sense of reasoning.

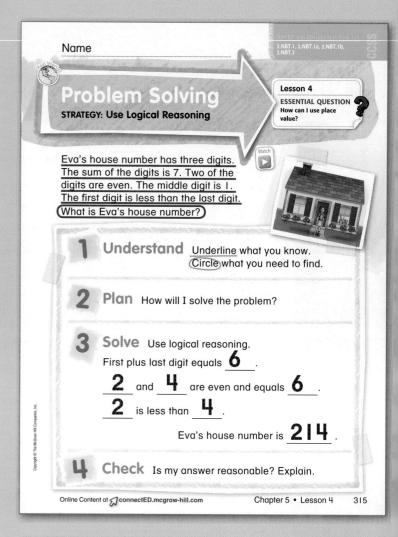

Name _____

2.NBT.1, 2.NBT.1a, 2.NBT.1b, 2.NBT.3

Problem Solving
STRATEGY: Use Logical Reasoning

Lesson 4
ESSENTIAL QUESTION
How can I use place value?

Eva's house number has three digits. The sum of the digits is 7. Two of the digits are even. The middle digit is 1. The first digit is less than the last digit. What is Eva's house number?

1 Understand Underline what you know. Circle what you need to find.

2 Plan How will I solve the problem?

3 Solve Use logical reasoning.
First plus last digit equals __6__.
__2__ and __4__ are even and equals __6__.
__2__ is less than __4__.
Eva's house number is __214__.

4 Check Is my answer reasonable? Explain.

Online Content at connectED.mcgraw-hill.com   Chapter 5 • Lesson 4   315

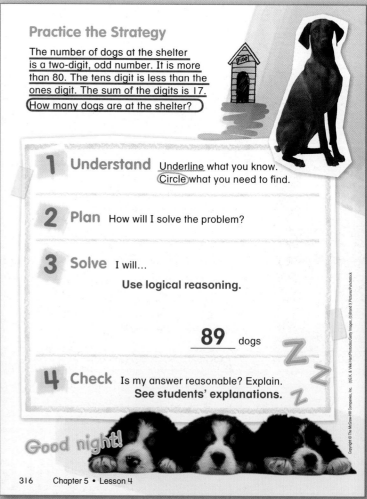

Practice the Strategy

The number of dogs at the shelter is a two-digit, odd number. It is more than 80. The tens digit is less than the ones digit. The sum of the digits is 17. How many dogs are at the shelter?

1 Understand Underline what you know. Circle what you need to find.

2 Plan How will I solve the problem?

3 Solve I will...
Use logical reasoning.

__89__ dogs

4 Check Is my answer reasonable? Explain.
See students' explanations.

Good night!

316   Chapter 5 • Lesson 4

Apply the Strategy

1. A number has three digits. The digit in the hundreds place is the difference of 4 and 2. The digit in the tens place is the sum of 2 and 3. The digit in the ones place is 2 more than the digit in the tens place. What is the number?

<u>**257**</u>

2. Sylvia writes this number: three ones, two tens, and seven hundreds. What number is it?

<u>**723**</u>

3. Ruby is trying to solve a number riddle. The digit in the tens place is less than 2. It is an odd number. The number in the hundreds place is greater than 8. The number in the ones place is the sum of 6 and 3. What is the number?

I LOVE riddles!

<u>**919**</u>

Chapter 5 • Lesson 4   317

Review the Strategies

Choose a strategy
• Make a model.
• Write a number sentence.
• Find a pattern.

4. Paco puts pennies into three groups. He counts 80 pennies in the first group, 3 pennies in the second group, and 500 pennies in the third group. How many pennies does he have?

<u>**583**</u> pennies

5. Ella's family is going to visit her cousins. They will drive for 3 days. Each day they will drive 60 miles. How many miles will they drive in all?

<u>**180**</u> miles

6. Jamie ate 20 cherries on Monday. She ate 20 cherries on Tuesday. She ate 20 cherries on Wednesday. If she continues, how many cherries will Jamie have eaten by Thursday?

<u>**80**</u> cherries

Mathematical
PRACTICE 1 Apply the Strategy

Have students work through the exercises on this page independently. You may choose to assign exercises based on the chart below.

DIFFERENTIATED ASSIGNMENTS

AL **Approaching Level** Pose simpler problems for the exercises given on the student page. Then demonstrate how to use logical reasoning to solve each simplified problem.

OL **On Level** Have students work through the problems independently using logical reasoning.

BL **Beyond Level** Have students work all the problems choosing what strategy to use.

Review the Strategies

Have students work through the problem-solving exercises on this page independently. They can use these strategies.

• Find a pattern
• Make a model
• Write a number sentence

RtI RESPONSE TO INTERVENTION

DIFFERENTIATED INSTRUCTION

AL **APPROACHING LEVEL**

IF my students struggle with using logical reasoning,

THEN choose a resource:

→ Use the Reteach worksheet with small groups.

→ Go online for a Differentiated Instruction activity.

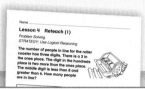

OL **ON LEVEL**

IF my students seem to know how to use logical reasoning, but need more practice,

THEN choose a resource:

→ Assign My Homework.

→ Go online for a Differentiated Instruction activity.

BL **BEYOND LEVEL**

IF my students have mastered using logical reasoning,

THEN choose a resource:

→ Use a Differentiated Instruction activity from p. 285B.

→ Use the Enrich worksheet in cooperative groups.

→ Assign My Homework.

→ Go online for a Differentiated Instruction activity.

AL Name _____

Lesson 4   Reteach (1)

Problem Solving
STRATEGY: Use Logical Reasoning

The number of people in line for the roller coaster has three digits. There is a 3 in the ones place. The digit in the hundreds place is two more than the ones place. The middle digit is less than 8 and greater than 6. How many people are in line?

Step 1 Understand	**What do I know?** There is a 3 in the ones place. The digit in the hundreds place is two more than the ones place. The middle digit is less than 8 and greater than 6. **What do I need to find?** The number of people in line.
Step 2 Plan	**How will I solve the problem?** Use logical reasoning.
Step 3 Solve	**Write the digits you already know.** __7__ is greater than 6 and less than 8. The number of people in line is __573__.
Step 4 Check	Is my answer reasonable? Explain. **See students' work.**

AL Name _____

Lesson 4   Reteach (2)

Problem Solving
STRATEGY: Use Logical Reasoning

Apply the strategy to solve.

1. Lee is training for a marathon. The number of miles he ran has two digits. The digit in the ones place is an even number less than 4. The number in the tens place is an odd number less than 3. How many miles did Lee run?

   __12__ miles

2. Bethany wrote this number: zero ones, 8 hundreds, and 1 ten. What number is it?

   __810__

3. Jacob saw a three-digit number on a street sign. The ones digit was the sum of 3 and 4. The tens digit was two less than the ones digit. The hundreds digit was the difference of 5 − 1. What number did Jacob see?

   __457__

BL Name _____

Lesson 4   Enrich

Problem Solving
STRATEGY: Use Logical Reasoning

Use logical reasoning to solve. Write the number of hundreds, tens, and ones.

1. I am a number between 400 and 500. My ones digit is 3 more than my tens digit. The sum of my digits is 13. What number am I?

hundreds	tens	ones
4	3	6

2. I am a number with 8 tens. The digit in my ones place is 4 more than the digit in my hundreds place. The sum of my digits is 16. What number am I?

hundreds	tens	ones
2	8	6

3. The sum of my digits is 6. The digit in my hundreds place is 1 less than the digit in my ones place. What number am I?

hundreds	tens	ones

   132 or 213

4. I am a number with 2 more tens than ones. I have 5 more ones than hundreds. The sum of my digits is 18. What number am I?

hundreds	tens	ones
2	9	7

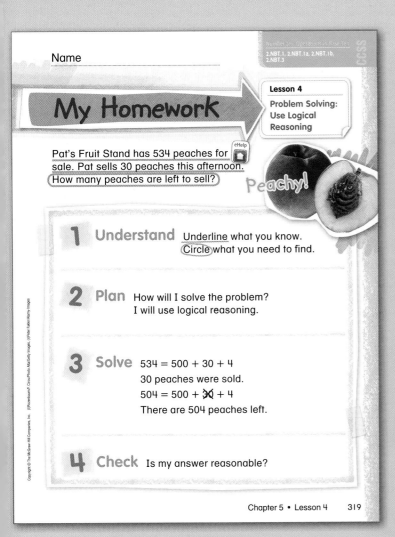

Name _____

2.NBT.1, 2.NBT.1a, 2.NBT.1b, 2.NBT.3

My Homework →

Lesson 4
Problem Solving: Use Logical Reasoning

Pat's Fruit Stand has 534 peaches for sale. Pat sells 30 peaches this afternoon. How many peaches are left to sell?

Peachy!

1 Understand Underline what you know.
Circle what you need to find.

2 Plan How will I solve the problem?
I will use logical reasoning.

3 Solve 534 = 500 + 30 + 4
30 peaches were sold.
504 = 500 + ~~30~~ + 4
There are 504 peaches left.

4 Check Is my answer reasonable?

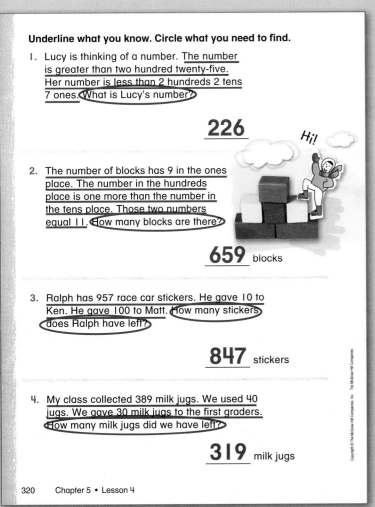

Underline what you know. Circle what you need to find.

1. Lucy is thinking of a number. The number is greater than two hundred twenty-five. Her number is less than 2 hundreds 2 tens 7 ones. What is Lucy's number?

226

Hi!

2. The number of blocks has 9 in the ones place. The number in the hundreds place is one more than the number in the tens place. Those two numbers equal 11. How many blocks are there?

659 blocks

3. Ralph has 957 race car stickers. He gave 10 to Ken. He gave 100 to Matt. How many stickers does Ralph have left?

847 stickers

4. My class collected 389 milk jugs. We used 40 jugs. We gave 30 milk jugs to the first graders. How many milk jugs did we have left?

319 milk jugs

---

4 WRAP IT UP

CCSS

My Homework

Assign homework after successful completion of the lesson. Students who understand the concepts may skip the **Homework Helper** section.

Formative Assessment

Ask students to explain how they solved Exercise 4.

LESSON 5
Read and Write Numbers to 1,000

OBJECTIVE Read and write numbers to 1,000.

What's the Math?

 Common Core State Standards
DOMAIN: Number and Operations in Base Ten

Standard: 2.NBT.3
The wording of this standard can be found on page 286.

What Students Should Understand

- You can read and write numbers with symbols (digits and commas) and words.
- One thousand equals 10 hundred. One thousand is written as 1,000.

What Students Should be Able to Do

Use symbols to write six hundred thirty-eight.

638

Use words to write 852.

eight hundred fifty-two

 Building on the Essential Question

In this lesson, students will build upon the concepts needed to answer the chapter's Essential Question "How can I use place value?"

Developing Vocabulary

New Vocabulary

thousand

Activity

- Discuss the word *hundred*. Write it on the board.
- Hold up one base-ten flat for students to see. Explain to students that it equals 100 units. Place it somewhere where students can see it, such as a board ledge.
- Hold up four flats. Ask students how many hundreds they represent. four hundreds
- Have a volunteer come to the front of the class. Have the student repeat the activity, using a different number of flats.
- Explain to students that 10 flats equals 1,000.

ELL **ELL Support Strategy** Use this vocabulary activity to use non-linguistic representations to support student understanding.

My Vocabulary Cards

Read the activity that matches the *thousands* card. Then organize students in pairs or small groups. Have them discuss their answers.

IWB **Virtual Word Wall**

Add the vocabulary card to the Virtual Word Wall for the chapter.

ELL Refer to the Multilingual eGlossary for interactive definitions in 13 languages.

Plan Online

Plan for your lesson by using the resources at
connectED.mcgraw-hill.com

Digital Dashboard

Interactive Whiteboard Ready

Vocab

The eBook **Glossary** shows the definition of the word and has audio for each definition. The **eGlossary** provides definitions in 13 languages.

Watch

Watch as concepts are brought to life through **animations**, **songs**, and a variety of visual instruction.

Tools

Virtual Manipulatives with work mats allow teachers and students to model the lesson.

Check

Use **eAssessment** for online assignments and customized assessments.

Use the **Common Core Quick Check** before the lesson to assess students' retention of previously learned concepts.

Use the interactive **Self-Check Quiz** after the lesson to provide immediate feedback on lesson concepts.

eHelp

Digital and print resources assist students and parents in completing My Homework.

Games

Online games and **apps** provide extra practice for lesson concepts.

PD

Professional development videos help teachers gain a deeper understanding of the lesson concepts and strategies.

RtI

Support for **approaching**, **on**- and **beyond-level** students as well as **English Language Learners**.

Masters

Reteach and **Enrich** worksheets, **Manipulative Masters**, the **Problem of the Day**, and other blackline masters are available for each lesson.

If your students are well-versed in numbers to 1,000, you may choose to begin instruction with Step 2, **TEACH**.

You will need

☐ base-ten blocks

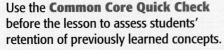
Mathematical **PRACTICE 4** **Modeling the Math**

Write the following numbers on the board: 139, 193, 319, 391, 913, and 931. Display a model of base-ten blocks showing 3 hundreds, 1 ten, and 9 ones.

Which number is modeled with the blocks? 319 *How do you know?* There are 3 hundreds, 1 ten, and 9 ones.

What is the expanded form of the number? 300 + 10 + 9

Repeat the activity by having the students model other numbers.

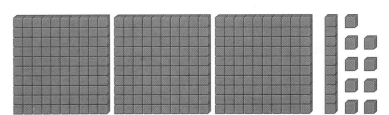

Begin core instruction here.

You will need

☐ crayons or colored pencils

Explore and Explain

Explain to students that they are going to use what they know about counting to find the missing numbers in the chart. Read the directions that are on the bottom of the student page. As a class, read and write the numbers.

Let's start at 101. Count and read the numbers. Write the missing numbers.

Have students color the numbers from 101 to 150 yellow. Have them color the numbers from 151 to 200 green.

Color the numbers from 101 to 150 yellow. Color the numbers from 151 to 200 green.

Discuss with students how they can count, read, and write numbers.

Vocabulary

Have students examine the chart in See and Show. Ask them to name the vocabulary words used in the chart that they have learned in this chapter. one, ten, hundred, thousand Ask students how they will use this chart when reading or writing numbers.

ELL Use this vocabulary activity to gain understanding by using information on a chart.

See and Show

Help students work through the example at the top of the page. Discuss the chart. Look at different numbers and how they are written. Have them trace the dashed numbers as they work the example.

Work through Exercises 1–4 as a class.

Mathematical PRACTICE 3 — Talk Math

Discuss with students "Explain how you would write 62 and 602 using words." Sample answer: 62 is sixty-two or 6 tens and 2 ones. 602 is six hundred two or 6 hundreds 2 ones.

ELL Use tiered questions to informally assess students' progress.

Beginning: Point to the chart in See and Show.

Intermediate: What are the two ways you can read and write numbers?

Advanced: Identify the symbol and word patterns in the chart.

Name _____ 2.NBT.3

Read and Write Numbers to 1,000

Lesson 5
ESSENTIAL QUESTION How can I use place value?

Explore and Explain

101	102	103	104	105	106	107	108	109	110
111	112	113	114	115	116	117	118	119	120
121	122	123	124	125	126	127	128	129	130
131	132	133	134	135	136	137	138	139	140
141	142	143	144	145	146	147	148	149	150
151	152	153	154	155	156	157	158	159	160
161	162	163	164	165	166	167	168	169	170
171	172	173	174	175	176	177	178	179	180
181	182	183	184	185	186	187	188	189	190
191	192	193	194	195	196	197	198	199	200

See students' work.

Teacher Directions: Fill in the missing numbers. Read the numbers from 101 to 150. Color them yellow. Read the numbers from 151 to 200. Color them green.

Online Content at connectED.mcgraw-hill.com   Chapter 5 • Lesson 5   321

See and Show   **Mathematical PRACTICE**

Helpful Hint
One thousand is equal to ten hundreds. We write this as 1,000.

You can read and write numbers with symbols and words.

1 one	11 eleven	10 ten	100 one hundred
2 two	12 twelve	20 twenty	200 two hundred
3 three	13 thirteen	30 thirty	300 three hundred
4 four	14 fourteen	40 forty	400 four hundred
5 five	15 fifteen	50 fifty	500 five hundred
6 six	16 sixteen	60 sixty	600 six hundred
7 seven	17 seventeen	70 seventy	700 seven hundred
8 eight	18 eighteen	80 eighty	800 eight hundred
9 nine	19 nineteen	90 ninety	900 nine hundred
			1,000 one **thousand**

Read five hundred thirty-eight.

Write the number. **538**

Read the number. Write the number.

1. thirty-eight   2. one hundred twenty-one

   38   **121**

Write the number in words. Read the number.

3. 710 **seven hundred ten**

4. 900 **nine hundred**

Talk Math Explain how you would write 62 and 602 using words.

322 Chapter 5 • Lesson 5

On My Own

Read the number.
Write the number.

Are you a Kangaroo or a squirrel?!

5. one hundred ninety-nine
   __199__

6. seven hundred twenty-eight
   __728__

7. three hundred ten
   __310__

8. two hundred eighty-five
   __285__

9. nine hundred seventy-seven
   __977__

10. four hundred sixty-four
    __464__

Write the number in words. Read the number.

11. 1,000 __one thousand__

12. 718 __seven hundred eighteen__

13. 614 __six hundred fourteen__

14. 244 __two hundred forty-four__

15. 321 __three hundred twenty-one__

Chapter 5 • Lesson 5   323

🌎 **Problem Solving**

Mathematical **PRACTICE**

16. There are 119 frogs in the pond. Write the number of frogs in the pond in words.

   __one hundred nineteen__

17. Amber is thinking of this number word: two hundred fifty-six. What is the number?

   __256__

18. There are four hundred twenty-seven geese in the lake. Write the number of geese in the lake.

   Which way to the lake?

   __427__ geese

Write Math Why is it important to know numbers and number names?

Sample answer: So that I can read numbers no matter how they are shown.

---

3 PRACTICE & APPLY

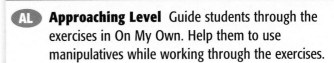
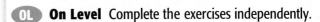
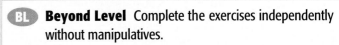

On My Own

Have students work the exercises on this page independently. You may choose to assign exercises based on the chart below.

DIFFERENTIATED ASSIGNMENTS

AL Approaching Level Guide students through the exercises in On My Own. Help them to use manipulatives while working through the exercises.

OL On Level Complete the exercises independently.

BL Beyond Level Complete the exercises independently without manipulatives.

Common Error!
Students may not remember when to use a hyphen between words when writing numbers. Explain that hyphens are used between a number in the tens place and a number in the ones place.

Problem Solving

Have students work through the problem-solving exercises on this page independently.

Mathematical **PRACTICE 2**   In Exercise 18, students **reason abstractly and quantitatively.**

Write Math

This exercise asks students to build upon their understanding of concepts needed to answer the chapter's Essential Question.

21ST CENTURY SKILLS

Have students take pictures of numbers they see in or around the school using a digital camera. Print out the pictures and glue them to flashcards. Students can pick a flashcard and practice writing the number in word form.

AL **APPROACHING LEVEL**

IF my students struggle with numbers to 1,000,

THEN choose a resource:

→ Use the Reteach worksheet with small groups.

→ Go online for a Differentiated Instruction activity.

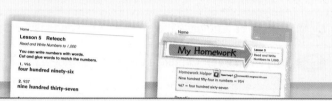

OL **ON LEVEL**

IF my students seem to know numbers to 1,000, but need more practice,

THEN choose a resource:

→ Assign My Homework.

→ Go online for a Differentiated Instruction activity.

BL **BEYOND LEVEL**

IF my students have mastered numbers to 1,000,

THEN choose a resource:

→ Use the Enrich worksheet in cooperative groups.

→ Assign My Homework.

→ Go online for a Differentiated Instruction activity.

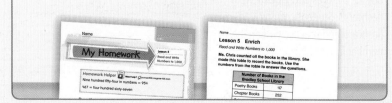

 AL

Name _____

Lesson 5   Reteach

Read and Write Numbers to 1,000

You can write numbers with words.
Cut and glue words to match the numbers.

1. 496
four hundred ninety-six

2. 937
nine hundred thirty-seven

3. 1,000
one thousand

4. 188
one hundred eighty-eight

5. 350
three hundred fifty

6. 625
six hundred twenty-five

✂- -

one hundred eighty-eight	one thousand
four hundred ninety-six	three hundred fifty
nine hundred thirty-seven	six hundred twenty-five

BL

Name _____

Lesson 5   Enrich

Read and Write Numbers to 1,000

Ms. Chris counted all the books in the library. She made this table to record the books. Use the numbers from the table to answer the questions.

Number of Books in the Bradley School Library	
Poetry Books	47
Chapter Books	252
Science Books	80
Picture Books	621
TOTAL	1,000

1. This is the number in expanded form: 200 + 50 + 2. This is the number of ___**chapter**___ books.

2. Write the number of picture books in expanded form.
600 + 20 + 1

3. Add the number of science books to the number of poetry books. What is the total? **127 books**

4. List the different types of books in order from *least* to *greatest* number of books in the library.
poetry, science, chapter, and picture books

5. Write a question of your own about the numbers shown in the table. Ask a friend to answer your question.
See students' work.

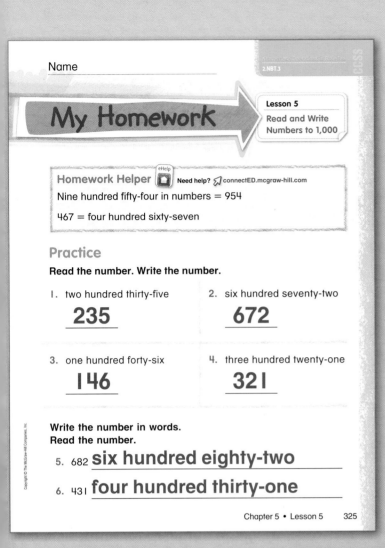

Name _____

My Homework →

Lesson 5
Read and Write
Numbers to 1,000

Homework Helper **Need help?** connectED.mcgraw-hill.com

Nine hundred fifty-four in numbers = 954

467 = four hundred sixty-seven

Practice

Read the number. Write the number.

1. two hundred thirty-five

   235

2. six hundred seventy-two

   672

3. one hundred forty-six

   146

4. three hundred twenty-one

   321

Write the number in words.
Read the number.

5. 682 **six hundred eighty-two**

6. 431 **four hundred thirty-one**

Chapter 5 • Lesson 5   325

Solve. Draw base-ten blocks if needed.

7. There are 429 students at Linden School. Cora wants to write the number in words to put in a newsletter. What should she write?

   four hundred twenty-nine students

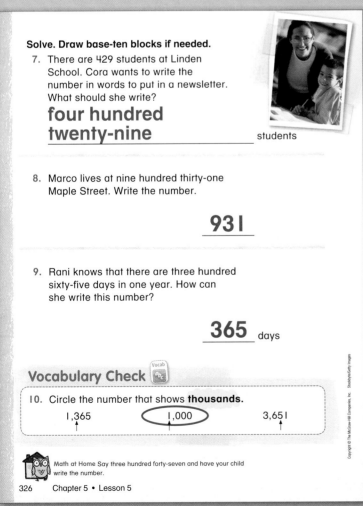

8. Marco lives at nine hundred thirty-one Maple Street. Write the number.

   931

9. Rani knows that there are three hundred sixty-five days in one year. How can she write this number?

   365 days

Vocabulary Check

10. Circle the number that shows **thousands**.

    1,365   (1,000)   3,651

Math at Home Say three hundred forty-seven and have your child write the number.

326   Chapter 5 • Lesson 5

4 WRAP IT UP

My Homework

Assign homework after successful completion of the lesson. Students who understand the concepts may skip the **Homework Helper** section.

Vocabulary Check

Explain to students that the arrow symbol will help them locate which number represents *thousands*. Tell students to circle the entire four-digit number.

Formative Assessment

Ask the students the following question.

How can you write 437 two different ways? 400 + 30 + 7; four hundred thirty-seven

MY Learning Stations

Use the activity card **Comparing Stories** after this lesson. The Teacher Guide provides suggestions for differentiated instruction.

LESSON 6
Count by 5s, 10s, and 100s
OBJECTIVE Find counting patterns.

What's the Math?

 Common Core State Standards
DOMAIN: Number and Operations in Base Ten
Standards: 2.NBT.2, 2.NBT.8
The wording of these standards can be found on page 286.

What Students Should Understand
• You can use number patterns like counting by 5s, 10s, and 100s, to help you count.
• In this lesson, the patterns contain numbers that increase in value. So, each number in a pattern is more than the previous number.

What Students Should be Able to Do
Write the missing numbers in this pattern: 230, _____, 240, 245, _____.
Then write the counting pattern.

Think: Do I count by 5s, 10s, or 100s to find the next number in the pattern?

230, _235_, 240, 245, _250_

The pattern is 5 more.

 Building on the Essential Question
In this lesson, students will build upon the skills and concepts needed to answer the chapter's Essential Question "How can I use place value?"

Developing Vocabulary

 Review Vocabulary
skip count

Review Activity
• Revisit the term *skip count*.
• Write the subtraction problem 260 − 40.
• Next to the problem, write the following column of numbers: 260, 250, 240, 230, 220.
• Explain that skip counting can be useful to solve a subtraction problem mentally. Ask students to describe how the example problem shows skip counting. Each number in the column shows mentally subtracting by 10s

ELL ELL Support Strategy Use this vocabulary activity to visualize what is being taught.

My Vocabulary Cards
Have students look at the set of cards for this chapter. Ask students which word they have read or written most. Have them explain why some words might be used more often than others.

IWB Virtual Word Wall
You may wish to add this review vocabulary word to the Virtual Word Wall for the chapter.

ELL Refer to the Multilingual eGlossary for interactive definitions in 13 languages.

Plan Online

Plan for your lesson by using the resources at

 connectED.mcgraw-hill.com

Digital Dashboard

Interactive Whiteboard Ready

 Vocab

The eBook **Glossary** shows the definition of the word and has audio for each definition. The **eGlossary** provides definitions in 13 languages.

 Watch

Watch as concepts are brought to life through **animations**, **songs**, and a variety of visual instruction.

 Tools

Virtual Manipulatives with work mats allow teachers and students to model the lesson.

 Check

Use **eAssessment** for online assignments and customized assessments.

Use the **Common Core Quick Check** before the lesson to assess students' retention of previously learned concepts.

Use the interactive **Self-Check Quiz** after the lesson to provide immediate feedback on lesson concepts.

 eHelp

Digital and print resources assist students and parents in completing My Homework.

 Games

Online games and **apps** provide extra practice for lesson concepts.

 PD

Professional development videos help teachers gain a deeper understanding of the lesson concepts and strategies.

 RtI

Support for **approaching**, **on**- and **beyond-level** students as well as **English Language Learners**.

 Masters

Reteach and **Enrich** worksheets, **Manipulative Masters**, the **Problem of the Day**, and other blackline masters are available for each lesson.

1 LAUNCH THE LESSON

🕐 If your students are well-versed in counting by 5s, 10s, and 100s, you may choose to begin instruction with Step 2, **TEACH**.

Mathematical PRACTICE 4 Modeling the Math

Write an increasing pattern on the board, such as 5, 10, 15, 20.

What number comes next? 25

Have students write the number on a piece of paper.

What is the pattern? skip counting by 5s

Write a decreasing pattern on the board, such as 90, 80, 70.

What is the next number? 60 *What is the pattern?* skip counting backwards by 10s

5, 10, 15, 20, _____

90, 80, 70, ____

Lunchroom Chat

Tips for New Teachers

To help students see which place value is involved in the skip counting, use grid paper and have students write the numbers using three grid columns so that the place values are aligned. Have them color the numbers that stay the same. Then ask them which place value has numbers that are not colored. This can help them determine whether they are counting by hundreds, tens, or fives.

Online Content at **connectED.mcgraw-hill.com**

🕐 **Begin core instruction here.**

What you need:

☐ yellow and red crayons or colored pencils

Explore and Explain

Model counting by fives from 5 to 30. Read the directions that are on the bottom of the student page.

Let's count by fives. You can start at any number. The chart starts with 201. Skip count by 5s and color those numbers yellow. What is the first number that you will color yellow? 205 *Why?* Sample answer: When you skip count by 5s, the numbers you count end in 5 or 0. 205 is the first number on this chart that ends in a 5 or 0.

Guide students in skip counting by 5s starting with 205. Have them color the numbers yellow.

Skip count by 10s and circle those numbers red. What is the first number that you will circle red? 210 *Why?* Sample answer: When you skip count by 10s, the numbers you count end in 0. 210 is the first number on this chart that ends in a 0.

Guide students in skip counting by 10s from 210 to 250. Have them circle those numbers red. Then have them continue skip counting by 10s and circling those numbers red independently.

How do you count by 100s? Sample answer: Start with one hundred. Skip count by adding 100 more each time. So, the second number is 200, then 300, and so on.

What would be the next number in the chart if you skip counted by 100s? 400 *Why?* Sample answer: When you skip count by 100s, you add 100 more each time. The last number in the chart that is a hundred is 300. 300 + 100 = 400

See and Show

Help students work through the example at the top of the page. Discuss what the number patterns are for each ladder. Have them trace the dashed numbers as they talk through the examples.

Work through Exercises 1–4 as a class.

Mathematical PRACTICE 3 → Talk Math

Discuss with students "How can you tell if a number pattern is counting by hundreds?" Sample answer: Each number is 100 more or 100 less.

Name _____

2.NBT.2, 2.NBT.8

Count by 5s, 10s, and 100s

Lesson 6
ESSENTIAL QUESTION
How can I use place value?

Explore and Explain ▶Watch

201	202	203	204	205	206	207	208	209	210
211	212	213	214	215	216	217	218	219	220
221	222	223	224	225	226	227	228	229	230
231	232	233	234	235	236	237	238	239	240
241	242	243	244	245	246	247	248	249	250
251	252	253	254	255	256	257	258	259	260
261	262	263	264	265	266	267	268	269	270
271	272	273	274	275	276	277	278	279	280
281	282	283	284	285	286	287	288	289	290
291	292	293	294	295	296	297	298	299	300

See students' work.

I can do it!

🦉 **Teacher Directions:** Skip count by 5. Color those numbers yellow. Skip count by 10. Circle those numbers red. If the chart continued, and you counted by hundreds, what would be the next number you would say?

Online Content at 🔗 connectED.mcgraw-hill.com   Chapter 5 • Lesson 6   327

See and Show

Mathematical PRACTICE

Helpful Hint
Patterns can also be 5 less, 10 less, or 100 less.

Number patterns can help you count. In these patterns, each number is *more*.

560
555
550
545

Count by **fives**.
Each number is **5** more.

575
565
555
545

Count by **tens**.
Each number is **10** more.

845
745
645
545

Count by **hundreds**.
Each number is **100** more.

Write the missing numbers. Then write the counting pattern.

1. 340, 350, 360, **370**, 380

   The pattern is **10 more**.

2. 575, 580, **585**, 590, **595**

   The pattern is **5 more**.

3. 941, 841, **741**, 641, 541

   The pattern is **100 less**.

4. 680, 675, **670**, **665**, 660

   The pattern is **5 less**.

Talk Math How can you tell if a number pattern is counting by hundreds?

On My Own

Name _____

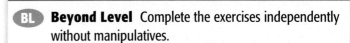

I will make the missing numbers appear!

On My Own
Write the missing numbers.
Then write the counting pattern.

5. 500, 510, **520**, 530, **540**

The pattern is **10 more**.

6. 310, **315**, 320, **325**, 330

The pattern is **5 more**.

7. 800, 790, 780, **770**, 760

The pattern is **10 less**.

8. 655, **555**, 455, 355, **255**

The pattern is **100 less**.

9. **386**, 486, 586, 686, **786**

The pattern is **100 more**.

10. 500, 600, 700, **800**, 900

The pattern is **100 more**.

11. 234, **244**, **254**, 264, 274

The pattern is **10 more**.

12. **520**, 515, 510, 505, **500**

The pattern is **5 less**.

Chapter 5 • Lesson 6   329

🌎 Problem Solving

Mathematical PRACTICE

13. Paul counts by hundreds. He starts with the number 123. Write the numbers Paul counts.

123, **223**, **323**, **423**, **523**, **623**

123

14. Ali counts by tens. She starts with 325. Ali counts 325, 335, 345, 365, 385. What numbers did Alli leave out?

355 and **375**

What's next?

15. Write the numbers you would say if you count backwards by fives. Start with 230 and end at 200.

230, **225**, **220**, **215**, **210**, **205**, 200

Write Math Felicia counts from 300 to 400. Would it be faster to count by 5s or by 10s? Explain.

Sample answer: 10s; each ten is bigger than each 5

so you would have to count less 10s than 5s.

_____

On My Own

Have students work through the exercises on this page independently. You may choose to assign exercises based on the chart below.

DIFFERENTIATED ASSIGNMENTS

AL **Approaching Level** Guide students through the exercises in On My Own. Help them to use manipulatives while the work through the exercises.

OL **On Level** Complete the exercises independently.

BL **Beyond Level** Complete the exercises independently without manipulatives.

Common Error!

Identifying patterns takes a great number of experiences for many students. Point out and discuss patterns of any type whenever you can to develop understanding.

Problem Solving

Have students work through the problem-solving exercises on this page independently.

Mathematical PRACTICE 8 In Exercise 13, students **look for and express regularity in repeated reasoning.**

Write Math

This exercise asks students to build upon their understanding of concepts needed to answer the chapter's Essential Question.

RESPONSE TO INTERVENTION

DIFFERENTIATED INSTRUCTION

AL **APPROACHING LEVEL**

IF my students struggle with counting by 5s, 10s, and 100s,

THEN choose a resource:

→ Use the Reteach worksheet with small groups.

→ Go online for a Differentiated Instruction activity.

→ **Act It Out** Have three students stand in front of the class. Count the students aloud and write 3 on the board. Ask three more students to join them. Count the students and write 6. Ask three more students to join. Count and write 9. *What is the next number in the pattern? What is the rule?* 12, skip count forward by 3s

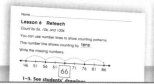

OL **ON LEVEL**

IF my students seem to know counting by 5s, 10s, and 100s, but need more practice,

THEN choose a resource:

→ Assign My Homework.

→ Go online for a Differentiated Instruction activity.

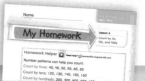

BL **BEYOND LEVEL**

IF my students have mastered counting by 5s, 10s, and 100s,

THEN choose a resource:

→ Use the Enrich worksheet in cooperative groups.

→ Assign My Homework.

→ Go online for a Differentiated Instruction activity.

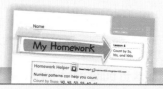

AL Name _____

Lesson 6   Reteach

Count by 5s, 10s, and 100s

You can use number lines to show counting patterns.

This number line shows counting by __tens__.

Write the missing numbers.

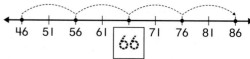

46   51   56   61   **66**   71   76   81   86

1–3. See students' drawings.

1. Draw a number line that models counting by fives.

2. Draw a number line that models counting by tens.

3. Draw a number line that models counting by hundreds.

BL Name _____

Lesson 6   Enrich

Count by 5, 10s, and 100s

Start with 433.				
Count by 10s.	443	453	463	473	End with 483.

Start with 525.				
Count by 5s.	530	535	540	545	End with 550.

Start with 383.				
Count by 100s.	483	583	683	783	End with 883.

Start with 650.				
Count by 10s.	660	670	680	690	End with 700.

Start with 975.				
Count by 5s.	980	985	990	995	End with 1,000.

Start with 119.				
Count by 100s.	219	319	419	519	End with 619.

Start with 702.				
Count by 10s.	712	722	732	742	End with 752.

Name _____

Number and Operations in Base Ten
2.NBT.2, 2.NBT.8

My Homework

Lesson 6
Count by 5s, 10s, and 100s

Homework Helper Need help? connectED.mcgraw-hill.com

Number patterns can help you count.

Count by fives: 40, 45, 50, 55, 60, 65

Count by tens: 120, 130, 140, 150, 160

Count by hundreds: 200, 300, 400, 500, 600

Practice

Write the missing numbers. Then write the counting pattern.

1. 1000, 995, **990**, 985, **980**

   The pattern is **5 less**.

2. 524, **534**, 544, 554, **564**

   The pattern is **10 more**.

3. **183**, 283, 383, **483**, 583

   The pattern is **100 more**.

4. **943**, 843, 743, 643, **543**

   The pattern is **100 less**.

5. 420, 430, **440**, 450, **460**

   The pattern is **10 more**.

6. 525, **530**, 535, **540**, 545

   The pattern is **5 more**.

Continue the counting pattern.

7. 835, 840, 845, **850**, **855**, **860**.

8. 410, 420, 430, **440**, **450**, **460**.

9. 900, 800, 700, **600**, **500**, **400**.

10. Shari counts: 169, 159, 149, 139, 129. Shari wants Miguel to guess her counting pattern. What should Miguel guess?

    The pattern is **10 less**.

Test Practice

11. Mark the number pattern that shows 10 less.

    ○ 820, 830, 840
    ● 980, 970, 960
    ○ 923, 922, 921
    ○ 400, 500, 600

 Math at Home Pick a three-digit number. Ask your child to count by ones, tens, and/or hundreds.

---

4 WRAP IT UP

My Homework

Assign homework after successful completion of the lesson. Students who understand the concepts may skip the **Homework Helper** section.

Test Practice

Diagnose Student Errors

Class trends in wrong answers may indicate common errors or misconceptions.

820, 830, 840 shows ten more

980, 970, 960 correct

921, 922, 923 counts by ones

400, 500, 600 counts by hundreds

Formative Assessment

What is the pattern: 22, 24, 28, 36? What number comes next? each increase is double the one before it: 52

Line Up!

When students line up, give them number patterns to complete.

- For example, give the number pattern 200, 210, 220.
- Have a volunteer tell what the next number is. 230 The last person to get in line tells the rule. Add 10

LESSON 7
Compare Numbers to 1,000

OBJECTIVE   Compare three-digit numbers using <, >, and =.

What's the Math?

 Common Core State Standards
DOMAIN: Number and Operations in Base Ten

Standard: 2.NBT.4

The wording of this standard can be found on page 286.

What Students Should Understand

You can compare numbers to 1,000 by following the steps below. Then use the symbols > (greater than), < (less than), and = (equal to) to compare numbers.

- First, write the numbers in a place-value chart. Make sure the digits are lined up correctly.
- Next, compare the digits in the greatest place value first. If they are the same then compare the digits in the next place value.
- Last, compare each digit until you find two digits that are not equal. Then decide whether the first number is greater than, equal to, or less than the second number.

What Students Should be Able to Do

Compare 459 and 495. Write >, <, or =.

hundreds	tens	ones
4	5	9
4	9	5

In the tens place, 5 is less than 9.

459 < 495

459 is less than 495.

? Building on the Essential Question

In this lesson, students will build upon the skills and concepts needed to answer the chapter's Essential Question "How can I use place value?"

Developing Vocabulary

 New Vocabulary

compare   greater than

less than   equal to

Activity

- Discuss the word *compare* and write it on the board. Ask students what they know about this word's meaning.
- Hold one object in your left hand, and five objects in your right hand. Tell students that the number of objects in your left hand is less than the number in your right hand.
- Explain that *greater* means "more" and *less* means "fewer." Tell students that the number of objects in your right hand is greater than the number in your left hand.
- Have a volunteer use objects to demonstrate the meaning of *equal to*.

ELL **ELL Support Strategy** Use this vocabulary activity to provide oral summaries of information.

My Vocabulary Cards

Read the activities for this lesson's vocabulary cards. Have students work in pairs to discuss the similarities and differences they notice on each card's visuals.

IWB **Virtual Word Wall**

Read the activities for this lesson's vocabulary cards. Have students work in pairs to discuss the similarities and differences they notice on each card's visuals.

ELL Refer to the Multilingual eGlossary for interactive definitions in 13 languages.

Plan Online
Plan for your lesson by using the resources at
 connectED.mcgraw-hill.com

1 LAUNCH THE LES

 If your students are well-versed i
numbers to 1,000, you may choos
instruction with Step 2, **TEACH.**

Digital Dashboard
Interactive Whiteboard Ready

 Vocab
The eBook **Glossary** shows the definition of the word and has audio for each definition. The **eGlossary** provides definitions in 13 languages.

 Watch
Watch as concepts are brought to life through **animations**, **songs**, and a variety of visual instruction.

 Tools
Virtual Manipulatives with work mats allow teachers and students to model the lesson.

 Check
Use **eAssessment** for online assignments and customized assessments.

Use the **Common Core Quick Check** before the lesson to assess students' retention of previously learned concepts.

Use the interactive **Self-Check Quiz** after the lesson to provide immediate feedback on lesson concepts.

 eHelp
Digital and print resources assist students and parents in completing My Homework.

 Games
Online games and **apps** provide extra practice for lesson concepts.

 PD
Professional development videos help teachers gain a deeper understanding of the lesson concepts and strategies.

 RtI
Support for **approaching**, **on-** and **beyond-level** students as well as **English Language Learners**.

 Masters
Reteach and **Enrich** worksheets, **Manipulative Masters**, the **Problem of the Day**, and other blackline masters are available for each lesson.

You will need
☐ number cards (from 1 to 10)
☐ blank index cards

Mathematical PRACTICE **Modeling the Math**

Distribute two sets of number cards from 1 to 10 and 3 blank index cards to each pair of students. Have students make signs for >, <, and =.

Students shuffle the number cards and place them facedown. Both students turn over one card from the pile.

The students put their number cards together, and partners compare their numbers using the <, >, or = sign. Place continues until all cards are drawn.

4	<	7

...CH

Begin core instruction here.

You will need

☐ base-ten blocks

Explore and Explain

Read the directions that are on the bottom of the student page. Guide students in modeling 331 and 208 with base-ten blocks.

How many hundreds did you use to model 331? 3 hundreds
How many hundreds did you use to model 208? 2 hundreds

Have students write 331 to the left of the sign, and write 208 to the right of the sign. Then have students sketch a picture of the base-ten blocks they used. Next, begin a discussion on how to compare numbers.

When you compare numbers, you start with the greatest place value. What is the greatest place value in this example? hundreds

How many hundreds are in 331? 3 hundreds *How many hundreds are in 208?* 2 hundreds

Compare 3 and 2. What is the greater number, 3 or 2? 3

Explain to students that 331 is greater than 208 since 3 hundreds is greater than 2 hundreds.

So, 331 is greater 208.

Lead a class discussion that > means is greater than.

See and Show

Help students work through the example at the top of the page.

Show examples on the board. Write numbers and have students decide if a >, <, or = should be placed between them.

Work through Exercises 1–12 as a class.

Mathematical PRACTICE 3 **Talk Math**

Discuss with students "Explain how you compare 567 and 575." Sample answer: First look at the hundreds. They are the same. Next look at the tens. 6 is less than 7. So, 567 is less than 576.

Name _____

Numbers and Operations in Base Ten
2.NBT.4

Compare Numbers to 1,000

Lesson 7
ESSENTIAL QUESTION
How can I use place value?

Explore and Explain

How much are you worth?

A lot, I'm sure!

>

See students' work.

Teacher Directions: Use base-ten blocks to show 331 and 208 on the mat. Place them on the appropriate side of the symbol. Draw the base-ten blocks.

Online Content at connectED.mcgraw-hill.com   Chapter 5 • Lesson 7   333

See and Show

Mathematical PRACTICE

Use these steps to compare numbers.

Step 1 Line up the numbers by place value in the chart.

Step 2 **Compare** the digits in the greatest place value first. If they are the same, compare digits in the next place value.

greater than			less than			equal to		
hundreds	tens	ones	hundreds	tens	ones	hundreds	tens	ones
6	1	8	8	4	6	9	7	8
6	3	4	8	2	3	9	7	8

634 > 618   823 < 846   978 = 978

634 is *greater*   823 is *less*   978 is *equal*
than 618.   than 846.   to 978.

Compare. Write >, <, or =.

1. 142 (>) 124   2. 253 (<) 257   3. 313 (=) 313

4. 842 (>) 795   5. 694 (=) 694   6. 203 (>) 153

7. 100 (<) 1,000   8. 999 (>) 99   9. 133 (=) 133

10. 743 (>) 734   11. 861 (<) 871   12. 542 (>) 452

Talk Math   Explain how to compare 567 and 576.

334   Chapter 5 • Lesson 7

Name _____

On My Own

Compare. Write >, <, or =.

13. 150 ⊜ 150   14. 132 ⓒ 213

15. 689 ⊜ 627   16. 425 ⊜ 425

17. 907 ⊜ 899   18. 533 ⊜ 533

19. 207 ⓒ 210   20. 697 ⊜ 667

21. 411 ⓒ 421   22. 619 ⓒ 621

23. 729 ⊜ 729   24. 325 ⊜ 300

25. 332 ⓒ 335   26. 984 ⊜ 894

Circle the number that is less than the purple number.

27.   568   28.   409

588   (464)   410   (406)

Circle the number that is greater than the purple number.

29.   311   30.   653

(313)   211   651   (655)

Chapter 5 • Lesson 7   335

Problem Solving

31. I am greater than 3 hundreds, 2 tens, and 2 ones. I am less than 3 hundreds, 2 tens, 4 ones. What number am I?

Hey, someone bit me!

323

32. Ravi is making cookies. He wants to have two equal groups of cookies. He made 45 cookies for one group. How many cookies does Ravi need for the other group?

45 _____ cookies

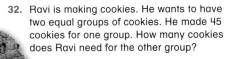

33. Demi collected 124 seashells. Eva collected 142 seashells. Who collected less seashells?

Demi

Mathematical PRACTICE

Write Math

Explain how you decide which number is greater than the other.

Sample answer: If hundreds are equal, move to tens.

If they are equal, move to ones. When comparing, if

you get to a digit that is higher, it is the greater number.

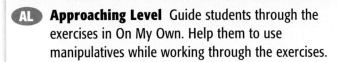

PRACTICE & APPLY

CCSS

On My Own

Have students work through the exercises on this page independently. You may choose to assign exercises based on the chart below.

Problem Solving

Have students work through the problem-solving exercises on this page independently.

Mathematical PRACTICE ① In Exercise 31, students **make sense of problems and persevere in solving them.**

Write Math

This exercise asks students to build upon their understanding of concepts needed to answer the chapter's Essential Question.

RESPONSE TO INTERVENTION

DIFFERENTIATED INSTRUCTION

AL | APPROACHING LEVEL

IF my students struggle with comparing numbers,

THEN choose a resource:

→ Use the Reteach worksheet with small groups.

→ Go online for a Differentiated Instruction activity.

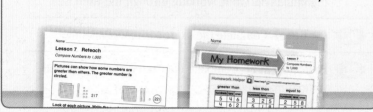

OL | ON LEVEL

IF my students seem to know how to compare numbers, but need more practice,

THEN choose a resource:

→ Assign My Homework.

→ Go online for a Differentiated Instruction activity.

BL | BEYOND LEVEL

IF my students have mastered comparing numbers,

THEN choose a resource:

→ Use the Enrich worksheet in cooperative groups.

→ Assign My Homework.

→ Go online for a Differentiated Instruction activity.

AL

Name _____

Lesson 7 Reteach

Compare Numbers to 1,000

> Pictures can show how some numbers are greater than others. The greater number is circled.

217   (221)

Look at each picture. Write the number that the picture shows. Then circle the number that is greater.

1. (192)   190

2. 270   (275)

3. 241   (251)

4. (833)   813

BL

Name _____

Lesson 7 Enrich

Compare Numbers to 1,000

Compare the numbers in the boxes. Cut the symbols from the bottom of the page, and glue the correct symbol in the box.

3 ones 4 tens 2 hundreds	>	200 + 10 + 4
600 + 30 + 0	<	6 ones 4 tens 6 hundreds
5 ones 6 tens 3 hundreds	=	300 + 60 + 5
9 ones 7 tens 1 hundred	>	10 tens

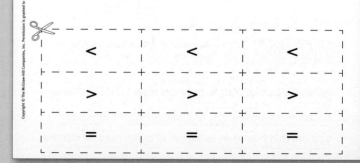

<	<	<
>	>	>
=	=	=

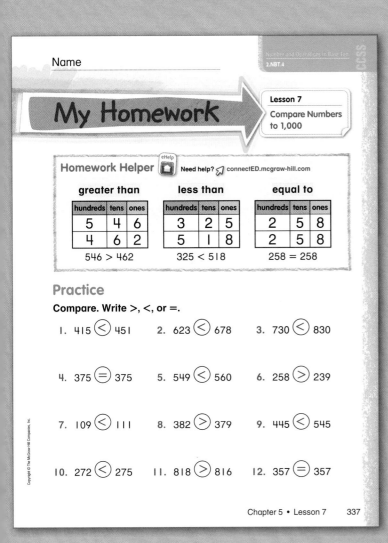

Name _____

My Homework

Lesson 7
Compare Numbers to 1,000

Homework Helper Need help? connectED.mcgraw-hill.com

greater than			less than			equal to		
hundreds	tens	ones	hundreds	tens	ones	hundreds	tens	ones
5	4	6	3	2	5	2	5	8
4	6	2	5	1	8	2	5	8

546 > 462　　　　325 < 518　　　　258 = 258

Practice

Compare. Write >, <, or =.

1. 415 $<$ 451　　2. 623 $<$ 678　　3. 730 $<$ 830

4. 375 $=$ 375　　5. 549 $<$ 560　　6. 258 $>$ 239

7. 109 $<$ 111　　8. 382 $>$ 379　　9. 445 $<$ 545

10. 272 $<$ 275　　11. 818 $>$ 816　　12. 357 $=$ 357

Chapter 5 • Lesson 7　　337

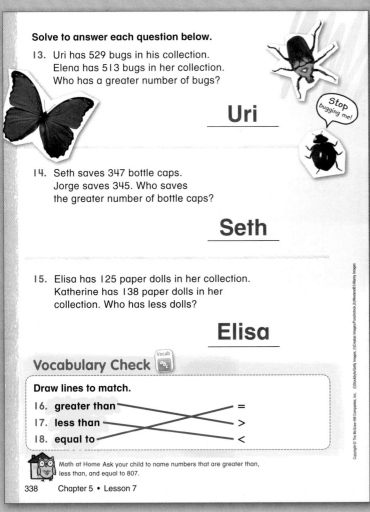

Solve to answer each question below.

13. Uri has 529 bugs in his collection. Elena has 513 bugs in her collection. Who has a greater number of bugs?

Uri

Stop bugging me!

14. Seth saves 347 bottle caps. Jorge saves 345. Who saves the greater number of bottle caps?

Seth

15. Elisa has 125 paper dolls in her collection. Katherine has 138 paper dolls in her collection. Who has less dolls?

Elisa

Vocabulary Check

Draw lines to match.

16. greater than —— =
17. less than —— >
18. equal to —— <

Math at Home Ask your child to name numbers that are greater than, less than, and equal to 807.

---

4 WRAP IT UP

My Homework

Assign homework after successful completion of the lesson. Students who understand the concepts may skip the **Homework Helper** section.

Vocabulary Check

Encourage students to refer to their My Vocabulary Cards if they need additional support.

Formative Assessment

Ask students the following question.

How do you compare 725 with 743 using <, >, or =?
725 < 743; 743 > 725

MY Learning Stations

Use the graphic novel **Home Run Records** after this lesson. The Teacher Guide provides suggestions for differentiated instruction.

My Review

Use these pages to assess your students' understanding of the vocabulary and key concepts in this chapter.

Vocabulary Check

Display this chapter's vocabulary on the virtual word wall. Encourage students to refer to the examples as they complete these exercises.

ELL **ELL Support Strategy** Use this vocabulary activity to demonstrate understanding drawing lines to match.

Concept Check

If students need reinforcement of skills after completing this section, use the Reteach worksheet to review the concepts again.

Exercise(s)	Concept	Review Lesson
7	Hundreds	1
8	Hundreds, tens, and ones	2
9–10	Place value to 1,000	3
11–12	Read and write numbers	5
13–16	Compare numbers	7

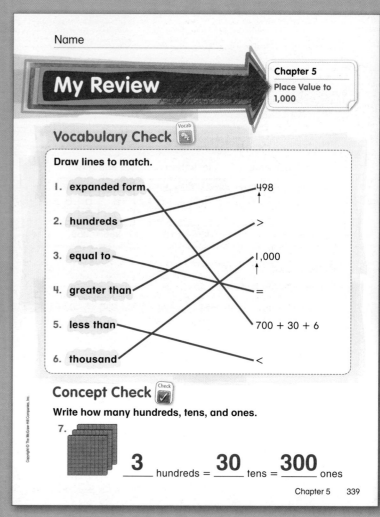

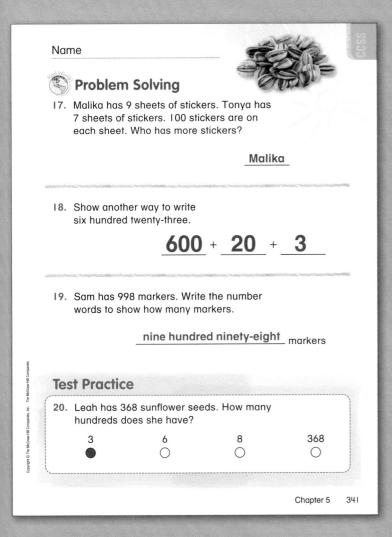

Name _____

🌐 Problem Solving

17. Malika has 9 sheets of stickers. Tonya has 7 sheets of stickers. 100 stickers are on each sheet. Who has more stickers?

   Malika

18. Show another way to write six hundred twenty-three.

   600 + **20** + **3**

19. Sam has 998 markers. Write the number words to show how many markers.

   nine hundred ninety-eight markers

Test Practice

20. Leah has 368 sunflower seeds. How many hundreds does she have?

   3 ●   6 ○   8 ○   368 ○

Reflect

Chapter 5
Answering the Essential Question ❓

Show the ways you can use place value.

Write the number. seven hundred sixty-three **763**	Write the number in expanded form. 233 **200** + **30** + **3**
ESSENTIAL QUESTION ❓ How can I use place value?	
Compare. 763 ⊙ 637	Write the missing numbers. 560, **570**, 580, **590**

Ready? Set? Solve!

Problem Solving

Remind students of the four-step plan for problem solving. For students who need help in reading comprehension, have them work with another student to read the problem aloud before attempting the four-step plan.

Test Practice

Diagnose Student Errors

Class trends in wrong answers may indicate common errors or misconceptions.

3   correct
6   this is the number of tens
8   this is the number of ones
368   this is the complete number

Reflect

Display this chapter's vocabulary on the Virtual Word Wall. Ask students to refer to the words as they complete the graphic organizer.

You may choose to have your students use a different graphic organizer for review.

Summative Assessment

Use these alternate leveled chapter tests from the Assessment Masters to differentiate assessment for the specific needs of your students.

Chapter Tests		
Level	**Type**	**Form**
AL	Multiple Choice	**1A**
AL	Multiple Choice	**1B**
OL	Multiple Choice / Free Choice	**2A**
OL	Multiple Choice / Free Choice	**2B**
BL	Free Choice	**3A**
BL	Free Choice	**3B**
Additional Chapter Resource Masters		
OL	Vocabulary Test	
OL	Listening Assessment	
OL	Oral Assessment	

Online Content at 🖊 connectED.mcgraw-hill.com

CHAPTER 6

Add Three-Digit Numbers

Chapter at a Glance

Suggested Pacing

Instruction*	Review & Assessment	TOTAL
11 days	2 days	**13 days**

*Includes additional time for remediation and differentiation.

Lesson	Objective	Materials & Manipulatives	Vocabulary	CCSS Standard
Lesson 1 *pp. 351–356* **Make a Hundred to Add**	Make a hundred to add a three-digit number.	• base-ten blocks • Work Mat 7	*All of the vocabulary words in this chapter are review words.*	2.NBT.7
Lesson 2 *pp. 357–362* **Add Hundreds**	Add numbers in the hundreds.	• base-ten blocks		2.NBT.7 2.NBT.9
Lesson 3 *pp. 363–368* **Mentally Add 10 or 100**	Students will add 10 or 100 mentally.			2.NBT.8
☑ **Check My Progress**				
Lesson 4 *pp. 371–376* **Regroup Ones to Add**	Regroup ones to add three-digit numbers.	• base-ten blocks • Work Mat 7		2.NBT.7 2.NBT.9
Lesson 5 *pp. 377–382* **Regroup Tens to Add**	Regroup tens to add three-digit numbers.	• base-ten blocks • Work Mat 7		2.NBT.7 2.NBT.9
Lesson 6 *pp. 383–388* **Add Three-Digit Numbers**	Add three-digit numbers.	• base-ten blocks • Work Mat 7		2.NBT.7 2.NBT.9
Lesson 7 *pp. 389–394* **Rewrite Three-Digit Addition**	Given a three-digit addition problem written horizontally, rewrite it vertically before adding.			2.NBT.7
Lesson 8 *pp. 395–400* **Problem-Solving Strategy: Guess, Check, and Revise**	Guess, Check, and Revise strategy to solve problems.			2.NBT.7
☑ **My Review and Reflect**				

  For customizable online assessment, go to **eAssessment** at ⚡ connectED.mcgraw-hill.com.

Planning for Differentiated Instruction

Use these differentiated instruction activity suggestions, along with the ongoing support provided in each lesson of this chapter, to meet individual learning needs.

AL APPROACHING LEVEL

Use with Lesson 2

Materials: index cards, base-ten blocks

- Have students work in small groups.
- On index cards, write addition problems with missing addends, such as $200 + \_\_\_\_ = 500$.
- Give each student in the groups an index card and base-ten blocks. Have students use the models to find the missing addends.
- Have students trade cards with students in their group and repeat the activity.
- Ask students to write how they used the models to help solve the problems.

BL BEYOND LEVEL

Use with Lesson 1

Materials: paper and pencil, index cards with addition problems

- Have students work in small groups.
- On index cards, write a three-digit addition problem, such as $637 + 98$. Give each group an index card.
- Ask students to make a hundred to add.
- Have each group member write how they determined which number to take apart to make a hundred.
- Students compare responses and solve.

OL ON LEVEL

Use with Lesson 2

Materials: 4-part spinner labeled *100, 200, 300, 400*

- Have students work with a partner.
- Each student spins the spinner twice, writes the numbers, and then adds the numbers.
- The student with the greatest sum is the winner. Students repeat for further practice.

ELL ENGLISH LANGUAGE LEARNERS

Support for English Language Learners is found throughout the chapter and includes:

- ELL strategies at point-of-use in each Teacher Edition lesson
- ELL tiered instruction suggestions for each lesson at connectED.mcgraw-hill.com
- Comprehensive ELL lessons and worksheets for additional instruction at connectED.mcgraw-hill.com
- Non-linguistic representations of concepts on My Math Words, My Vocabulary Cards, and My Foldables

Additional online resources at connectED.mcgraw-hill.com include:

- Visual Vocabulary Cards
- Multilingual eGlossary
- Professional Development support

Looking for more DIFFERENTIATED INSTRUCTION?
Find additional support in each lesson of this chapter and online at connectED.mcgraw-hill.com

- AL Approaching Level
- OL On Level
- BL Beyond Level
- ELL English Language Learners

What's the Math in This Chapter?

CCSS Points of Intersection

Where
CONTENT STANDARDS

Meet
Mathematical PRACTICE ➡ **8**

NBT
Number and Operations in Base Ten

Look for and express regularity in repeated reasoning.

This chapter concentrates on the **Number and Operations in Base Ten (NBT)** domain.

As you teach addition of three-digit numbers, emphasize that the addition process involves repeated calculation. Students can use the same algorithm repeatedly with any addition problem they encounter. The algorithm consists of adding each place value, starting with the ones place, and regrouping when needed.

What should my students already know?

In the previous grade, students used **Operations and Algebraic Thinking (OA)** in their study of addition:

- Use addition within 20 to solve word problems.
  1.OA.1, 1.OA.6

Students used **Number and Operations in Base Ten (NBT)** in their study of place value and addition:

- Understand that the two digits of a two-digit number represent amounts of tens and ones.
  1.NBT.2

- Add within 100, using concrete models or drawings and strategies based on place value. Understand that when adding two-digit numbers, one adds tens and tens, ones and ones; and sometimes it is necessary to compose a ten.
  1.NBT.4

- Given a two-digit number, mentally find 10 more than the number, without having to count.
  1.NBT.5

WHAT STUDENTS SHOULD UNDERSTAND

Make a Hundred to Add
 2.NBT.7

How to take apart an addend to make a hundred to add.

- It is easier to add a two-digit and a three-digit number if one of the numbers is a hundred.

Add Hundreds
 2.NBT.7

How to add two hundreds.

- You can use addition facts to add hundreds.

WHAT STUDENTS SHOULD BE ABLE TO DO

Find 34 + 297 by taking apart an addend to make a hundred.

$34 + 297$ Take apart 34 to make $31 + 3$.

$31 + 3 + 297$ Add $3 + 297$.

$31 + 300 = 331$ Add 31 to that sum.

So, $34 + 297 = 331$.

Find 200 + 400.

2 hundreds
+ 4 hundreds
6 hundreds

THINK
You know that $2 + 4 = 6$.
So, $200 + 400 = 600$.

| **WHAT STUDENTS SHOULD UNDERSTAND** | **WHAT STUDENTS SHOULD BE ABLE TO DO** |

Mentally Add 10 or 100

 2.NBT.8

How to mentally add 10 or 100 to a three-digit number.

- You can use mental math to add 10 or 100 to a number by thinking of addition facts.

Mentally add 100.

```
   530
+  100
```

> **THINK**
> 5 + 1 = 6, so
> ```
>    530
> +  100
>    630
> ```

Mentally add 10.

```
   565
+   10
```

> **THINK**
> 6 + 1 = 7, so
> ```
>    565
> +   10
>    575
> ```

Add Three-Digit Numbers with Regrouping

 2.NBT.7

How to add three-digit numbers that involve regrouping the ones, tens, or both place values.

- When adding with three-digit numbers, add the ones, the tens, and then the hundreds.
- Regroup 10 ones as 1 ten if there are ten or more ones.
- Regroup 10 tens as 1 hundred if there are ten or more tens.

Find 146 + 273.

Step 1 Add the ones.

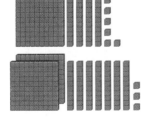

	hundreds	tens	ones
	1	4	6
+	2	7	3
			9

Step 2 Add the tens. Regroup.

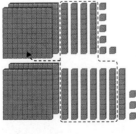

	hundreds	tens	ones
	[1]		
	1	4	6
+	2	7	3
		1	9

Step 3 Add the hundreds.

	hundreds	tens	ones
	[1]		
	1	4	6
+	2	7	3
	4	1	9

So, 146 + 273 = 419.

> ## What will my students do next with these skills?
>
> **After this chapter,** students will learn to:
>
> - subtract three-digit numbers. 2.NBT.7
>
> **In the next grade,** students will learn to:
>
> - use patterns and algebraic thinking. 3.OA.9

Reading Connections

Real-World Problem Solving Library

Math and Social Studies: Moving Along

Use these leveled books to reinforce and extend problem-solving skills and strategies.

Leveled for:

AL Approaching Level

OL On Level Also available in Spanish

BL Beyond Level

For additional support, see the *Real-World Problem Solving Readers Teacher Guide.* This reader is also featured in *My Learning Stations* (see page 350A).

Leveled Reader Database

Available at leveledreaderdatabase.macmillanmh.com
Search by:

- Content Area
- Guided Reading Level
- Lexile Score
- Benchmark Level

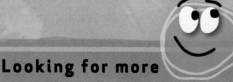

**Looking for more Reading and Language Arts Support?
go online to
connectED.mcgraw-hill.com**

Library Books

Check with your school library or your local public library for these titles.

Roman Numerals
David Adler

Coyotes All Around
Stuart J. Murphy

The 329th Friend
Marjorie W. Sharmat

Animal Giants
Sara Louise Kras

Mission: Addition
Loreen Leedy

Reading and Language Arts Support

Math in Our World

Distribute copies of the front page of a newspaper. Have students search for numbers and circle them. Remind students to also look carefully for numbers written as words. Lead a discussion about the numbers students found and what they refer to. Ask them if they see any pattern in which numbers are written as digits and which are written as words. Choose several pairs of numbers to practice regrouping to add. Finally, lead a brief discussion about which stories are on the front page. Who decided that they are the most important stories? Do students agree?

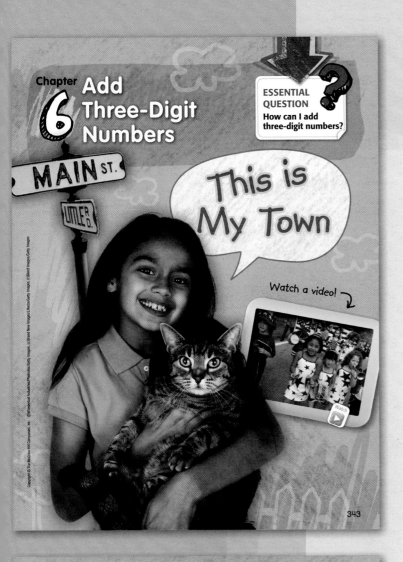

ESSENTIAL QUESTION
How can I add three-digit numbers?

This is My Town

Watch a video!

343

LAUNCH
THE CHAPTER

Theme:
This is My Town

All of the lessons in Chapter 6 will connect with the theme of This is My Town, which centers on maps and travel. This is reflected in problem solving and the visuals used throughout the chapter.

Video

Have students watch the video about towns. You may want to spark a discussion about how math is used in operating a town.

Building on the Essential Question

Once students have completed this chapter they should be able to answer the question "How can I add three-digit numbers?". In each lesson, students build upon their understanding by answering a simpler question. These are indicated in the exercises as Building on the Essential Question. At the end of the chapter, students use a graphic organizer to help them answer the Essential Question.

My Common Core State Standards (CCSS)

Number and Operations in Base Ten

2.NBT.7 Add and subtract within 1000, using concrete models or drawings and strategies based on place value, properties of operations, and/or the relationship between addition and subtraction; relate the strategy to a written method. Understand that in adding or subtracting three digit numbers, one adds or subtracts hundreds and hundreds, tens and tens, ones and ones; and sometimes it is necessary to compose or decompose tens or hundreds.

2.NBT.8 Mentally add 10 or 100 to a given number 100–900, and mentally subtract 10 or 100 from a given number 100–900.

2.NBT.9 Explain why addition and subtraction strategies work, using place value and the properties of operations.

Standards for Mathematical PRACTICE

1. Make sense of problems and persevere in solving them.
2. Reason abstractly and quantitatively.
3. Construct viable arguments and critique the reasoning of others.
4. Model with mathematics.
5. Use appropriate tools strategically.
6. Attend to precision.
7. Look for and make use of structure.
8. Look for and express regularity in repeated reasoning.

= focused on in this chapter

Professional Development

Common Core State Standards

Learn more about how the Common Core State Standards can be implemented in your classroom at mhpdonline.com.

Look for
- **eImplementation**
- **eVideo Clip Libraries**
- **eTech Training**
- **ePD Webinars**

Feature video for mathematical content in this chapter:
CGI-Join Result
Unknown-Invented Strategy

ASSESS READINESS

1 Assess

You have two options for assessing student readiness for this chapter. Use student results to determine which level of instruction is needed to help students get ready for the chapter and to determine what ongoing support they will need during the chapter.

Option 1: Am I Ready?

Have students complete the Am I Ready? page in their student books.

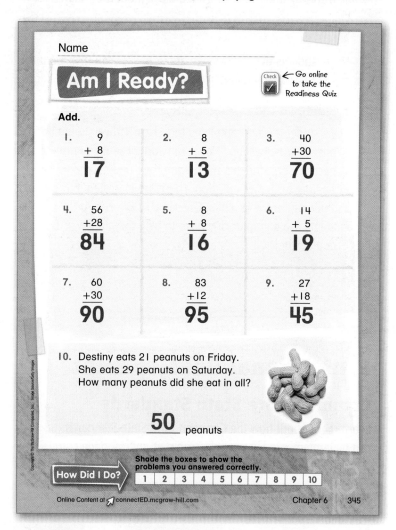

Name

Am I Ready?

 Go online to take the Readiness Quiz

Add.

1. $\begin{array}{r} 9 \\ + 8 \\ \hline 17 \end{array}$	2. $\begin{array}{r} 8 \\ + 5 \\ \hline 13 \end{array}$	3. $\begin{array}{r} 40 \\ +30 \\ \hline 70 \end{array}$
4. $\begin{array}{r} 56 \\ +28 \\ \hline 84 \end{array}$	5. $\begin{array}{r} 8 \\ + 8 \\ \hline 16 \end{array}$	6. $\begin{array}{r} 14 \\ + 5 \\ \hline 19 \end{array}$
7. $\begin{array}{r} 60 \\ +30 \\ \hline 90 \end{array}$	8. $\begin{array}{r} 83 \\ +12 \\ \hline 95 \end{array}$	9. $\begin{array}{r} 27 \\ +18 \\ \hline 45 \end{array}$

10. Destiny eats 21 peanuts on Friday. She eats 29 peanuts on Saturday. How many peanuts did she eat in all?

    <u>50</u> peanuts

How Did I Do?
Shade the boxes to show the problems you answered correctly.

| 1 | 2 | 3 | 4 | 5 | 6 | 7 | 8 | 9 | 10 |

Online Content at connectED.mcgraw-hill.com

Chapter 6   345

Option 2: Online Readiness Quiz

Have students take the Online Readiness Quiz.

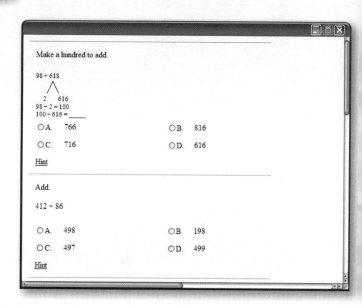

Make a hundred to add.

$98 + 618$

$\begin{array}{cc} 2 & 616 \end{array}$
$98 + 2 = 100$
$100 + 616 = \underline{}$

○ A. 766   ○ B. 816
○ C. 716   ○ D. 616

<u>Hint</u>

Add.

$412 + 86$

○ A. 498   ○ B. 198
○ C. 497   ○ D. 499

<u>Hint</u>

OPTION 2

Common Core Review

Exercises	Skill	Standard
1–10*	Addition	2.NBT.7

*These questions are randomly generated from a bank of 15 questions.

OPTION 1

Common Core Review

Exercises	Skill	Standard
1–10	Addition	2.NBT.7

345   Chapter 6 Add Three-Digit Numbers

2 Diagnose and Prescribe

Based on the results of the Am I Ready? in the student edition, use the charts below to address individual needs **before** beginning the chapter.

Use the **ONGOING** resources to support differentiated instruction as new skills and concepts are presented in the chapter.

TIER 1

OL — ON LEVEL

IF students miss 2 in Exercises 1–10,

THEN choose a resource:

→ Am I Ready? Practice
→ Online Readiness Quiz

ONGOING Self-Check Quizzes • Chapter Project • Differentiated Assignments • My Learning Stations • Differentiated Instruction activities

TIER 2

AL — STRATEGIC INTERVENTION

(Approaching Grade Level)

IF students miss 3–4 in Exercises 1–10,

THEN choose a resource:

→ Online Strategic Intervention activity
→ Am I Ready? Review

ONGOING Common Errors • Differentiated Assignments • Online support • Reteach worksheets • Homework Helper • My Learning Stations • RtI lesson support • Differentiated Instruction activities

TIER 3

INTENSIVE INTERVENTION

(2 or more years below grade level)

IF students miss 5 or more in Exercises 1–10,

THEN use *Math Triumphs,* an intensive math intervention program from McGraw-Hill.

BL — BEYOND LEVEL

IF students miss 1 or less in Exercises 1–10,

THEN choose a resource:

→ Online Games
→ Am I Ready? Apply

ONGOING 21st Century Skills • Chapter Project • Differentiated Assignments • Enrich worksheets • My Learning Stations • Differentiated Instruction activities

Online Content at **connectED.mcgraw-hill.com**

3 Reassess

If reassessment is necessary, administer the chapter Diagnostic Test in the **Assessment Masters** or go online for eAssessment.

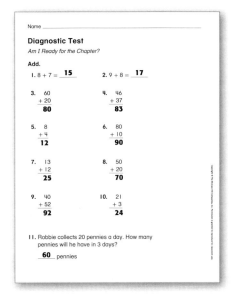

Name _____

Diagnostic Test
Am I Ready for the Chapter?

Add.

1. $8 + 7 = $ __15__   2. $9 + 8 = $ __17__

3. $\begin{array}{r} 60 \\ + 20 \\ \hline 80 \end{array}$ 4. $\begin{array}{r} 46 \\ + 37 \\ \hline 83 \end{array}$

5. $\begin{array}{r} 8 \\ + 4 \\ \hline 12 \end{array}$ 6. $\begin{array}{r} 80 \\ + 10 \\ \hline 90 \end{array}$

7. $\begin{array}{r} 13 \\ + 12 \\ \hline 25 \end{array}$ 8. $\begin{array}{r} 50 \\ + 20 \\ \hline 70 \end{array}$

9. $\begin{array}{r} 40 \\ + 52 \\ \hline 92 \end{array}$ 10. $\begin{array}{r} 21 \\ + 3 \\ \hline 24 \end{array}$

11. Robbie collects 20 pennies a day. How many pennies will he have in 3 days?

__60__ pennies

 For additional chapter readiness assessment, go to eAssessment at connectED.mcgraw-hill.com.

DEVELOP VOCABULARY

My Math Words

Review Vocabulary

Where did they learn it?

- ones   (Lesson 5-1)
- regroup   (Lesson 3-2)
- sum   (Lesson 1-1)
- tens   (Lesson 5-1)

Making Connections

Ask students to describe or show what they know about the review vocabulary. Encourage students to describe, draw, act out, or model their examples. Discuss with students that circling or highlighting signal words or signal phrases will help them read and solve word problems.

Ask students to examine the graphic organizer. Ask a volunteer to read aloud the problem in the middle category. Discuss with students what word or words tells them they should add. in all

My Vocabulary Cards

There is no new vocabulary in this chapter. Encourage students to use the blank cards to review vocabulary words, draw examples of important concepts, or write questions they have about what they have learned. More ideas for using the blank cards can be found on the backs of the cards.

Students should clip and store their cards in one place, such as a small envelope, where they can access them as needed throughout the chapter.

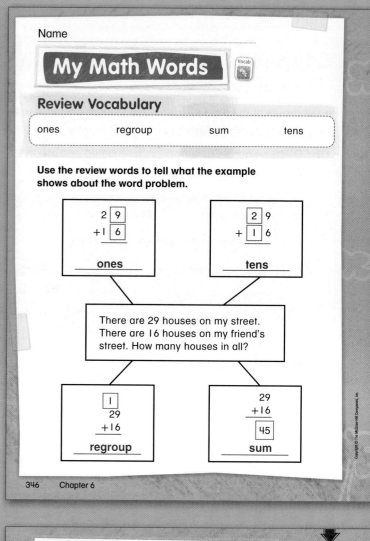

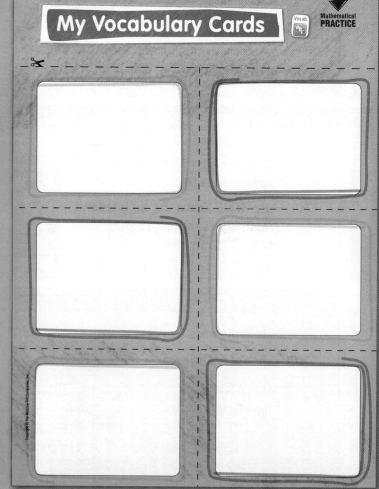

Directions:
Ideas for Use
• Have students use the blank cards to write words from previous chapters that they would like to review.

• Ask students to use the blank cards to write their own vocabulary cards.

Mathematical
PRACTICE 3 **My Vocabulary Card Activities**

Suggestions for using blank cards appear in some Developing Vocabulary Activities.

My Foldable

What's the Math?

Content Standard: 2.NBT.7

Mathematical PRACTICE 5 **Use appropriate tools strategically.**

This Foldable allows students to practice adding three-digit numbers. The yellow column requires no regrouping. The blue column requires regrouping of ones. The green column requires students to regroup both ones and tens.

How Do I Make It?

• Tear out the page and cut off the top banner.

• Fold along the two green dotted lines.

• Cut along the orange dashed lines in four places to make six tabs.

When Do I Use It?

Use after Lesson 5 and as a review tool at the end of the chapter.

How Could I Use It?

• Start with all tabs closed.

• Have students open the yellow tabs and use the base-ten block images to add the numbers. Have students close the tabs and write the answer in the white box.

• Repeat with the blue and green tabs. Some students may benefit from the use of actual base-ten blocks from the manipulative kit.

ELL **ELL Support Strategy** Use this Foldable to provide multiple exposures to three-digit addition.

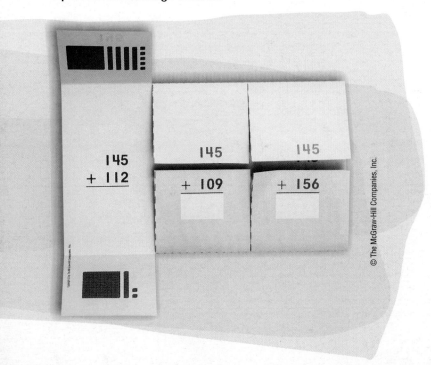

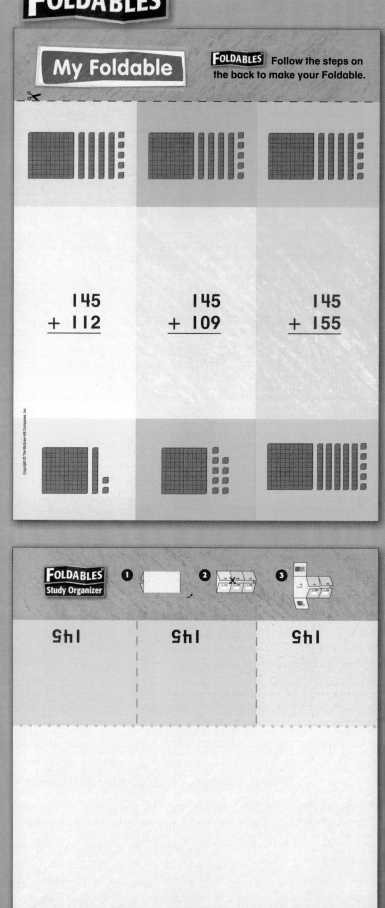

Lunchroom Chat

Building a Learning Community

Sometimes, it may be difficult to relate the mathematical concepts students are studying in the classroom to the real-world. In this chapter, you can relate mathematics to science topics by talking about characteristics of animals. For examples, students may learn that a female tiger weighs about 310 pounds. Ask students how many pounds in all would two female tigers weigh?

Another example might be to ask students to find the number of teeth in all for two dolphins that have 200 teeth each. Have them add mentally. Talk with your colleagues about other examples in science and in other subjects that you could use with three-digit addition.

MY Learning Stations

Use the following learning stations to differentiate the instruction for Chapter 6. Includes Spanish!

Learning Station	Title	Use after Lesson(s)
Game	*Three-Digit Fruit*	6
RWPS Reader	*Lady Liberty*	6
RWPS Reader	*Moving Along*	6
Graphic Novel	*Enchanted Palace Park*	6
Activity Card	*How Many Calories?*	6

RWPS = Real-World Problem Solving

Chapter Project

Practice Game

Students will design and specify rules for an addition game.

- Have students work with a partner or in small groups to design and create a three-digit addition card game or board game.
- Ask students to design their game on paper before they begin to construct it.
- Have all necessary materials available for students to use as they begin the construction of their games.
- Invite students to share their games with the class and explain how their games show three-digit addition.
- Allow time for students to play the addition games before the chapter review and test.

📅 CALENDAR TIME

Adding Days

- Have students choose three months on a calendar.
- Ask students to write an addition sentence to find the total number of days in these months.
- Repeat using three additional months.
- Add the two totals together.

_____ + _____ + _____ = _____

LESSON 1
Make a Hundred to Add

OBJECTIVE Make a hundred to add a three-digit number.

What's the Math?

 Common Core State Standards
DOMAIN: Number and Operations in Base Ten

Standard: 2.NBT.7
The wording of this standard can be found on page 344.

What Students Should Understand

- It is easier to add a two-digit and a three-digit number if one of the numbers is a hundred, or ends in two zeros.
- You can take apart the addends to create a number that is a hundred.

What Students Should be Able to Do

Find $26 + 198$ by taking apart the addends to create a number that is a hundred.

Take apart 26 to make $24 + 2$.

Add $2 + 198$.

Add 24 to that sum.

$$26 + 198$$
$$24 + 2 + 198$$
$$24 + 200 = 224$$

So, $26 + 198 = 224$.

Building on the Essential Question

In this lesson, students will build upon the skills and concepts needed to answer the chapter's Essential Question "How can I add three-digit numbers?"

Developing Vocabulary

 Review Vocabulary

add   hundred

Review Activity

- Write the review words on the board. Ask students what they learned about these words in previous grades or chapters. For example, they might recall that *hundred* can be shown as 100.
- Next, have students browse the lesson. Ask a volunteer to identify the name of the lesson. Make a Hundred to Add
- Ask students why it might be easier to make a hundred before adding greater numbers. It is easy to work with zeroes.

ELL ELL Support Strategy Use this vocabulary activity to assess students' ability to read for understanding.

My Vocabulary Cards

Ask students to use a blank card to write a tip that will help them make a hundred to add.

IWB Virtual Word Wall

All of the words in this chapter are review words. You may wish to add these review words to begin the Virtual Word Wall for this chapter.

ELL Refer to the Multilingual eGlossary for interactive definitions in 13 languages.

Plan Online

Plan for your lesson by using the resources at

connectED.mcgraw-hill.com

Digital Dashboard

Interactive Whiteboard Ready

Vocab
The eBook **Glossary** shows the definition of the word and has audio for each definition. The **eGlossary** provides definitions in 13 languages.

Watch
Watch as concepts are brought to life through **animations**, **songs**, and a variety of visual instruction.

Tools
Virtual Manipulatives with work mats allow teachers and students to model the lesson.

Check
Use **eAssessment** for online assignments and customized assessments.

Use the **Common Core Quick Check** before the lesson to assess students' retention of previously learned concepts.

Use the interactive **Self-Check Quiz** after the lesson to provide immediate feedback on lesson concepts.

eHelp
Digital and print resources assist students and parents in completing My Homework.

Games
Online games and **apps** provide extra practice for lesson concepts.

PD
Professional development videos help teachers gain a deeper understanding of the lesson concepts and strategies.

RtI
Support for **approaching**, **on-** and **beyond-level** students as well as **English Language Learners**.

Masters
Reteach and **Enrich** worksheets, **Manipulative Masters**, the **Problem of the Day**, and other blackline masters are available for each lesson.

LAUNCH THE LESSON

If your students are well-versed in making a hundred to add, you may choose to begin instruction with Step 2, **TEACH**.

You will need

☐ base-ten blocks
☐ Work Mat 7

Mathematical PRACTICE

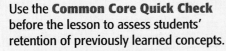

Modeling the Math

Have students use base-ten blocks and Work Mat 7 to model the following problems.

What is 200 + 43? 243

What is 700 + 69? 769

What is 500 + 32? 532

Are you able to add these numbers mentally, without the base-ten blocks? yes *Why?* Sample answer: It is easier to add when there is a hundred.

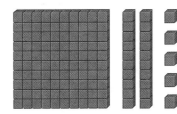

hundreds	tens	ones
☐	☐	

 **Begin core instruction here.**

You will need

☐ base-ten blocks

Explore and Explain

Read the directions that are on the bottom of the student page. Guide students in using base-ten blocks to model 97 and 16. Then lead them through moving some ones from 16 to 97 to make 100.

How many ones do you need to move from 16 to 97 to make 100? 3 ones

How many base-ten blocks are left after removing 3 from 16? 13 base-ten blocks

Write the numbers modeled by the base-ten blocks as the addends in the addition number sentence. What is the sum of 100 + 13? 113

Is it easier to find 97 + 16, or 100 + 13? 100 + 13 *Why?* Sample answer: One of the addends ends in 0.

See and Show

Help students work through the example at the top of the page. Help students recognize that the goal is to take apart an addend to make a hundred with the other addend. In the example shown, 43 was taken apart into 42 and 1 so that 199 could become 200. Then the student is adding 200 + 42 rather than 199 + 43.

Using hundreds simplifies the addition. Have students trace the dashed numbers as they work through the problems.

Work through Exercises 1 and 2 as a class.

Mathematical PRACTICE 3 **Talk Math**

Discuss with students "Explain how you know which addend to take apart to make a hundred to add." Sample answer: I decide which number is closest to a hundred and take that many from the other number.

Name _____

Numbers and Operations in Base Ten
2.NBT.7

Make a Hundred to Add

Lesson 1
ESSENTIAL QUESTION
How can I add three-digit numbers?

Explore and Explain ▶ Watch Tools

Gee, how do I get to G Street?

97 + 16 = _____

<u>100</u> + <u>13</u> = <u>113</u>

Teacher Directions: Model using base-ten blocks. My town has 97 streets named by numbers and 16 streets named by letters of the alphabet. How many streets are named by numbers or letters of the alphabet? Take the ones from 16 and add them to 97 to make 100. Write the new problem. Add.

Online Content at ✏connectED.mcgraw-hill.com   Chapter 6 • Lesson 1   351

See and Show

 Mathematical PRACTICE

You can make a hundred to help you add.
Find 199 + 43.

Take apart 43 to make 1 + 42.
Then add 1 + 199. Add 42 to that sum.

Helpful Hint
1 + 199 = 200

$$199 + 43$$
$$199 + 1 + 42$$
$$200 + 42 = \textbf{242}$$
So, 199 + 43 = **242**.

Make a hundred to add.

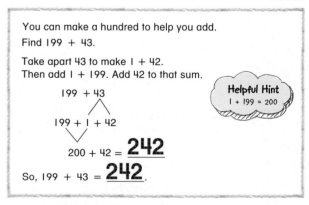
1.   77 + 298

<u>75</u> + <u>2</u> + 298

75 + <u>**300**</u> = <u>375</u>

So, 77 + 298 = <u>**375**</u>.

2.   237 + 99

<u>236</u> + <u>1</u> + 99

236 + <u>**100**</u> = <u>336</u>

So, 237 + 99 = <u>**336**</u>.

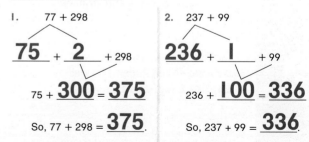
Talk Math Explain how you know which addend to take apart to make a hundred to add.

352   Chapter 6 • Lesson 1

③ PRACTICE & APPLY

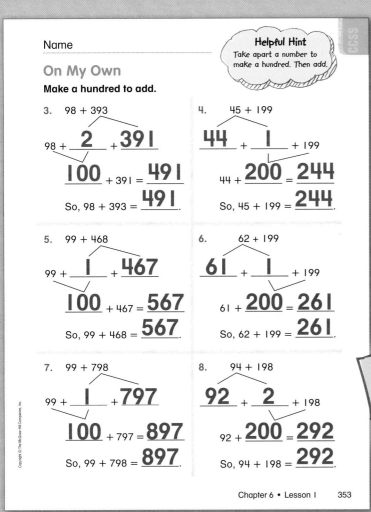

Name ....

Helpful Hint
Take apart a number to make a hundred. Then add.

On My Own

Make a hundred to add.

3. 98 + 393

98 + **2** + 391

100 + 391 = **491**

So, 98 + 393 = **491**.

4. 45 + 199

44 + **1** + 199

44 + **200** = **244**

So, 45 + 199 = **244**.

5. 99 + 468

99 + **1** + 467

100 + 467 = **567**

So, 99 + 468 = **567**.

6. 62 + 199

61 + **1** + 199

61 + **200** = **261**

So, 62 + 199 = **261**.

7. 99 + 798

99 + **1** + 797

100 + 797 = **897**

So, 99 + 798 = **897**.

8. 94 + 198

92 + **2** + 198

92 + **200** = **292**

So, 94 + 198 = **292**.

Chapter 6 • Lesson 1   353

On My Own

Have students work through the exercises on this page independently. You may choose to assign exercises based on the chart below.

DIFFERENTIATED ASSIGNMENTS

AL **Approaching Level** Guide students through the exercises in On My Own. Help them to use manipulatives while working on the exercises.

OL **On Level** Complete the exercises independently.

BL **Beyond Level** Complete the exercises independently without manipulatives.

Common Error!

Some students may have trouble breaking apart the addends to make a hundred. If they are making mistakes, have them talk you through the process step by step to discover where the error is being made.

Problem Solving

Have students work through the problem-solving exercises on this page independently.

Mathematical PRACTICE ④ In Exercise 11, students **model with mathematics.**

Write Math

This exercise asks students to build upon their understanding of concepts needed to answer the chapter's Essential Question.

🌎 **Problem Solving**

Mathematical **PRACTICE**

9. There are 299 animals at the fair. 76 more animals are brought to the fair. How many animals are at the fair now?

I'm the prettiest pig at the fair!

375 animals

10. There are 334 people at the town fair. 89 more people come to the fair. How many people are at the fair in all?

423 people

11. Leon is adding a number to 35. He takes apart 35 into 33 and 2 so he can use the 2 to make a hundred. Is Leon adding 199 or 198 to 35?

198

Write Math How does taking apart a number help you add to a three-digit number?

Sample answer: When you take apart a number you can

make another number that is easier to add to take off.

RtI RESPONSE TO INTERVENTION

DIFFERENTIATED INSTRUCTION

AL APPROACHING LEVEL

IF my students struggle with making a hundred to add,

THEN choose a resource:

→ Use the Reteach worksheet with small groups.

→ Go online for a Differentiated Instruction activity.

→ **Another Way to Add** Explore a different strategy for adding numbers. Start with 65 + 498. Explain that you are going to add the same number to both addends to make it easier to add.

If you add 2 to both addends, what is the new problem and sum? 67 + 500 = 567

Are we done? No; we need to subtract the 2 we added to each addend. So to find our final sum we subtract 567 − 4. *What is the sum?* 563

OL ON LEVEL

IF my students seem to know how to make a hundred to add, but need more practice,

THEN choose a resource:

→ Assign My Homework.

→ Go online for a Differentiated Instruction activity.

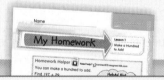

BL BEYOND LEVEL

IF my students have mastered making a hundred to add,

THEN choose a resource:

→ Use a Differentiated Instruction activity from p. 343B.

→ Use the Enrich worksheet in cooperative groups.

→ Assign My Homework.

→ Go online for a Differentiated Instruction activity.

AL Name _____

Lesson 1   Reteach

Make a Hundred to Add

> **Make a hundred to help you add.**
>
> 299 + 34   You can make a hundred by breaking apart a number.
>   / \
>   1 33   Break apart 34. 34 can break apart into 1 + 33. Add 1 + 299.
>
> 299 + 1 = __300__.
>
> And then you add __300__ + __33__ = __333__.

Make a hundred to add.

1.   138 + 99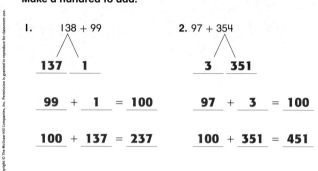

    137   **1**

    99 + **1** = **100**

    100 + **137** = **237**

2. 97 + 354

    3   **351**

    97 + **3** = **100**

    100 + **351** = **451**

BL Name _____

Lesson 1   Enrich

Make a Hundred to Add

Find the missing digits in the place-value chart.
Write the missing digits in the chart.

hundreds	tens	ones
5	3	5
3	4	**6**
8	8	1

(+ shown before the second row)

    Player 1   **Player 2**

Spinner Player 1: 8 1 2 3 4 5 6 7
Spinner Player 2: 8 1 2 3 4 5 6 7

Directions:

1. Use a pencil and a paper clip to make a spinner on each game board.
2. Take turns spinning for the missing digits.
3. If your spinner stops on a missing digit, color the space red.
4. The first player to color 3 spaces red is the winner.

355A   Chapter 6 Add Three-Digit Numbers

My Homework

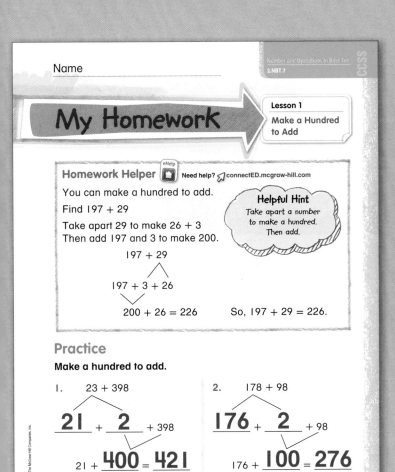

Name _____

Number and Operations in Base Ten
2.NBT.7

CCSS

My Homework →

Lesson 1
Make a Hundred
to Add

Homework Helper 🖥 Need help? 🔗 connectED.mcgraw-hill.com

You can make a hundred to add.

Find 197 + 29

Take apart 29 to make 26 + 3
Then add 197 and 3 to make 200.

Helpful Hint
Take apart a number to make a hundred. Then add.

197 + 29

197 + 3 + 26

200 + 26 = 226   So, 197 + 29 = 226.

Practice

Make a hundred to add.

1.   23 + 398

21 + **2** + 398

21 + **400** = **421**

So, 23 + 398 = **421**.

2.   178 + 98

176 + **2** + 98

176 + **100** = **276**

So, 178 + 98 = **276**.

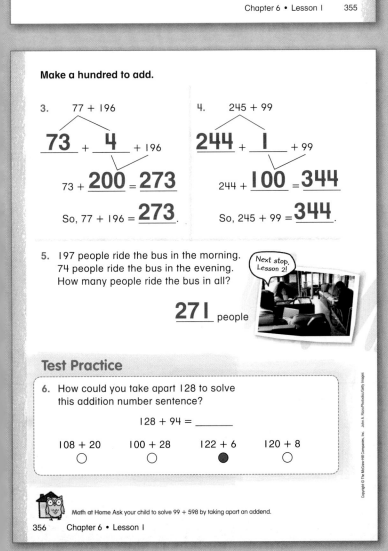

Make a hundred to add.

3.   77 + 196

73 + **4** + 196

73 + **200** = **273**

So, 77 + 196 = **273**.

4.   245 + 99

244 + **1** + 99

244 + **100** = **344**

So, 245 + 99 = **344**.

5. 197 people ride the bus in the morning. 74 people ride the bus in the evening. How many people ride the bus in all?

271 people

Next stop, Lesson 2!

Test Practice

6. How could you take apart 128 to solve this addition number sentence?

128 + 94 = _____

| 108 + 20 | 100 + 28 | 122 + 6 | 120 + 8 |
| ○ | ○ | ● | ○ |

Math at Home Ask your child to solve 99 + 598 by taking apart an addend.

My Homework

Assign homework after successful completion of the lesson. Students who understand the concepts may skip the **Homework Helper** section.

Test Practice

Diagnose Student Errors

Class trends in wrong answers may indicate common errors or misconceptions.

108 + 20 94 + 108 do not make a hundred

100 + 28 usual assumption, but when added will not make a hundred

122 + 6   correct

120 + 8   94 + 8 do not make a hundred

Formative Assessment

Ask students to model and solve 115 + 99 using base-ten blocks and Work Mat 7. Have students show you how to take apart the numbers to make it easier to add.

Line Up!
As students line up for recess, lunch, or dismissal, give addition problems that can be taken apart to add. For example, 345 + 99. Have students explain how they would make a hundred to add.
344 + 100 = 444

LESSON 2
Add Hundreds
OBJECTIVE   Add numbers in the hundreds.

What's the Math?

 Common Core State Standards
DOMAIN: Number and Operations in Base Ten

Standards: 2.NBT.7, 2.NBT.9
The wording of these standards can be found on page 344.

What Students Should Understand
- You can use addition facts to add numbers in the hundreds.

What Students Should be Able to Do
Find $500 + 300$.

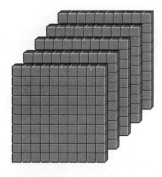 

You know that $5 + 3 = 8$.

$$\begin{array}{r} 5 \text{ hundreds} \\ + 3 \text{ hundreds} \\ \hline 8 \text{ hundreds} \end{array}$$

$500 + 300 = 800$

 Building on the Essential Question

In this lesson, students will build upon the skills and concepts needed to answer the chapter's Essential Question "How can I add three-digit numbers?"

Developing Vocabulary

 Review Vocabulary
zero

Review Activity
- Have students browse the first two pages of the lesson. Ask them what they notice about the addition sentences. The addends are all numbers in the hundreds place, with zeroes in the ones and tens places.
- Direct students' attention to the cloud at the top of the second page. Explain that recalling basic facts will help them solve the exercises in this lesson. Remind students that text in text features like this is a signal to readers to reread for important information.

ELL **ELL Support Strategy** Use this vocabulary activity to develop and advance mathematical language skills.

My Vocabulary Cards
Have students use blank cards to write problems showing adding hundreds. Have them work with a partner to answer each other's problems.

Plan Online

Plan for your lesson by using the resources at
connectED.mcgraw-hill.com

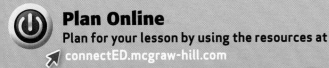

Digital Dashboard

Interactive Whiteboard Ready

Vocab

The eBook **Glossary** shows the definition of the word and has audio for each definition. The **eGlossary** provides definitions in 13 languages.

Watch

Watch as concepts are brought to life through **animations**, **songs**, and a variety of visual instruction.

Tools

Virtual Manipulatives with work mats allow teachers and students to model the lesson.

Check

Use **eAssessment** for online assignments and customized assessments.

Use the **Common Core Quick Check** before the lesson to assess students' retention of previously learned concepts.

Use the interactive **Self-Check Quiz** after the lesson to provide immediate feedback on lesson concepts.

eHelp

Digital and print resources assist students and parents in completing My Homework.

Games

Online games and **apps** provide extra practice for lesson concepts.

PD

Professional development videos help teachers gain a deeper understanding of the lesson concepts and strategies.

RtI

Support for **approaching**, **on**- and **beyond-level** students as well as **English Language Learners**.

Masters

Reteach and **Enrich** worksheets, **Manipulative Masters**, the **Problem of the Day**, and other blackline masters are available for each lesson.

---

1 LAUNCH THE LESSON

CCSS

If your students are well-versed in adding hundreds, you may choose to begin instruction with Step 2, **TEACH**.

You will need
☐ hundred flats

Mathematical PRACTICE 4 Modeling the Math

Display a hundred flat for students.

> *How many hundreds?* 1

Put two more hundred flats near the first.

> *How many more hundreds?* 2
> *How many hundreds altogether?* 3

Give groups of students several hundred flats, and ask them to make hundreds problems for one another. After a few minutes, ask one person from each group to share a problem with the entire group.

TEACH

🕐 **Begin core instruction here.**

You will need

☐ base-ten blocks

Explore and Explain

Read the directions that are at the bottom of the student page.

Which base-ten blocks will you use to model 200 and 100? 2 hundreds flats and 1 hundred flat

These two numbers are the addends in the addition number sentence. Write them in the blanks.

Point to the 2 and the 1 in the hundreds place in the two addends.

You can use a basic addition fact to find 200 + 100. What basic addition fact can you use with these two numbers? 2 + 1 = 3

Write the sum of the basic addition fact. In this case, the sum is 3. Then, to the right of the 3, write the same number of zeros that are in the addends. How many zeros will you write to the right of 3? 2 zeros

What is 200 + 100? 300

See and Show

Help students work through the example at the top of the page. Have them trace the dashed numbers as they work through the problems.

Work through Exercises 1–9 as a class.

 **Talk Math**

Discuss with students "What addition fact can help you find 600 + 100? Explain." Sample answer: 6 + 1, or 1 + 6. I know that 6 + 1 = 7, so 600 + 100 = 700

Name _____

2.NBT.7, 2.NBT.9

Add Hundreds

Lesson 2
ESSENTIAL QUESTION
How can I add three-digit numbers?

Explore and Explain ▶ Watch 🔧 Tools

WOW!

Say ah!

$$200 + 100 = 300 \text{ patients}$$

🦉 **Teacher Directions:** Model using base-ten blocks. The doctor in my town saw 200 patients last month. This month he has seen 100 patients. How many patients has the doctor seen in all? Write the addition sentence.

Online Content at 🖱 connectED.mcgraw-hill.com   Chapter 6 • Lesson 2   357

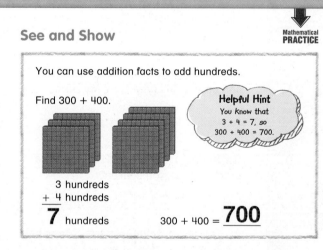

See and Show   Mathematical **PRACTICE**

You can use addition facts to add hundreds.

Find 300 + 400.

Helpful Hint
You know that
3 + 4 = 7, so
300 + 400 = 700.

3 hundreds
+ 4 hundreds
7 hundreds

$$300 + 400 = 700$$

Add.

1. $600 + 100 = 700$
2. $300 + 300 = 600$
3. $200 + 300 = 500$
4. $700 + 200 = 900$
5. $400 + 200 = 600$
6. $800 + 100 = 900$

7. $\begin{array}{r} 200 \\ + 100 \\ \hline 300 \end{array}$
8. $\begin{array}{r} 100 \\ + 300 \\ \hline 400 \end{array}$
9. $\begin{array}{r} 500 \\ + 200 \\ \hline 700 \end{array}$

 Talk Math   What addition fact can help you find 600 + 100? Explain.

358   Chapter 6 • Lesson 2

357-358   Chapter 6 Add Three-Digit Numbers

Name _____

On My Own

Add.

10. 200 + 300 = **500**   11. 400 + 400 = **800**

12. 700 + 100 = **800**   13. 600 + 300 = **900**

14. 400 + 200 = **600**   15. 100 + 100 = **200**

16. 300 + 400 **700**	17. 100 + 800 **900**	18. 200 + 600 **800**
19. 500 + 300 **800**	20. 200 + 700 **900**	21. 400 + 300 **700**
22. 600 + 200 **800**	23. 300 + 100 **400**	24. 900 + 0 **900**

25. 700
    + 100
    800

Here's the news...
You can add 100s!

Chapter 6 • Lesson 2   359

Problem Solving

Mathematical
PRACTICE

26. Ava counts 100 cars in a parking lot. She counts 200 cars in another parking lot. How many cars did Ava count in all?

    300 cars

27. A baker bakes 400 bagels on Saturday. He bakes 200 bagels on Sunday. How many bagels does he bake on those two days?

    600 bagels

28. Jan delivers 300 newspapers on Friday. She delivers 400 newspapers on Sunday. How many newspapers did she deliver in all?

    700 newspapers

HOT Problem Pam has collected 100 pull-tabs for charity. Jake has 100 of them and Pat has 200. How many do they have altogether? Tell how knowing addition facts can help you solve this problem. Solve.

Sample answer: I know that 1 + 1 + 2 = 4

so 100 + 100 + 200 = 400

---

³PRACTICE & APPLY

On My Own

Have students work through the exercises on this page independently. You may choose to assign exercises based on the chart below.

DIFFERENTIATED ASSIGNMENTS

AL **Approaching Level** Guide students through the exercises in On My Own. Help them to use manipulatives while working through the exercises.

OL **On Level** Complete the exercises independently.

BL **Beyond Level** Complete the exercises independently without manipulatives.

Common Error!
Students may write the wrong number of zeros after the hundreds digit. Review place value and stress that a hundreds number always has three digits, and that the third digit to the left is the hundreds digit.

Problem Solving

Have students work through the problem-solving exercises on this page independently.

Mathematical
PRACTICE 1 In Exercise 28, students **make sense of problems and persevere in solving them.**

HOT Problem This exercise asks students to build upon their understanding of concepts needed to answer the chapter's Essential Question.

RESPONSE TO INTERVENTION

DIFFERENTIATED INSTRUCTION

AL APPROACHING LEVEL

IF my students struggle with adding hundreds,

THEN choose a resource:

→ Use a Differentiated Instruction activity from p. 343B.

→ Use the Reteach worksheet with small groups.

→ Go online for a Differentiated Instruction activity.

→ **Addition Facts Review** Have partners use or create a set of basic addition facts on index cards or paper cut to approximately the same size to quiz each other.

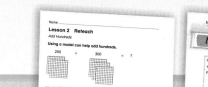

OL ON LEVEL

IF my students seem to know how to add hundreds, but need more practice,

THEN choose a resource:

→ Use a Differentiated Instruction activity from p. 343B.

→ Assign My Homework.

→ Go online for a Differentiated Instruction activity.

BL BEYOND LEVEL

IF my students have mastered adding hundreds,

THEN choose a resource:

→ Use the Enrich worksheet in cooperative groups.

→ Assign My Homework.

→ Go online for a Differentiated Instruction activity.

AL

Name _____

Lesson 2 Reteach
Add Hundreds

Using a model can help add hundreds.

$$200 \quad + \quad 300 \quad = \quad ?$$

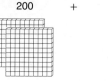

count: 100, 200   count on: 300, 400, 500

$$200 \quad + \quad 300 \quad = \quad 500$$

Model using base-ten blocks. Write the sum.

1. $100 \quad + \quad 200 \quad = \quad \underline{300}$

---

2. $100 + 300 = \underline{400}$ 3. $200 + 200 = \underline{400}$

4. $100 + 100 = \underline{200}$ 5. $200 + 300 = \underline{500}$

6. $200 + 100 = \underline{300}$ 7. $400 + 100 = \underline{500}$

8. $300 + 400 = \underline{700}$ 9. $200 + 400 = \underline{600}$

BL

Name _____

Lesson 2 Enrich
Add Hundreds

Draw lines to connect two or more numbers whose sums are greater than 1,000.

See students' work, but sum must be > 1,000.

100	200	300
200	300	400
300	400	500
500	600	700
600	700	800
700	800	900

Write six of the number combinations on the lines.

See students' work.

_____

_____

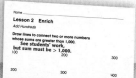
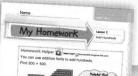

My Homework

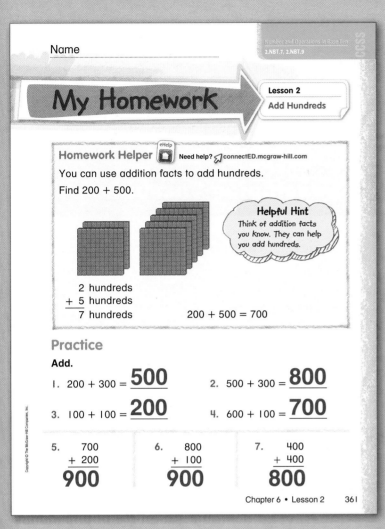

Name _____

Number and Operations in Base Ten
2.NBT.7, 2.NBT.9

Lesson 2
Add Hundreds

Homework Helper 🖲 Need help? 🔍 connectED.mcgraw-hill.com

You can use addition facts to add hundreds.

Find 200 + 500.

Helpful Hint
Think of addition facts you know. They can help you add hundreds.

2 hundreds
+ 5 hundreds
7 hundreds   200 + 500 = 700

Practice

Add.

1. 200 + 300 = **500**

2. 500 + 300 = **800**

3. 100 + 100 = **200**

4. 600 + 100 = **700**

5. 700
  + 200
  900

6. 800
  + 100
  900

7. 400
  + 400
  800

Chapter 6 • Lesson 2   361

Add.

8.   100
  + 200
  300

9.   500
  + 100
  600

10.   200
  + 400
  600

11.   100
  + 700
  800

12.   100
  + 400
  500

13.   300
  + 300
  600

14.   700
  + 200
  900

15.   500
  + 400
  900

16.   200
  + 600
  800

17. Zoe counts 300 seeds in her pumpkin.
Michael counts 500 seeds in his pumpkin.
How many seeds do they count in all?
800 seeds

Test Practice

18. Find the sum.

600 + 300 = _____

○ 900 ●   ○ 300 ○   ○ 9 ○   ○ 3 ○

Math at Home Ask your child how knowing 4 + 5 = 9 helps him or her find 400 + 500.

---

4 WRAP IT UP

My Homework

Assign homework after successful completion of the lesson. Students who understand the concepts may skip the **Homework Helper** section.

Test Practice

Diagnose Student Errors

Class trends in wrong answers may indicate common errors or misconceptions.

900 correct

300 subtracted

9 omitted the zeros in the tens and ones places

3 misunderstood concept

Formative Assessment

How would I begin adding 300 + 200? Remember the addition fact, 3 + 2 = 5, then make sure that you fill in the right number of zeros after the 5 in the sum.

Line Up!

As students line up for recess, lunch, or dismissal, ask each one a true or false addition question such as:

- *True or false: 200 + 200 = 400.* true
- *True or false: 100 + 250 = 200.* false
- *If the student answers incorrectly, have the next student tell the correct answer.*

LESSON 3
Mentally Add 10 or 100
OBJECTIVE Students will add 10 or 100 mentally.

What's the Math?

 Common Core State Standards
DOMAIN: Number and Operations in Base Ten

Standard: 2.NBT.8
The wording of this standard can be found on page 344.

What Students Should Understand
- You can use mental math to add 10 or 100 to a number.
- You can use base-ten blocks to model adding 10 or 100 to a number if needed.

What Students Should be Able to Do
Mentally add 100.

$$\begin{array}{r} 325 \\ +\ 100 \end{array} \quad \text{Think: } 3 + 1 = 4, \text{ so} \quad \begin{array}{r} 325 \\ +\ 100 \\ \hline 425 \end{array}$$

Mentally add 10.

$$\begin{array}{r} 370 \\ +\ 10 \end{array} \quad \text{Think: } 7 + 1 = 8, \text{ so} \quad \begin{array}{r} 370 \\ +\ 10 \\ \hline 380 \end{array}$$

 Building on the Essential Question
In this lesson, students will build upon the skills and concepts needed to answer the chapter's Essential Question "How can I add three-digit numbers?"

Developing Vocabulary

Review Vocabulary
addition

Review Activity
- Discuss with students how they use basic facts when adding two-digit numbers. For example, they might explain that they use basic facts when adding the numbers in the ones place, and then in the tens place.
- Have students browse the text box on the second page of the lesson. Have volunteers point out examples of how basic facts are used to solve the three-digit addition examples.

ELL **ELL Support Strategy** Use this vocabulary activity to link to familiar contexts and prior knowledge.

My Vocabulary Cards
Have students work in small groups. Tell them to use a blank card to write a main idea about adding three-digit numbers. Ask each group to share their main idea.

Plan Online
Plan for your lesson by using the resources at
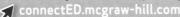 connectED.mcgraw-hill.com

Digital Dashboard

Interactive Whiteboard Ready

 Vocab The eBook **Glossary** shows the definition of the word and has audio for each definition. The **eGlossary** provides definitions in 13 languages.

 Watch Watch as concepts are brought to life through **animations**, **songs**, and a variety of visual instruction.

 Tools **Virtual Manipulatives** with work mats allow teachers and students to model the lesson.

 Check Use **eAssessment** for online assignments and customized assessments.

Use the **Common Core Quick Check** before the lesson to assess students' retention of previously learned concepts.

Use the interactive **Self-Check Quiz** after the lesson to provide immediate feedback on lesson concepts.

 eHelp Digital and print resources assist students and parents in completing My Homework.

 Games **Online games** and **apps** provide extra practice for lesson concepts.

 PD **Professional development videos** help teachers gain a deeper understanding of the lesson concepts and strategies.

 RtI Support for **approaching**, **on-** and **beyond-level** students as well as **English Language Learners**.

 Masters **Reteach** and **Enrich** worksheets, **Manipulative Masters**, the **Problem of the Day**, and other blackline masters are available for each lesson.

 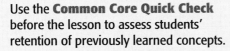

1 LAUNCH THE LESSON

 If your students are well-versed in mentally adding 10 or 100, you may choose to begin instruction with Step 2, **TEACH**.

Mathematical PRACTICE 4 Modeling the Math

Use a number line to demonstrate counting by 100s. You may wish to either draw a number line that has the hundreds marked to 1,000, or use one from the virtual manipulatives.

Let's start at 100, and skip count by 100s. Students should count 100, 200, 300, 400… 1,000.

Count again. Start at 100 and stop at 400.

At what number did we stop? 400 *If you want to add 100, what number would we land on?* 500 *Suppose you stopped at 400 and you want to add 200. What number do you end on now?* 600

Discuss with students how they can add 100 mentally to a number such as 100, 400, and 600. Then ask students how they would go about mentally adding 100 to a number such as 350.

Suppose you start at 350. Where would you be on the number line if you add 100? 450

Suppose you start at 750. Where would you be on the number line if you add 100? 850

Have students explain how they would mentally add 100 to 234.

Suppose you begin at 234 and you add one hundred. Where would you land on a number line? 334

Continue to give examples to reinforce the concept of mentally adding 100 to numbers such as 600, 340, and 569.

21ST CENTURY SKILLS

Critical Thinking

Mental arithmetic may be challenging for some students. This is a chance to reinforce place value and have them think critically about which digits of the number may change with the addition of 10s or 100s to the number. Even more so, students can be challenged in a later lesson on adding a multiple of 10 when it will result in renaming.

TEACH

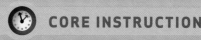 **Begin core instruction here.**

You will need

☐ base-ten blocks

Explore and Explain

Read the directions that are at the bottom of the student page. Explain to students that there are a few steps involved in solving this problem. Tell them that you will work on solving this problem one step at a time.

Guide students in using base-ten blocks to model 126 to represent the number of students that are waiting in line for each bus.

> *Let's use base-ten blocks to model the number 126. How many hundreds, tens, and ones will you use?* 1 hundred, 2 tens, and 6 ones

Discuss that 100 more students get in line for the yellow bus. Guide students to use base-ten blocks to add 100 to 126.

> *There are 126 students in line for the yellow bus, and 100 more students get in line for the yellow bus. You have modeled 126. Place another hundred flat with your models. How many hundreds, tens, and ones do you have now?* 2 hundreds, 2 tens, and 6 ones *How many students are in line in all for the yellow bus?* 226 students

Have students remove one of the hundreds flats from the model.

Discuss that 10 more students get in line for the green bus. Guide students to use base-ten blocks to add 10 to 126.

> *There are 126 students in line for the green bus, and 10 more students get in line for the green bus. You have modeled 126. Place another tens rod with your models. How many hundreds, tens, and ones do you have now?* 1 hundred, 3 tens, and 6 ones *How many students are in line in all for the green bus?* 136 students

See and Show

Help students work through the example at the top of the page. Stress that to add 10 or 100 they only need to look at a simple fact they already know. Have them trace the dashed numbers as they work through the problems.

Work through Exercises 1–8 as a class.

Mathematical PRACTICE ③ Talk Math

Discuss with students "Why is it easy to mentally add 10 or 100?" Sample answer: Because you are only adding 1 to either the tens or the hundreds place. All other numbers stay the same.

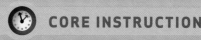 **CORE INSTRUCTION**

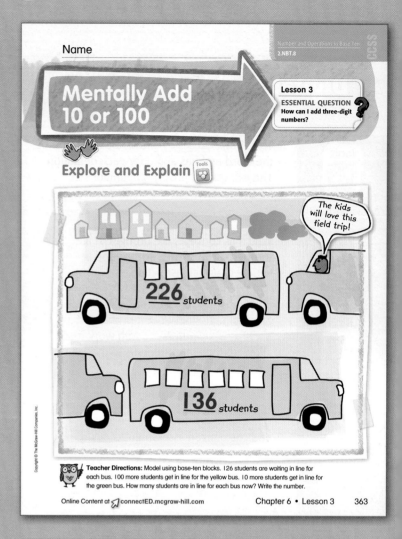

Name _____

Number and Operations in Base Ten
2.NBT.8

Mentally Add 10 or 100

Lesson 3

ESSENTIAL QUESTION
How can I add three-digit numbers?

Explore and Explain

The kids will love this field trip!

226 students

136 students

Teacher Directions: Model using base-ten blocks. 126 students are waiting in line for each bus. 100 more students get in line for the yellow bus. 10 more students get in line for the green bus. How many students are in line for each bus now? Write the number.

Online Content at connectED.mcgraw-hill.com   Chapter 6 • Lesson 3   363

See and Show

 Mathematical PRACTICE

To add 10 or 100, think of addition facts you know.

Mentally add 100.

$$\begin{array}{r} 215 \\ + 100 \\ \hline \end{array}$$

Helpful Hint
You Know that
2 + 1 = 3.

$$\begin{array}{r} 215 \\ + 100 \\ \hline 315 \end{array}$$

Mentally add 10.

$$\begin{array}{r} 250 \\ + 10 \\ \hline \end{array}$$

Helpful Hint
You Know that
5 + 1 = 6.

$$\begin{array}{r} 250 \\ + 10 \\ \hline 260 \end{array}$$

Add.

1. $\begin{array}{r} 450 \\ + 100 \\ \hline 550 \end{array}$	2. $\begin{array}{r} 630 \\ + 10 \\ \hline 640 \end{array}$	3. $\begin{array}{r} 801 \\ + 100 \\ \hline 901 \end{array}$
4. $\begin{array}{r} 115 \\ + 10 \\ \hline 125 \end{array}$	5. $\begin{array}{r} 500 \\ + 10 \\ \hline 510 \end{array}$	6. $\begin{array}{r} 237 \\ + 100 \\ \hline 337 \end{array}$

7. $327 + 100 = $ **427**   8. $755 + 10 = $ **765**

Talk Math  Why is it easy to mentally add 10 or 100?

364   Chapter 6 • Lesson 3

Name _____

On My Own

Add.

9.	122 + 100 **222**	10.	378 + 10 **388**	11.	500 + 10 **510**
12.	200 + 100 **300**	13.	747 + 100 **847**	14.	800 + 10 **810**
15.	400 + 10 **410**	16.	668 + 100 **768**	17.	817 + 100 **917**

Find the missing addend.

18. 392 + **100** = 492

19. 815 + 10 = **825**

20. 101 + **10** = 111

21. 756 + 100 = **856**

22. **723** + 100 = 823

23. **836** + 10 = 846

24. 385 + **100** = 485

Hi neighbor!

Chapter 6 • Lesson 3   365

 ## Problem Solving

Mathematical PRACTICE

25. 448 birds are in the park. 100 more birds fly into the park. How many birds are in the park now?

548 birds

26. A mail carrier delivered 352 packages last month. She delivered 10 more packages last week. How many packages did she deliver in all?

362 packages

Do you like my hair style?

27. There are 112 sheep in a barn. More sheep come into the barn. Now there are 122 sheep. How many sheep came into the barn?

10 sheep

Write Math Explain how to add 100 to 899.

Sample answer: Mentally add 100 and 800 to get 900, and keep 99 the same. So, 100 + 899 is 999.

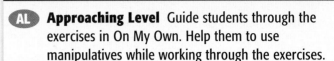

On My Own

Have students work through the exercises on this page independently. You may choose to assign exercises based on the chart below.

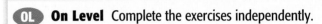
DIFFERENTIATED ASSIGNMENTS

AL **Approaching Level** Guide students through the exercises in On My Own. Help them to use manipulatives while working through the exercises.

OL **On Level** Complete the exercises independently.

BL **Beyond Level** Complete the exercises independently without manipulatives.

Problem Solving

Have students work through the problem-solving exercises on this page independently.

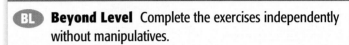
Mathematical PRACTICE 2   In Exercise 27, students **reason abstractly and quantitatively.**

Write Math

This exercise asks students to build upon their understanding of concepts needed to answer the chapter's Essential Question.

AL APPROACHING LEVEL

IF my students struggle with mentally adding 10 or 100,

THEN choose a resource:

→ Use the Reteach worksheet with small groups.

→ Go online for a Differentiated Instruction activity.

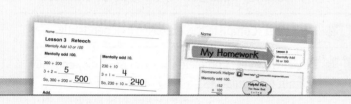

OL ON LEVEL

IF my students seem to know how to mentally add 10 or 100, but need more practice,

THEN choose a resource:

→ Assign My Homework.

→ Go online for a Differentiated Instruction activity.

BL BEYOND LEVEL

IF my students have mastered mentally adding 10 or 100,

THEN choose a resource:

→ Use the Enrich worksheet in cooperative groups.

→ Assign My Homework.

→ Go online for a Differentiated Instruction activity.

AL Name _____

Lesson 3   Reteach
Mentally Add 10 or 100

Mentally add 100.

300 + 200

3 + 2 = ___5___

So, 300 + 200 = __500__.

Mentally add 10.

230 + 10

3 + 1 = ___4___

So, 230 + 10 = __240__.

Add.

1. 500 + 200

   5 + 2 = ___7___

   So, 500 + 200 = __700__

2. 650 + 20

   5 + 2 = ___7___

   So, 650 + 20 = __670__.

3. 600 + 300

   6 + 3 = ___9___

   So, 600 + 300 = __900__.

4. 870 + 10

   7 + 1 = ___8___

   So, 870 + 10 = __880__.

5. 400 + 400

   4 + 4 = ___8___

   So, 400 + 400 = __800__.

6. 330 + 30

   3 + 3 = ___6___

   So, 330 + 30 = __360__.

BL Name _____

Lesson 3   Enrich
Mentally Add 10 or 100

Mentally add 100.

300 + 200 = __500__

Mentally add 10.

230 + 10 = __240__

Add.

1. 500 + 200 = __700__

2. 650 + 20 = __670__

3. 600 + 300 = __900__

4. 870 + 10 = __880__

5. 400 + 400 = __800__

6. 330 + 30 = __360__

7. 800 + 100 = __900__

8. 820 + 70 = __890__

9. 400 + 300 = __700__

10. 460 + 20 = __480__

11. 600 + 200 = __800__

12. 210 + 10 = __220__

13. 200 + 200 = __400__

14. 660 + 30 = __690__

15. 100 + 600 = __700__

16. 250 + 40 = __290__

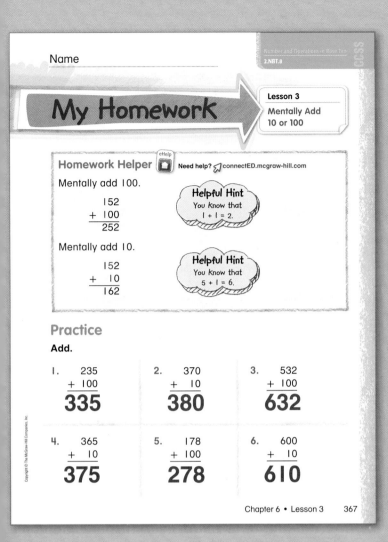

Name _____

My Homework

Lesson 3
Mentally Add
10 or 100

Homework Helper Need help? connectED.mcgraw-hill.com

Mentally add 100.

$$\begin{array}{r} 152 \\ + 100 \\ \hline 252 \end{array}$$

Helpful Hint
You know that
1 + 1 = 2.

Mentally add 10.

$$\begin{array}{r} 152 \\ + 10 \\ \hline 162 \end{array}$$

Helpful Hint
You know that
5 + 1 = 6.

Practice

Add.

1. $\begin{array}{r} 235 \\ + 100 \\ \hline \mathbf{335} \end{array}$ 2. $\begin{array}{r} 370 \\ + 10 \\ \hline \mathbf{380} \end{array}$ 3. $\begin{array}{r} 532 \\ + 100 \\ \hline \mathbf{632} \end{array}$

4. $\begin{array}{r} 365 \\ + 10 \\ \hline \mathbf{375} \end{array}$ 5. $\begin{array}{r} 178 \\ + 100 \\ \hline \mathbf{278} \end{array}$ 6. $\begin{array}{r} 600 \\ + 10 \\ \hline \mathbf{610} \end{array}$

Chapter 6 • Lesson 3   367

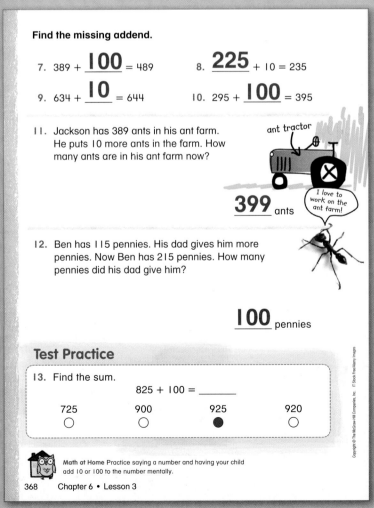

Find the missing addend.

7. $389 + \mathbf{100} = 489$ 8. $\mathbf{225} + 10 = 235$

9. $634 + \mathbf{10} = 644$ 10. $295 + \mathbf{100} = 395$

11. Jackson has 389 ants in his ant farm. He puts 10 more ants in the farm. How many ants are in his ant farm now?

ant tractor

I love to work on the ant farm!

399 ants

12. Ben has 115 pennies. His dad gives him more pennies. Now Ben has 215 pennies. How many pennies did his dad give him?

100 pennies

Test Practice

13. Find the sum.

$$825 + 100 = \underline{\hspace{1cm}}$$

725 ○   900 ○   925 ●   920 ○

Math at Home Practice saying a number and having your child add 10 or 100 to the number mentally.

---

4 WRAP IT UP

CCSS

My Homework

Assign homework after successful completion of the lesson. Students who understand the concepts may skip the **Homework Helper** section.

Test Practice

Diagnose Student Errors

Class trends in wrong answers may indicate common errors or misconceptions.

725 subtracted instead of added

900 added the hundreds and omitted the other numbers

925 correct

920 added the hundreds and tens and omitted the ones

Formative Assessment

Give students a number and ask them what number is 100 more.

Check My Progress

Use this as a formative assessment to determine if your students are struggling, and if so, with which topics they struggle. The criteria for differentiation are on the next page.

Vocabulary Check

Ask students to describe the relationship between the words in the word bank. They are all used when adding greater numbers.

ELL ELL Support Strategy Use this information to participate in purposeful, cooperative learning activities.

Concept Check

These concepts are covered in Lessons 1–3.

Exercises	Concept	Review Lesson
4–5	Add hundreds	2
6–7, 14–15	Mentally add 10 or 100	3
8–13	Add three-digit numbers	3
16–17	Find the missing addend	3

Test Practice

Diagnose Student Errors

Class trends in wrong answers may indicate common errors or misconceptions

- **100** answered using the number 100 given in the problem
- **197** subtracted instead of added
- **297** same number as what Sophia counted
- **397** correct

369-370 **Chapter 6** Three-Digit Numbers

Name _____

Check My Progress

Vocabulary Check

Complete each sentence.

tens   regroup   ones

1. In the number 352, the 5 is in the __tens__ place.

2. In the number 352, the 2 is in the __ones__ place.

3. If the ones add up to more than 9, you must __regroup__.

Concept Check

Make a hundred to add.

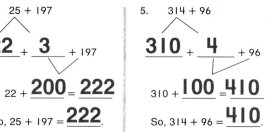

4. 25 + 197

$$22 + 3 + 197$$

$$22 + 200 = 222$$

So, 25 + 197 = **222**.

5. 314 + 96

$$310 + 4 + 96$$

$$310 + 100 = 410$$

So, 314 + 96 = **410**.

Chapter 6   369

Add.

6. 200 + 100 = **300**		7. 400 + 200 = **600**
8. 100 + 300 = **400**	9. 700 + 100 = **800**	10. 500 + 400 = **900**
11. 836 + 100 = **936**	12. 390 + 100 = **490**	13. 567 + 10 = **577**
14. 564 + 10 = **574**		15. 626 + 100 = **726**

Find the missing addend.

16. 239 + **10** = 249

17. 853 + **100** = 953

Test Practice

18. Sophia counts 297 watermelon seeds. Isabella counts 100 more seeds than Sophia. How many seeds does Isabella count?

100	197	297	397
○	○	○	●

370   Chapter 6

Name _____

Check My Progress *(Lessons 1 through 3)*

Make a hundred to add.

1. $23 + 297$

   $20 + \underline{\textbf{3}}$

   $297 + \underline{\textbf{3}} = \underline{\textbf{300}}$

   $\underline{\textbf{20}} + \underline{\textbf{300}} = \underline{\textbf{320}}$

   So, $23 + 297 = \underline{\textbf{320}}$

2. $95 + 315$

   $310 + \underline{\textbf{5}}$

   $95 + \underline{\textbf{5}} = \underline{\textbf{100}}$

   $\underline{\textbf{310}} + \underline{\textbf{100}} = \underline{\textbf{410}}$

   So, $95 + 315 = \underline{\textbf{410}}$

Add.

3. $300 + 100 = \underline{\textbf{400}}$ 4. $500 + 400 = \underline{\textbf{900}}$

5. $700 + 200 = \underline{\textbf{900}}$ 6. $600 + 100 = \underline{\textbf{700}}$

7. $\quad 600$ 8. $\quad 587$ 9. $\quad 359$
   $+ 300$ $+ 10$ $+ 100$
   $\boxed{\textbf{900}}$ $\boxed{\textbf{597}}$ $\boxed{\textbf{459}}$

10. Julia counted 145 baseballs fans. Bailey counted 100 more baseball fans than Julia. How many baseball fans did Bailey count? $\underline{\textbf{245}}$ baseball fans

RESPONSE TO INTERVENTION

DIFFERENTIATED INSTRUCTION

CCSS

AL   STRATEGIC INTERVENTION

(Approaching Grade Level)

IF **students miss 8 or more in Exercises 1–10,**

THEN **choose a resource:**

→ Check My Progress
→ Self-Check Quiz
→ Use the Reteach worksheets.

OL   ON LEVEL

IF **students miss 4 to 5 in Exercises 1–10,**

THEN **choose a resource:**

→ Chapter Project
→ Proceed to the next lesson.

BL   BEYOND LEVEL

IF **students miss 3 or less in Exercises 1–10,**

THEN **choose a resource:**

→ Chapter Project
→ Use the Enrich worksheets.
→ Proceed to the next lesson.

LESSON 4
Regroup Ones to Add

OBJECTIVE Regroup the ones to add three-digit numbers.

What's the Math?

 Common Core State Standards
DOMAIN: Number and Operations in Base Ten

Standards: 2.NBT.7, 2.NBT.9

The wording of these standards can be found on page 344.

What Students Should Understand

• When adding with three-digit numbers, add the ones, the tens, and then the hundreds.

• Regroup 10 ones as 1 ten if there are ten or more ones.

• You can use base-ten blocks to help you regroup and find the sum.

What Students Should be Able to Do

Find 226 + 118.

Step 1

Add the ones. If there are 10 or more ones, regroup 10 ones as 1 ten. Write the 1 in the tens column.

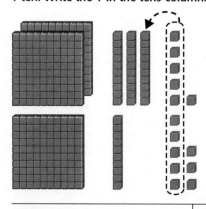

hundreds	tens	ones
	☐1	
2	2	6
+ 1	1	8
		4

Step 2
Add the tens.

hundreds	tens	ones
	☐1	
2	2	6
+ 1	1	8
	4	4

Step 3
Add the hundreds.

hundreds	tens	ones
	☐1	
2	2	6
+ 1	1	8
3	4	4

Developing Vocabulary

 Review Vocabulary

regroup

Activity

• Write *regroup* on the board. Ask students when they have used this word previously. For example, they might recall regrouping to add or subtract.

• Explain that *regroup* means "to take apart a number to write it in a new way." For example, you can show 14 by regrouping the ones to be 1 ten and 4 ones.

• Tell students that regrouping is needed when there are 10 or more ones.

ELL **ELL Support Strategy** Use this vocabulary activity to develop and advance mathematical language skills.

My Vocabulary Cards

Read the activity for this lesson's card to students. Have them share and explain their drawings with the class.

ELL Refer to the multilingual eGlossary for interactive definitions in 13 languages.

Building on the Essential Question

In this lesson, students will build upon the skills and concepts needed to answer the chapter's Essential Question "How can I add three-digit numbers?"

Plan Online

Plan for your lesson by using the resources at

connectED.mcgraw-hill.com

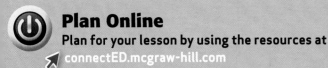

Digital Dashboard

Interactive Whiteboard Ready

Vocab

The eBook **Glossary** shows the definition of the word and has audio for each definition. The **eGlossary** provides definitions in 13 languages.

Watch

Watch as concepts are brought to life through **animations**, **songs**, and a variety of visual instruction.

Tools

Virtual Manipulatives with work mats allow teachers and students to model the lesson.

Check

Use **eAssessment** for online assignments and customized assessments.

Use the **Common Core Quick Check** before the lesson to assess students' retention of previously learned concepts.

Use the interactive **Self-Check Quiz** after the lesson to provide immediate feedback on lesson concepts.

eHelp

Digital and print resources assist students and parents in completing My Homework.

Games

Online games and **apps** provide extra practice for lesson concepts.

PD

Professional development videos help teachers gain a deeper understanding of the lesson concepts and strategies.

Rtl

Support for **approaching**, **on**- and **beyond-level** students as well as **English Language Learners**.

Masters

Reteach and **Enrich** worksheets, **Manipulative Masters**, the **Problem of the Day**, and other blackline masters are available for each lesson.

---

1 LAUNCH THE LESSON

 If your students are well-versed in regrouping, you may choose to begin instruction with Step 2, TEACH.

You will need

☐ base-ten blocks

Mathematical PRACTICE 4 Modeling the Math

Review how to add. Then have students use base-ten blocks to act out the meaning of *regroup*.

Using actual or virtual base-ten blocks, count out one group having 2 tens and 7 ones, and another group having 4 tens and 4 ones.

What do we add together first, the tens or the ones? ones
What is their sum? 7 ones and 4 ones is 11 ones

Do you need to regroup? Explain. Yes; regroup 11 ones as 1 ten and 1 one; That is, trade 10 ones for one tens rod.

Let's now add the tens. How many tens are there? 2 tens, 4 tens, and 1 ten, or 7 tens

What is the sum of 2 tens, 7 ones, and 4 tens, 4 ones? 7 tens and 1 one, or 71

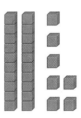

🕐 **Begin core instruction here.**

You will need

☐ base-ten blocks
☐ Work Mat 7

Explore and Explain

Read the directions that are at the bottom of the student page.

You need to find how many dog books and cat books the library has in all. How can you do this? Find 146 + 145.

Write 146 + 145 on the board vertically in a place-value chart. Then point to the number 146.

Which base-ten blocks should you use to show 146?
1 hundred flat, 4 tens rods, and 6 unit cubes

Next, point to the number 145.

Which base-ten blocks should you use to show 145?
1 hundred flat, 4 tens rods, and 5 unit cubes

Let's add the ones first. Are there 10 or more ones? yes
What do you do when there are 10 or more ones? regroup

Have students trade 10 unit cubes for 1 tens rod. Then write 1 above the tens place on the board and tell students that it represents the regrouped ones.

How many ones are left after you regroup? 1 one

Write 1 in the sum in the ones place on the board.

Add the tens next. How many tens are there? Do not forget to add the regrouped ten. 9 tens

Write 9 in the tens place of the sum on the board.

Add the hundreds next. How many hundreds are there? 2

What are you going to write to complete the number sentence? The addends are 146 and 145 and the sum is 291

So, the library has 291 dog books and cat books.

See and Show

Help students work through the example at the top of the page. Walk students through the steps using virtual or actual base-ten blocks and Work Mat 7. Point out that they will have to regroup if the total in the ones is 10 or more. Have them trace the dashed numbers as they work through the problems.

Work through Exercises 1 and 2 as a class.

Mathematical PRACTICE ➌ **Talk Math**

Discuss with students "How is three-digit addition like two-digit addition?" Sample answer: You add the ones first. If needed, you regroup, then add the tens.

Name _____

2.NBT.7, 2.NBT.9

Regroup Ones to Add

Lesson 4
ESSENTIAL QUESTION
How can I add three-digit numbers?

Explore and Explain

Woof!

$146 + 145 = 291$ books

Teacher Directions: Model using base-ten blocks. Our library has 146 books about dogs. It has 145 books about cats. How many books about cats and dogs does the library have? Write the number sentence.

Online Content at connectED.mcgraw-hill.com   Chapter 6 • Lesson 4   371

See and Show

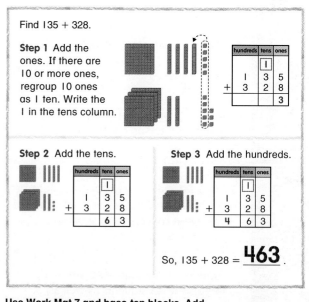

Find 135 + 328.

Step 1 Add the ones. If there are 10 or more ones, regroup 10 ones as 1 ten. Write the 1 in the tens column.

hundreds	tens	ones
	1	
1	3	5
+ 3	2	8
		3

Step 2 Add the tens.

hundreds	tens	ones
	1	
1	3	5
+ 3	2	8
	6	3

Step 3 Add the hundreds.

hundreds	tens	ones
	1	
1	3	5
+ 3	2	8
4	6	3

So, $135 + 328 = $ **463**.

Use Work Mat 7 and base-ten blocks. Add.

1.
hundreds	tens	ones
	1	
4	3	6
+ 2	4	5
6	8	1

2.
hundreds	tens	ones
	1	
1	2	7
+ 6	4	8
7	7	5

Talk Math How is three-digit addition like two-digit addition?

372   Chapter 6 • Lesson 4

Name _____

On My Own

Add. Use base-ten blocks if needed.

> **Helpful Hint**
> Remember to write 1 in the tens column if you regroup.

3.
```
    1
  4 6 8
+   2 3
-------
  4 9 1
```

4.
```
    □
  5 6 1
+   2 6
-------
  5 8 7
```

5.
```
    1
  4 1 1
+ 3 7 9
-------
  7 9 0
```

6.
```
    236
 +  518
 ------
    754
```

7.
```
    468
 +   18
 ------
    486
```

8.
```
    427
 +  144
 ------
    571
```

9.
```
    306
 +  408
 ------
    714
```

10.
```
     28
 +  515
 ------
    543
```

11.
```
    273
 +  224
 ------
    497
```

12.
```
    749
 +    9
 ------
    758
```

13.
```
    146
 +  253
 ------
    399
```

14.
```
    135
 +   16
 ------
    151
```

15.
```
    305
 +  306
 ------
    611
```

16.
```
    607
 +   13
 ------
    620
```

17.
```
    782
 +  103
 ------
    885
```

Chapter 6 • Lesson 4   373

Problem Solving

Mathematical PRACTICE

18. There are 247 red cars. There are 438 black cars. How many red and black cars in all?

    685 cars

19. Mr. Archer picked 416 apples last month. He picked 336 apples this month. How many apples did he pick in all?

    752 apples

> I can't wait to meet the new family on the block!

20. The park ranger counted 105 black bears last year. This year, he counts 128 black bears. How many black bears did he count in all?

    233 black bears

Write Math Explain how to regroup ones to make a ten when adding three-digit numbers.

Sample answer: If there are 10 or more ones, regroup

10 ones as 1 ten and add it to the other tens.

---

3 PRACTICE & APPLY

On My Own

Have students work through the exercises on this page independently. You may choose to assign exercises based on the chart below.

DIFFERENTIATED ASSIGNMENTS

AL Approaching Level Guide students through the exercises in On My Own. Help them to use manipulatives while working through the exercises.

OL On Level Complete the exercises independently.

BL Beyond Level Complete the exercises independently without manipulatives.

Common Error!

Students may forget to regroup as they add. Remind them to write the number they have regrouped in the appropriate place above the problem so that they remember it.

Problem Solving

Have students work through the problem-solving exercises on this page independently.

Mathematical PRACTICE 1 In Exercise 20, students **make sense of problems and persevere in solving them.**

Write Math

This exercise asks students to build upon their understanding of concepts needed to answer the chapter's Essential Question.

RESPONSE TO INTERVENTION

DIFFERENTIATED INSTRUCTION

 APPROACHING LEVEL

IF my students struggle with regrouping,

THEN choose a resource:

→ Use the Reteach worksheet with small groups.

→ Go online for a Differentiated Instruction activity.

→ **Make a Ten** Have students find 46 + 8. Have them count on to find how many more must be added to 46 to make 50. 4 Ask students to break apart 8 to include 4 and 4. Then have them add 46 + 4 to find 50, and then 50 + 4 to find the sum of 54.

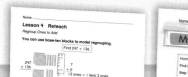

 ON LEVEL

IF my students seem to know how to regroup, but need more practice,

THEN choose a resource:

→ Assign My Homework.

→ Go online for a Differentiated Instruction activity.

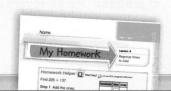

 BEYOND LEVEL

IF my students have mastered regrouping,

THEN choose a resource:

→ Use the Enrich worksheet in cooperative groups.

→ Assign My Homework.

→ Go online for a Differentiated Instruction activity.

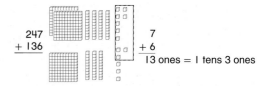

Name _____

Lesson 4   Reteach

Regroup Ones to Add

You can use base-ten blocks to model regrouping.

Find 247 + 136.

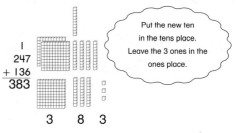

$\begin{array}{r} 247 \\ + 136 \end{array}$

$\begin{array}{r} 7 \\ + 6 \\ \hline \end{array}$
13 ones = 1 tens 3 ones

Regroup the ones. Then add the tens and hundreds.

$\begin{array}{r} 1 \\ 247 \\ + 136 \\ \hline 383 \end{array}$

Put the new ten in the tens place. Leave the 3 ones in the ones place.

3   8   3

So, 247 + 136 = 383.

Model using base-ten blocks. Regroup blocks to solve.

1. 129 + 203 = **332**

2. 262 + 119 = **381**

3. 288 + 306 = **594**

4. 469 + 228 = **697**

Name _____

Lesson 4   Enrich

Regroup Ones to Add

Play a game with a partner.

How to Play:

- Toss two cubes onto the game board. Each cube should land on a box with a number.

- Write the two numbers as an addition problem. Solve it.

- Check your answer. If it is correct, you get one point.

- If your answer is not correct, the other player gets a point.

- If you had to regroup the ones, you get another point.

- The first person to get 5 points is the winner.

516	142	435	535
638	941	123	424
723	227	524	629
331	817	425	622

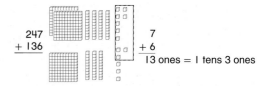

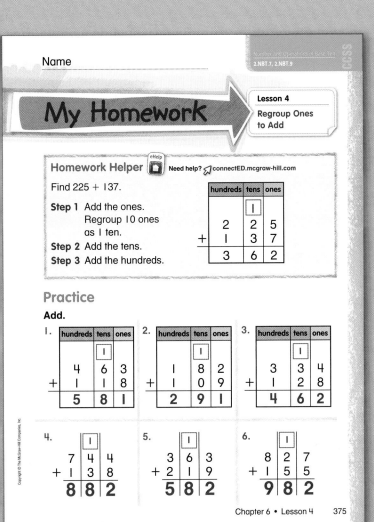

My Homework

Lesson 4
Regroup Ones to Add

Homework Helper

Need help? connectED.mcgraw-hill.com

Find 225 + 137.

Step 1 Add the ones.
Regroup 10 ones
as 1 ten.
Step 2 Add the tens.
Step 3 Add the hundreds.

hundreds	tens	ones
	1	
2	2	5
+ 1	3	7
3	6	2

Practice

Add.

1.
hundreds	tens	ones
	1	
4	6	3
+ 1	1	8
5	8	1

2.
hundreds	tens	ones
	1	
1	8	2
+ 1	0	9
2	9	1

3.
hundreds	tens	ones
	1	
3	3	4
+ 1	2	8
4	6	2

4.
	1	
7	4	4
+ 1	3	8
8	8	2

5.
	1	
3	6	3
+ 2	1	9
5	8	2

6.
	1	
8	2	7
+ 1	5	5
9	8	2

Chapter 6 • Lesson 4   375

Add.

7.
$$335$$
$$+ 116$$
$$451$$

8.
$$135$$
$$+ 219$$
$$354$$

9.
$$425$$
$$+ 148$$
$$573$$

10. 149 children are on a playground. 131 more children come to the playground. How many children are on the playground now?

280 children

The pond in our town rules!

11. There are 152 tadpoles and 138 frogs in a pond. How many frogs and tadpoles are there in all?

290 frogs and tadpoles

Test Practice

12. Find the sum.

$$368 + 619 = \underline{\hspace{1cm}}$$

919 ○   968 ○   987 ●   997 ○

Math at Home Have your child explain how to regroup to add 215 + 215.

---

4 WRAP IT UP

CCSS

My Homework

Assign homework after successful completion of the lesson. Students who understand the concepts may skip the **Homework Helper** section.

Test Practice

Class trends in wrong answers may indicate common errors or misconceptions.

919 incorrect

968 added wrong

987 correct

997 regrouped wrong

Formative Assessment

Ask students the following question.

When solving an addition problem, how do you know that you have to regroup ones? when the sum of the addends in the ones place is greater than 9

Line Up!

As students line up, ask each student joining the line a question such as: *Is 114 + 342 greater than 200?* yes *Is 231 + 427 greater than 700?* no

They should add the hundreds as a starting point to determine their answer.

LESSON 5
Regroup Tens to Add

OBJECTIVE   Regroup tens to add three-digit numbers.

What's the Math?

 Common Core State Standards
DOMAIN: Number and Operations in Base Ten

Standards: 2.NBT.7, 2.NBT.9
The wording of these standards can be found on page 344.

What Students Should Understand
- When adding with three-digit numbers, add the ones, the tens, and then the hundreds.
- Regroup 10 tens as 1 hundred if there are ten or more tens.
- You can use base-ten blocks to help you regroup and find the sum.

What Students Should be Able to Do
Find 364 + 253.

Step 1 Add the ones.

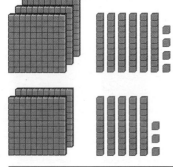

hundreds	tens	ones
3	6	4
+ 2	5	3
		7

Step 2 Add the tens. Regroup if needed.

hundreds	tens	ones
[1]		
3	6	4
+ 2	5	3
	1	7

Step 3 Add the hundreds.

hundreds	tens	ones
[1]		
3	6	4
+ 2	5	3
6	1	7

So, 364 + 253 = 617.

Developing Vocabulary

 Review Vocabulary
regroup

Review Activity
- Divide the class into groups of four. Ask each group to browse their textbooks to identify three-digit numbers.
- Have each group choose 6 numbers. Tell them to list the numbers on a piece of paper.
- Ask a volunteer from each group to provide 2 of their three-digit numbers. Write each set as a three-digit addition problem.
- Work with the class to solve each addition problem. (Do not introduce problems with a four-digit sum.) Discuss the steps for regrouping in each example.

ELL **ELL Support Strategy** Use this vocabulary activity to provide multiple exposures to regrouping while adding three-digit numbers.

My Vocabulary Cards
Have students use a blank card to review a vocabulary word such as *sum*.

 Building on the Essential Question
The Write Math problem at the end of the lesson will help students build on the Essential question "How can I add three-digit number?"

Plan Online
Plan for your lesson by using the resources at
 connectED.mcgraw-hill.com

Digital Dashboard

Interactive Whiteboard Ready

Vocab

The eBook **Glossary** shows the definition of the word and has audio for each definition. The **eGlossary** provides definitions in 13 languages.

Watch

Watch as concepts are brought to life through **animations**, **songs**, and a variety of visual instruction.

Tools

Virtual Manipulatives with work mats allow teachers and students to model the lesson.

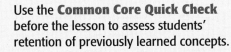
Check

Use **eAssessment** for online assignments and customized assessments.

Use the **Common Core Quick Check** before the lesson to assess students' retention of previously learned concepts.

Use the interactive **Self-Check Quiz** after the lesson to provide immediate feedback on lesson concepts.

eHelp

Digital and print resources assist students and parents in completing My Homework.

Games

Online games and **apps** provide extra practice for lesson concepts.

PD

Professional development videos help teachers gain a deeper understanding of the lesson concepts and strategies.

RtI

Support for **approaching**, **on-** and **beyond-level** students as well as **English Language Learners**.

Masters

Reteach and **Enrich** worksheets, **Manipulative Masters**, the **Problem of the Day**, and other blackline masters are available for each lesson.

Online Content at connectED.mcgraw-hill.com

If your students are well-versed in regrouping tens, you may choose to begin instruction with Step 2, **TEACH**.

You will need
☐ base-ten blocks
☐ Work Mat 7

Mathematical PRACTICE  Modeling the Math

Give small groups of students base-ten blocks and Work Mat 7. Have students work through the problem as you demonstrate and think aloud.

Show 6 hundreds, 3 tens, and 7 ones and 1 hundred, 8 tens, and 8 ones. Have the groups show the same. Remind students to start with the ones.

How many ones are there altogether? 15 *Can we regroup 15 ones for 1 ten and 5 ones?* yes

Regroup. *Can we regroup 12 tens for 1 hundred and 2 tens?* yes

Regroup. *How much do we have altogether?* 8 hundreds, 2 tens, 5 ones

hundreds	tens	ones
I	I	
6	3	7
+ 1	8	8
8	2	5

2 TEACH

🕐 **Begin core instruction here.**

You will need
- ☐ base-ten blocks
- ☐ Work Mat 7

Explore and Explain

Read the directions that are on the bottom of the student page.

What do you need to find? the number of stop signs and street lights in the town *What two numbers can you add together to find this?* 163 and 181

Write 163 + 181 on the board vertically in a place-value chart. Point to the addends in the problem.

Which base-ten blocks are you going to use to model the problem? 1 hundreds flat, 6 tens rods, and 3 unit cubes to show 163, and 1 hundred flat, 8 tens rods, and 1 unit cube to show 181

Let's add the ones first. Are there 10 or more ones? no *How many ones are there?* 4 ones

Write a 4 in the sum in the ones place on the board.

Let's add the tens next. Are there 10 or more tens? yes *What do you do when there are 10 or more tens?* regroup

Guide students in regrouping 10 tens rods as 1 hundreds flat. Then write 1 above the hundreds place on the board. Tell students that it represents the regrouped tens.

How many tens are left after you regroup? 4 tens

Write a 4 in the sum in the tens place on the board.

Add the hundreds next. How many hundreds are there? Do not forget to add the regrouped hundred. 3 hundreds

Write a 3 in the sum in the hundreds place on the board.

What are you going to write to complete the number sentence? The addends are 163 and 181 and the sum is 344.

So, the town has 344 stop signs and street lights.

See and Show

Help students work through the example at the top of the page. Be sure to point out the steps and regroupings shown. Have them trace the dashed number as they work through the problems.

Work through Exercises 1 and 2 as a class.

Mathematical PRACTICE ③ Talk Math

Discuss with students "How is regrouping ones different from regrouping tens?" Sample answer: You regroup 10 ones as 1 ten. You regroup 10 tens as 1 hundred.

Name _____ 2.NBT.7, 2.NBT.9

Regroup Tens to Add

Lesson 5
ESSENTIAL QUESTION
How can I add three-digit numbers?

Explore and Explain 🔲Watch 🔲Tools

Get ready to GO!

163 + 181 = 344

Teacher Directions: Model using base-ten blocks. My town has 163 stop signs. There are also 181 street lights. How many stop signs and street lights does my town have? Write the number sentence.

Online Content at 🔗 connectED.mcgraw-hill.com   Chapter 6 • Lesson 5   377

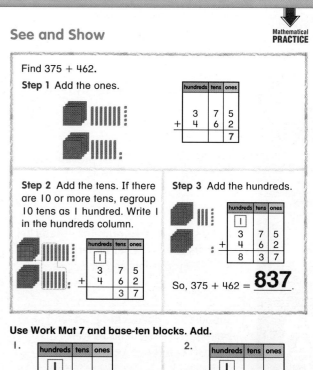

See and Show

Mathematical PRACTICE

Find 375 + 462.

Step 1 Add the ones.

hundreds	tens	ones
3	7	5
+ 4	6	2
		7

Step 2 Add the tens. If there are 10 or more tens, regroup 10 tens as 1 hundred. Write 1 in the hundreds column.

	hundreds	tens	ones
1			
	3	7	5
+	4	6	2
		3	7

Step 3 Add the hundreds.

	hundreds	tens	ones
1			
	3	7	5
+	4	6	2
	8	3	7

So, 375 + 462 = **837**.

Use Work Mat 7 and base-ten blocks. Add.

1.
hundreds	tens	ones
1		
2	4	3
+ 3	8	5
6	2	8

2.
hundreds	tens	ones
1		
5	6	2
+ 1	7	4
7	3	6

Talk Math How is regrouping ones different from regrouping tens?

378   Chapter 6 • Lesson 5

Name _____

On My Own

Add. Use base-ten blocks if needed.

3.
```
  1
  4 5 6
+ 2 9 1
-------
  7 4 7
```

4.
```
  □
  7 3 2
+ 1 6 7
-------
  8 9 9
```

5.
```
    1
  3 2 4
+   9 3
-------
  4 1 7
```

6.
```
  1
  6 8 4
+   2 4
-------
  7 0 8
```

7.
```
  1
  4 8 5
+ 3 3 2
-------
  8 1 7
```

8.
```
  1
  8 9 5
+   1 1
-------
  9 0 6
```

9.
```
  363
+ 281
-----
 644
```

10.
```
  286
+ 121
-----
 407
```

11.
```
  384
+ 134
-----
 518
```

12.
```
  466
+  60
-----
 526
```

13.
```
  352
+ 475
-----
 827
```

14.
```
  382
+  51
-----
 433
```

15.
```
  601
+ 281
-----
 882
```

16.
```
  558
+ 360
-----
 918
```

17.
```
  387
+ 122
-----
 509
```

Chapter 6 • Lesson 5   379

Copyright © The McGraw-Hill Companies, Inc.

Problem Solving

Mathematical **PRACTICE**

18. There are 156 men and 163 women at the town meeting. How many people came to the meeting?

319 people

19. A forest ranger plants 132 pine trees and 191 oak trees. How many trees did the ranger plant in all?

Finally, a chance to rest!

323 trees

20. There are 124 red park benches and 185 blue park benches. How many red and blue park benches are there in all?

309 benches

Write Math   How do you know when to regroup?

Sample answer: When two numbers added together

are 10 or more you must regroup.

380   Chapter 6 • Lesson 5

Copyright © The McGraw-Hill Companies, Inc.   Ingram Publishing/SuperStock

---

On My Own

Have students work through the exercises on this page independently. You may choose to assign exercises based on the chart below.

DIFFERENTIATED ASSIGNMENTS

AL Approaching Level Guide students through the exercises in On My Own. Help them to use manipulatives while working through the exercises.

OL On Level Complete the exercises independently.

BL Beyond Level Complete the exercises independently without manipulatives.

Common Error!

Students may not regroup the tens when adding, writing instead the full number in the sum. Remind them that when regrouping, only the ones are written in the sum, while the tens are regrouped over to be added into the next column.

Problem Solving

Have students work through the problem-solving exercises on this page independently.

Mathematical **PRACTICE** **1**   In Exercise 20, students **make sense of problems and persevere in solving them.**

Write Math

This exercise asks students to build upon their understanding of concepts needed to answer the chapter's Essential Question.

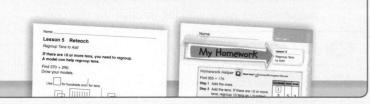

AL APPROACHING LEVEL

IF my students struggle with regrouping tens,

THEN choose a resource:

→ Use the Reteach worksheet with small groups.

→ Go online for a Differentiated Instruction activity.

OL ON LEVEL

IF my students seem to know how to regroup tens, but need more practice,

THEN choose a resource:

→ Assign My Homework.

→ Go online for a Differentiated Instruction activity.

BL BEYOND LEVEL

IF my students have mastered regrouping tens,

THEN choose a resource:

→ Use the Enrich worksheet in cooperative groups.

→ Assign My Homework.

→ Go online for a Differentiated Instruction activity.

381A **Chapter 6** Add Three-Digit Numbers

Name _____

AL

Lesson 5   Reteach
Regroup Tens to Add

If there are 10 or more tens, you need to regroup. A model can help regroup tens.

Find 370 + 290.
Draw your models.

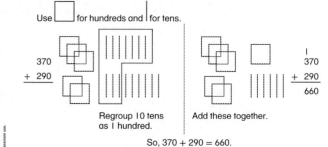

Use ☐ for hundreds and | for tens.

$$370 + 290$$

Regroup 10 tens as 1 hundred.   Add these together.

$$\begin{array}{r} 1 \\ 370 \\ + 290 \\ \hline 660 \end{array}$$

So, 370 + 290 = 660.

Draw a model to help you add.

Show your work here.

1. 290 + 350 = **640**

2. 120 + 280 = **400**

See students' drawings.

Name _____

BL

Lesson 5   Enrich
Regroup Tens to Add

Day	Miles Driven
Monday	324
Tuesday	686
Wednesday	144

Tonya and her family are taking a trip to visit her Aunt Lisa. Tonya keeps track of the miles they drive each day. Use the data from the table to answer these questions.

1. Which two days' totals are closest to 1,000 miles?
Monday and Tuesday

2. Did they travel more than 1,000 miles? **yes**

3. How do you know?
The two-day total is more than 1,000, and they drove another day.

4. How many miles do they travel altogether?
1,154 miles

5. Which two day totals are closest to 500 miles?
Monday and Wednesday

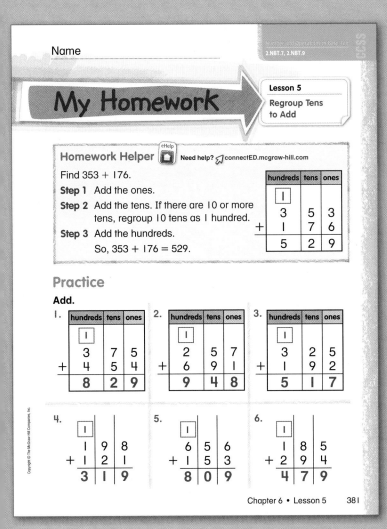

My Homework →

Lesson 5
Regroup Tens
to Add

Homework Helper 🔲 eHelp   Need help? ✍ connectED.mcgraw-hill.com

Find 353 + 176.

Step 1 Add the ones.

Step 2 Add the tens. If there are 10 or more tens, regroup 10 tens as 1 hundred.

Step 3 Add the hundreds.

So, 353 + 176 = 529.

hundreds	tens	ones
1		
3	5	3
+ 1	7	6
5	2	9

Practice

Add.

1.
hundreds	tens	ones
1		
3	7	5
+ 4	5	4
8	2	9

2.
hundreds	tens	ones
1		
2	5	7
+ 6	9	1
9	4	8

3.
hundreds	tens	ones
1		
3	2	5
+ 1	9	2
5	1	7

4.
1		
1	9	8
+ 1	2	1
3	1	9

5.
1		
6	5	6
+ 1	5	3
8	0	9

6.
1		
1	8	5
+ 2	9	4
4	7	9

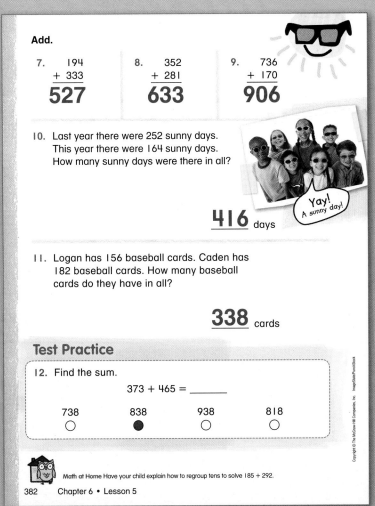

Add.

7.
```
  194
+ 333
```
527

8.
```
  352
+ 281
```
633

9.
```
  736
+ 170
```
906

10. Last year there were 252 sunny days. This year there were 164 sunny days. How many sunny days were there in all?

Yay!
A sunny day!

416 days

11. Logan has 156 baseball cards. Caden has 182 baseball cards. How many baseball cards do they have in all?

338 cards

Test Practice

12. Find the sum.

373 + 465 = _____

738 ○   838 ●   938 ○   818 ○

Math at Home Have your child explain how to regroup tens to solve 185 + 292.

4 WRAP IT UP

CCSS

My Homework

Assign homework after successful completion of the lesson. Students who understand the concepts may skip the **Homework Helper** section.

Test Practice

Diagnose Student Errors

Class trends in wrong answers may indicate common errors or misconceptions.

738 forgot to add the 1 that was regrouped

838 correct

938 added the hundreds incorrectly

818 subtracted the tens

Formative Assessment

Ask students the following question.

How do you add 233 + 681? Add 3 + 1. Add 3 + 8 and regroup. Add 1 to 2 + 6. So 233 + 681 = 914.

Line Up!

As students line up for recess, lunch, or dismissal, ask addition questions such as: 4 + 8 = 12, 10 + 9 = 19, 400 + 5 = 405, 300 + 500 = 800

LESSON 6
Add Three-Digit Numbers

OBJECTIVE Regroup hundreds to add three-digit numbers.

What's the Math?

 Common Core State Standards
DOMAIN: Number and Operations in Base Ten

Standards: 2.NBT.7, 2.NBT.9
The wording of these standards can be found on page 344.

What Students Should Understand

• When adding with three-digit numbers, add the ones, the tens, and then the hundreds.

• Regroup 10 ones as 1 ten if there are ten or more ones.

• Regroup 10 tens as 1 hundred if there are ten or more tens.

What Students Should be Able to Do

Find 449 + 472.

Step 1 Add the ones, regroup.

hundreds	tens	ones
	1	
4	4	9
+ 4	7	2
		1

Step 2 Add the tens, regroup.

hundreds	tens	ones
1	1	
4	4	9
+ 4	7	2
	2	1

Step 3 Add the hundreds.

hundreds	tens	ones
1	1	
4	4	9
+ 4	7	2
9	2	1

So, 449 + 472 = 921.

Developing Vocabulary

 Review Vocabulary

add   regroup

Review Activity

• Write the review words on the board. Have students browse the lesson to identify where they see each word.

• Point out the text box on the second page. Ask students how many steps are shown. 3

• Have a volunteer explain what pattern they notice in the steps. The addition is shown from right to left. The ones and tens are regrouped.

• Explain that this example will help students as they solve the exercises in this lesson.

ELL ELL Support Strategy Use this vocabulary activity to provide oral summaries of information.

My Vocabulary Cards

Have students use a blank card to write a question they have about adding three-digit numbers. Collect the cards, and choose random questions to read aloud. Ask volunteers to help answer the questions.

 Building on the Essential Question

In this lesson, students will build upon the skills and concepts needed to answer the chapter's Essential Question "How can I add three-digit numbers?"

Digital Dashboard

Interactive Whiteboard Ready

Vocab

The eBook **Glossary** shows the definition of the word and has audio for each definition. The **eGlossary** provides definitions in 13 languages.

Watch

Watch as concepts are brought to life through **animations**, **songs**, and a variety of visual instruction.

Tools

Virtual Manipulatives with work mats allow teachers and students to model the lesson.

Check

Use **eAssessment** for online assignments and customized assessments.

Use the **Common Core Quick Check** before the lesson to assess students' retention of previously learned concepts.

Use the interactive **Self-Check Quiz** after the lesson to provide immediate feedback on lesson concepts.

eHelp

Digital and print resources assist students and parents in completing My Homework.

Games

Online games and **apps** provide extra practice for lesson concepts.

PD

Professional development videos help teachers gain a deeper understanding of the lesson concepts and strategies.

RtI

Support for **approaching**, **on**- and **beyond-level** students as well as **English Language Learners**.

Masters

Reteach and **Enrich** worksheets, **Manipulative Masters**, the **Problem of the Day**, and other blackline masters are available for each lesson.

CCSS

1 LAUNCH THE LESSON

 If your students are well-versed in regrouping to add three-digit numbers, you may choose to begin instruction with Step 2, **TEACH**.

You will need

☐ Work Mat 7

Mathematical PRACTICE 4 **Modeling the Math**

Use Work Mat 7 to model 148 + 153. Make sure you point out to students that it is important to keep the hundreds, tens, and ones aligned.

Do the ones need to be regrouped? yes *How?* Regroup 10 ones for one ten.

Do the tens need to be regrouped? yes *How?* Regroup 10 ones for one hundred.

Do you always have to regroup ones and tens when adding three-digit numbers? Sample answer: No; only if the sum in any place is 10 or more.

hundreds	tens	ones
1	1	
1	4	8
+ 1	5	3
3	0	1

🕐 **Begin core instruction here.**

You will need

☐ base-ten blocks

Explore and Explain

Read the directions that are on the bottom of the student page.

You need to find how many people went to the movies on Friday and Saturday. What two numbers should you add to find this? 347 and 485

Write 347 + 485 on the board vertically in a place-value chart. Point to the addends in the problem.

Which base-ten blocks should you use to model the problem? 3 hundreds flats, 4 tens rods, and 7 unit cubes to show 347, and 4 hundreds flats, 8 tens rods, and 5 unit cubes to show 485

Let's add the ones first. Do you need to regroup? Explain. Yes; there are more than 10 ones so trade 10 ones for 1 ten.

Write 1 above the tens place on the board and tell students that it represents the regrouped ones.

How many ones are left after you regroup? 2 ones

Write 2 in the ones place on the board.

Let's add the tens next. Do you need to regroup? yes

Guide students in trading 10 tens rods for 1 hundreds flat. Then write 1 above the hundreds place on the board and tell students that it represents the regrouped tens.

How many tens are left after you regroup? 3 tens

Write 3 in the sum in the tens place on the board.

Add the hundreds next. How many hundreds are there? 8

Write 8 in the sum in the hundreds place on the board. Then ask students to write the number sentence.

Write the number sentence. 347 + 485 = 832

So, 832 people went to the movies on Friday and Saturday.

See and Show

Help students work through the example at the top of the page. Explain that this is just like the previous lessons except now they may be regrouping ones and/or tens in a problem. Have them trace the dashed numbers as they work through the problems.

Work through Exercises 1–4 as a class.

Mathematical PRACTICE ➌   Talk Math

Discuss with students "Explain how you solved Exercise 2." Sample answer: See students' explanations.

Name _____

Add Three-Digit Numbers

Lesson 6

ESSENTIAL QUESTION
How can I add three-digit numbers?

Explore and Explain ▶ 🔧

"I'm crunchy!"

$$347 + 485 = 832 \text{ people}$$

Teacher Directions: Model using base-ten blocks. On Friday, 347 people went to the movies. On Saturday, 485 people went to the movies. How many people went to the movies on these two days in all? Write the number sentence.

Online Content at 🔗connectED.mcgraw-hill.com   Chapter 6 • Lesson 6   383

See and Show

Find 582 + 268.

Step 1 Add the ones, regroup.
Step 2 Add the tens, regroup.
Step 3 Add the hundreds.

So, 582 + 268 = **850**.

	hundreds	tens	ones
	☐	☐	
	5	8	2
+	2	6	8
	8	**5**	**0**

Mathematical PRACTICE

Use Work Mat 7 and base-ten blocks. Add.

1.

	hundreds	tens	ones
	☐	☐	
	3	5	7
+	4	5	4
	8	**1**	**1**

2.

	hundreds	tens	ones
		☐	☐
		2	6
+		6	9
	3	**3**	**0**

3.

	hundreds	tens	ones
	☐	☐	
	1	1	8
+	1	9	9
	3	**1**	**7**

4.

	hundreds	tens	ones
	☐	☐	
	5	2	3
+	2	8	7
	8	**1**	**0**

Talk Math Explain how you solved Exercise 2.

Name _____

On My Own

Add. Use base-ten blocks if needed.

5. ☐ ☐
    1 6 6
  + 1 4 7
  _____
    3 1 3

6. ☐ ☐
    7 2 0
  + 1 9 5
  _____
    9 1 5

7. ☐ ☐
    4 5 8
  +   6 6
  _____
    5 2 4

8.   34
  + 515
  _____
    549

9.   632
  + 299
  _____
    931

10.   327
  + 127
  _____
    454

11. 129
  + 386
  _____
    515

12. 103
  + 609
  _____
    712

13. 123
  + 785
  _____
    908

14. 843
  + 77
  _____
    920

15. 422
  + 309
  _____
    731

16. 215
  + 193
  _____
    408

17. 395
  + 238
  _____
    633

18. 725
  + 174
  _____
    899

19. 662
  + 199
  _____
    861

Chapter 6 • Lesson 6   385

🌎 Problem Solving

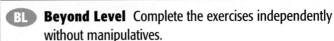

Mathematical PRACTICE

20. One day Keith skipped 145 rocks over the river. The next day he skipped 165 rocks. How many rocks did he skip altogether?

  310 rocks

21. One karate class has 156 students. The other karate class has 176 students. How many students are in both karate classes?

  I get a big KICK out of karate!

  332 students

22. 389 people went to the zoo on Saturday. 592 people went to the zoo on Sunday. How many people went to the zoo in all?

  981 people

Write Math Explain how adding three-digit numbers is different than adding two-digit numbers.

Sample Answer: The only difference is that with a three

digit number you need to add the hundreds after you

add the tens.

386   Chapter 6 • Lesson 6

On My Own

Have students work through the exercises on this page independently. You may choose to assign exercises based on the chart below.

DIFFERENTIATED ASSIGNMENTS

AL Approaching Level Guide students through the exercises in On My Own. Help them to use manipulatives while working through the exercises.

OL On Level Complete the exercises independently.

BL Beyond Level Complete the exercises independently without manipulatives.

Common Error!

Some students might try to add the hundreds first, then the tens, and finally the ones. Remind them that they need to start with the ones column first. Point out that if regrouping is necessary, they will get an incorrect answer if they start in the hundreds column and they will have to go back and change all of their answers.

Problem Solving

Have students work through the problem-solving exercises on this page independently.

Mathematical PRACTICE 2 ➡ In Exercise 21, students **reason abstractly and quantitatively.**

Write Math

This exercise asks students to build upon their understanding of concepts needed to answer the chapter's Essential Question.

RESPONSE TO INTERVENTION

DIFFERENTIATED INSTRUCTION

AL · APPROACHING LEVEL

IF my students struggle with adding three-digit numbers,

THEN choose a resource:

→ Use the Reteach worksheet with small groups.

→ Go online for a Differentiated Instruction activity.

OL · ON LEVEL

IF my students seem to know how to add three-digit numbers, but need more practice,

THEN choose a resource:

→ Assign My Homework.

→ Go online for a Differentiated Instruction activity.

BL · BEYOND LEVEL

IF my students have mastered adding three-digit numbers,

THEN choose a resource:

→ Use the Enrich worksheet in cooperative groups.

→ Assign My Homework.

→ Go online for a Differentiated Instruction activity.

AL Name _____

Lesson 6 Reteach

Add Three-Digit Numbers

You can use base-ten blocks to add.

Find 267 + 464.

Step 1	Step 2	Step 3
Add the ones. You will need to regroup	Add the tens. You will need to regroup	Add the hundreds.

Think 11 ones = 1 ten, 1 one	Think 13 tens = 1 hundred, 3 tens	Think 1 hundred + 2 hundreds + 3 hundreds = 7 hundreds

	hundreds	tens	ones
			1
	2	6	7
+	4	6	4
			1

	hundreds	tens	ones
	1	1	
	2	6	7
+	4	6	4
		3	1

	hundreds	tens	ones
	1	1	
	2	6	7
+	4	6	4
	7	3	1

Find each sum. Use base-ten blocks to help.

1.
```
  146
+ 129
-----
  275
```

2.
```
  245
+ 128
-----
  373
```

BL Name _____

Lesson 6 Enrich

Add Three-Digit Numbers

Jerry, Pedro, and Beth belong to a stamp collectors club. Club members must have at least 225 stamps to join. Emily is thinking about joining. The table shows how many stamps each member has.

Pedro	Beth	Jerry	Emily
376	268	458	

1. Find the total number of stamps for the current members. Show how you regroup.

```
  22
  376
  268
+ 458
------
1,102
```

2. Emily has 139 more stamps than Beth. Write a number sentence that shows how many stamps Emily has.

268 + 139 = 407

Which places needed to be regrouped to solve 268 + 139?

ones and tens

387A **Chapter 6** Add Three-Digit Numbers

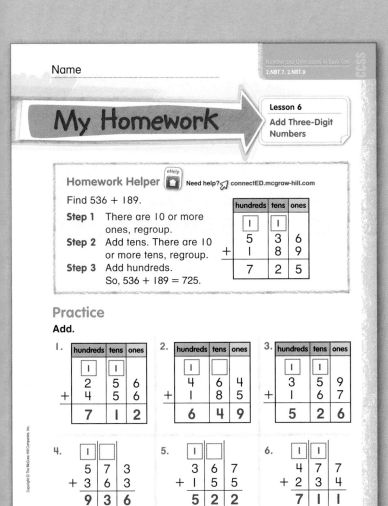

My Homework →

Lesson 6
Add Three-Digit Numbers

Homework Helper Need help? ☞ connectED.mcgraw-hill.com

Find 536 + 189.

Step 1 There are 10 or more ones, regroup.
Step 2 Add tens. There are 10 or more tens, regroup.
Step 3 Add hundreds.
So, 536 + 189 = 725.

hundreds	tens	ones
1	1	
5	3	6
+ 1	8	9
7	2	5

Practice
Add.

1.
hundreds	tens	ones
1	1	
2	5	6
+ 4	5	5
7	1	2

2.
hundreds	tens	ones
1		
4	6	4
+ 1	8	5
6	4	9

3.
hundreds	tens	ones
1		
3	5	9
+ 1	6	7
5	2	6

4.
```
   1   
  5 7 3
+ 3 6 3
  9 3 6
```

5.
```
  1    
  3 6 7
+ 1 5 5
  5 2 2
```

6.
```
  1 1  
  4 7 7
+ 2 3 4
  7 1 1
```

Chapter 6 • Lesson 6   387

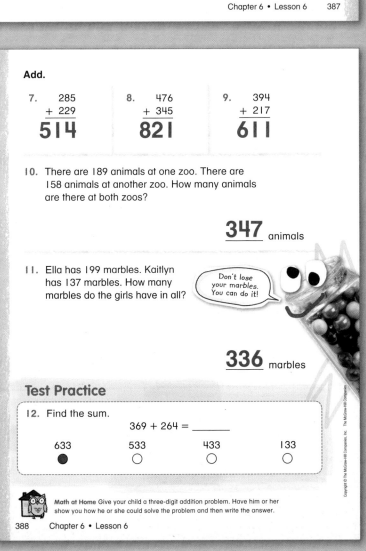

Add.

7.
```
  285
+ 229
  514
```

8.
```
  476
+ 345
  821
```

9.
```
  394
+ 217
  611
```

10. There are 189 animals at one zoo. There are 158 animals at another zoo. How many animals are there at both zoos?

347 animals

11. Ella has 199 marbles. Kaitlyn has 137 marbles. How many marbles do the girls have in all?

Don't lose your marbles. You can do it!

336 marbles

Test Practice

12. Find the sum.

369 + 264 = _____

  ● 633   ○ 533   ○ 433   ○ 133

Math at Home Give your child a three-digit addition problem. Have him or her show you how he or she could solve the problem and then write the answer.

---

4 WRAP IT UP

CCSS

My Homework

Assign homework after successful completion of the lesson. Students who understand the concepts may skip the **Homework Helper** section.

Test Practice
Diagnose Student Errors

Class trends in wrong answer may indicate common errors or misconceptions.

633 correct

533 forgot to regroup to hundreds

433 incorrect

133 subtracted hundreds

Formative Assessment

Ask students the following question.

How many times do you have to regroup when adding 795 and 116? Explain. You have to regroup twice; once with the ones to tens and again with tens to hundreds.

MY Learning Stations

Use the game **Three-Digit Fruit**, the graphic novel **Enchanted Palace Park**, the Real-World Problem Solving Readers **Lady Liberty**, and **Moving Along**, and the activity card **How Many Calories?** after this lesson. The Teacher Guide provides suggestions for differentiated instruction.

Line Up!
Before students line up for recess, lunch, or dismissal, write 357 + 23 = 587 on the board. As students line up, ask them to explain to you why the sum is incorrect. Sample answer: The sum is incorrect because the numbers were not lined up properly. The correct sum is 380.

LESSON 7
Rewrite Three-Digit Addition

OBJECTIVE Given a three-digit addition problem written horizontally, rewrite it vertically before adding.

What's the Math?

 Common Core State Standards
DOMAIN: Number and Operations in Base Ten

Standard: 2.NBT.7

The wording of this standard can be found on page 344.

What Students Should Understand

• You can rewrite a horizontal addition problem vertically before finding the sum.

• After rewriting the problem, add the ones, regroup if needed, add the tens, regroup if needed, then add the hundreds.

What Students Should be Able to Do

Find 382 + 279.

Step 1 Write one addend below the other addend. Line up the ones, tens, and hundreds.

Step 2 Add. Regroup if necessary. So, 382 + 279 = 661.

hundreds	tens	ones
1	1	
3	8	2
+ 2	7	9
6	6	1

 Building on the Essential Question

In this lesson, students will build upon the skills and concepts needed to answer the chapter's Essential Question "How can I add three-digit numbers?"

Developing Vocabulary

Review Vocabulary

regroup   ones

tens   hundreds

Review Activity

• Write the review words on the board. Then have students identify where the words appear in this lesson. Have them circle or highlight each example.

• Afterward, have students describe how each word they circled is used in the examples.

ELL **ELL Support Strategy** Use this vocabulary activity to assess students' ability to read for understanding.

My Vocabulary Cards

Have students use a blank card to answer this chapter's Essential Question.

Digital Dashboard

Interactive Whiteboard Ready

Vocab
The eBook **Glossary** shows the definition of the word and has audio for each definition. The **eGlossary** provides definitions in 13 languages.

Watch
Watch as concepts are brought to life through **animations**, **songs**, and a variety of visual instruction.

Tools
Virtual Manipulatives with work mats allow teachers and students to model the lesson.

Check
Use **eAssessment** for online assignments and customized assessments.

Use the **Common Core Quick Check** before the lesson to assess students' retention of previously learned concepts.

Use the interactive **Self-Check Quiz** after the lesson to provide immediate feedback on lesson concepts.

eHelp
Digital and print resources assist students and parents in completing My Homework.

Games
Online games and **apps** provide extra practice for lesson concepts.

PD
Professional development videos help teachers gain a deeper understanding of the lesson concepts and strategies.

RtI
Support for **approaching**, **on**- and **beyond-level** students as well as **English Language Learners**.

Masters
Reteach and **Enrich** worksheets, **Manipulative Masters**, the **Problem of the Day**, and other blackline masters are available for each lesson.

---

1 LAUNCH THE LESSON

 If your students are well-versed in rewriting three-digit addition, you may choose to begin instruction with Step 2, **TEACH**.

Mathematical PRACTICE 4  **Modeling the Math**

Write 247 + 342 on the board horizontally. Ask students to find the sum without rewriting the problem vertically.

Suppose you have this addition problem. Find the sum by adding the ones, the tens, and the hundreds. Do not write the problem vertically. What is the sum? 589

As a class, discuss the difficulties in adding without rewriting the problem vertically. Remind students that they rewrote horizontal addition problems vertically in Chapter 3. Explain that they will continue this skill but the addition problems will involve three-digit numbers.

Now have students rewrite 247 + 342 vertically, and then find the sum. As a class, discuss the benefits of rewriting the problem vertically before carrying out the addition.

Lunchroom Chat

Tips for New Teachers

Students often have difficulty keeping numbers aligned in vertical addition with multi-digit addends. You may want to use grid paper to help students keep their numbers aligned. For those students that might have vision difficulties, you might consider highlighting each place-value column with a different highlighter color to help them focus on the digits they are adding. This is especially helpful when they begin to use more than two addends.

 Begin core instruction here.

You will need
☐ base-ten blocks

Explore and Explain

Read the directions that are on the bottom of the student page.

What do you need to find? How many firefighters and police officers are in the town in all. *How can you do this?* Find 143 + 167.

Write 143 + 167 horizontally on the board. Have students write the addition problem vertically in the place-value chart.

Rewrite this addition problem in the place-value chart with one addend above the other addend. Which place value should you add first? ones

Have students add the ones.

Add the ones. Do you need to regroup 10 ones as 1 ten? yes *Why?* Sample answer: There are 10 or more ones.

Lead students in regrouping 10 ones as 1 ten.

After regrouping 10 ones as 1 ten, how many ones should you write in the sum? 0 ones *Next, add the tens. Do you need to regroup the tens?* yes *Why?* Sample answer: There are 10 or more tens.

Lead students in regrouping 10 tens as 1 hundred.

After regrouping 10 tens as 1 hundred, how many tens should you write in the sum? 1 ten

Add the hundreds. How many hundreds are there? 3 hundreds

How many hundreds do you write in the sum? 3 hundreds

So, how many firefighters and police officers are in the town in all? 310 firefighters and police officers

See and Show

Help students work through the example at the top of the page. Have them trace the dashed numbers as they work through the problems.

Work through Exercises 1 through 6 as a class.

Mathematical PRACTICE 3 ▷ **Talk Math**

Discuss with students "How is rewriting three-digit addition different than rewriting two-digit addition?" Sample answer: You will have numbers in 3 columns instead of just 2.

Name _____

2.NBT.7

Rewrite Three-Digit Addition

Lesson 7
ESSENTIAL QUESTION
How can I add three-digit numbers?

Explore and Explain

143 + 167

hundreds	tens	ones
1	1	
1	4	3
+ 1	6	7
3	**1**	**0**

310 firefighters and police officers

Be proud of your town!

🦉 **Teacher Directions:** There are 143 firefighters and 167 police officers in my town. How many firefighters and police officers are in my town in all? Write the number in the place-value chart and add.

Online Content at connectED.mcgraw-hill.com   Chapter 6 • Lesson 7   389

See and Show

Mathematical PRACTICE

You can rewrite a problem to add.
Find 366 + 264.

Step 1 Write one addend below the other addend. Line up the ones, tens, and hundreds.

Step 2 Add. Regroup if necessary.

hundreds	tens	ones
1	1	
3	6	6
+ 2	6	4
6	**3**	**0**

Rewrite the problems. Add.

1. 634 + 125

```
    6 3 4
  + 1 2 5
  -------
    7 5 9
```

2. 245 + 236

```
      1
    2 4 5
  + 2 3 6
  -------
    4 8 1
```

3. 743 + 163

```
      1
    7 4 3
  + 1 6 3
  -------
    9 0 6
```

4. 264 + 566

```
    1 1
    2 6 4
  + 5 6 6
  -------
    8 3 0
```

5. 396 + 378

```
    1 1
    3 9 6
  + 3 7 8
  -------
    7 7 4
```

6. 237 + 592

```
      1
    2 3 7
  + 5 9 2
  -------
    8 2 9
```

Talk Math How is rewriting three-digit addition different than rewriting two-digit addition?

CORE INSTRUCTION

Name _____

On My Own

Rewrite the problems. Add.

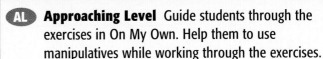
Our town recycles!

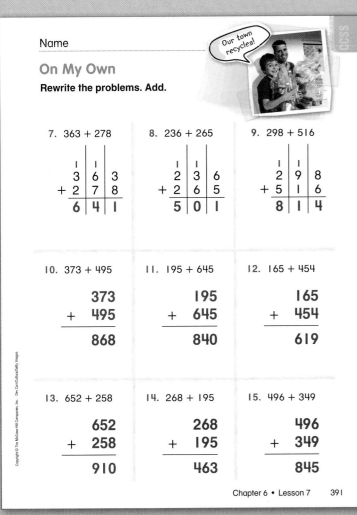

7. 363 + 278

```
  1 1
  3 6 3
+ 2 7 8
-------
  6 4 1
```

8. 236 + 265

```
  1 1
  2 3 6
+ 2 6 5
-------
  5 0 1
```

9. 298 + 516

```
  1 1
  2 9 8
+ 5 1 6
-------
  8 1 4
```

10. 373 + 495

```
   373
+  495
------
   868
```

11. 195 + 645

```
   195
+  645
------
   840
```

12. 165 + 454

```
   165
+  454
------
   619
```

13. 652 + 258

```
   652
+  258
------
   910
```

14. 268 + 195

```
   268
+  195
------
   463
```

15. 496 + 349

```
   496
+  349
------
   845
```

Chapter 6 • Lesson 7   391

Problem Solving

Mathematical
PRACTICE

16. 395 ants crawled around the ant hill. 111 more ants came over to the ant hill. How many ants are there now?

506 ants

17. There are 153 yellow houses and 168 blue houses in the neighborhood. How many yellow and blue houses are there in all?

My house

321 yellow and blue houses

18. Last week, Amelia sold 193 cups of lemonade. This week, she sold 129 cups. How many cups of lemonade has she sold in both weeks?

322 cups

Write Math   Explain how you rewrite three-digit addition problems to solve.

Sample answer: Write one number below the other

number. Line up the ones, tens, and hundreds.

Then subtract and regroup if needed.

392   Chapter 6 • Lesson 7

³PRACTICE & APPLY

On My Own

Have students work through the exercises on this page independently. You may choose to assign exercises based on the chart below.

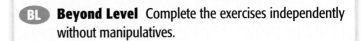

DIFFERENTIATED ASSIGNMENTS

AL **Approaching Level** Guide students through the exercises in On My Own. Help them to use manipulatives while working through the exercises.

OL **On Level** Complete the exercises independently.

BL **Beyond Level** Complete the exercises independently without manipulatives.

Problem Solving

Have students work through the problem-solving exercises on this page independently.

Mathematical
PRACTICE 1   In Exercise 18, students **make sense of problems and persevere in solving them.**

Write Math

This exercise asks students to build upon their understanding of concepts needed to answer the chapter's Essential Question.

RESPONSE TO INTERVENTION
DIFFERENTIATED INSTRUCTION

AL **APPROACHING LEVEL**

IF my students struggle with rewriting three-digit addition,

THEN choose a resource:

→ Use the Reteach worksheet with small groups.

→ Go online for a Differentiated Instruction activity.

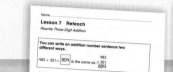

OL **ON LEVEL**

IF my students seem to know how to rewrite three-digit addition, but need more practice,

THEN choose a resource:

→ Assign My Homework.

→ Go online for a Differentiated Instruction activity.

BL **BEYOND LEVEL**

IF my students have mastered rewriting three-digit addition,

THEN choose a resource:

→ Use the Enrich worksheet in cooperative groups.

→ Assign My Homework.

→ Go online for a Differentiated Instruction activity.

AL Name _____

Lesson 7   Reteach
Rewrite Three-Digit Addition

> **You can write an addition number sentence two different ways.**
>
> $483 + 321 = \boxed{804}$ is the same as
> $$\begin{array}{r} 483 \\ +\,321 \\ \hline 804 \end{array}$$

Add.

1. $208 + 501 = \boxed{709}$ is the same as
$$\begin{array}{r} 208 \\ +\,501 \\ \hline \mathbf{709} \end{array}$$

2. $132 + 175 = \boxed{307}$ is the same as
$$\begin{array}{r} 132 \\ +\,175 \\ \hline \mathbf{307} \end{array}$$

3. $369 + 258 = \boxed{627}$ is the same as
$$\begin{array}{r} 369 \\ +\,258 \\ \hline \mathbf{627} \end{array}$$

4. $602 + 199 = \boxed{801}$ is the same as
$$\begin{array}{r} 602 \\ +\,199 \\ \hline \mathbf{801} \end{array}$$

BL Name _____

Lesson 7   Enrich
Rewrite Three-Digit Addition

Solve. Write each addition number sentence two ways.

1. Kenny has been in school for 178 days. Cameron has been in school for 163 days. How many days altogether have they been in school?

   $\mathbf{178 + 163 = 341}$

   $$\begin{array}{r} 178 \\ +\,163 \\ \hline 341 \end{array}$$
   _____**341**_____ days

2. Grace read 362 chapters in a year. Julia read 218 chapters. How many chapters did they read in all?

   $\mathbf{362 + 218 = 580}$

   $$\begin{array}{r} 362 \\ +\,218 \\ \hline 580 \end{array}$$
   _____**580**_____ chapters

3. Gail's Groceries sold 483 bags of apples and 382 bags of oranges in one month. How many bags of fruit did Gail's Groceries sell in all?

   $\mathbf{483 + 382 = 865}$

   $$\begin{array}{r} 483 \\ +\,382 \\ \hline 865 \end{array}$$
   _____**865**_____ bags

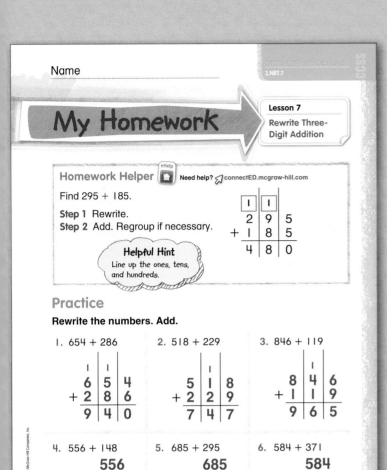

Name _____

2.NBT.7

My Homework

Lesson 7
Rewrite Three-Digit Addition

Homework Helper 🖥 Need help? connectED.mcgraw-hill.com

Find 295 + 185.

Step 1 Rewrite.
Step 2 Add. Regroup if necessary.

```
  1 1
  2 9 5
+ 1 8 5
-------
  4 8 0
```

Helpful Hint
Line up the ones, tens, and hundreds.

Practice

Rewrite the numbers. Add.

1. 654 + 286
```
  1 1
  6 5 4
+ 2 8 6
-------
  9 4 0
```

2. 518 + 229
```
    1
  5 1 8
+ 2 2 9
-------
  7 4 7
```

3. 846 + 119
```
    1
  8 4 6
+ 1 1 9
-------
  9 6 5
```

4. 556 + 148
```
   556
 + 148
------
   704
```

5. 685 + 295
```
   685
 + 295
------
   980
```

6. 584 + 371
```
   584
 + 371
------
   955
```

Chapter 6 • Lesson 7   393

Rewrite the problems. Add.

7. 172 + 217
```
   172
 + 217
------
   389
```

8. 362 + 264
```
   362
 + 264
------
   626
```

9. 239 + 375
```
   239
 + 375
------
   614
```

10. There are 129 boats in the lake. There are 197 jet skis in the lake. How many boats and jet skis are in the lake?

Weeeeee!

326 boats and jet skis

Test Practice

11. Mark the answer that shows how to rewrite and solve the number sentence.

427 + 228 = _____

```
   427          427          427          427
 + 228        - 228        + 228        + 228
------       ------       ------       ------
  6415          199          645          655
```
   ○   ○   ○   ●

 Math at Home Write 374 + 185 on a piece of paper. Have your child rewrite the problem and solve it.

---

4 WRAP IT UP

CCSS

My Homework

Assign homework after successful completion of the lesson. Students who understand the concepts may skip the **Homework Helper** section.

Test Practice

Diagnose Student Errors

Class trends in wrong answers may indicate common errors or misconceptions.

427 + 228 = 6415   student has sum of 8 + 7 as 15 and did not regroup

427 − 228 = 199   subtracted

427 + 228 = 645   forgot to regroup ones to tens

427 + 228 = 655   correct

Formative Assessment

In the problem 445 + 345 =, how many times do you need to regroup? only 1 time in the ones column

LESSON 8
Problem Solving
STRATEGY: Guess, Check, and Revise
OBJECTIVE Guess, check, and revise to solve problems.

What's the Math?

 Common Core State Standards
DOMAIN: Number and Operations in Base Ten

Standard: 2.NBT.7

The wording of this standard can be found on page 344.

Mathematical PRACTICE 1 Make sense of problems and persevere in solving them.

What Students Should Understand

- You can guess, check, and revise to solve real-world problems.
- First, make sure you understand the meaning of the problem. Determine what facts are important and the question being asked.
- Make a plan and follow through to solve the problem.
- Justify your conclusion by checking your answer to determine whether it is correct and makes sense.

What Students Should be Able to Do

A store sells beads in packages of 150, 250, and 300. Sheila wants to buy 400 beads to make necklaces. Which two packages will she buy?

1 Understand

Underline what you know. Circle what you need to find.

2 Plan

How will I solve this problem?

I can guess, check, and revise.

3 Solve

I will guess, check, and revise.

Guess: 150 + 300
Check: 150 + 300 = 450

Revise: 450 is too high, one of the addends needs to be smaller.

Guess: 150 + 250
Check: 150 + 250 = 400

So, Sheila should buy a package that has 150 beads and a package that has 250 beads.

4 Check

Is my answer reasonable? Explain.

Developing the Strategy

What's the Strategy?

Guess, Check, and Revise Students use the guess, check, and revise strategy as a method to solve many everyday problems. This strategy helps students understand how to make an educated guess and determine if their guess is reasonable. If it is not, they can revise their answer to the problem.

Example: Samson has 50 collectable cards in album A. He has 55 cards in album B, and 40 cards in Album C. He wants to take as close to 100 cards as he can to school. Which two albums should he take?

Guess: Album A and C
Check: 50 + 40 = 90; 90 is 10 away from 100
Revise: This may not be the best choice. So, guess again.

Guess: Album A and B
Check: 50 + 55 = 105; 105 is 5 away from 100

So, Albums A and B are the better choice.

Other strategies that have been taught and that students may choose to use are:

- Act it out
- Use logical reasoning

Mathematical PRACTICE

The Mathematical Practices are especially evident in problem-solving situations, in which students connect procedures and processes with mathematical understanding. In this lesson, the following Mathematical Practices are addressed.

 Make sense of problems and persevere in solving them.

 Attend to precision.

 Look for and express regularity in repeated reasoning.

Digital Dashboard

Interactive Whiteboard Ready

Vocab

The eBook **Glossary** shows the definition of the word and has audio for each definition. The **eGlossary** provides definitions in 13 languages.

Tools

Virtual Manipulatives along with work mats allow teachers and students to model the lesson.

Check

Use **eAssessment** for online assignments and customized assessments.

Use the **Common Core Quick Check** before the lesson to assess students' retention of previously learned concepts.

eHelp

Digital and print resources assist students and parents in completing My Homework.

PD

Professional development videos help teachers gain a deeper understanding of the lesson concepts and strategies.

RtI

Support for **approaching**, **on**- and **beyond-level** students as well as **English Language Learners**.

Masters

Reteach and **Enrich** worksheets, **Manipulative Masters**, the **Problem of the Day**, and other blackline masters are available for each lesson.

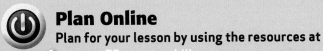
LAUNCH THE LESSON

CCSS

If your students are well-versed in problem solving, you may choose to begin instruction with Step 2, **TEACH**.

Review

Write and read aloud the following problem:

Alexis has 125 toy dinosaurs. Jean has 159 toy dinosaurs.

About how many toy dinosaurs do they have together?

Explain to students that they can round the numbers to the nearest hundred to estimate the sums.

> *What is 125 to the nearest hundred?* 100 *What is 159 to the nearest hundred?* 200
>
> *About how many dinosaurs do they have together?* 300; $100 + 200 = 300$

Repeat the activity, this time rounding to the nearest ten.

100   125

159   200

🕐 **Begin your instruction here.**

Problem Solving

1 Understand

Reread the problem with the students. Point out information as you read it.

2 Plan

Discuss several ideas. Lead the students toward the process of guess, check, and revise to solve the problem.

3 Solve

Work through the problem step-by-step using the student page with the students. Show how to solve the problem using the guess, check, and revise method.

4 Check

Discuss why the answer makes sense. Try to develop a sense of reasoning.

Practice the Strategy

1 Understand

Reread the problem with the students. Ask students to point out information that is important as you read.

2 Plan

Lead the students in discussing several ideas. Direct the students toward the guess, check, and revise method to solve the problem.

3 Solve

Work through the problem using the student page with the class. Show how to solve the problem step-by-step.

4 Check

Discuss why the answer makes sense. Try to develop a sense of reasoning.

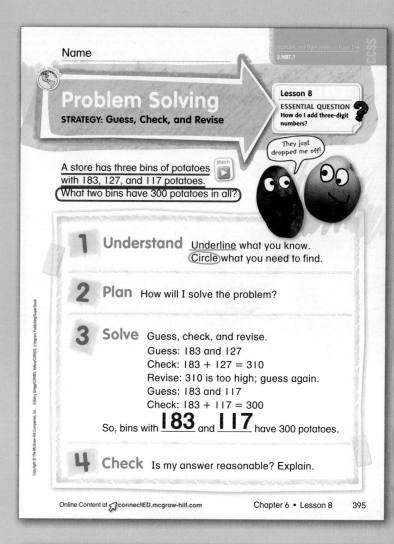

Name _____

Number and Operations in Base Ten
2.NBT.7

Problem Solving
STRATEGY: Guess, Check, and Revise

Lesson 8
ESSENTIAL QUESTION
How do I add three-digit numbers?

They just dropped me off!

A store has three bins of potatoes with 183, 127, and 117 potatoes. What two bins have 300 potatoes in all?

1 Understand Underline what you know. Circle what you need to find.

2 Plan How will I solve the problem?

3 Solve Guess, check, and revise.
Guess: 183 and 127
Check: 183 + 127 = 310
Revise: 310 is too high; guess again.
Guess: 183 and 117
Check: 183 + 117 = 300
So, bins with **183** and **117** have 300 potatoes.

4 Check Is my answer reasonable? Explain.

Online Content at connectED.mcgraw-hill.com   Chapter 6 • Lesson 8   395

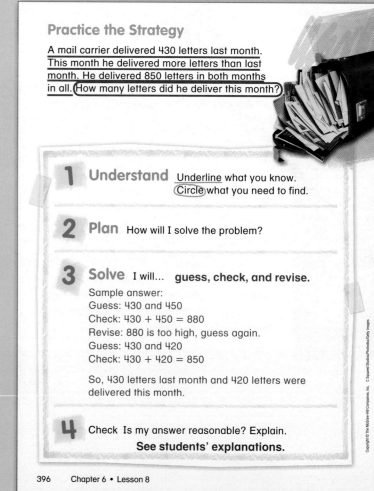

Practice the Strategy

A mail carrier delivered 430 letters last month. This month he delivered more letters than last month. He delivered 850 letters in both months in all. How many letters did he deliver this month?

1 Understand Underline what you know. Circle what you need to find.

2 Plan How will I solve the problem?

3 Solve I will... **guess, check, and revise.**
Sample answer:
Guess: 430 and 450
Check: 430 + 450 = 880
Revise: 880 is too high, guess again.
Guess: 430 and 420
Check: 430 + 420 = 850

So, 430 letters last month and 420 letters were delivered this month.

4 Check Is my answer reasonable? Explain.
See students' explanations.

396   Chapter 6 • Lesson 8

Name _____

Apply the Strategy

1. A store sells raisins in packages of 130, 165, and 170. Rosa wants to buy 300 raisins. Which two packages will she buy?

packages of __130__ and __170__

2. Alexa's ant farm has 120 ants. She buys another ant farm. She now has 300 ants. How many ants are in the second ant farm?

Guys, look what I found!

__180__ ants

3. Tao needs to read three books that total 500 pages. Which three books should he read?

Book	Pages
1	115
2	150
3	200
4	185

Books __1__, __3__, and __4__

Review the Strategies

Choose a strategy
• Guess, check, and revise.
• Act it out.
• Use logical reasoning.

4. Clara counted 185 flowers on her walk. Her dad counted 139 flowers. How many flowers did they count altogether?

__324__ flowers

5. Chelsea collects sand dollars. The number she has collected is greater than 400 and less than 460. The number in the hundreds place is one less than the number in the tens place. The number in the ones place is two more than the number in the tens place. How many sand dollars did Chelsea collect?

__457__ sand dollars

6. One pet store has 289 angel fish. Another pet store has 132 angel fish. How many angel fish do the stores have altogether?

__421__ angel fish

ꓱPRACTICE & APPLY

Mathematical
PRACTICE 1 Apply the Strategy

Have students work through the exercises on these pages independently. You may choose to assign exercises based on the chart below.

DIFFERENTIATED ASSIGNMENTS

AL **Approaching Level** Guide students through the exercises in On My Own. Help them to use manipulatives while working through the exercises.

OL **On Level** Complete the excercises independently.

BL **Beyond Level** Complete the excercises independently without manipulatives.

Review the Strategies

Students may use other strategies they have learned to solve these exercises such as:

• Act it out

• Use logical reasoning

Mathematical
PRACTICE 8 In Exercise 5, students apply **Mathematical Practice: Look for and express regularity in repeated reasoning.**

AL APPROACHING LEVEL

IF my students struggle with problem solving,

THEN choose a resource:

→ Use the Reteach worksheet with small groups.

→ Go online for a Differentiated Instruction activity.

→ **Make a Model** Write 279 + 203 on the board. Use base-ten blocks and Work Mat 7 to show each addend rounded to the nearest hundred. Combine models and find the estimated sum. 3 hundreds + 2 hundreds = 5 hundreds or 500

OL ON LEVEL

IF my students seem to know problem solving, but need more practice,

THEN choose a resource:

→ Assign My Homework.

→ Go online for a Differentiated Instruction activity.

BL BEYOND LEVEL

IF my students have mastered problem solving,

THEN choose a resource:

→ Use the Enrich worksheet in cooperative groups.

→ Assign My Homework.

→ Go online for a Differentiated Instruction activity.

AL

Name _____

Lesson 8   Reteach (1)

Problem Solving
STRATEGY: Guess, Check, and Revise

There were 80 people on the plane. More people boarded the plane. Now there are 200 people. How many new people boarded the plane?

Step 1 Understand	**What do I know?** There were 80 people on the plane. There were 200 people after more boarded the plane.
	What do I need to find? The number of new people that boarded the plane.
Step 2 Plan	**How will I solve the problem?** I can guess, check, and revise.
Step 3 Solve	**Guess, check, and revise.** Guess: 200 passengers Check: 80 + 100 = 180 Revise: 180 is less than 200 Guess: 100 passengers Check: 80 + 120 = 200 **120** new passengers boarded the plane.
Step 4 Check	Is my answer reasonable? ___**yes**___

AL

Name _____

Lesson 8   Reteach (2)

Problem Solving
STRATEGY: Guess, Check, and Revise

Guess, check, and revise to solve.

1. Amy's family took a road trip to the nature center. Their home is 272 miles away from the nature center. If they drove there and back, how many total miles did they travel?   **544** miles

2. There are 192 steps to the pedestal of the Statue of Liberty. There are 162 more steps to the crown. How many total steps are there to climb the Statue of Liberty?   **354** steps

3. If there are 286 pages in a math workbook, how many pages are in 2 books?   **572** pages

4. There are 386 calories in a turkey sandwich and 115 calories in an apple. How many calories are there in all?   **501** calories

BL

Name _____

Lesson 8   Enrich

Problem Solving
STRATEGY: Guess, Check, and Revise

Play this game with a partner.

• Use three [1][1][1].
• Roll each number cube once for hundreds, once for tens, and once for ones.
• Write the numbers you roll for each digit in the charts.
• Repeat 3 rolls for the second addend.
• Guess the sum.
• Then find the actual sum.
• The player with the greater sum wins.
• Circle the winner's name.

Player 1 Name ____			Player 2 Name ____		
hundreds	tens	ones	hundreds	tens	ones
+			+		
hundreds	tens	ones	hundreds	tens	ones

Guess: ____   Guess: ____

Actual: ____   Actual: ____

See students' work.

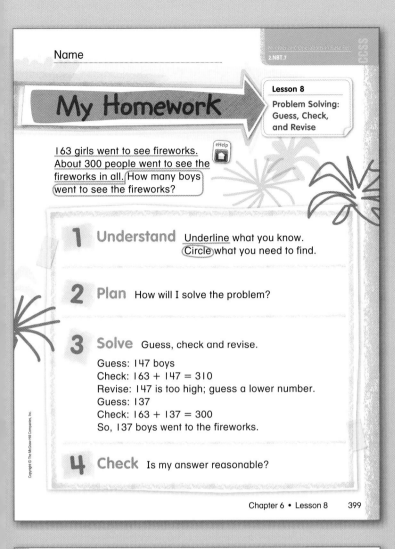

My Homework

Lesson 8
Problem Solving:
Guess, Check,
and Revise

163 girls went to see fireworks. About 300 people went to see the fireworks in all. How many boys went to see the fireworks?

1 Understand Underline what you know.
Circle what you need to find.

2 Plan How will I solve the problem?

3 Solve Guess, check and revise.

Guess: 147 boys
Check: 163 + 147 = 310
Revise: 147 is too high; guess a lower number.
Guess: 137
Check: 163 + 137 = 300
So, 137 boys went to the fireworks.

4 Check Is my answer reasonable?

Chapter 6 • Lesson 8   399

Underline what you know. Circle what you need to find out. Guess, check, and revise to solve.

1. 350 people went to the movie on Saturday. More people went to the movie on Sunday. About 600 people went to the movies in all. How many people went to the movie on Sunday?

   250 people

2. Pam has 65 purple flowers, 50 yellow flowers, and 75 red flowers in her garden. She needs a total of 125 flowers in 2 colors. Which flowers should she pick?

   yellow and red flowers

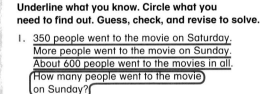

3. My garden has 145 corn stalks. It also has some tomato plants. There are about 245 corn and tomato plants in my garden. About how many tomato plants are in my garden?

   I love corny jokes!

   100 tomato plants

 Math at Home Tell story problems to your child. Have him or her practice guessing an answer and then checking it.

400   Chapter 6 • Lesson 8

---

4 WRAP IT UP

CCSS

My Homework

Assign homework after successful completion of the lesson. Students who understand the concepts may skip the **Homework Helper** section.

Formative Assessment

Ask students the following question.

Why is it important to check your guesses? Sometimes you guess too high or too low. It is good to check your answer against the facts in the problem to make sure you guessed correctly.

Review

Use these pages to assess your students' understanding of the vocabulary and key concepts in this chapter.

Vocabulary Check

Have students use each word in the word bank in a sentence.

ELL **ELL Support Strategy** Use this information to participate in purposeful, cooperative learning activities.

Concept Check

If students need reinforcement of skills after completing this section, use the Reteach worksheet to review the concepts again.

Exercises	Concept	Review Lesson(s)
6–8	Add hundreds	2
9–11	Mentally add 10 or 100	3
12–17	Add three-digit numbers	4, 5, 6
18–20	Rewrite three-digit addition	7

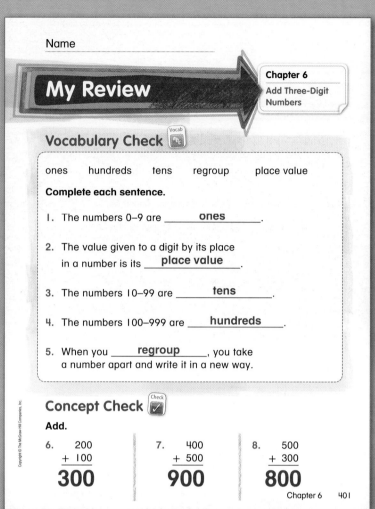

Name _____

My Review

Vocabulary Check

> ones   hundreds   tens   regroup   place value
>
> **Complete each sentence.**
>
> 1. The numbers 0–9 are ____**ones**____.
>
> 2. The value given to a digit by its place in a number is its ____**place value**____.
>
> 3. The numbers 10–99 are ____**tens**____.
>
> 4. The numbers 100–999 are ____**hundreds**____.
>
> 5. When you ____**regroup**____, you take a number apart and write it in a new way.

Concept Check

Add.

6.
```
  200
+ 100
  300
```

7.
```
  400
+ 500
  900
```

8.
```
  500
+ 300
  800
```

Chapter 6   401

Add.

9.
```
  354
+ 100
  454
```

10.
```
  327
+  10
  337
```

11.
```
  356
+ 100
  456
```

12.
```
  275
+ 116
  391
```

13.
```
  434
+ 247
  681
```

14.
```
  367
+ 226
  593
```

15.
```
  777
+ 133
  910
```

16.
```
  397
+ 159
  556
```

17.
```
  487
+ 247
  734
```

Rewrite the problems. Add.

18. 395 + 154
```
  395
+ 154
  549
```

19. 225 + 353
```
  225
+ 353
  578
```

20. 348 + 273
```
  348
+ 273
  621
```

402   Chapter 6

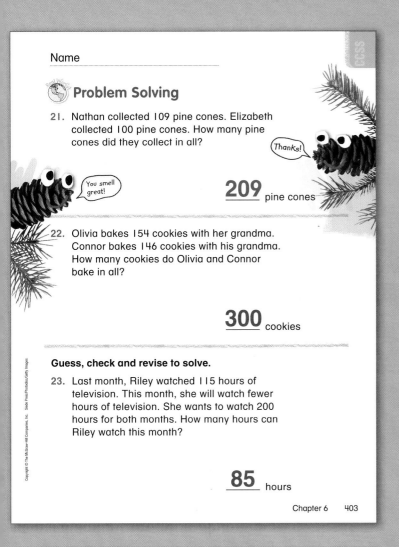

Name _____

🌐 Problem Solving

21. Nathan collected 109 pine cones. Elizabeth collected 100 pine cones. How many pine cones did they collect in all?

You smell great!

Thanks!

209 pine cones

22. Olivia bakes 154 cookies with her grandma. Connor bakes 146 cookies with his grandma. How many cookies do Olivia and Connor bake in all?

300 cookies

Guess, check and revise to solve.

23. Last month, Riley watched 115 hours of television. This month, she will watch fewer hours of television. She wants to watch 200 hours for both months. How many hours can Riley watch this month?

85 hours

Reflect

Show the ways you can add three-digit numbers.

Regroup ones.

$$\begin{array}{r} {}^{1} \\ 1\ 0\ 1 \\ +\ 1\ 2\ 9 \\ \hline 2\ 3\ 0 \end{array}$$

Regroup tens.

$$\begin{array}{r} {}^{1} \\ 2\ 3\ 4 \\ +\ 3\ 8\ 3 \\ \hline 6\ 1\ 7 \end{array}$$

ESSENTIAL QUESTION ❓
How do I add three-digit numbers?

Regroup tens and ones.

$$\begin{array}{r} {}^{1}\ {}^{1} \\ 3\ 6\ 4 \\ +\ 4\ 5\ 8 \\ \hline 8\ 2\ 2 \end{array}$$

Add mentally.

$358 + 100 = $ **458**

$782 + $ **10** $= 792$

MAIN ST.

Remember to visit me!

You will go far!

Problem Solving

Remind students of the four-step plan for problem solving. For students who need help in reading comprehension, have them work with another student to read the problem aloud before attempting the four-step plan.

Reflect

Display this chapter's vocabulary on the Virtual Word Wall. Ask students to refer to the words as they complete the graphic organizer.

You may choose to have your students use a different graphic organizer for review.

Summative Assessment

Use these alternate leveled chapter tests from the Assessment Masters to differentiate assessment for the specific needs of your students.

Chapter Tests		
Level	**Type**	**Form**
AL	Multiple Choice	**1A**
AL	Multiple Choice	**1B**
OL	Multiple Choice / Free Choice	**2A**
OL	Multiple Choice / Free Choice	**2B**
BL	Free Choice	**3A**
BL	Free Choice	**3B**
Additional Chapter Resource Masters		
OL	Vocabulary Test	
OL	Listening Assessment	
OL	Oral Assessment	

CHAPTER 7

Subtract Three-Digit Numbers

Suggested Pacing		
Instruction*	**Review & Assessment**	**TOTAL**
12 days	2 days	**14 days**

*Includes additional time for remediation and differentiation.

Chapter at a Glance

CCSS

Lesson	Objective	Materials & Manipulatives	Vocabulary	CCSS Standard
Lesson 1 *pp. 413–418* **Take Apart Hundreds to Subtract**	Make a hundred to subtract a three-digit number.	• base-ten blocks	*All of the vocabulary in this chapter are review words.*	2.NBT.7
Lesson 2 *pp. 419–424* **Subtract Hundreds**	Subtract numbers in the hundreds.	• spinner		2.NBT.7 2.NBT.9
Lesson 3 *pp. 425–430* **Mentally Subtract 10 or 100**	Subtract 10 or 100 mentally.	• base-ten blocks		2.NBT.8
✓ Check My Progress				
Lesson 4 *pp. 433–438* **Regroup Tens**	Regroup tens to subtract three-digit numbers.	• base-ten blocks • Work Mat 7		2.NBT.7 2.NBT.9
Lesson 5 *pp. 439–444* **Regroup Hundreds**	Regroup hundreds to subtract three-digit numbers.	• base-ten blocks • Work Mat 7		2.NBT.7 2.NBT.9

Lesson	Objective	Materials & Manipulatives	Vocabulary	CCSS Standard
Lesson 6 *pp. 445–450* **Subtract Three-Digit Numbers**	Subtract three-digit numbers.	• base-ten blocks • Work Mat 7		2.NBT.7 2.NBT.9
Lesson 7 *pp. 451–456* **Rewrite Three-Digit Subtraction**	Rewrite horizontal three-digit subtraction as vertical three-digit subtraction.	• base-ten blocks		2.NBT.7
Lesson 8 *pp. 457–462* **Problem-Solving Strategy: Write a Number Sentence**	Write a number sentence to solve problems.			2.NBT.7
Lesson 9 *pp. 463–468* **Subtract Across Zeros**	Subtract from numbers ending in zero.	• base-ten blocks • Work Mat 7		2.NBT.7 2.NBT.9

 My Review and Reflect

For customizable online assessment, go to **eAssessment** at connectED.mcgraw-hill.com.

Planning for Differentiated Instruction

Use these differentiated instruction activity suggestions, along with the ongoing support provided in each lesson of this chapter, to meet individual learning needs.

AL APPROACHING LEVEL

Use with Lesson 3

Materials: number cube, index cards labeled 98 or 99, paper, pencil

- Have students work in pairs. One student rolls a number cube three times and records a three-digit number. Each roll of the number cube represents a digit in the three-digit number.
- The second student picks an index card labeled 98 or 99.
- Have students work together to take apart one of the numbers to make a hundred to subtract. Record the difference on paper.
- Repeat the activity.

AL APPROACHING LEVEL

Use with Lesson 2

Materials: index cards (labeled with hundred numbers such as 0 hundred, 1 hundred, 2 hundred … 9 hundred on each card), blank number line, transparent chips

- Label the number line with multiples of 100 (0–900).
- Choose an index card and read the number aloud. Place a chip on that number on the number line.
- Choose another index card to generate the number to subtract.
- Tell students to use the number line to find the difference. Start with the first number and count back to subtract. Place a chip on the difference.
- Have the students write the number sentence.

AL APPROACHING LEVEL

Use with Lesson 6

Materials: base-ten blocks, 0–9 digit cards

- Pick six 0–9 digit cards to generate the greatest and least three-digit numbers.
- Instruct students to write a subtraction problem on paper using these two numbers. Have them write the problem using hundreds, tens, and ones.
- Have students model the greater number with base-ten blocks.
- Have them decide whether regrouping a ten as 10 ones is needed.
- Explain that regrouping is needed if the digit in the place value is less than the digit to be subtracted from it.
- Work the problem together. Discuss whether the answer is reasonable, and why.

AL APPROACHING LEVEL

Use with Lesson 5

Materials: books with over 100 pages, base-ten blocks

- Have students work in pairs.
- Have the students take turns opening the book to random pages and recording the page number. Tell them that it is important that they turn to pages later in the book so that they record pages numbered over 100.
- They should then write the two numbers in a subtraction problem with the greater number on top.
- Together the students should work to solve the subtraction problem using the base-ten blocks and regrouping as needed.

OL ON LEVEL

Use with Lesson 2

Materials: number cube

- Have students work in groups of three.
- One student rolls a number cube twice and adds zeros to the numbers to form two numbers in the hundreds.
- A second student writes a subtraction sentence that takes the lower number away from the higher.
- A third student does the subtraction while others check.

OL ON LEVEL

Use with Lesson 6

Materials: spinner

- A student spins a spinner to get and record six numbers.
- A second student arranges the numbers into a subtraction problem.
- A third student works through the problem, and a fourth student checks the work.
- Students rotate roles and repeat.

BL BEYOND LEVEL

Use with Lesson 9

Materials: number cards (0–9), index cards (labeled 0, 100, 200, 300, ... 800; two of each label)

- Have students work in groups of three.
- Spread out the index cards, faceup.
- The first student draws three number cards. Another student generates 2 three-digit numbers and records them.
- The next student estimates the difference in hundreds and points to the index card with that estimate.
- Students rotate roles and repeat.

ELL ENGLISH LANGUAGE LEARNERS

Support for English Language Learners is found throughout the chapter and includes:

- ELL strategies at point-of-use in each Teacher Edition lesson
- ELL tiered instruction suggestions for each lesson at connectED.mcgraw-hill.com
- Comprehensive ELL lessons and worksheets for additional instruction at connectED.mcgraw-hill.com
- Non-linguistic representations of concepts on My Math Words, My Vocabulary Cards, and My Foldables

Additional online resources at connectED.mcgraw-hill.com include:

- Visual Vocabulary Cards
- Multilingual eGlossary
- Professional Development support

Looking for more DIFFERENTIATED INSTRUCTION?
Find additional support in each lesson of this chapter and online at connectED.mcgraw-hill.com

AL Approaching Level
OL On Level
BL Beyond Level
ELL English Language Learners

What's the Math in This Chapter?

Points of Intersection

Where

CONTENT STANDARDS

Meet

Mathematical **PRACTICE**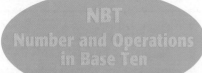

Look for and express regularity in repeated reasoning.

NBT
Number and Operations in Base Ten

This chapter concentrates on the **Number and Operations in Base Ten (NBT)** domain.

As you teach subtraction of three-digit numbers, emphasize that the subtraction process involves repeated calculation. Students can use the same algorithm repeatedly with any addition problem they encounter. The algorithm consists of subtracting each place value, starting with the ones place, and regrouping when needed.

What should my students already know?

In the previous grade, students used **Operations and Algebraic Thinking (OA)** in their study of **subtraction**:

- Use subtraction within 20 to solve word problems.
  1.OA.1

- Subtract within 20, demonstrating fluency for subtraction within 10.
  1.OA.6

Students also used **Number and Operations in Base Ten (NBT)** in their study of **subtraction**:

- Understand that the two digits of a two-digit number represent amounts of tens and ones.
  1.NBT.2

- Given a two-digit number, mentally find 10 less than the number, without having to count.
  1.NBT.5

- Subtract multiples of 10 in the range 10–90 from multiples of 10 in the range 10–90.
  1.NBT.6

WHAT STUDENTS SHOULD UNDERSTAND

Take Apart Hundreds to Subtract

 2.NBT.7

How to take apart one of the numbers in a subtraction problem to make a hundred so that it is easier to subtract.

- Take apart the minuend. Next, subtract the subtrahend from 100. Then add the difference to what was left from the minuend.

Subtract Hundreds

 2.NBT.7

How to subtract two hundreds.

- You can use basic subtraction facts to subtract hundreds.

WHAT STUDENTS SHOULD BE ABLE TO DO

Find 502 − 98.

Take apart 502 as 402 and 100 since it is easier to subtract 98 from 100.

$$502 - 98$$
$$\diagdown\diagup$$
$$402 \quad 100$$

$$100 - 98 = 2$$

$$402 + 2 = 404$$

So, $502 - 98 = 404$.

Find 500 − 300.

You know that $5 - 3 = 2$.

$$\begin{array}{r} 5 \text{ hundreds} \\ - \ 3 \text{ hundreds} \\ \hline 2 \text{ hundreds} \end{array}$$

So, $500 - 300 = 200$.

WHAT STUDENTS SHOULD UNDERSTAND	WHAT STUDENTS SHOULD BE ABLE TO DO

Mentally Subtract 10 or 100

 2.NBT.8

How to mentally subtract 10 or 100 from a three-digit number.

- You can use mental math to subtract 10 or 100 from a number by thinking of subtraction facts.

Mentally subtract 100.

$$\begin{array}{r} 745 \\ -\ 100 \end{array}$$

THINK

$7 - 1 = 6$, so
$$\begin{array}{r} 745 \\ -\ 100 \\ \hline 645 \end{array}$$

Mentally subtract 10.

$$\begin{array}{r} 831 \\ -\ 10 \end{array}$$

THINK

$3 - 1 = 2$, so
$$\begin{array}{r} 831 \\ -\ 10 \\ \hline 821 \end{array}$$

Subtract Three-Digit Numbers with Regrouping

 2.NBT.7

How to subtract three-digit numbers that involve regrouping the tens, hundreds, or both place values.

- When subtracting with three-digit numbers, subtract the ones, the tens, and then the hundreds.
- Regroup 1 ten as 10 ones if there are not enough ones to subtract from.
- Regroup 1 hundred as 10 tens if there are not enough tens to subtract from.

Find 411 - 273.

Step 1 Subtract the ones, regroup.

Step 2 Subtract the tens, regroup.

Step 3 Subtract the hundreds.

hundreds	tens	ones
3	10	11
4̶	1̶	1̶
− 2	7	3
1	3	8

Subtract Across Zeros

 2.NBT.7

How to subtract three-digit numbers when the top number ends in two zeros.

- When the top number ends with two zeros and you need to regroup the tens, the first step you will take is to regroup 1 hundred as 10 tens and 1 ten as 10 ones.

Find 400 − 155.

Step 1 Subtract the ones, regroup. There are no tens to regroup. Look at the hundreds. Regroup 1 hundred as 10 tens. Then regroup 1 ten as 10 ones.

Step 2 Subtract the tens.

hundreds	tens	ones
3	9	10
4̶	0̶	0̶
− 1	5	5
2	4	5

What will my students do next with these skills?

After this chapter, students will learn to:
- solve problems involving money.

In the next grade, students will learn to:
- solve multiplication and division problems.

Reading Connections

Real-World Problem Solving Library

Maths and Social Studies: A Mountain of Presidents

Real-World Problem Solving
Math and Social Studies
A Mountain of Presidents
Measurement

Use these leveled books to reinforce and extend problem-solving skills and strategies.

Leveled for:

AL **Approaching Level**

OL **On Level** Also available in Spanish

BL **Beyond Level**

For additional support, see the *Real-World Problem Solving Readers Teacher Guide.*

Leveled Reader Database

Available at leveledreaderdatabase.macmillanmh.com
Search by:

- Content Area
- Guided Reading Level
- Lexile Score
- Benchmark Level

Library Books

Check with your school library or your local public library for these titles.

Shark Swimathon
Stuart J. Murphy

"You and the Statue"* from *Math Mini Mysteries
Sandra Markle

Panda Math: Learning About Subtraction from Hua Mei and Mei Sheng
Ann Whitehead Nagda

The Case of the $hrunken Allowance
Joanne Rocklin

The Water Hole
Graeme Base

Tightwad Tod
Daphne Skinner

Reading and Language Arts Support

Examining Math

Have students work in pairs, and distribute an index card to each pair. Ask them to discuss the similarities and differences between addition and subtraction of three-digit numbers. Each pair will record 2 similarities on one side of their index card and 2 differences on the other side. Collect the cards, and come together again as a class to discuss what students have written.

Looking for more Reading and Language Arts Support? go online to connectED.mcgraw-hill.com

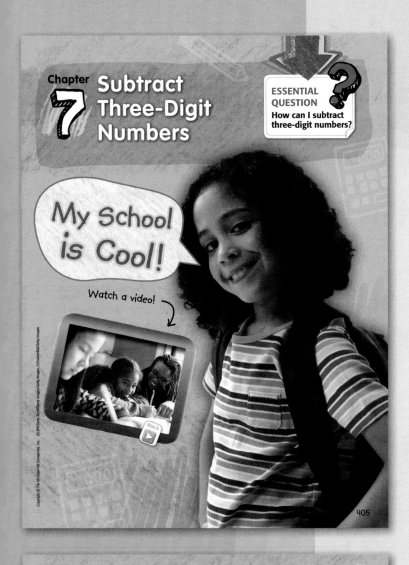

My School is Cool!

Watch a video!

405

LAUNCH THE CHAPTER

Theme:

My School is Cool!

All of the lessons in Chapter 7 will connect with the theme of My School is Cool!, which centers around school activities. This is reflected in problem solving and the visuals used throughout the chapter.

Video

Have students watch the video about school. You may want to spark a discussion about how math is used in school.

Building on the Essential Question

Once students have completed this chapter, they should be able to answer the question "How can I subtract three-digit numbers?" In each lesson, students build upon their understanding of this question by answering a simpler question. These are indicated in the exercises as Building on the Essential Question. At the end of the chapter, students use a graphic organizer to help them answer the Essential Question.

CCSS

My Common Core State Standards CCSS

Number and Operations in Base Ten

2.NBT.7 Add and subtract within 1000, using concrete models or drawings and strategies based on place value, properties of operations, and/or the relationship between addition and subtraction; relate the strategy to a written method. Understand that in adding or subtracting three-digit numbers, one adds or subtracts hundreds and hundreds, tens and tens, ones and ones; and sometimes it is necessary to compose or decompose tens or hundreds.

2.NBT.8 Mentally add 10 or 100 to a given number 100–900, and mentally subtract 10 or 100 from a given number 100–900.

2.NBT.9 Explain why addition and subtraction strategies work, using place value and the properties of operations.

Standards for Mathematical PRACTICE

1. Make sense of problems and persevere in solving them.
2. Reason abstractly and quantitatively.
3. Construct viable arguments and critique the reasoning of others.
4. Model with mathematics.
5. Use appropriate tools strategically.
6. Attend to precision.
7. Look for and make use of structure.
8. Look for and express regularity in repeated reasoning.

= focused on in this chapter

406   Chapter 7

Professional Development

CCSS Common Core State Standards

Learn more about how the Common Core State Standards can be implemented in your classroom at mhpdonline.com.

Look for
- eImplementation
- eVideo Clip Libraries
- eTech Training
- ePD Webinars

Feature video for mathematical content in this chapter:
Operations and Algorithms

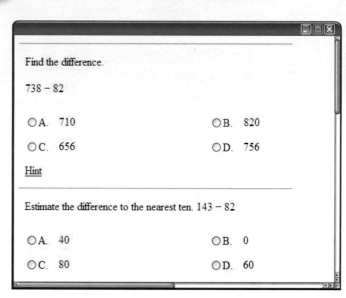

1 Assess

You have two options for assessing student readiness for this chapter. Use student results to determine which level of instruction is needed to help students get ready for the chapter and to determine what ongoing support they will need during the chapter.

Option 1: Am I Ready?

Have students complete the Am I Ready? page in their student books.

Option 2: Online Readiness Quiz

Have students take the **Online Readiness Quiz.**

Name _____

Am I Ready?

← Go online to take the Readiness Quiz

Subtract.

1. 9 − 6 **3**	2. 8 − 8 **0**	3. 17 − 8 **9**	4. 14 − 5 **9**
5. 60 − 30 **30**	6. 87 − 53 **34**	7. 62 − 37 **25**	8. 72 − 25 **47**
9. 95 − 14 **81**	10. 90 − 60 **30**	11. 88 − 61 **27**	12. 43 − 25 **18**

13. Aiden sees eight squirrels. Two run away. How many squirrels does Aiden see now?

6 squirrels

How Did I Do? Shade the boxes to show the problems you answered correctly.
1 2 3 4 5 6 7 8 9 10 11 12 13

Online Content at connectED.mcgraw-hill.com   Chapter 7   407

Find the difference.

738 − 82

○ A. 710   ○ B. 820

○ C. 656   ○ D. 756

Hint

Estimate the difference to the nearest ten. 143 − 82

○ A. 40   ○ B. 0

○ C. 80   ○ D. 60

OPTION 2

Common Core Review

Exercises	Skill	Standard
1–10*	Subtraction	2.NBT.7

*These questions are randomly generated from a bank of 15 questions.

OPTION 1

Common Core Review

Exercises	Skill	Standard
1–13	Subtraction	2.NBT.7

2 Diagnose and Prescribe

Based on the results of the Am I Ready? in the student edition, use the charts below to address individual needs **before** beginning the chapter.

Use the **ONGOING** resources to support differentiated instruction as new skills and concepts are presented in the chapter.

TIER 1

OL ON LEVEL

IF students miss 3–4 in Exercises 1–13,

THEN choose a resource:

→ Am I Ready? Practice

→ Online Readiness Quiz

ONGOING Self-Check Quizzes • Chapter Project • Differentiated Assignments • My Learning Stations • Differentiated Instruction activities

TIER 2

AL STRATEGIC INTERVENTION

(Approaching Grade Level)

IF students miss 4–5 in Exercises 1–13,

THEN choose a resource:

→ Online Strategic Intervention activity

→ Am I Ready? Review

ONGOING Common Errors • Differentiated Assignments • Online support • Reteach worksheets • Homework Helper • My Learning Stations • RtI lesson support • Differentiated Instruction activities

TIER 3

INTENSIVE INTERVENTION

(2 or more years below grade level)

IF students miss 6 or more in Exercises 1–13,

THEN use *Math Triumphs,* an intensive math intervention program from McGraw-Hill.

BL BEYOND LEVEL

IF students miss 2 or less in Exercises 1–13,

THEN choose a resource:

→ Online Games

→ Am I Ready? Apply

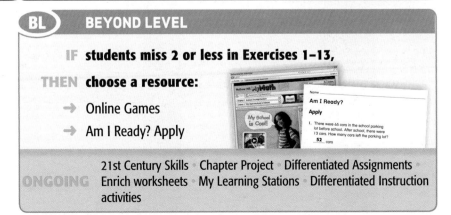

ONGOING 21st Century Skills • Chapter Project • Differentiated Assignments • Enrich worksheets • My Learning Stations • Differentiated Instruction activities

3 Reassess

If reassessment is necessary, administer the chapter Diagnostic Test in the **Assessment Masters** or go online for eAssessment.

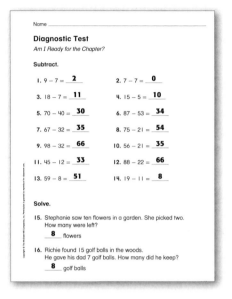

Name _____

Diagnostic Test
Am I Ready for the Chapter?

Subtract.

1. $9 - 7 =$ __2__
2. $7 - 7 =$ __0__
3. $18 - 7 =$ __11__
4. $15 - 5 =$ __10__
5. $70 - 40 =$ __30__
6. $87 - 53 =$ __34__
7. $67 - 32 =$ __35__
8. $75 - 21 =$ __54__
9. $98 - 32 =$ __66__
10. $56 - 21 =$ __35__
11. $45 - 12 =$ __33__
12. $88 - 22 =$ __66__
13. $59 - 8 =$ __51__
14. $19 - 11 =$ __8__

Solve.

15. Stephanie saw ten flowers in a garden. She picked two. How many were left?
__8__ flowers

16. Richie found 15 golf balls in the woods. He gave his dad 7 golf balls. How many did he keep?
__8__ golf balls

Check For additional chapter readiness assessment, go to eAssessment at connectED.mcgraw-hill.com.

My Math Words

Review Vocabulary

Where did they learn it?

- difference   (Lesson 1-7)
- ones   (Lesson 5-1)
- regroup   (Lesson 3-2)
- subtract   (Lesson 1-7)
- tens   (Lesson 5-1)

Making Connections

Ask students to describe or show what they know about the review vocabulary. Encourage students to describe, draw, act out, or model their examples.

Ask students to examine the graphic organizer. Have them compare and contrast the subtraction sentence on the left with the subtraction sentence on the right.

After students complete the page, have them draw a similar graphic organizer. Tell them to solve these three-digit addition problems: 388 + 111; 507 + 197. Have them describe the place value in each addend.

My Vocabulary Cards

There is no new vocabulary in this chapter. Encourage students to use the blank cards to review vocabulary words, draw examples of important concepts, or write questions they have about what they have learned.

Students should clip and store their cards in one place, such as a small envelope, where they can access them as needed throughout the chapter.

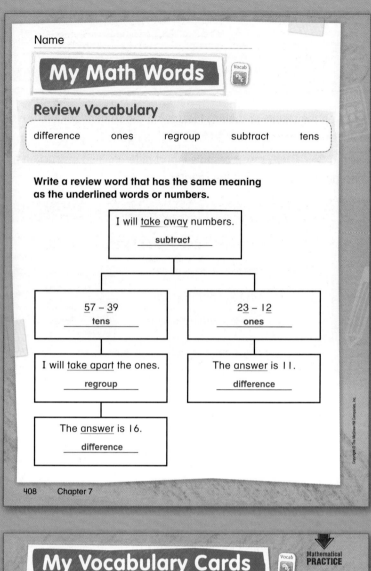

Name _____

My Math Words

Review Vocabulary

| difference | ones | regroup | subtract | tens |

Write a review word that has the same meaning as the underlined words or numbers.

I will take away numbers.
subtract

57 – 39
tens

23 – 12
ones

I will take apart the ones.
regroup

The answer is 11.
difference

The answer is 16.
difference

408   Chapter 7

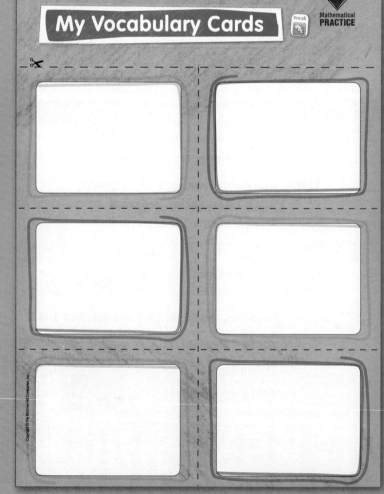

My Vocabulary Cards

Mathematical PRACTICE

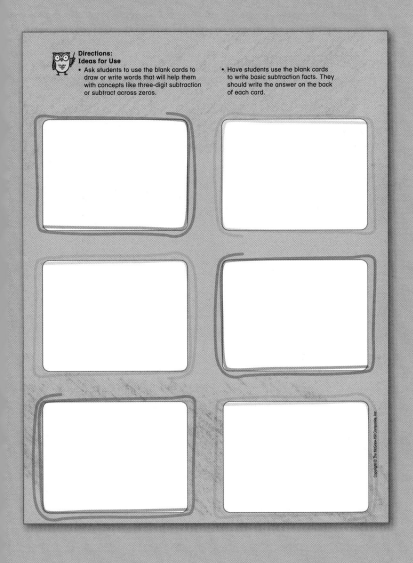

Directions:
Ideas for Use

- Ask students to use the blank cards to draw or write words that will help them with concepts like three-digit subtraction or subtract across zeros.

- Have students use the blank cards to write basic subtraction facts. They should write the answer on the back of each card.

Copyright © The McGraw-Hill Companies, Inc.

Mathematical
PRACTICE 3   **My Vocabulary Card Activities**

Suggestions for using blank cards appear in some Developing Vocabulary Activities.

My Foldable

What's the Math?

Content Standard: 2.NBT.7

Mathematical PRACTICE 5 **Use appropriate tools strategically.**

This Foldable has students practice subtracting three-digit numbers when regrouping is necessary.

How Do I Make It?

• Tear out the page and cut off the top banner.

• Fold along the two green dotted lines.

• Cut along the orange dashed lines in four places to make six tabs.

When Do I Use It?

Use after Lesson 4 and as a review tool at the end of the chapter.

How Could I Use It?

• Start with all tabs closed to show the problem 125 − 109.

• Have students look at the 5 on the green tab. Ask students if they can subtract 9 from 5. If they cannot, they must regroup a ten as ten ones. Have students open the 2 tab and change the number to 1. Have students open the 5 tab and change the number to 15.

• Students may then continue with the subtraction problem, working from right to left, writing the answer in the white box under the bottom tab.

ELL **ELL Support Strategy** Use this Foldable to assess students' ability extend their understanding.

© The McGraw-Hill Companies, Inc.

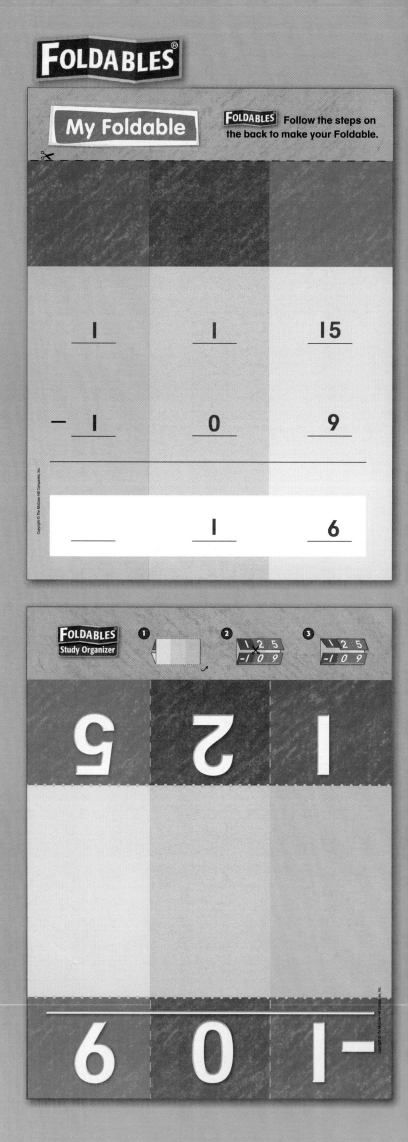

Lunchroom Chat

Building a Learning Community

Students will now be able to subtract three-digit numbers. This provides an opportunity for your teaching team to create word problems involving other disciplines so students can see how their mathematics skills relate to the real world. Brainstorm with your fellow teachers to make lists of related quantities that could be subtracted. Categorize the lists by discipline and make a plan for possibly creating a math snapshot feature for each of the subjects being taught at this time.

MY Learning Stations

Use the following learning stations to differentiate the instruction for Chapter 7. Includes Spanish!

Learning Station	Title	Use after Lesson
Game	*Subtract It!*	6
Graphic Novel	*Ice Cream Favorites*	6
Activity Card	*The Boiling Point*	6

Chapter Project

Reference Posters for Subtracting Three-Digit Numbers

To help students remember the steps and strategies for subtracting three-digit numbers, have them work in small groups to create a poster to illustrate a concept.

- Encourage students to plan what they will include in their poster and remind them to refer back to the lessons to check their work for accuracy.
- Have students include an example problem that uses the steps or strategy they are illustrating.
- Provide groups with construction paper, poster board and art materials to create their poster.
- Ask students to share their poster. Display them to be used for reference by the class.

CALENDAR TIME

Calendar Time

Month by Month Subtraction

- Choose a month from the calendar.
- Inform students that there are 365 days in a year.
- Start with January and ask how many days would be left in the year if we subtract the days for that month.
- Ask a volunteer to do the subtraction to find out.
- Repeat with February and the following months until the number of days left is a two-digit number.

LESSON 1
Take Apart Hundreds to Subtract

OBJECTIVE   Make a hundred to subtract a three-digit number.

What's the Math?

 Common Core State Standards
DOMAIN: Number and Operations in Base Ten

Standard: 2.NBT.7
The wording of this standard can be found on page 406.

What Students Should Understand

- You can take apart the first number to create two numbers: a number that is one hundred and what is left of the first number. Then subtract the second number from 100. Last, add the difference to what was left from the first number.

- This subtraction strategy is useful when the second number is close to, but less than 100.

What Students Should be Able to Do

Find 305 − 96 by taking apart 305 to create a number that is a hundred.

$$305 - 96$$

205 100

$$100 - 96 = 4$$

$$205 + 4 = 209$$

So, 305 − 96 = 209.

 Building on the Essential Question

In this lesson, students will build upon the skills and concepts needed to answer the chapter's Essential Question "How can I subtract three-digit numbers?"

Developing Vocabulary

 Review Vocabulary

hundreds

Review Activity

- Write *hundreds* on the board. Have students explain what they have learned about hundreds in previous chapters or grades. For example, they might recall that hundreds are easy to work with because they end in zero.

- Have students work in small groups to take apart base-ten blocks. Each group should have 4 flats and tens rods.

- Have each group show 2 groups of hundreds and six groups of ten. Ask a volunteers to name the number they are showing. 260

- Tell students that numbers in a subtraction sentence can be broken apart into hundreds to make them easier to work with.

ELL **ELL Support Strategy**   Use this vocabulary activity to visualize what is being taught and participate in purposeful, cooperative learning activities.

My Vocabulary Cards

Have students use a blank card write the example problem 800 − 98 as shown in the lesson. They can refer to this example as they solve the exercises in the lesson.

IWB **Virtual Word Wall**

You may wish to begin the Virtual Word Wall for this chapter by adding this review word.

ELL Refer to the Multilingual eGlossary for interactive definitions in 13 languages.

Plan Online

Plan for your lesson by using the resources at

 connectED.mcgraw-hill.com

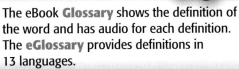

Digital Dashboard

Interactive Whiteboard Ready

Vocab

The eBook **Glossary** shows the definition of the word and has audio for each definition. The **eGlossary** provides definitions in 13 languages.

Watch

Watch as concepts are brought to life through **animations**, **songs**, and a variety of visual instruction.

Tools

Virtual Manipulatives with work mats allow teachers and students to model the lesson.

Check

Use **eAssessment** for online assignments and customized assessments.

Use the **Common Core Quick Check** before the lesson to assess students' retention of previously learned concepts.

Use the interactive **Self-Check Quiz** after the lesson to provide immediate feedback on lesson concepts.

eHelp

Digital and print resources assist students and parents in completing My Homework.

Games

Online games and **apps** provide extra practice for lesson concepts.

PD

Professional development videos help teachers gain a deeper understanding of the lesson concepts and strategies.

RtI

Support for **approaching**, **on-** and **beyond-level** students as well as **English Language Learners**.

Masters

Reteach and **Enrich** worksheets, **Manipulative Masters**, the **Problem of the Day**, and other blackline masters are available for each lesson.

---

1 LAUNCH THE LESSON

CCSS

 If your students are well-versed in taking apart hundreds to subtract, you may choose to begin instruction with Step 2, **TEACH**.

You will need

☐ base-ten blocks

Mathematical PRACTICE 4  **Modeling the Math**

Model 301 − 100 using base-ten blocks as shown below.

What is 301 − 100? 201

Model 530 − 100 using base-ten blocks.

What is 530 − 100? 430

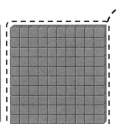

Online Content at  **connectED.mcgraw-hill.com**

 Begin core instruction here.

You will need

☐ base-ten blocks

Explore and Explain

Read the directions that are on the bottom of the student page.

Discuss how to model the problem.

How many new crayons are in the crayon bucket?
403 crayons

Which base-ten blocks can you use to model 403?
4 hundreds flats, 0 tens rods, 3 unit cubes

How many crayons were lost after the first month of school? 97 crayons

If you take apart one of the hundreds and take away 97 from it, how many are left? 3

Guide students in showing 403 − 97 by taking away one of the hundreds flats and replacing it with the 3 unit cubes that are left.

How many base-ten blocks are left after you took away 97?
306 base-ten blocks

What is 403 − 97? 306

So, there are 306 crayons left in the bucket.

See and Show

Help students work through the example at the top of the page.

Help students understand that the first number is being taken apart so that it is easier to subtract mentally.

Have them trace the dashed numbers as they work through the problems.

Work through Exercises 1 and 2 as a class.

 **PRACTICE 3** **Talk Math**

Discuss with students "In Exercise 2, why is 2 added back?"
Sample answer: The 3 is added back because it was taken away from 100.

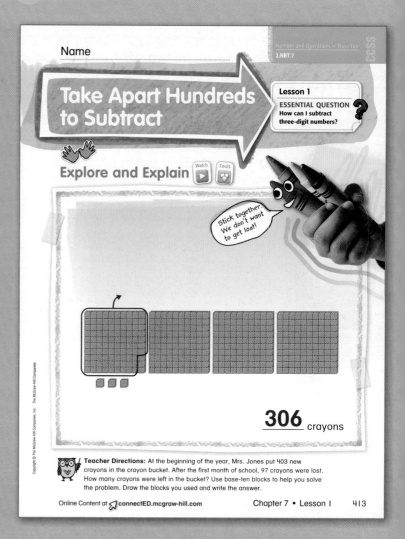

Name _____

Number and Operations in Base Ten
2.NBT.7

Take Apart Hundreds to Subtract

Lesson 1
ESSENTIAL QUESTION
How can I subtract three-digit numbers?

Explore and Explain Watch Tools

Stick together. We don't want to get lost!

306 crayons

Teacher Directions: At the beginning of the year, Mrs. Jones put 403 new crayons in the crayon bucket. After the first month of school, 97 crayons were lost. How many crayons were left in the bucket? Use base-ten blocks to help you solve the problem. Draw the blocks you used and write the answer.

Online Content at connectED.mcgraw-hill.com   Chapter 7 • Lesson 1   413

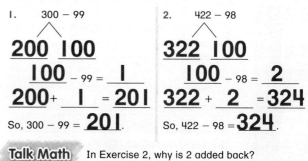

See and Show

You can take apart hundreds to subtract mentally.

Take apart 800 as 700 and 100 since it is easier to subtract 98 from 100.

800 − 98

700   100

$100 - 98 = $ **2**

$700 + 2 = $ **702**

So, $800 - 98 = $ **702**.

Take apart 401 as 301 and 100 since it is easier to subtract 97 from 100.

401 − 97

Helpful Hint
What hundreds do you need to use?

301   100

$100 - 97 = $ **3**

$301 + 3 = $ **304**

So, $401 - 97 = $ **304**.

Take apart hundreds to subtract.

1.   300 − 99

200 100

100 − 99 = **1**

200+ **1** = **201**

So, 300 − 99 = **201**.

2.   422 − 98

322 100

100 − 98 = **2**

322 + **2** = **324**

So, 422 − 98 = **324**.

Talk Math   In Exercise 2, why is 2 added back?

414   Chapter 7 • Lesson 1

PRACTICE & APPLY

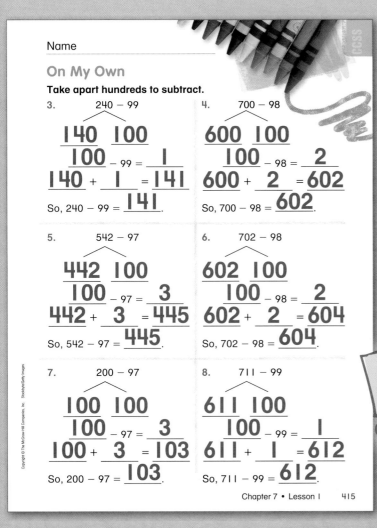

Name _____

On My Own

Take apart hundreds to subtract.

3.   240 − 99

$$\underline{140} \quad \underline{100}$$
$$\underline{100} - 99 = \underline{1}$$
$$140 + 1 = 141$$

So, 240 − 99 = __141__.

4.   700 − 98

$$\underline{600} \quad \underline{100}$$
$$\underline{100} - 98 = \underline{2}$$
$$600 + 2 = 602$$

So, 700 − 98 = __602__.

5.   542 − 97

$$\underline{442} \quad \underline{100}$$
$$\underline{100} - 97 = \underline{3}$$
$$442 + 3 = 445$$

So, 542 − 97 = __445__.

6.   702 − 98

$$\underline{602} \quad \underline{100}$$
$$\underline{100} - 98 = \underline{2}$$
$$602 + 2 = 604$$

So, 702 − 98 = __604__.

7.   200 − 97

$$\underline{100} \quad \underline{100}$$
$$\underline{100} - 97 = \underline{3}$$
$$100 + 3 = 103$$

So, 200 − 97 = __103__.

8.   711 − 99

$$\underline{611} \quad \underline{100}$$
$$\underline{100} - 99 = \underline{1}$$
$$611 + 1 = 612$$

So, 711 − 99 = __612__.

On My Own

Have students work through the exercises on this page independently. You may choose to assign exercises based on the chart below.

DIFFERENTIATED ASSIGNMENTS

AL Approaching Level Guide students through the exercises in On My Own. Help them to use manipulatives while working through the exercises.

OL On Level Complete the exercises independently.

BL Beyond Level Complete the exercises independently without manipulatives.

Common Error!

Students might have difficulty remembering to add back the 1 or 2 they received from subtracting 98 or 99 from 100. Have them circle the number so that they do not forget to add it back in at the end of the problem.

Problem Solving

Have students work through the problem-solving exercises on this page independently.

Mathematical PRACTICE 4 In Exercise 11, students **model with mathematics.**

HOT Problem This exercise asks students to build upon their understanding of concepts needed to answer the chapter's Essential Question.

Problem Solving

Mathematical PRACTICE

9. Eli counts 335 sunflower seeds. He places 98 of the seeds in a bowl. How many seeds were left?

   237 sunflower seeds

10. Rachel has 148 blueberries. She gives 97 blueberries to her brother. How many blueberries does Rachel have left?

    51 blueberries

11. 382 people were in our school auditorium. 99 people left. How many people are still in the auditorium?

    283 people

HOT Problem Explain in words how to solve 700 − 97.

Sample answer: First, take apart 700 as 600 and 100.

Then subtract 97 from 100 and get 3. Add 3 to 600 to

get the answer, 600 + 3 = 603. See students' work.

AL APPROACHING LEVEL

IF my students struggle with taking apart hundreds to subtract,

THEN choose a resource:

→ Use the Reteach worksheet with small groups.

→ Go online for a Differentiated Instruction activity.

→ **Another Way to Subtract** Explore with students a different strategy for subtracting numbers. Start with 501 − 98. Explain to students that you are going to add the same number to both sides to make it easier to subtract. *What would that number be?* 2 *If we add 2 to both sides, what is our new problem?* 503 − 100 *What is the difference?* 403

OL ON LEVEL

IF my students seem to know taking apart hundreds to subtract, but need more practice,

THEN choose a resource:

→ Assign My Homework.

→ Go online for a Differentiated Instruction activity.

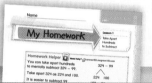

BL BEYOND LEVEL

IF my students have mastered taking apart hundreds to subtract,

THEN choose a resource:

→ Use the Enrich worksheet in cooperative groups.

→ Assign My Homework.

→ Go online for a Differentiated Instruction activity.

AL

Name _____

Lesson 1   Reteach

Take Apart Hundreds to Subtract

Mental math can make subtraction easier.

$$600 - 99 = \boxed{501}$$
$$\diagdown\ \diagdown$$
$$100\ \ 500$$

You can break apart 600 to be 100 and 500.

$$100 - 99 = 1$$
$$500 + 1 = 501$$

99 is 1 away from 100. Add the 1 to 500 to get your answer.

Break apart hundreds to subtract mentally.

1. $303 - 98 = \boxed{205}$
    $\diagup\ \diagdown$
    $100\ \ 203$

    $100 - 98 = \underline{\textbf{2}}$

    $203 + \underline{\textbf{2}} = \textbf{205}$

2. $500 - 97 = \boxed{403}$
    $\diagup\ \diagdown$
    $\underline{\textbf{100}}\ \ \underline{\textbf{400}}$

    $100 - 97 = \underline{\textbf{3}}$

    $400 + \underline{\textbf{3}} = \textbf{403}$

3. $360 - 99 = \boxed{261}$
    $\diagup\ \diagdown$
    $\textbf{100}\ \ \textbf{260}$

    $\textbf{100} - \textbf{99} = \textbf{1}$

    $\textbf{260} + \textbf{1} = \textbf{261}$

4. $304 - 98 = \boxed{206}$
    $\diagup\ \diagdown$
    $\textbf{100}\ \ \textbf{204}$

    $\textbf{100} - \textbf{98} = \textbf{2}$

    $\textbf{204} + \textbf{2} = \textbf{206}$

BL

Name _____

Lesson 1   Enrich

Take Apart Hundreds to Subtract

Draw lines to match each mouse to the cheese.

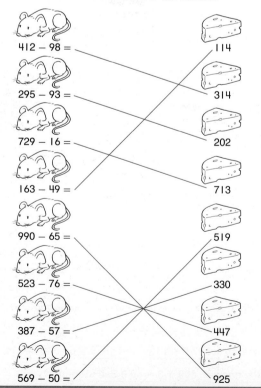

$412 - 98 =$	114
$295 - 93 =$	314
$729 - 16 =$	202
$163 - 49 =$	713
$990 - 65 =$	519
$523 - 76 =$	330
$387 - 57 =$	447
$569 - 50 =$	925

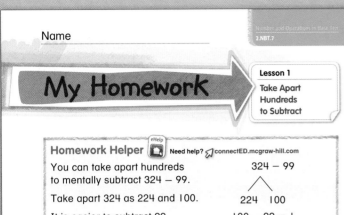

My Homework

Lesson 1
Take Apart Hundreds to Subtract

Homework Helper Need help? connectED.mcgraw-hill.com

You can take apart hundreds to mentally subtract 324 − 99.

Take apart 324 as 224 and 100.

It is easier to subtract 99 from 100.

324 − 99

224 100

$100 - 99 = 1$

$224 + 1 = 225$

So, $324 - 99 = 225$.

Practice

Take apart hundreds to subtract.

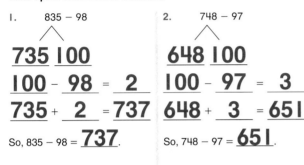

1.   835 − 98

735 100

$100 - 98 = 2$

$735 + 2 = 737$

So, $835 - 98 = 737$.

2.   748 − 97

648 100

$100 - 97 = 3$

$648 + 3 = 651$

So, $748 - 97 = 651$.

Take apart hundreds to subtract.

3.   395 − 99

295 100

$100 - 99 = 1$

$295 + 1 = 296$

So, $395 - 99 = 296$.

4.   600 − 97

500 100

$100 - 97 = 3$

$500 + 3 = 503$

So, $600 - 97 = 503$.

5. Students go to school for 180 days. 96 school days were sunny. How many school days were not sunny?

____84____ days

It's definitely "not sunny" today.

Test Practice

6. How would you take apart 355 to solve 355 − 94?

○ 355 and 100   ○ 300 and 55

● 255 and 100   ○ 255 and 94

Math at Home Have your child solve 321 − 99 using mental math.

---

4 WRAP IT UP

CCSS

My Homework

Assign homework after successful completion of the lesson. Students who understand the concepts may skip the **Homework Helper** section.

Test Practice

Diagnose Student Errors

Class trends in wrong answers may indicate common errors or misconceptions.

355 and 100 didn't take apart 355, did know they needed to get 100

300 and 55 need to create 100 to be able to subtract 94

255 and 100 correct

255 and 94 took 100 away from 355

Formative Assessment

- Ask students to model 302 − 99 and solve using base-ten blocks and Work Mat 7.
- Have students show you how to take apart the numbers to make it easier to subtract.

Line Up!

As students line up for recess, lunch, or dismissal, ask each one a true or false subtraction question such as

- True or false: 760 − 100 = 860 false
- True or false: 208 − 100 = 108 true

LESSON 2
Subtract Hundreds

OBJECTIVE Subtract numbers in the hundreds.

What's the Math?

 Common Core State Standards
DOMAIN: Number and Operations in Base Ten

Standards: 2.NBT.7, 2.NBT.9
The wording of these standards can be found on page 406.

What Students Should Understand
• You can use basic subtraction facts to subtract numbers in the hundreds.

What Students Should be Able to Do
Find 400 − 200.

You know that 4 − 2 = 2.

```
  4 hundreds
− 2 hundreds
  2 hundreds
```

400 − 200 = 200

 Building on the Essential Question

In this lesson, students will build upon the skills and concepts needed to answer the chapter's Essential Question "How can I subtract three-digit numbers?"

Developing Vocabulary

 Review Vocabulary

subtract

Review Activity

• Write *subtract* on the board. Have volunteers come to the front of the class and present what they have learned about subtracting. For example, they might write and solve a subtraction sentence, or act out subtraction using models.

• Browse the lesson with students. Ask them what they notice about the exercises. The subtraction exercises show subtracting hundreds.

• Explain to students that using basic subtraction facts will help them in this lesson.

ELL ELL Support Strategy Use this vocabulary activity to demonstrate understanding by summarizing.

My Vocabulary Cards

Have students use a blank card to write a question they having about subtracting hundreds. Collect the cards. Read the questions aloud, and have the class help you answer each question.

IWB Virtual Word Wall

Add this review word to the Virtual Word Wall for the chapter.

Plan Online

Plan for your lesson by using the resources at
connectED.mcgraw-hill.com

Digital Dashboard

Interactive Whiteboard Ready

Vocab

The eBook **Glossary** shows the definition of the word and has audio for each definition. The **eGlossary** provides definitions in 13 languages.

Watch

Watch as concepts are brought to life through **animations**, **songs**, and a variety of visual instruction.

Tools

Virtual Manipulatives with work mats allow teachers and students to model the lesson.

Check

Use **eAssessment** for online assignments and customized assessments.

Use the **Common Core Quick Check** before the lesson to assess students' retention of previously learned concepts.

Use the interactive **Self-Check Quiz** after the lesson to provide immediate feedback on lesson concepts.

eHelp

Digital and print resources assist students and parents in completing My Homework.

Games

Online games and **apps** provide extra practice for lesson concepts.

PD

Professional development videos help teachers gain a deeper understanding of the lesson concepts and strategies.

RtI

Support for **approaching**, **on**- and **beyond-level** students as well as **English Language Learners**.

Masters

Reteach and **Enrich** worksheets, **Manipulative Masters**, the **Problem of the Day**, and other blackline masters are available for each lesson.

---

1 LAUNCH THE LESSON

CCSS

If your students are well-versed in subtracting hundreds, you may choose to begin instruction with Step 2, **TEACH**.

You will need

☐ spinner labeled 0–9

Mathematical PRACTICE 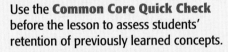 **Modeling the Math**

Have a volunteer spin a spinner labeled 0–9 twice to get two one-digit numbers. Have students write the pair of numbers. Guide students to write a number sentence reviewing the basic facts.

What is the greater number? See student response. *What is the lesser number?* See student response. *Write a subtraction sentence. What is the difference?* See student response.

Repeat the activity until all basic subtraction facts have been reviewed.

🕐 **Begin core instruction here.**

You will need
☐ base-ten blocks

Explore and Explain

Read the directions that are on the bottom of the student page.

What do you need to find to solve this problem? The number of steps the class has left to climb. *How will you do this?* Find 400 – 300.

Which base-ten blocks will you use to model 400? 4 hundreds flats

How do you use the base-ten blocks to show 400 – 300? Take away 3 hundreds flats.

How many hundreds are left? 1 hundred

What is 400 – 300? 100

Write 500 – 200 on the board. Explain that basic subtraction facts can also be used to solve the problem.

This problem is like the previous problem. You can also use base-ten blocks to find 500 – 200. However, you can also use a basic subtraction fact.

Point to 5 and 2 in the hundreds places.

What basic subtraction fact can you use with these two numbers? 5 – 2 = 3

Write a 3 in the difference of the problem on the board. Then write 2 zeros to the right of the 3. Explain to students that you write the same number of zeros that are in the two numbers in the problem to the right of the difference from the basic subtraction fact.

What is 500 – 200? 300

See and Show

Help students work through the example at the top of the page. Use actual or virtual base-ten blocks to demonstrate as you are talking.

Have them trace the dashed numbers as they work through the problems.

Work through Exercises 1–6 as a class.

PRACTICE **3** 🖋 **Talk Math**

Discuss with students "What subtraction fact can you use to find 900–800?" Sample answer: 9–8

Subtract Hundreds

Lesson 2
ESSENTIAL QUESTION
How can I subtract three-digit numbers?

Explore and Explain

What goes up, must come down!

100 steps

Teacher Directions: There are 400 steps in my school. My class decided to walk up all of the steps. We have walked up 300 steps already. How many steps do we have left? Use base-ten blocks. Draw the blocks. Write how many steps are left.

Online Content at connectED.mcgraw-hill.com   Chapter 7 • Lesson 2   419

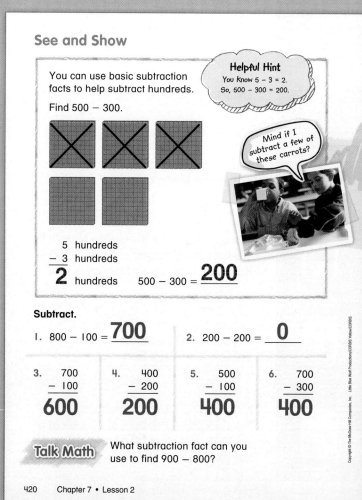

See and Show

You can use basic subtraction facts to help subtract hundreds.

Helpful Hint
You Know 5 – 3 = 2.
So, 500 – 300 = 200.

Find 500 – 300.

Mind if I subtract a few of these carrots?

    5 hundreds
 – 3 hundreds
    2 hundreds   500 – 300 = **200**

Subtract.

1. 800 – 100 = **700**   2. 200 – 200 = **0**

3.   700   4.   400   5.   500   6.   700
   – 100   – 200   – 100   – 300
   600   **200**   **400**   **400**

Talk Math What subtraction fact can you use to find 900 – 800?

420   Chapter 7 • Lesson 2

On My Own

Helpful Hint
Use the subtraction facts you know to subtract hundreds.

Subtract.

7. $800 - 300 =$ **500**

8. $600 - 600 =$ **0**

9. $300 - 100 =$ **200**

10. $900 - 200 =$ **700**

11. $800 - 400 =$ **400**

12. $700 - 500 =$ **200**

13. $200 - 200 =$ **0**

14. $400 - 100 =$ **300**

15. $\begin{array}{r} 700 \\ -\ 400 \\ \hline \textbf{300} \end{array}$	16. $\begin{array}{r} 800 \\ -\ 200 \\ \hline \textbf{600} \end{array}$	17. $\begin{array}{r} 300 \\ -\ 300 \\ \hline \textbf{0} \end{array}$	18. $\begin{array}{r} 500 \\ -\ 400 \\ \hline \textbf{100} \end{array}$
19. $\begin{array}{r} 500 \\ -\ 300 \\ \hline \textbf{200} \end{array}$	20. $\begin{array}{r} 200 \\ -\ 100 \\ \hline \textbf{100} \end{array}$	21. $\begin{array}{r} 600 \\ -\ 200 \\ \hline \textbf{400} \end{array}$	22. $\begin{array}{r} 900 \\ -\ 700 \\ \hline \textbf{200} \end{array}$
23. $\begin{array}{r} 700 \\ -\ 200 \\ \hline \textbf{500} \end{array}$	24. $\begin{array}{r} 400 \\ -\ 300 \\ \hline \textbf{100} \end{array}$	25. $\begin{array}{r} 800 \\ -\ 0 \\ \hline \textbf{800} \end{array}$	26. $\begin{array}{r} 800 \\ -\ 800 \\ \hline \textbf{0} \end{array}$

Problem Solving

27. 700 people came to my school's spring concert. 500 people came to our winter concert. How many more people came to the spring concert?

200 people

28. My school made flags for Memorial Day. There were 600 flags. 200 students took their flags home. How many flags are left?

Stars and stripes FOREVER!

400 flags

29. The floor in my classroom has 200 tiles. 100 tiles are blue. The rest of the tiles are white. How many white tiles are there?

100 tiles

Write Math How is subtracting hundreds like subtracting ones?

Sample answer: You can subtract the same way you subtract ones, then just add two zeros onto the answer to tell how many hundreds are left.

On My Own

Have students work through the exercises on this page independently. You may choose to assign exercises based on the chart below.

DIFFERENTIATED ASSIGNMENTS

AL Approaching Level Guide students through the exercises in On My Own. Help them to use manipulatives while working through the exercises.

OL On Level Complete the exercises independently.

BL Beyond Level Complete the exercises independently without manipulatives.

Common Error!
Students might have difficulty keeping numbers in the right place for their value. Have students draw vertical lines to separate the numbers and zeros and line them up with digits below.

Problem Solving

Have students work through the problem-solving exercises on this page independently.

Mathematical PRACTICE 2 In Exercise 29, students **reason abstractly and quantitatively.**

Write Math

This exercise asks students to build upon their understanding of concepts needed to answer the chapter's Essential Question.

AL APPROACHING LEVEL

IF my students struggle with subtracting hundreds,

THEN choose a resource:

→ Use a Differentiated Instruction activity from p. 405C.

→ Use the Reteach worksheet with small groups.

→ Go online for a Differentiated Instruction activity.

→ **Flash Cards** Remind students that subtracting hundreds begins with using the number facts for single digits. Have students work with flash cards to strengthen their abilities.

OL ON LEVEL

IF my students seem to know subtracting hundreds, but need more practice,

THEN choose a resource:

→ Use Differentiated Instruction activity from p. 405D.

→ Assign My Homework.

→ Go online for a Differentiated Instruction activity.

BL BEYOND LEVEL

IF my students have mastered subtracting hundreds,

THEN choose a resource:

→ Use the Enrich worksheet in cooperative groups.

→ Assign My Homework.

→ Go online for a Differentiated Instruction activity.

AL 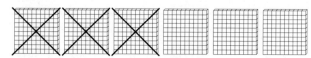 Name _____

Lesson 2   Reteach
Subtract Hundreds

Find 600 − 300.

6 hundreds − 3 hundreds = __3__ hundreds

600 − 300 = __300__

Subtract.

1. 4 hundreds − 1 hundred = __3__ hundreds

   400 − 100 = __300__

2. 7 hundreds − 3 hundreds = __4__ hundreds

   700 − 300 = __400__

3. 8 hundreds − 5 hundreds = __3__ hundreds

   800 − 500 = __300__

4.
600	500	800	600	500
− 100	− 200	− 300	− 200	− 100
500	**300**	**500**	**400**	**400**

BL Name _____

Lesson 2   Enrich
Subtract Hundreds

Solve.

1. Write a subtraction sentence with a difference of 300.

   See students' work.

2. Write a subtraction sentence with a difference of 200.

   See students' work.

3. Write a subtraction sentence with a difference of 400.

   See students' work.

4. Write a subtraction sentence with a difference of 500.

   See students' work.

5. Write a subtraction sentence with a difference of 100.

   See students' work.

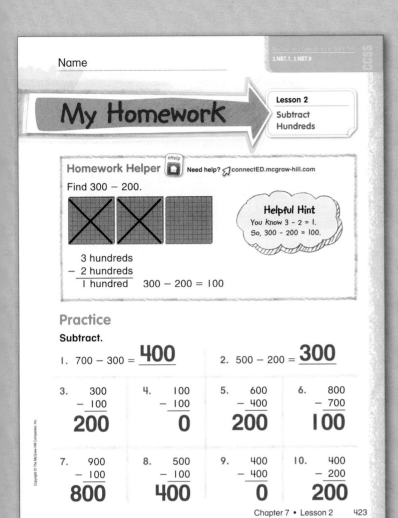

Name _____

Number and Operations in Base Ten
2.NBT.7, 2.NBT.9

My Homework ➡ Lesson 2
Subtract Hundreds

Homework Helper eHelp   Need help? connectED.mcgraw-hill.com

Find 300 − 200.

Helpful Hint
You know 3 − 2 = 1.
So, 300 − 200 = 100.

3 hundreds
− 2 hundreds
‾‾‾‾‾‾‾‾‾‾‾
1 hundred   300 − 200 = 100

Practice

Subtract.

1. 700 − 300 = **400**   2. 500 − 200 = **300**

3. 300
  − 100
  ‾‾‾‾‾
  200

4. 100
  − 100
  ‾‾‾‾‾
  0

5. 600
  − 400
  ‾‾‾‾‾
  200

6. 800
  − 700
  ‾‾‾‾‾
  100

7. 900
  − 100
  ‾‾‾‾‾
  800

8. 500
  − 100
  ‾‾‾‾‾
  400

9. 400
  − 400
  ‾‾‾‾‾
  0

10. 400
   − 200
   ‾‾‾‾‾
   200

Copyright © The McGraw-Hill Companies, Inc.

Chapter 7 • Lesson 2   423

Solve each word problem.

11. 800 people went to watch the ballet. 200 people left early. How many people stayed at the ballet?

600 people

12. 500 boys and girls went to the basketball game. 300 girls were at the game. How many boys were at the game?

200 boys

13. The cafeteria had pizza slices and hot dogs for lunch. 900 lunches were sold. 300 people bought hot dogs. How many pizza slices were sold?

600 pizza slices

Test Practice

14. Which number sentence could help you solve 700 − 500?

7 − 2   2 + 5   5 + 2   7 − 5
○   ○   ○   ●

 Math at Home Ask your child what number is 100 less than 500.

424   Chapter 7 • Lesson 2

Copyright © The McGraw-Hill Companies, Inc.   Punkstock/SuperFusion/SuperStock

---

CCSS

4 WRAP IT UP

My Homework

Assign homework after successful completion of the lesson.

Students who understand the concepts may skip the **Homework Helper** section.

Test Practice

Diagnose Student Errors

Class trends in wrong answer may indicate common errors or misconceptions.

7 − 2 not the correct numbers

2 + 5 incorrect numbers; addition

5 + 2 incorrect numbers; addition

7 − 5 correct

Formative Assessment

Ask students the following question.

Why can you use single-digit number facts to subtract hundreds? because the hundreds are the single-digit numbers with 2 zeros added on

Line Up!

When students line up for recess, have them skip-count backwards by hundreds from 900. The first student should say "800," the second "700," the third "600," and so on.

Online Content at connectED.mcgraw-hill.com

Lesson 2 Subtract Hundreds   **423-424**

LESSON 3
Mentally Subtract 10 or 100

OBJECTIVE   Subtract 10 or 100 mentally.

What's the Math?

 Common Core State Standards
DOMAIN: Number and Operations in Base Ten

Standard: 2.NBT.8
The wording of this standard can be found on page 406.

 CCSS

What Students Should Understand

• You can use mental math to subtract 10 or 100 from a number.

• You can use base-ten blocks to model subtracting 10 or 100 from a number if needed.

What Students Should be Able to Do

Mentally subtract 100.

$$\begin{array}{r} 538 \\ -100 \\ \hline \end{array}$$ Think: 5 − 1 = 4, so $$\begin{array}{r} 538 \\ -100 \\ \hline 438 \end{array}$$

Mentally subtract 10.

$$\begin{array}{r} 675 \\ -10 \\ \hline \end{array}$$ Think: 7 − 1 = 6, so $$\begin{array}{r} 675 \\ -10 \\ \hline 665 \end{array}$$

 Building on the Essential Question

In this lesson, students will build upon the skills and concepts needed to answer the chapter's Essential Question "How can I subtract three-digit numbers?"

Developing Vocabulary

Review Vocabulary
subtraction

Review Activity

• Discuss with students how they use basic facts when subtracting two-digit numbers. For example, they might explain that they use basic facts when subtracting the numbers in the ones place, and then in the tens place.

• Have students browse the text box on the second page of the lesson. Have volunteers point out examples of how basic facts are used to solve the three-digit subtraction examples.

ELL **ELL Support Strategy** Use this vocabulary activity to recognize text features, such as text boxes.

My Vocabulary Cards

Have students work in small groups. Tell them to use a blank card to write a key idea about subtracting three-digit numbers. Ask each group to share their key idea.

IWB **Virtual Word Wall**

Add this review word to the Virtual Word Wall for the chapter.

Plan Online

Plan for your lesson by using the resources at
connectED.mcgraw-hill.com

Digital Dashboard

Interactive Whiteboard Ready

Vocab
The eBook **Glossary** shows the definition of the word and has audio for each definition. The **eGlossary** provides definitions in 13 languages.

Watch
Watch as concepts are brought to life through **animations**, **songs**, and a variety of visual instruction.

Tools
Virtual Manipulatives with work mats allow teachers and students to model the lesson.

Check
Use **eAssessment** for online assignments and customized assessments.

Use the **Common Core Quick Check** before the lesson to assess students' retention of previously learned concepts.

Use the interactive **Self-Check Quiz** after the lesson to provide immediate feedback on lesson concepts.

eHelp
Digital and print resources assist students and parents in completing My Homework.

Games
Online games and **apps** provide extra practice for lesson concepts.

PD
Professional development videos help teachers gain a deeper understanding of the lesson concepts and strategies.

RtI
Support for **approaching**, **on-** and **beyond-level** students as well as **English Language Learners**.

Masters
Reteach and **Enrich** worksheets, **Manipulative Masters**, the **Problem of the Day**, and other blackline masters are available for each lesson.

---

1 LAUNCH THE LESSON

 If your students are well-versed in mentally subtracting 10 or 100, you may choose to begin instruction with Step 2, **TEACH**.

You will need

☐ number lines (labeled 0–10 and 100–900)

Mathematical PRACTICE 4 Modeling the Math

Show the class a number line labeled 0–10. Show the class a number line labeled 100–900.

Do you see anything that is alike on these two number lines?

Guide students toward recognizing that both number lines have ten increments.

Suppose you have 6 and you take away 4. How many do you have left? 2 *Suppose you have 7 and take away 4. How many do you have left?* 3

Point out the hundreds number line.

Suppose you have 600 and you take away 400. How many do you have left? 200 *Suppose you have 700 and take away 400. How many do you have left?* 300

As a class, discuss how basic subtraction facts can help you subtract hundreds. Take the number line away and try a few more examples together.

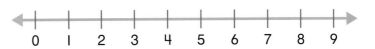

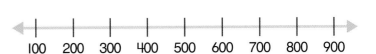

TEACH

Begin core instruction here.

You will need
☐ base-ten blocks

Explore and Explain

Read the directions that are on the bottom of the student page.

Guide students in using base-ten blocks to model 135 to represent the number of students that are on the playground.

How can you find the number of students who are still on the playground? Subtract 100 from 135. *Let's model the problem. What base-ten blocks will you use to show 135?* 1 hundred flat, 3 tens rods, 5 unit cubes

Guide students in showing the subtraction of 100.

Subtract 100. If you remove one hundred flat, what are you left with? 3 tens rods and 5 unit cubes

As a class, discuss how to mentally find the difference.

Think of a basic subtraction fact to find the number of hundreds when you subtract 100 from 135. What is the basic subtraction fact? 1 − 1 = 0

How many hundreds are in the difference? 0 hundreds

So, what is the difference? 35

How many students are still on the playground? 35 students

See and Show

Help students work through the example at the top of page. Be sure to stress mental subtraction involves using facts you know or can do easily without paper.

Have them trace the dashed numbers as they work through the problems.

Work through Exercises 1–8 as a class.

Mathematical PRACTICE ③ Talk Math

Discuss with students "Tell how to mentally subtract 10 or 100." Sample answer: You subtract 1 from either the hundreds or the tens place.

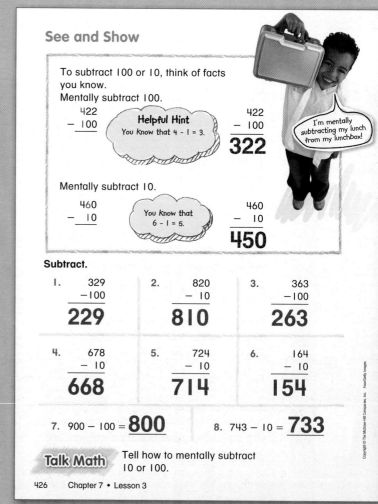

425-426 **Chapter 7** Subtract Three-Digit Numbers

Name _____

On My Own

Subtract.

9.
```
   491
  -100
   391
```

10.
```
   942
  - 10
   932
```

11.
```
   770
  - 10
   760
```

12.
```
   672
  -100
   572
```

13.
```
   853
  -100
   753
```

14.
```
   269
  - 10
   259
```

15.
```
   368
  - 10
   358
```

16.
```
   374
  -100
   274
```

17.
```
   982
  -100
   882
```

18. $498 - 100 =$ **398**

19. $533 - 100 =$ **433**

Find the missing number.

20. $434 -$ **10** $= 424$

21. $371 -$ **100** $= 271$

22. $738 -$ **100** $= 638$

23. $270 -$ **10** $= 260$

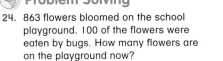 **Problem Solving**

Mathematical **PRACTICE**

24. 863 flowers bloomed on the school playground. 100 of the flowers were eaten by bugs. How many flowers are on the playground now?

    763 flowers

25. 299 people came to the school play. 10 people had to leave early. How many people were still at the play?

     The play must go on!

    289 people

26. 423 wildflowers grew in the field. Embry picked 10 of them. How many wildflowers are left in the field?

    413 wildflowers

Write Math Explain how you would mentally subtract 10 from 900.

Sample answer: You count back by 10.

$900 - 10 = 890.$

_____

On My Own

Have students work through the exercises on this page independently. You may choose to assign exercises based on the chart below.

DIFFERENTIATED ASSIGNMENTS

AL **Approaching Level** Guide students through the exercises in On My Own. Help them to use manipulatives while working through the exercises.

OL **On Level** Complete the exercises independently.

BL **Beyond Level** Complete the exercises independently without manipulatives.

Problem Solving

Have students work through the problem-solving exercises on this page independently.

Mathematical **PRACTICE 2** In Exercise 25, students **reason abstractly and quantitatively.**

Write Math

This exercise asks students to build upon their understanding of concepts needed to answer the chapter's Essential Question.

RESPONSE TO INTERVENTION
DIFFERENTIATED INSTRUCTION

AL **APPROACHING LEVEL**

IF my students struggle with mentally subtracting 10 or 100,

THEN choose a resource:

→ Use a Differentiated Instruction activity from p. 405C.
→ Use the Reteach worksheet with small groups.
→ Go online for a Differentiated Instruction activity.

OL **ON LEVEL**

IF my students seem to know mentally subtracting 10 or 100, but need more practice,

THEN choose a resource:

→ Assign My Homework.
→ Go online for a Differentiated Instruction activity.

BL **BEYOND LEVEL**

IF my students have mastered mentally subtracting 10 or 100,

THEN choose a resource:

→ Use the Enrich worksheet in cooperative groups.
→ Assign My Homework.
→ Go online for a Differentiated Instruction activity.

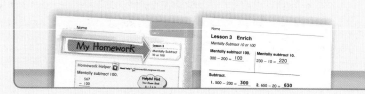

AL

Name _____

Lesson 3   Reteach
Mentally Subtract 10 or 100

Mentally subtract 100.	Mentally subtract 10.
$300 - 200$	$230 - 10$
$3 - 2 = \underline{1}$	$3 - 1 = \underline{2}$
So, $300 - 200 = \underline{100}$.	So, $230 - 10 = \underline{220}$.

Subtract.

1. $500 - 200$
   $5 - 2 = \underline{3}$
   So, $500 - 200 = \underline{300}$.

2. $650 - 20$
   $5 - 2 = \underline{3}$
   So, $650 - 20 = \underline{630}$.

3. $600 - 300$
   $6 - 3 = \underline{3}$
   So, $600 - 300 = \underline{300}$.

4. $870 - 10$
   $7 - 1 = \underline{6}$
   So, $870 - 10 = \underline{860}$.

5. $400 - 400$
   $4 - 4 = \underline{0}$
   So, $400 - 400 = \underline{0}$.

6. $330 - 30$
   $3 - 3 = \underline{0}$
   So, $330 - 30 = \underline{300}$.

BL

Name _____

Lesson 3   Enrich
Mentally Subtract 10 or 100

Mentally subtract 100.	Mentally subtract 10.
$300 - 200 = \underline{100}$	$230 - 10 = \underline{220}$

Subtract.

1. $500 - 200 = \underline{300}$
2. $650 - 20 = \underline{630}$
3. $600 - 300 = \underline{300}$
4. $870 - 10 = \underline{860}$
5. $400 - 400 = \underline{0}$
6. $330 - 30 = \underline{300}$
7. $800 - 100 = \underline{700}$
8. $870 - 20 = \underline{850}$
9. $400 - 300 = \underline{100}$
10. $460 - 20 = \underline{440}$
11. $600 - 200 = \underline{400}$
12. $210 - 10 = \underline{200}$
13. $200 - 200 = \underline{0}$
14. $660 - 30 = \underline{630}$
15. $900 - 600 = \underline{300}$
16. $250 - 40 = \underline{210}$

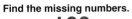

Name _____

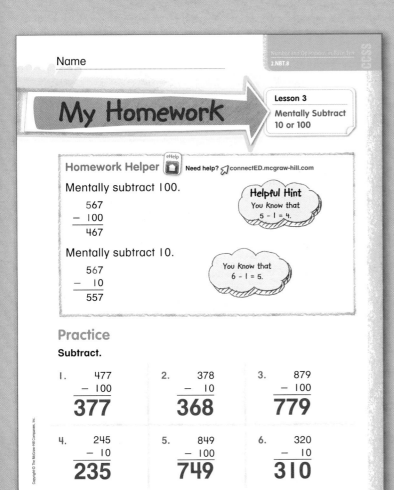

My Homework

Lesson 3
Mentally Subtract
10 or 100

2.NBT.8

Homework Helper 🔲 Need help? connectED.mcgraw-hill.com

Mentally subtract 100.

$$\begin{array}{r} 567 \\ -\ 100 \\ \hline 467 \end{array}$$

Helpful Hint
You Know that
5 - 1 = 4.

Mentally subtract 10.

$$\begin{array}{r} 567 \\ -\ 10 \\ \hline 557 \end{array}$$

You Know that
6 - 1 = 5.

Practice

Subtract.

1. $\begin{array}{r} 477 \\ -\ 100 \\ \hline \mathbf{377} \end{array}$

2. $\begin{array}{r} 378 \\ -\ 10 \\ \hline \mathbf{368} \end{array}$

3. $\begin{array}{r} 879 \\ -\ 100 \\ \hline \mathbf{779} \end{array}$

4. $\begin{array}{r} 245 \\ -\ 10 \\ \hline \mathbf{235} \end{array}$

5. $\begin{array}{r} 849 \\ -\ 100 \\ \hline \mathbf{749} \end{array}$

6. $\begin{array}{r} 320 \\ -\ 10 \\ \hline \mathbf{310} \end{array}$

Find the missing numbers.

7. $358 - \mathbf{100} = 258$

8. $843 - \mathbf{10} = 833$

9. $954 - \mathbf{10} = 944$

10. $700 - \mathbf{100} = 600$

11. Joan counts 143 birds by the pond. 100 birds fly away. How many birds are left by the pond?

    Where's your tail?

    43 birds

12. There were 694 tadpoles in the lake. 100 of the tadpoles turned into frogs. How many tadpoles were left in the lake?

    594 tadpoles

Test Practice

13. Find $363 - 100$.

    163 ○   263 ●   363 ○   463 ○

Math at Home Practice saying a number and having your child subtract 10 or 100 from the number mentally.

---

4 WRAP IT UP

CCSS

My Homework

Assign homework after successful completion of the lesson. Students who understand the concepts may skip the **Homework Helper** section.

Test Practice

Diagnose Student Errors

Class trends in wrong answers may indicate common errors or misconceptions.

163 subtracted hundreds incorrectly

263 correct

363 did not add or subtract

463 added instead of subtracted

Formative Assessment

Give students any number up to 999 and ask them what they would have left if you took 10 or 100 away from it.

Check My Progress

Use this as a formative assessment to determine if your students are struggling, and if so, with which topics they struggle. The criteria for differentiation are on the next page.

Vocabulary Check

Have students use each word in a sentence.

ELL **ELL Support Strategy** Use the activity described in the Vocabulary Check to develop students' oral language skills with computer vocabulary.

Concept Check

These concepts are covered in Lesson 1–3.

Exercises	Concept	Review Lesson
4–5	Take apart hundreds to subtract	1
6–10	Subtract hundreds	2
11–14	Mentally subtract 10 or 100	3

Problem Solving

Exercise 15 uses a word problem to check for understanding of the same concepts.

Test Practice

Diagnose Student Errors

Class trends in wrong answers may indicate common errors or misconceptions.

600 added
300 used one of the numbers given
100 misunderstood concept
0 correct

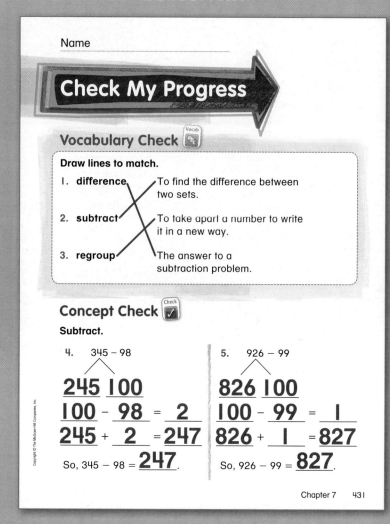

Name

Check My Progress

Vocabulary Check

Draw lines to match.

1. difference — The answer to a subtraction problem.
2. subtract — To find the difference between two sets.
3. regroup — To take apart a number to write it in a new way.

Concept Check

Subtract.

4. $345 - 98$

$245 \quad 100$
$100 - 98 = 2$
$245 + 2 = 247$
So, $345 - 98 = 247$.

5. $926 - 99$

$826 \quad 100$
$100 - 99 = 1$
$826 + 1 = 827$
So, $926 - 99 = 827$.

Chapter 7   431

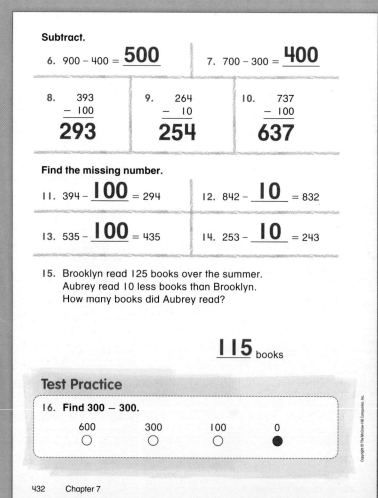

Subtract.

6. $900 - 400 = 500$ 7. $700 - 300 = 400$

8. $\begin{array}{r} 393 \\ -\ 100 \\ \hline 293 \end{array}$ 9. $\begin{array}{r} 264 \\ -\ 10 \\ \hline 254 \end{array}$ 10. $\begin{array}{r} 737 \\ -\ 100 \\ \hline 637 \end{array}$

Find the missing number.

11. $394 - 100 = 294$ 12. $842 - 10 = 832$

13. $535 - 100 = 435$ 14. $253 - 10 = 243$

15. Brooklyn read 125 books over the summer. Aubrey read 10 less books than Brooklyn. How many books did Aubrey read?

115 books

Test Practice

16. Find $300 - 300$.

   600   300   100   0
   ○   ○   ○   ●

432   Chapter 7

Name _____

Check My Progress *(Lessons 1 through 3)*

Subtract.

1.   236 − 97

136 ⟋⟍ **100**

$\underline{100} - \underline{97} = \underline{3}$

$\underline{136} + \underline{3} = \underline{139}$

So, 236 − 97 = __139__

2.   395 − 99

295 ⟋⟍ 100

$\underline{100} - \underline{99} = \underline{1}$

$\underline{295} + \underline{1} = \underline{296}$

So, 395 − 93 = __296__

3. 300 − 100 = __200__   4. 900 − 400 = __500__

5. 700 − 200 = __500__   6. 600 − 100 = __500__

7.   600
    − 300
   ┌─────┐
   │ 300 │
   └─────┘

8.   587
    − 10
   ┌─────┐
   │ 577 │
   └─────┘

9.   359
    − 100
   ┌─────┐
   │ 259 │
   └─────┘

10. Molly scored 527 points on her video game. Annabelle scored 10 points less than Molly. How many points did Annabelle score? __517__ points

RESPONSE TO INTERVENTION

DIFFERENTIATED INSTRUCTION

AL   STRATEGIC INTERVENTION

(Approaching Grade Level)

IF students miss 6 or more in Exercises 1–15,

THEN choose a resource:

→ Check My Progress

→ Self-Check Quiz

→ Use the Reteach worksheets.

OL   ON LEVEL

IF students miss 3 to 4 in Exercises 1–15,

THEN choose a resource:

→ Chapter Project

→ Proceed to the next lesson.

BL   BEYOND LEVEL

IF students miss 2 or less in Exercises 1–15,

THEN choose a resource:

→ Chapter Project

→ Use the Enrich worksheets.

→ Proceed to the next lesson.

LESSON 4
Regroup Tens

OBJECTIVE Regroup tens to subtract three-digit numbers.

What's the Math?

 Common Core State Standards
DOMAIN: Number and Operations in Base Ten

Standards: 2.NBT.7, 2.NBT.9

The wording of these standards can be found on page 406.

What Students Should Understand

• When subtracting with three-digit numbers, subtract the ones, the tens, and then the hundreds.

• If there are not enough ones to subtract from, regroup 1 ten as 10 ones.

• You can use base-ten blocks to help you regroup and find the difference.

What Students Should be Able to Do

Find 362 − 134.

Step 1

Subtract the ones. You cannot subtract 4 ones from 2 ones. Regroup 1 ten as 10 ones.

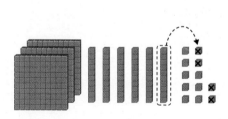

hundreds	tens	ones
	5	12
3	6̷	2̷
− 1	3	4
		8

Step 2

Subtract the tens.

hundreds	tens	ones
	5	12
3	6̷	2̷
− 1	3	4
	2	8

Step 3

Subtract the hundreds.

hundreds	tens	ones
	5	12
3	6̷	2̷
− 1	3	4
2	2	8

So, 362 − 134 = 228.

Developing Vocabulary

 Review Vocabulary

regroup

Review Activity

• Write *regroup* on the board. Ask students when they have used this word previously. For example, they might recall regrouping to add or subtract.

• Explain that regroup means "to take apart a number to write it in a new way." For example, you can show 14 by regrouping the ones to be 1 ten and 4 ones. Tell students that regrouping is needed when there are 10 or more ones.

ELL **ELL Support Strategy** Use this vocabulary activity to link familiar contexts and prior knowledge.

My Vocabulary Cards

Read the activity for this lesson's card to students. Have them share and explain their drawings with the class.

IWB **Virtual Word Wall**

You may wish to add this review word to the Virtual Word Wall for the chapter.

 Building on the Essential Question

In this lesson, students will build upon the skills and concepts needed to answer the chapter's Essential Question "How can I subtract three-digit numbers?"

Plan Online
Plan for your lesson by using the resources at
 connectED.mcgraw-hill.com

Digital Dashboard
Interactive Whiteboard Ready

The eBook **Glossary** shows the definition of the word and has audio for each definition. The **eGlossary** provides definitions in 13 languages.

Watch as concepts are brought to life through **animations**, **songs**, and a variety of visual instruction.

Virtual Manipulatives with work mats allow teachers and students to model the lesson.

Use **eAssessment** for online assignments and customized assessments.

Use the **Common Core Quick Check** before the lesson to assess students' retention of previously learned concepts.

Use the interactive **Self-Check Quiz** after the lesson to provide immediate feedback on lesson concepts.

Digital and print resources assist students and parents in completing My Homework.

Online games and **apps** provide extra practice for lesson concepts.

Professional development videos help teachers gain a deeper understanding of the lesson concepts and strategies.

Support for **approaching**, **on**- and **beyond-level** students as well as **English Language Learners**.

Reteach and **Enrich** worksheets, **Manipulative Masters**, the **Problem of the Day**, and other blackline masters are available for each lesson.

---

1 LAUNCH THE LESSON

 If your students are well-versed in regrouping tens, you may choose to begin instruction with Step 2, **TEACH**.

You will need
☐ base-ten blocks

Mathematical PRACTICE 4  **Modeling the Math**

Have 12 students come to the front of the class. Separate them into a line of 10 and a line of 2. Point out that the number 12 is composed of 2 ones and 1 ten. Students may model this formation at their desks with base-ten blocks.

Tell students you want to subtract 4 students from the front. Point out that there are only 2 students in the ones line.

Say that you will regroup the 12 students so you can subtract 4. Move the students in the tens line into line behind the 2 in the ones line. Then have 4 students sit down.

How many are left? 8

Have the students left in front count off to show that there are 8.

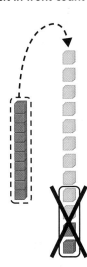

 Begin core instruction here.

You will need

☐ base-ten blocks

☐ Work Mat 7

Explore and Explain

Read the directions that are on the bottom of the student page.

What do you need to find? how many jump ropes Mr. Hicks has left *How can you do this?* Find 145 − 36.

Write 145 − 36 on the board vertically.

Which base-ten blocks will you use to show 145? 1 hundred flat, 4 tens rods, and 5 unit cubes

Guide students to solve the problem.

Subtract the ones first. Are there enough ones in the top number to subtract from? No *What do you need to do when there are not enough ones?* Regroup 1 ten as 10 ones

Cross out 4 in the tens place and write 3 above it. Tell students this shows 1 ten has been regrouped as 10 ones.

How many ones are there after you regroup? 15 ones

Cross out 5 in the ones place and write 15 above it.

What is 15 ones − 6 ones? 9 ones

Have students take away 6 unit cubes.

What number should go in the ones place as the difference? 9

Continue on with students using their base-ten blocks and you or a volunteer filling the problem in on the board.

See and Show

Help students work through the example at the top of page. Use actual or virtual base-ten blocks and Work Mat 7 to help assure the students understand the regrouping.

Have them trace the dashed numbers as they work through the problems.

Work through Exercises 1 and 2 as a class.

Mathematical PRACTICE ❸ **Talk Math**

Discuss with students "How is subtracting three-digit numbers like subtracting two-digit numbers?" Sample answer: You have to regroup the tens if you do not have enough ones.

CORE INSTRUCTION

Name _____

2.NBT.7, 2.NBT.9

Regroup Tens

Lesson 4

ESSENTIAL QUESTION
How can I subtract three-digit numbers?

Only 360 more and I break the school record!

Explore and Explain Watch ▶ Tools

Go!

109 jump ropes

Teacher Directions: Use base-ten blocks to solve. Mr. Hicks, our gym teacher, had 145 jump ropes. 36 jump ropes broke this year. How many jump ropes does Mr. Hicks have left? Write the number.

Online Content at connectED.mcgraw-hill.com   Chapter 7 • Lesson 4   433

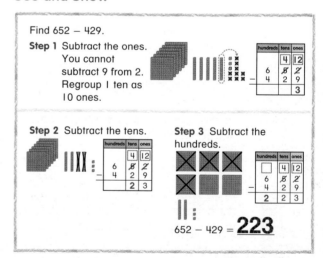

See and Show

Find 652 − 429.

Step 1 Subtract the ones. You cannot subtract 9 from 2. Regroup 1 ten as 10 ones.

	hundreds	tens	ones
		4	12
	6	5	2
−	4	2	9
			3

Step 2 Subtract the tens.

	hundreds	tens	ones
		4	12
	6	5	2
−	4	2	9
		2	3

Step 3 Subtract the hundreds.

	hundreds	tens	ones
		4	12
	6	5	2
−	4	2	9
	2	2	3

652 − 429 = **223**

Use Work Mat 7 and base-ten blocks. Subtract.

1.
hundreds	tens	ones
	3	16
5	4	6
	1	7
5	2	9

2.
hundreds	tens	ones
	7	13
7	8	3
4	3	9
3	4	4

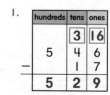 **Talk Math** How is subtracting three-digit numbers like subtracting two-digit numbers?

434   Chapter 7 • Lesson 4

3 PRACTICE & APPLY

CCSS

On My Own

Use Work Mat 7 and base-ten blocks. Subtract.

3.
hundreds	tens	ones
	7	**12**
3	8	2
− 1	2	8
2	5	4

4.
hundreds	tens	ones
	5	**17**
4	6	7
−	4	9
4	1	8

5.
```
      6  15
   5  7  5
 −    6  6
   5  0  9
```

6.
```
      5  13
   8  6  3
 −  2  1  8
   6  4  5
```

7.
```
      5  14
   2  6  4
 −  1  3  5
   1  2  9
```

8.
```
   754
 − 507
   247
```

9.
```
   455
 − 326
   129
```

10.
```
   930
 − 428
   502
```

11.
```
   780
 − 436
   344
```

12.
```
   652
 −  35
   617
```

13.
```
   931
 −   6
   925
```

14.
```
   387
 −  18
   369
```

15.
```
   423
 − 119
   304
```

16.
```
   540
 −  15
   525
```

Chapter 7 • Lesson 4   435

On My Own

Have students work through the exercises on this page independently. You may choose to assign exercises based on the chart below.

DIFFERENTIATED ASSIGNMENTS

AL Approaching Level Guide students through the exercises in On My Own. Help them to use manipulatives while working through the exercises.

OL On Level Complete the exercises independently.

BL Beyond Level Complete the exercises independently without manipulatives.

> **Common Error!**
> Students may have trouble remembering to add the regrouped ten to the number that is already in the ones place. Have them circle that number so they notice it.

Problem Solving

Have students work through the problem-solving exercises on this page independently.

Mathematical PRACTICE ➊ In Exercise 19, students **make sense of problems and persevere in solving them.**

HOT Problem This exercise asks students to build upon their understanding of concepts needed to answer the chapter's Essential Question.

 Problem Solving   **Mathematical PRACTICE**

17. Ada jumped 382 times in a row. Helen jumped 277 times in a row. How many more jumps in a row did Ada do than Helen?

105 jumps

18. A store had 472 bouncy balls. They sold 155. How many bouncy balls were left?

317 bouncy balls

19. Lisa hit 294 golf balls in one day. She hit 149 in the morning. How many golf balls did she hit in the afternoon?

145 golf balls

HOT Problem Andre wrote 381 − 165 = 224. Tell why Andre is wrong. Make it right.

Sample answer: Andre took 1 from 5 instead of

regrouping 11 ones. 381 − 165 = 216.

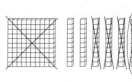

AL APPROACHING LEVEL

IF my students struggle with regrouping tens,

THEN choose a resource:

→ Use the Reteach worksheet with small groups.

→ Go online for a Differentiated Instruction activity.

→ **Borrowing 10 Ones** Point out that regrouping tens is like borrowing ten ones from the tens place and putting them in the ones place. You add the ten ones to the number already there. This gives the number of ones to subtract from.

OL ON LEVEL

IF my students seem to know how to regroup tens, but need more practice,

THEN choose a resource:

→ Assign My Homework.

→ Go online for a Differentiated Instruction activity.

BL BEYOND LEVEL

IF my students have mastered regrouping tens,

THEN choose a resource:

→ Use the Enrich worksheet in cooperative groups.

→ Assign My Homework.

→ Go online for a Differentiated Instruction activity.

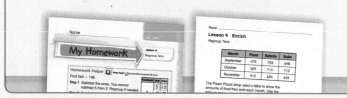

AL

Name _____

Lesson 4   Reteach
Regroup Tens

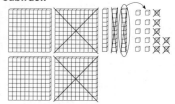

hundreds	tens	ones
	5	13
1	6̸	3̸
− 1	3	5
	2	8

Remember: Regroup 1 ten as 10 ones.

Use the base-ten blocks to subtract.

1.

hundreds	tens	ones
	2	17
4	3̸	7̸
− 2	1	8
	2	1	9

Use base-ten blocks and Work Mat 7. Subtract.

2. 321 − 13 = **308**   3. 543 − 215 = **328**

4. 865 − 9 = **856**   5. 623 − 415 = **208**

6. 460 − 152 = **308**   7. 746 − 28 = **718**

BL

Name _____

Lesson 4   Enrich
Regroup Tens

Month	Pizza	Salads	Subs
September	479	753	648
October	429	719	712
November	410	634	639

The Pizza! Pizza! shop used a table to show the amounts of food they sold each month. Use the table to answer these questions.

1. In September, how many more subs were sold than pizzas? **169 more subs**

2. In September, how many more salads were sold than subs? **105 more salads**

3. How many more salads were sold in September than November? **119 more salads**

4. How many more subs were sold in September than November? **9 more subs**

5. In October, how many more subs were sold than pizzas? **283 more subs**

Name _____

Number and Operations in Base Ten
2.NBT.7, 2.NBT.9

My Homework

Lesson 4
Regroup Tens

Homework Helper
eHelp Need help? connectED.mcgraw-hill.com

Find 362 − 145.

Step 1 Subtract the ones. You cannot subtract 5 from 2. Regroup if needed.

Step 2 Subtract the tens.

Step 3 Subtract the hundreds.

hundreds	tens	ones
	5	12
3	6	2
− 1	4	5
2	1	7

Practice

Subtract.

1.

hundreds	tens	ones
	2	15
8	3	5
− 2	1	6
6	1	9

2.

hundreds	tens	ones
	4	12
9	5	2
− 6	3	7
3	1	5

3.

	4	13
1	5	3
−	4	4
1	0	9

4.

	3	12
6	4	2
− 2	1	8
4	2	4

5.

	2	14
7	3	4
− 2	2	8
5	0	6

Copyright © The McGraw-Hill Companies, Inc.

Chapter 7 • Lesson 4   437

Subtract.

6.
```
   153
 −  47
  106
```

7.
```
   642
 − 215
  427
```

8.
```
   754
 − 225
  529
```

9.
```
   438
 − 129
  309
```

10.
```
   362
 − 148
  214
```

11.
```
   762
 − 349
  413
```

12.
```
   647
 − 518
  129
```

13.
```
   377
 − 163
  214
```

14. 725 people came to my school's pancake breakfast. 318 of those people were children. How many adults were at the breakfast?

Hmmm! How many can I eat?

407 adults

Test Practice

15. Which subtraction problem needs regrouping to solve?

○ 392 − 222   ● 385 − 266

○ 692 − 321   ○ 295 − 172

Math at Home Write a subtraction problem that requires regrouping tens on a piece of paper for your child to solve. Have your child explain each step to solving the problem. Try one-, two-, and three-digit subtraction problems.

Copyright © The McGraw-Hill Companies, Inc. Randy Faris/Fancy/CORBIS

438   Chapter 7 • Lesson 4

My Homework

Assign homework after successful completion of the lesson. Students who understand the concepts may skip the **Homework Helper** section.

Test Practice

Diagnose Student Errors

Class trends in wrong answers may indicate common errors or misconceptions.

392 − 222 does not need regrouping

385 − 266 correct

692 − 321 does not need regrouping

295 − 172 does not need regrouping

Formative Assessment

Ask students the following question.

Why do you sometimes have to regroup tens in order to subtract? Sometimes the number of ones to take away is greater than the number of ones in the number to subtract from.

Line Up!

When students line up, have the first three suggest numbers. Write them on the board. Ask the fourth student to name a number greater than the number in the ones place. Write it in the correct place to subtract it. Then show students how to regroup tens to do the subtraction.

LESSON 5
Regroup Hundreds

OBJECTIVE Regroup hundreds to subtract three-digit numbers.

What's the Math?

 Common Core State Standards
DOMAIN: Number and Operations in Base Ten

Standards: 2.NBT.7, 2.NBT.9
The wording of these standards can be found on page 406.

The wording of these standards can be found on page 406.

What Students Should Understand

• When subtracting with three-digit numbers, subtract the ones, the tens, and then the hundreds.

• If there are not enough tens to subtract from, regroup 1 hundred as 10 tens.

• You can use base-ten blocks to help you regroup and find the difference.

What Students Should be Able to Do

Find 417 − 256.

Step 1 Subtract the ones.

hundreds	tens	ones
4	1	7
− 2	5	6
		1

Step 2 Subtract the tens. You cannot subtract 5 tens from 1 ten. Regroup 1 hundred as 10 tens.

hundreds	tens	ones
3	11	
4̶	1̶	7
− 2	5	6
	6	1

Step 3 Subtract the hundreds

hundreds	tens	ones
3	11	
4̶	1̶	7̶
− 2	5	6
1	6	1

So, 417 − 256 = 161.

Developing Vocabulary

 Review Vocabulary

regroup

Review Activity

• Divide the class into groups of 4. Ask each group to browse their textbook to identify three-digit numbers.

• Have each group choose 6 three-digit numbers. Tell them to list the numbers on a piece of paper.

• Ask a volunteer from each group to provide two of their three-digit numbers. Write each set as a three-digit subtraction problem.

• Work with the class to solve each subtraction problem. (Do not introduce problems with a four-digit difference.) Discuss the steps for regrouping in each example.

ELL **ELL Support Strategy** Use this vocabulary activity to provide exposures to regrouping when subtracting.

My Vocabulary Cards

Have students use a blank card to review a vocabulary word such as *difference*.

 Building on the Essential Question

In this lesson, students will build upon the skills and concepts needed to answer the chapter's Essential Question "How can I subtract three-digit numbers?"

Plan Online

Plan for your lesson by using the resources at
connectED.mcgraw-hill.com

Digital Dashboard

Interactive Whiteboard Ready

Vocab

The eBook **Glossary** shows the definition of the word and has audio for each definition. The **eGlossary** provides definitions in 13 languages.

Watch

Watch as concepts are brought to life through **animations**, **songs**, and a variety of visual instruction.

Tools

Virtual Manipulatives with work mats allow teachers and students to model the lesson.

Check

Use **eAssessment** for online assignments and customized assessments.

Use the **Common Core Quick Check** before the lesson to assess students' retention of previously learned concepts.

Use the interactive **Self-Check Quiz** after the lesson to provide immediate feedback on lesson concepts.

eHelp

Digital and print resources assist students and parents in completing My Homework.

Games

Online games and **apps** provide extra practice for lesson concepts.

PD

Professional development videos help teachers gain a deeper understanding of the lesson concepts and strategies.

RtI

Support for **approaching**, **on**- and **beyond-level** students as well as **English Language Learners**.

Masters

Reteach and **Enrich** worksheets, **Manipulative Masters**, the **Problem of the Day**, and other blackline masters are available for each lesson.

---

1 LAUNCH THE LESSON

 If your students are well-versed in regrouping hundreds, you may choose to begin instruction with Step 2, **TEACH**.

You will need

☐ base-ten blocks
☐ Work Mat 7

Mathematical PRACTICE 4 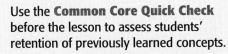 Modeling the Math

Have students form small groups. Then have students model 428–172 with base-ten blocks and Work Mat 7, without solving.

Before solving, say, *do we need to regroup tens?* no

Will you need to regroup hundreds? yes *How do you know?* You cannot subtract 7 tens from 2 tens, so you have to regroup hundreds to solve.

hundreds	tens	ones
3	12	
4̶	2̶	8
− 1	7	2
2	5	6

🕐 **Begin core instruction here.**

You will need

☐ base-ten blocks
☐ Work Mat 7

Explore and Explain

Read the directions that are on the bottom of the student page.

What do you need to find? I need to find how many pieces of macaroni are still on Gwen's picture. *How can you do this?* Find 214 − 120.

Write 214 − 120 on the board. Point to 214 in the problem.

Which base-ten blocks are you going to use to show this number? 2 hundred flats, 1 tens rod, and 4 unit cubes

Guide students to solve the problem.

Subtract the ones first. Are there enough ones in the top number to subtract? yes *What is 4 ones − 0 ones?* 4 ones

Write a 4 in the difference in the ones place on the board.

Subtract the tens next. Are there enough tens in the top number to subtract? no *What is our next step?* Regroup 1 hundred as 10 tens.

Guide students in regrouping 1 hundred flat for 10 tens rods. On the board, cross out 2 in the hundreds place and write a 1 above it. Tell students that it shows that 1 hundred has been regrouped as 10 tens.

How many tens are there after you regroup? 11 tens

Cross out 1 in the tens place. Then write 11 above it.

What is 11 tens − 2 tens? 9 tens

Have students take away 2 tens rods. Finish by subtracting hundreds.

So, how many pieces of macaroni are still on Gwen's picture? 94 pieces of macaroni

See and Show

Help students work through the example at the top of the page. Walk through the steps with the students using actual or virtual base-ten blocks and Work Mat 7. Have them trace the dashed numbers as they work through the problems.

Work through Exercises 1 and 2 as a class.

Mathematical PRACTICE 3 ➡ **Talk Math**

Discuss with students "How do you know when to regroup?" Sample answer: Regroup when there are not enough ones or tens to subtract.

🕐 **CORE INSTRUCTION**

Name _____

Number and Operations in Base Ten
2.NBT.7, 2.NBT.9 | CCSS

Regroup Hundreds

Lesson 5
ESSENTIAL QUESTION
How can I subtract three-digit numbers?

Explore and Explain [Watch] [Tools]

I am the most famous macaroni artist!

See students' work.

94 pieces of macaroni

🦉 **Teacher Directions:** Use base-ten blocks to solve. Gwen put 214 pieces of macaroni on her picture in art class. 120 pieces fell off. How many pieces of macaroni are still on the picture? Draw the blocks you used. Write the number.

Online Content at ⌁ connectED.mcgraw-hill.com   Chapter 7 • Lesson 5   439

See and Show

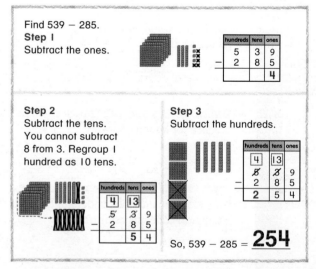

Find 539 − 285.
Step 1
Subtract the ones.

hundreds	tens	ones
5	3	9
− 2	8	5
		4

Step 2
Subtract the tens. You cannot subtract 8 from 3. Regroup 1 hundred as 10 tens.

hundreds	tens	ones
4	13	
5̶	3̶	9
− 2	8	5
	5	4

Step 3
Subtract the hundreds.

hundreds	tens	ones
4	13	
5̶	3̶	9
− 2	8	5
2	5	4

So, 539 − 285 = **254**

Use Work Mat 7 and base-ten blocks. Subtract.

1.
hundreds	tens	ones
4	16	
5	6̶	8
− 1	9	7
3	7	1

2.
hundreds	tens	ones
5	12	
6̶	2̶	8
− 4	4	2
1	8	6

Talk Math How do you know when to regroup?

Name _____

On My Own

Use Work Mat 7 and base-ten blocks. Subtract.

3.
hundreds	tens	ones
[4]	[18]	
5	8	6
− 2	9	5
2	9	1

4.
hundreds	tens	ones
[5]	[13]	
6	3	8
−	4	3
5	9	5

5.
[3] [15]
4 5 9
−   6 9
3 9 0

6.
[6] [13]
7 3 9
− 5 4 1
1 9 8

7.
[7] [12]
8 2 7
− 2 4 7
5 8 0

8.   638
   − 36
   602

9.   232
   − 170
   62

10.   948
   − 472
   476

11.   565
   − 272
   293

12.   640
   − 50
   590

13.   729
   − 135
   594

14.   225
   − 133
   92

15.   485
   − 194
   291

16.   529
   − 395
   134

Chapter 7 • Lesson 5   441

On My Own

Have students work through the exercises on this page independently. You may choose to assign exercises based on the chart below.

DIFFERENTIATED ASSIGNMENTS

AL **Approaching Level** Guide students through the exercises in On My Own. Help them to use manipulatives while working through the exercises.

OL **On Level** Complete the exercises independently.

BL **Beyond Level** Complete the exercises independently without manipulatives.

Common Error!
If students have difficulty adding the regrouped hundred to the number that is already in the tens place, have them write out the addition problem in the margin. For example: 4 tens plus 10 tens, or 40 plus 100, equals 140.

Problem Solving

Have students work through the problem-solving exercises on this page independently.

Mathematical **PRACTICE** In Exercise 18, students **make sense of problems and persevere in solving them.**

Write Math

This exercise asks students to build upon their understanding of concepts needed to answer the chapter's Essential Question.

Problem Solving

Mathematical **PRACTICE**

17. Lucy went to basketball camp. 325 second graders and 234 first graders were there. How many more second graders were at camp?

91 more second graders

18. 417 boys were at the museum. 286 girls were at the museum. How many more boys were at the museum than girls?

131 more boys

A macaroni artist masterpiece
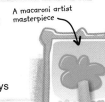

19. 475 parents came to the school's fall party. 294 parents had to leave early. How many parents are still at the fall party?

181 parents

Write Math Explain how to regroup hundreds.

Sample answer: Subtract tens. To regroup, cross out the hundreds and tens digits in the top number. Write the number that is one less above the hundred and one more above the ten. Subtract hundreds.

442   Chapter 7 • Lesson 5

AL | APPROACHING LEVEL

IF my students struggle with regrouping hundreds,

THEN choose a resource:

→ Use a Differentiated Instruction activity from p. 405C.

→ Use the Reteach worksheet with small groups.

→ Go online for a Differentiated Instruction activity.

→ **Borrowing 10 Tens** Point out that regrouping the hundreds is like borrowing 10 tens from the hundreds place and putting them in the tens place. You then add the 10 tens (100) to the number that is already there. This gives the number of tens from which you can subtract.

OL | ON LEVEL

IF my students seem to know how to regroup hundreds, but need more practice,

THEN choose a resource:

→ Assign My Homework.

→ Go online for a Differentiated Instruction activity.

BL | BEYOND LEVEL

IF my students have mastered regrouping hundreds,

THEN choose a resource:

→ Use the Enrich worksheet in cooperative groups.

→ Assign My Homework.

→ Go online for a Differentiated Instruction activity.

AL

Name _____

Lesson 5   Reteach
Regroup Hundreds

Step 1
Subtract the ones.
Write how many ones are left.

Step 2
Subtract the tens.
Regroup 1 hundred as 10 tens. Write the new number of hundreds and tens in the boxes.

Step 3
Subtract the hundreds.
Write how many hundreds are left.

   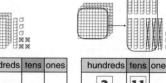

hundreds	tens	ones
3	1	7
− 1	3	4
		3

hundreds	tens	ones
[2]	[11]	
3̸	1̸	7
− 1	3	4
	8	3

hundreds	tens	ones
2	11	
3̸	1̸	7
− 1	3	4
1	8	3

Use base-ten blocks and Work Mat 7. Subtract.

1. 827 − 433 = __394__

2. 245 − 153 = __92__

3. 597 − 489 = __108__

4. 762 − 234 = __528__

5. 624 − 325 = __299__

6. 943 − 144 = __799__

BL

Name _____

Lesson 5   Enrich
Regroup Hundreds

Put the scores in order from *least* to *greatest*.

735, 873, 182, 549, 317, 284

182	284	317	549	735	873
First	Second	Third	Fourth	Fifth	Sixth

1. What is the difference between first place and sixth place? __691__

2. What is the difference between first place and fifth place? __553__

3. What is the difference between second place and third place? __33__

4. What is the difference between fourth place and fifth place? __186__

5. What is the difference between third place and first place? __135__

6. Which two positions have a difference of 451 points? __fifth__ and __second__

7. Which two positions have a difference of 324 points? __sixth__ and __fourth__

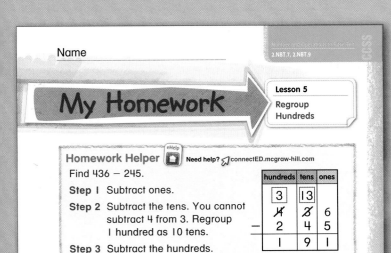

Name _____

Number and Operations in Base Ten
2.NBT.7, 2.NBT.9

My Homework

Lesson 5
Regroup Hundreds

Homework Helper eHelp Need help? connectED.mcgraw-hill.com

Find 436 − 245.

Step 1 Subtract ones.

Step 2 Subtract the tens. You cannot subtract 4 from 3. Regroup 1 hundred as 10 tens.

Step 3 Subtract the hundreds.

hundreds	tens	ones
3	13	
̸4	̸3	6
− 2	4	5
1	9	1

Practice

Subtract.

1.
hundreds	tens	ones
3	16	
3	6	2
− 2	7	1
	9	1

2.
hundreds	tens	ones
6	13	
7	3	2
− 4	4	1
2	9	1

3.
7	13	
8	3	5
−	5	5
7	8	0

4.
6	13	
7	3	5
− 6	7	2
	6	3

5.
1	11	
2	1	7
− 1	4	4
	7	3

Copyright © The McGraw-Hill Companies, Inc.

Chapter 7 • Lesson 5   443

Subtract.

6.   453
   − 62
   391

7.   721
   − 131
   590

8.   745
   − 552
   193

9.   375
   − 292
   83

10. 423
   − 282
   141

11. 434
   − 243
   191

12. 625
   − 462
   163

13. 278
   − 184
   94

14. 835 cows are in the field. 251 cows go in the barn. How many cows are still in the field?

584 cows

I wish I could go to school!

Test Practice

15. Which subtraction problem does not need regrouping to solve?

363 − 148 ○

734 − 371 ○

357 − 147 ●

367 − 288 ○

 Math at Home Have your child explain when you need to regroup to solve a problem.

Copyright © The McGraw-Hill Companies, Inc. D.K. & Vikki Hart/Photodisc/Getty Images

444   Chapter 7 • Lesson 5

My Homework

Assign homework after successful completion of the lesson. Students who understand the concepts may skip the **Homework Helper** section.

Test Practice

Diagnose Student Errors

Class trends in wrong answers may indicate common errors or misconceptions.

363–148 needs regrouping

734–371 needs regrouping

357–147 correct

367–288 needs regrouping

Formative Assessment

Why do you sometimes have to regroup hundreds to subtract?
Sometimes the number of tens to take away is greater than the number of tens in the number to subtract from.

Line Up!

When students line up, ask questions such as: What is 345–1? 344 What is 180–80? 100

LESSON 6
Subtract Three-Digit Numbers

OBJECTIVE   Subtract three-digit numbers.

What's the Math?

 Common Core State Standards
DOMAIN: Number and Operations in Base Ten

Standards: 2.NBT.7, 2.NBT.9
The wording of these standards can be found on page 406.

What Students Should Understand

• When subtracting with three-digit numbers, subtract the ones, the tens, and then the hundreds.

• Regroup 1 ten as 10 ones if there are not enough ones to subtract from.

• If there are not enough tens to subtract from, regroup 1 hundred as 10 tens.

• You can use base-ten blocks to help you regroup and find the difference.

What Students Should be Able to Do

Find 523 − 387.

Step 1

Subtract the ones. You cannot subtract 7 ones from 3 ones. Regroup 1 ten as 10 ones.

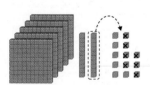

hundreds	tens	ones
	1	13
5	2	3
− 3	8	7
		6

Step 2

Subtract the tens. You cannot subtract 8 tens from 1 ten. Regroup 1 hundred as 10 tens.

hundreds	tens	ones
4	11	13
5	2	3
− 3	8	7
	3	6

Step 3

Subtract the hundreds.

hundreds	tens	ones
4	11	13
5	2	3
− 3	8	7
1	3	6

So, 523 − 387 = 136.

Developing Vocabulary

 Review Vocabulary

subtract   regroup

Review Activity

• Write the review words on the board. Have students browse the lesson to identify where each word occurs.

• Point out the text box on the second page. Ask students how many steps are shown. 3

• Have a volunteers explain what pattern they notice in the steps. The subtraction is shown from right to left. The ones and tens are regrouped.

• Explain that this example will help students as they solve the exercises in this lesson.

ELL **ELL Support Strategy** Use this vocabulary activity to provide oral summaries of information and to recognize text features, such as charts.

My Vocabulary Cards

Have students use a blank card to write a question they have about subtracting three-digit numbers. Collect the cards, and choose random questions to read aloud. Ask volunteers to help answer the questions.

 Building on the Essential Question

In this lesson, students will build upon the skills and concepts needed to answer the chapter's Essential Question "How can I subtract three-digit numbers?"

Digital Dashboard

Interactive Whiteboard Ready

Vocab

The eBook **Glossary** shows the definition of the word and has audio for each definition. The **eGlossary** provides definitions in 13 languages.

Watch

Watch as concepts are brought to life through **animations**, **songs**, and a variety of visual instruction.

Tools

Virtual Manipulatives with work mats allow teachers and students to model the lesson.

Check

Use **eAssessment** for online assignments and customized assessments.

Use the **Common Core Quick Check** before the lesson to assess students' retention of previously learned concepts.

Use the interactive **Self-Check Quiz** after the lesson to provide immediate feedback on lesson concepts.

eHelp

Digital and print resources assist students and parents in completing My Homework.

Games

Online games and **apps** provide extra practice for lesson concepts.

PD

Professional development videos help teachers gain a deeper understanding of the lesson concepts and strategies.

RtI

Support for **approaching**, **on-** and **beyond-level** students as well as **English Language Learners**.

Masters

Reteach and **Enrich** worksheets, **Manipulative Masters**, the **Problem of the Day**, and other blackline masters are available for each lesson.

---

1 LAUNCH THE LESSON

CCSS

If your students are well-versed in subtracting three-digit numbers, you may choose to begin instruction with Step 2, **TEACH**.

You will need

☐ base-ten blocks
☐ Work Mat 7

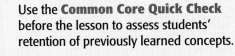
Mathematical PRACTICE 4 **Modeling the Math**

Have students use base-ten blocks and Work Mat 7 to model subtraction.

Tell students to subtract 546 and 325.

Did you regroup? Explain. No; I can subtract without regrouping.

Have students subtract 546 and 217.

Did you regroup? Explain. Yes; I regrouped 1 ten as 10 ones because 7 is greater than 6.

Ask students to subtract 546 and 259.

Did you regroup? Explain. Yes; I regrouped 1 ten as 10 ones because 9 is greater than 6. I regrouped 1 hundred as 10 tens because 5 is greater than 3.

hundreds	tens	ones
☐	☐	
5	4	6
− 3	2	5
2	2	1

TEACH

 **CORE INSTRUCTION**

(V) Begin core instruction here.

You will need

☐ base-ten blocks

☐ Work Mat 7

Explore and Explain

Read the directions that are on the bottom of the student page.

What is the question? How many students bought their lunch? *How can you do this?* Find 355 – 166.

Write 355 – 166 on the board vertically. Guide student in using base-ten blocks to solve the problem.

Which base-ten blocks should you use to model this problem? 3 hundreds flats, 5 tens rods, and 5 unit cubes and 1 hundred flat, 6 tens rods, and 6 unit cubes.

Subtract the ones first. Do you need to regroup? Explain. Yes; Regroup 1 ten for 10 ones.

As students model the regrouping, show the work by crossing out 5 in the tens place and writing 4 above it. Tell students that it represents regrouping 1 ten as 10 ones.

How many ones are there after you regroup? 15 ones

Cross out 5 in the ones and write 15 above it.

What is 15 ones – 6 ones? 9 ones

Have students take away 6 unit cubes. Write 9 as the difference in the ones place.

Subtract the tens next. Do you need to regroup? yes

Guide students in regrouping 1 hundred flat for 10 tens rods. Show your work on the board or have a volunteer do it. Have students follow along at their seats using their tens rods.

How many students bought their lunch? 189 students

See and Show

Help students work through the example at the top of the page. Have them trace the dashed numbers as they work through the problems.

Mathematical PRACTICE 3 ➤ **Talk Math**

Discuss with students "Explain what you write in the box above the ones and tens when you regroup tens and hundreds."
Sample answer: The box above the ones is ten more of that number. The box above the tens is ten more of that number and one less.

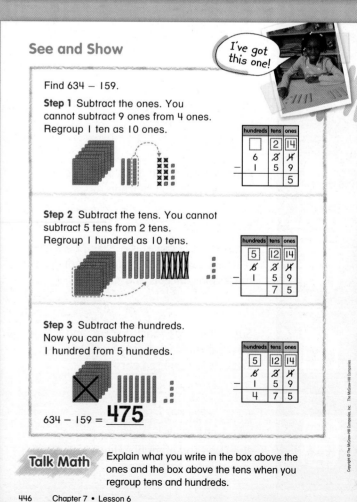

Name

On My Own

Use Work Mat 7 and base-ten blocks. Subtract.

1.
```
  3 12 11
  4  3  1
-    3  4  5
     8  6
```

2.
```
  6 15 12
  7  6  2
-       8  8
     6  7  4
```

3.
```
  8 14 13
  9  5  3
-    7  6  4
     1  8  9
```

4.
```
   702
 - 211
 ‾‾‾‾‾
   491
```

5.
```
   884
 - 197
 ‾‾‾‾‾
   687
```

6.
```
   632
 - 444
 ‾‾‾‾‾
   188
```

7.
```
   485
 - 296
 ‾‾‾‾‾
   189
```

8.
```
   357
 - 169
 ‾‾‾‾‾
   188
```

9.
```
   625
 - 438
 ‾‾‾‾‾
   187
```

10.
```
   590
 - 184
 ‾‾‾‾‾
   406
```

11.
```
   718
 - 628
 ‾‾‾‾‾
    90
```

12.
```
   394
 - 185
 ‾‾‾‾‾
   209
```

13.
```
   561
 - 273
 ‾‾‾‾‾
   288
```

14.
```
   934
 - 395
 ‾‾‾‾‾
   539
```

15.
```
   533
 - 203
 ‾‾‾‾‾
   330
```

Problem Solving

16. The post office had 912 stamps on Friday. By Saturday 189 stamps were left. How many stamps were sold on Friday?

723 stamps

17. Dakota had 200 plastic bugs. He lost some bugs. He has 155 bugs left. How many bugs did he lose?

45 bugs

18. There are 350 pieces of popcorn. Ayana and Gabby eat 177 pieces. How many pieces are left?

173 pieces

HOT Problem 228 students like red. 293 students like blue. 154 students like green. How many more students like red or green than blue? Explain.

Sample answer: 89; You have to add 228 + 154.

Then subtract 293 from that sum. 382 − 293 = 89.

---

3 PRACTICE & APPLY

CCSS

On My Own

Have students work through the exercises on this page independently. You may choose to assign exercises based on the chart below.

DIFFERENTIATED ASSIGNMENTS

AL **Approaching Level** Guide students through the exercises in On My Own. Help them to use manipulatives while working through the exercises.

OL **On Level** Complete the exercises independently.

BL **Beyond Level** Complete the exercises independently without manipulatives.

Common Error!

Students may forget to rename the tens digit when they regroup for more ones. Remind them that when they regroup 1 ten as 10 ones, the 1 ten in the tens column must be taken away.

Problem Solving

Have students work through the problem-solving exercises on this page independently.

Mathematical PRACTICE 2 In Exercise 17, students **reason abstractly and quantitatively.**

HOT Problem This exercise asks students to build upon their understanding of concepts needed to answer the chapter's Essential Question.

ELL Use tiered questions to informally assess students' progress. Refer students to page 446.

Beginning: Point to the first example showing 634–159.

Intermediate: What are the three categories shown in the place-value chart?

Advanced: Explain the steps shown to subtract 159 from 634 in your own words.

RESPONSE TO INTERVENTION

DIFFERENTIATED INSTRUCTION

AL APPROACHING LEVEL

IF my students struggle with subtracting three-digit numbers,

THEN choose a resource:

→ Use a Differentiated Instruction activity from p. 405C.

→ Use the Reteach worksheet with small groups.

→ Go online for a Differentiated Instruction activity.

→ **Make a Model** Have students subtract 235 from 422 using pencil and paper. Ask students to prove their answer by modeling the problem with base-ten blocks and Work Mat 7.

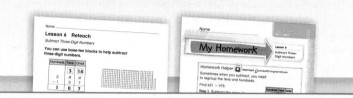

OL ON LEVEL

IF my students seem to know how to subtract three-digit numbers, but need more practice,

THEN choose a resource:

→ Use a Differentiated Instruction activity from p. 405D.

→ Assign My Homework.

→ Go online for a Differentiated Instruction activity.

BL BEYOND LEVEL

IF my students have mastered subtracting three-digit numbers,

THEN choose a resource:

→ Use the Enrich worksheet in cooperative groups.

→ Assign My Homework.

→ Go online for a Differentiated Instruction activity.

AL

Name _____

Lesson 6   Reteach

Subtract Three-Digit Numbers

You can use base-ten blocks to help subtract three-digit numbers.

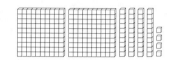

Hundreds	Tens	Ones
	3	14
2	̶4̶	̶4̶
− 1	3	7
1	**0**	**7**

Step 1 Subtract ones.

You cannot take 7 ones from 4 ones. Regroup 1 ten as 10 ones. Now you can subtract 7.

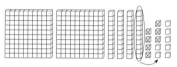

Step 2 Subtract tens.

You can cross out 3 tens.

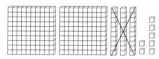

Step 3 Subtract hundreds.

You can cross out 1 hundred.

Count the blocks you have left. You have 1 hundred and 7 ones.

$244 - 137 =$ **107**

BL

Name _____

Lesson 6   Enrich

Subtract Three-Digit Numbers

Miranda and Marty are two very popular monkeys at the zoo. The zoo keeps track of how many bananas each monkey eats throughout the week. Miranda and Marty start with 225 bananas at the beginning of the week.

Use the chart to help answer the questions.

Monkeys	Weekly Bananas	Monday	Tuesday	Wednesday	Thursday	Friday	Saturday	Sunday
Miranda	225	32	27	25	30	26	39	21
Marty	225	33	35	28	29	34	37	25

1. Who ate more bananas from Monday to Wednesday? How many more bananas?
   Marty ate **12** more bananas than **Miranda**.

2. How many bananas did Marty have left after Thursday? **100** bananas

3. Is the total number of bananas Miranda ate on Saturday and Sunday odd or even? **even**

4. How many bananas did both Miranda and Marty have left at the end of the week? **29** bananas

Name

My Homework

Lesson 6
Subtract Three-Digit Numbers

2.NBT.7, 2.NBT.9

Homework Helper

Need help? connectED.mcgraw-hill.com

Sometimes when you subtract, you need to regroup the tens and hundreds.

Find 621 − 475.

Step 1 Subtract the ones. You cannot subtract 5 from 1. Regroup 1 ten as 10 ones.

Step 2 Subtract the tens. You cannot subtract 7 from 1. Regroup.

Step 3 Subtract the hundreds.

hundreds	tens	ones
5	11	11
6̶	2̶	1̶
− 4	7	5
1	4	6

Practice

Subtract.

1.
```
    4 5 3
  − 3 5 1
    1 0 2
```

2.
```
  5 10 12
  6  1  2
− 1  5  9
  4  5  3
```

Chapter 7 • Lesson 6   449

Subtract.

3.
```
    5 3 7
  −   2 6
    5 1 1
```

4.
```
  5 12 14
  6  3  4
− 2  7  8
  3  5  6
```

5.
```
  2 16
  3  6  4
− 1  7  2
  1  9  2
```

6.
```
  634
−  26
  608
```

7.
```
  264
− 168
   96
```

8.
```
  524
− 445
   79
```

9.
```
  347
− 168
  179
```

10. 344 people are at a game. 198 people leave at half time. How many people are still at the game?

Touchdown!

146 people

Test Practice

11. Which problem needs to be regrouped twice?

354 − 134 ○

367 − 263 ○

364 − 274 ○

364 − 278 ●

 Math at Home Have your child explain how regrouping tens and hundreds are the same.

450   Chapter 7 • Lesson 6

---

4 WRAP IT UP

My Homework

Assign homework after successful completion of the lesson. Students who understand the concepts may skip the **Homework Helper** section.

Test Practice

Diagnose Student Errors

Class trends in wrong answers may indicate common errors or misconceptions.

354–134 does not need regrouped

367–263 does not need regrouped

364–274 only regrouped once

364–278 correct

Formative Assessment

Binta has 215 baseball cards. Susana has 88. What is the difference in the number of cards they have? 127 cards

 **MY Learning Stations**

Use the game **Subtract It!**, the graphic novel **Ice Cream Favorites**, and the activity card **The Boiling Point** after this lesson. The Teacher Guide provides suggestions for differentiated instruction.

Line Up! As students line up for recess, lunch, or dismissal, display flash cards of three-digit subtraction problems. Without solving, ask students to identify if they think regrouping will be necessary, and in which place value.

LESSON 7
Rewrite Three-Digit Subtraction

OBJECTIVE Rewrite horizontal three-digit subtraction as vertical three-digit subtraction.

What's the Math?

 Common Core State Standards
DOMAIN: Number and Operations in Base Ten

Standard: 2.NBT.7
The wording of this standard can be found on page 406.

What Students Should Understand

- You can rewrite a horizontal subtraction problem vertically before finding the difference.

- When you rewrite the problem, write the greater number on top and the other number below it.

- After rewriting the problem, subtract the ones, regroup if needed, subtract the tens, regroup if needed, then subtract the hundreds.

What Students Should be Able to Do

Find 736 − 468.

Rewrite 736 − 468 vertically to solve.

Write the greater number above the other number. Line up the ones, tens, and hundreds.
Subtract. Regroup if necessary.

$736 - 468 = 268$

$$
\begin{array}{c|c|c}
6 & 12 & 16 \\
\not{7} & \not{3} & \not{6} \\
- \quad 4 & 6 & 8 \\
\hline
2 & 6 & 8
\end{array}
$$

 Building on the Essential Question

In this lesson, students will build upon the skills and concepts needed to answer the chapter's Essential Question "How can I subtract three-digit numbers?"

Developing Vocabulary

 Review Vocabulary

regroup	ones
tens	hundreds

Review Activity

- Write the review words on the board. Then have students identify where the words appear in this lesson. Have them circle or highlight each example.

- Afterward, have students describe how each word is used in the examples they circled.

ELL **ELL Support Strategy** Use this vocabulary activity to assess students' ability to read for understanding and to develop oral language with content-specific vocabulary.

My Vocabulary Cards

Have students use a blank card to answer this chapter's essential question.

Plan Online

Plan for your lesson by using the resources at
connectED.mcgraw-hill.com

Digital Dashboard

Interactive Whiteboard Ready

Vocab

The eBook **Glossary** shows the definition of the word and has audio for each definition. The **eGlossary** provides definitions in 13 languages.

Watch

Watch as concepts are brought to life through **animations**, **songs**, and a variety of visual instruction.

Tools

Virtual Manipulatives with work mats allow teachers and students to model the lesson.

Check

Use **eAssessment** for online assignments and customized assessments.

Use the **Common Core Quick Check** before the lesson to assess students' retention of previously learned concepts.

Use the interactive **Self-Check Quiz** after the lesson to provide immediate feedback on lesson concepts.

eHelp

Digital and print resources assist students and parents in completing My Homework.

Games

Online games and **apps** provide extra practice for lesson concepts.

PD

Professional development videos help teachers gain a deeper understanding of the lesson concepts and strategies.

RtI

Support for **approaching**, **on-** and **beyond-level** students as well as **English Language Learners**.

Masters

Reteach and **Enrich** worksheets, **Manipulative Masters**, the **Problem of the Day**, and other blackline masters are available for each lesson.

---

1 LAUNCH THE LESSON

 If your students are well-versed in rewriting three-digit subtraction, you may choose to begin instruction with Step 2, **TEACH**.

Mathematical PRACTICE 4 → Modeling the Math

Write $512 - 424$ horizontally on the board. Write $978 - 764$ vertically on the board. Ask students which format makes the subtraction easier.

Look at these problems. Which format makes it easier to subtract? See students' responses.

As a class, discuss how it is easier to subtract when a problem is written in vertical form. Remind students that they have rewritten horizontal problems vertically before. Tell them that, in this lesson, they will rewrite horizontal three-digit subtraction problems vertically before subtracting.

Allow students to rewrite the problem and solve the problem. $512 - 424 = 88$

Lunchroom Chat

Tips for New Teachers

Students sometimes have difficulty keeping place value numbers aligned when they first learn to write vertical subtraction problems. You might want to use the centimeter grid paper to help students learn to keep place value aligned. Use a color pencil to encase the column for ones, another for tens, and a third color for hundreds. Have them write their problem, making sure the numbers are in the proper column.

Begin core instruction here.

You will need

☐ base-ten blocks

Explore and Explain

Read the directions that are on the bottom of the student page.

What do you need to find? The number of pages left to read. *How can you do this?* Find 385 − 266.

Explain to students that they are going to write a subtraction number sentence to solve the problem. Tell them that they can use base-ten blocks to model the problem if they need to.

Write 385 − 266 on the board horizontally.

You can rewrite this subtraction problem in the place-value chart with the greater number on top of the other number.

Guide students in writing 385 − 266 vertically on Work Mat 7.

Subtract the ones. Do you need to regroup? Why or why not? Yes; There are not enough ones.

Lead students in regrouping 1 ten as 10 ones. Use both base-ten blocks and the written algorithm.

After you regroup 1 ten as 10 ones, how many tens and ones are there? 7 tens, 15 ones *What is 15 ones − 6 ones?* 9 ones

Have students take away 6 unit cubes and write 9 in the ones place as the difference.

Next, we will continue the process with the tens and hundreds columns.

How many pages does the teacher have left to read? 119 pages

See and Show

Help students work through the example at the top of the page. Be sure to point out that the first couple steps are what they have already been doing. They are just adding another step. Ask what they think would be different with 4-digit numbers. They would just do another step of the same.

Have them trace the dashed numbers as they work through the problems.

Work through Exercises 1–6 as a class.

Mathematical PRACTICE 3 · **Talk Math**

Discuss with students "How is rewriting three-digit subtraction different than rewriting two-digit subtraction?" Sample answer: You have to line up the hundreds place and you may need to regroup hundreds.

Name _____

2.NBT.7

Rewrite Three-Digit Subtraction

Lesson 7

ESSENTIAL QUESTION
How can I subtract three-digit numbers?

Explore and Explain

385 − 266

hundreds	tens	ones
−		

119 pages

Teacher Directions: Our teacher is reading a very long book to our class. The book has 385 pages. So far, she has read 266 pages of the book. How many pages does she have left to read? Write the numbers in the place-value chart and subtract.

Online Content at connectED.mcgraw-hill.com   Chapter 7 • Lesson 7   451

See and Show

You can rewrite a problem to subtract.
Find 368 − 279.
Step 1 Rewrite.
Step 2 Subtract.

$$\begin{array}{ccc} 2 & 15 & 18 \\ \cancel{3} & \cancel{6} & \cancel{8} \\ -2 & 7 & 9 \\ \hline & 8 & 9 \end{array}$$

Helpful Hint
Write the greater number at the top. Write the other number below it.

Line up the ones, tens, and hundreds.

Rewrite the problem. Subtract.

1. 336 − 272

$$\begin{array}{ccc} 2 & 13 & \\ \cancel{3} & \cancel{3} & 6 \\ -2 & 7 & 2 \\ \hline & 6 & 4 \end{array}$$

2. 377 − 264

$$\begin{array}{ccc} 3 & 7 & 7 \\ -2 & 6 & 4 \\ \hline 1 & 1 & 3 \end{array}$$

3. 633 − 265

$$\begin{array}{ccc} 5 & 12 & 13 \\ \cancel{6} & \cancel{3} & \cancel{3} \\ -2 & 6 & 5 \\ \hline 3 & 6 & 8 \end{array}$$

4. 264 − 175

$$\begin{array}{ccc} 1 & 15 & 14 \\ \cancel{2} & \cancel{6} & \cancel{4} \\ -1 & 7 & 5 \\ \hline & 8 & 9 \end{array}$$

5. 845 − 378

$$\begin{array}{ccc} 7 & 13 & 15 \\ \cancel{8} & \cancel{4} & \cancel{5} \\ -3 & 7 & 8 \\ \hline 4 & 6 & 7 \end{array}$$

6. 555 − 428

$$\begin{array}{ccc} & 4 & 15 \\ 5 & \cancel{5} & \cancel{5} \\ -4 & 2 & 8 \\ \hline 1 & 2 & 7 \end{array}$$

Talk Math How is rewriting three-digit subtraction different than when you rewrite two-digit subtraction?

452   Chapter 7 • Lesson 7

Name _____

On My Own

Rewrite the problem. Subtract.

7. 363 − 278

```
  2 15 13
  3  6  3
− 2  7  8
─────────
     8  5
```

8. 285 − 185

```
  2  8  5
− 1  8  5
─────────
  1  0  0
```

9. 634 − 175

```
  5 12 14
  6  3  4
− 1  7  5
─────────
  4  5  9
```

10. 375 − 142

```
  3  7  5
− 1  4  2
─────────
  2  3  3
```

11. 825 − 195

```
  7 12
  8  2  5
− 1  9  5
─────────
  6  3  0
```

12. 647 − 373

```
  5 14
  6  4  7
− 3  7  3
─────────
  2  7  4
```

13. 695 − 295

```
  6  9  5
− 2  9  5
─────────
  4  0  0
```

14. 853 − 259

```
  7 14 13
  8  5  3
− 2  5  9
─────────
  5  9  4
```

15. 496 − 349

```
     8 16
  4  9  6
− 3  4  9
─────────
  1  4  7
```

16. 495 − 267

```
     8 15
  4  9  5
− 2  6  7
─────────
  2  2  8
```

17. 845 − 264

```
  7 14
  8  4  5
− 2  6  4
─────────
  5  8  1
```

18. 764 − 375

```
  6 15 14
  7  6  4
− 3  7  5
─────────
  3  8  9
```

Chapter 7 • Lesson 7   453

Problem Solving

19. Lucas is reading a book that is 239 pages long. He has read 159 pages. How many pages does he have left to read?

80 pages

20. Our class read 753 books over the summer. The girls read 394 books. How many books did the boys read?

I do a lot of summer reading!

359 books

21. Our school library has 125 books about pets. I have read 96 of the books. How many books do I have left to read?

29 books

Mathematical PRACTICE

Write Math Explain how you rewrite three-digit subtraction problems to solve.

Sample answer: Put the greatest number on top. Write the other number below it. Line up the ones, tens, and hundreds. Then subtract, regrouping if needed.

454   Chapter 7 • Lesson 7

---

③ PRACTICE & APPLY

On My Own

Have students work through the exercises on this page independently. You may choose to assign exercises based on the chart below.

DIFFERENTIATED ASSIGNMENTS

AL Approaching Level Guide students through the exercises in On My Own. Help them to use manipulatives while working through the exercises.

OL On Level Complete the exercises independently.

BL Beyond Level Complete the exercises independently without manipulatives.

Problem Solving

Have students work through the problem-solving exercises on this page independently.

Mathematical PRACTICE ① In Exercise 20, students **make sense of problems and persevere in solving them.**

Write Math

This exercise asks students to build upon their understanding of concepts needed to answer the chapter's Essential Question.

RESPONSE TO INTERVENTION
DIFFERENTIATED INSTRUCTION

AL ▸ APPROACHING LEVEL

IF my students struggle with rewriting three-digit subtraction,

THEN choose a resource:

→ Use the Reteach worksheet with small groups.

→ Go online for a Differentiated Instruction activity.

OL ▸ ON LEVEL

IF my students seem to know how to rewrite three-digit subtraction, but need more practice,

THEN choose a resource:

→ Assign My Homework.

→ Go online for a Differentiated Instruction activity.

BL ▸ BEYOND LEVEL

IF my students have mastered rewriting three-digit subtraction,

THEN choose a resource:

→ Use the Enrich worksheet in cooperative groups.

→ Assign My Homework.

→ Go online for a Differentiated Instruction activity.

AL Name _____

Lesson 7   Reteach

Rewrite Three-Digit Subtraction

You can write a subtraction fact two different ways.

$$548 - 230 = \boxed{318} \text{ is the same as } \begin{array}{r} 548 \\ -\ 230 \\ \hline 318 \end{array}$$

Subtract.

1. $708 - 501 = \boxed{207}$ is the same as $\begin{array}{r} 708 \\ -\ 501 \\ \hline \mathbf{207} \end{array}$

2. $100 - 75 = \boxed{25}$ is the same as $\begin{array}{r} 100 \\ -\ 75 \\ \hline \mathbf{25} \end{array}$

3. $369 - 258 = \boxed{111}$ is the same as $\begin{array}{r} 369 \\ -\ 258 \\ \hline \mathbf{111} \end{array}$

4. $602 - 199 = \boxed{403}$ is the same as $\begin{array}{r} 602 \\ -\ 199 \\ \hline \mathbf{403} \end{array}$

BL Name _____

Lesson 7   Enrich

Rewrite Three-Digit Subtraction

Solve. Write each subtraction sentence two ways.

1. Ida received 230 votes for class president. Amelia received 108 votes. How many more votes did Ida receive?

   $$\mathbf{230 - 108 = 122}$$
   $$\begin{array}{r} 230 \\ -\ 108 \\ \hline 122 \end{array}$$
   _____**122**_ votes

2. There are 593 fish in the aquarium. There were 287 birds in the cage. How many more fish are there?

   $$\mathbf{593 - 287 = 306}$$
   $$\begin{array}{r} 593 \\ -\ 287 \\ \hline 306 \end{array}$$
   _____**306**_ fish

3. Jay scored 704 points during the first round of his video game. He scored 908 points during the second round. How many more points did he score during the second round?

   $$\mathbf{908 - 704 = 204}$$
   $$\begin{array}{r} 908 \\ -\ 704 \\ \hline 204 \end{array}$$
   _____**204**_ points

My Homework

Name _____

2.NBT.7

CCSS

My Homework ➡

Lesson 7
Rewrite Three-Digit Subtraction

Homework Helper 📱 eHelp Need help? ✍ connectED.mcgraw-hill.com

Find 356 − 298.

Step 1 Rewrite. Place the greater number on top.

Step 2 Subtract. Regroup if necessary.

$$\begin{array}{r} 2\ |\ 14\ |\ 16 \\ \cancel{3}\ \ \cancel{5}\ \ \cancel{6} \\ -\ 2\ \ \ 9\ \ \ 8 \\ \hline 5\ \ \ 8 \end{array}$$

Practice

Rewrite the problem. Subtract.

1. 724 − 235

$$\begin{array}{r} 6\ |\ 11\ |\ 14 \\ \cancel{7}\ \ \cancel{2}\ \ \cancel{4} \\ -\ 2\ \ \ 3\ \ \ 5 \\ \hline 4\ \ \ 8\ \ \ 9 \end{array}$$

2. 616 − 337

$$\begin{array}{r} 5\ |\ 10\ |\ 16 \\ \cancel{6}\ \ \cancel{1}\ \ \cancel{6} \\ -\ 3\ \ \ 3\ \ \ 7 \\ \hline 2\ \ \ 7\ \ \ 9 \end{array}$$

3. 374 − 286

$$\begin{array}{r} 2\ |\ 16\ |\ 14 \\ \cancel{3}\ \ \cancel{7}\ \ \cancel{4} \\ -\ 2\ \ \ 8\ \ \ 6 \\ \hline 8\ \ \ 8 \end{array}$$

4. 875 − 596

$$\begin{array}{r} 7\ |\ 16\ |\ 15 \\ \cancel{8}\ \ \cancel{7}\ \ \cancel{5} \\ -\ 5\ \ \ 9\ \ \ 6 \\ \hline 2\ \ \ 7\ \ \ 9 \end{array}$$

5. 945 − 387

$$\begin{array}{r} 8\ |\ 13\ |\ 15 \\ \cancel{9}\ \ \cancel{4}\ \ \cancel{5} \\ -\ 3\ \ \ 8\ \ \ 7 \\ \hline 5\ \ \ 5\ \ \ 8 \end{array}$$

6. 435 − 294

$$\begin{array}{r} 3\ |\ 13\ | \\ \cancel{4}\ \ \cancel{3}\ \ 5 \\ -\ 2\ \ \ 9\ \ \ 4 \\ \hline 1\ \ \ 4\ \ \ 1 \end{array}$$

Chapter 7 • Lesson 7   455

Rewrite the problem. Subtract.

7. 162 − 89

$$\begin{array}{r} 0\ |\ 15\ |\ 12 \\ \cancel{1}\ \ \cancel{6}\ \ \cancel{2} \\ -\ \ \ \ \ 8\ \ \ 9 \\ \hline 7\ \ \ 3 \end{array}$$

8. 619 − 254

$$\begin{array}{r} 5\ |\ 11\ | \\ \cancel{6}\ \ \cancel{1}\ \ 9 \\ -\ 2\ \ \ 5\ \ \ 4 \\ \hline 3\ \ \ 6\ \ \ 5 \end{array}$$

9. 195 − 99

$$\begin{array}{r} 0\ |\ 18\ |\ 15 \\ \cancel{1}\ \ \cancel{9}\ \ \cancel{5} \\ -\ \ \ \ \ 9\ \ \ 9 \\ \hline 9\ \ \ 6 \end{array}$$

10. 835 people are on a boat. 295 people get off of the boat. How many people are still on the boat?

Ahoy!

540 people

Test Practice

11. Which problem shows how to rewrite the problem?

368 − 179 = _____

368 − 179 = 200	179 − 368 = 411	368 − 179 = 189	368 + 179 = 547
○	○	●	○

  Math at Home Write a three-digit subtraction number sentence for your child. Have him or her rewrite the number sentence vertically and then subtract.

456   Chapter 7 • Lesson 7

My Homework

Assign homework after successful completion of the lesson. Students who understand the concepts may skip the **Homework Helper** section.

Test Practice

Diagnose Student Errors

Class trends in wrong answers may indicate common errors or misconceptions.

$$\begin{array}{r} 368 \\ -\ 179 \\ \hline 200 \end{array}$$ subtracted incorrectly

$$\begin{array}{r} 179 \\ -\ 368 \\ \hline 411 \end{array}$$ put the smaller number on top and added

$$\begin{array}{r} 368 \\ -\ 179 \\ \hline 189 \end{array}$$ correct

$$\begin{array}{r} 368 \\ +\ 179 \\ \hline 547 \end{array}$$ added

Formative Assessment

Write the problem 486 − 273 = on the board in horizontal form and ask student to solve it using what they have learned. If they rewrite it in vertical form and solve it, then they are on the correct path and understanding the process. 486 − 273 = 213

LESSON 8

Problem Solving
STRATEGY: Write a Number Sentence

OBJECTIVE Write a number sentence to solve problems.

What's the Math?

 Common Core State Standards
DOMAIN: Number and Operations in Base Ten

Standard: 2.NBT.7
The wording of this standard can be found on page 406.

 Model with mathematics.

What Students Should Understand

• You can write a number sentence to solve real-world problems.

• First, make sure you understand the meaning of the problem. Determine what facts are important and what question is being asked.

• Then make a plan to solve the problem. Follow through with the plan.

• Justify your conclusion by checking your answer to determine whether it is correct and makes sense.

What Students Should be Able to Do

The Gomez family is traveling 248 miles to go on vacation. So far, they have driven 115 miles. How many miles do they have left to drive?

1 Understand

Underline what you know. Circle what you need to find.

2 Plan

How will I solve this problem?
I can write a number sentence.

3 Solve

I will write a number sentence.
$248 - 115 = 133$
So, the Gomez family has 133 miles left to drive.

4 Check

Is my answer reasonable? Explain.
Sample answer: yes; $115 + 133 = 248$. So, my answer is correct.

Developing the Strategy

Make a Number Sentence

People use language to communicate in a comprehensible way. By translating English phrases/sentences into "Math" phrases/sentences (in mathematics, phrases are called expressions, and sentences are called equations), solution become clearer. Students translate the word problems in this lesson into number sentences to solve.

Example:

Mandy saw 2 bears.

Jamie saw 7 lions.

How many bears and lions did Mandy and Jamie see?

This word problem translates into $2 + 7 = ?$
Students then solve the number sentence to find:
$2 + 7 = 9$

Other Strategies

Other strategies that have been taught and that students may choose to use in the Review the Strategies section are:

• Make a model

• Guess, check, and revise

ELL **Signal Words** Encourage English-language learners to identify signal phrases, such as *how many were not* and *how many more*, as they read word problems.

Mathematical PRACTICE

The Mathematical Practices are especially evident in problem-solving situations, in which students connect procedures and processes with mathematical understanding. In this lesson, the following Mathematical Practices are addressed.

 Make sense of problems and persevere in solving them.

 Model with mathematics.

Plan Online
Plan for your lesson by using the resources at
connectED.mcgraw-hill.com

Digital Dashboard

Interactive Whiteboard Ready

The eBook **Glossary** shows the definition of the word and has audio for each definition. The **eGlossary** provides definitions in 13 languages.

Virtual Manipulatives along with work mats allow teachers and students to model the lesson.

Use **eAssessment** for online assignments and customized assessments.

Use the **Common Core Quick Check** before the lesson to assess students' retention of previously learned concepts.

Digital and print resources assist students and parents in completing My Homework.

Professional development videos help teachers gain a deeper understanding of the lesson concepts and strategies.

Support for **approaching**, **on**- and **beyond-level** students as well as **English Language Learners**.

Reteach and **Enrich** worksheets, **Manipulative Masters**, the **Problem of the Day**, and other blackline masters are available for each lesson.

---

1 LAUNCH THE LESSON

 CCSS

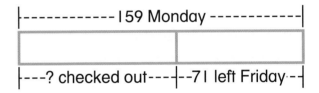

If your students are well-versed in problem solving, you may choose to begin instruction with Step 2, **TEACH**.

Review

Write and read aloud the following: *Elena saw 159 books at the library on Monday. On Friday there were 71 books left. How many books had been checked out?*

Set up a bar diagram to show students what they know and what they need to find out.

What should I write above the bar diagram? 159 across the entire top *Why?* This represents what we know; the whole.

What should I write below the bar diagram? there should be a ? across one part of the bottom of the diagram and 71 across the other part *Why?* We know one part is 71 and the other part is missing.

How many books had been checked out of the library? How do you know? 88; $159 - 71 = 88$

```
|------------159 Monday------------|
|                    |                    |
|----? checked out----|--71 left Friday--|
```

TEACH

🕐 **Begin core instruction here.**

Problem Solving

1 Understand

Reread the problem with the students. Point out information as you read it.

2 Plan

Discuss several ideas. Lead the students towards writing the number sentence needed to solve the problem.

3 Solve

Work through the problem step-by-step using the student page with the students. Show how to solve the problem.

4 Check

Discuss why the answer makes sense. Try to develop a sense of reasoning.

Practice the Strategy

1 Understand

Reread the problem with the students. Ask students to point out information that is important as you read it.

2 Plan

Lead the students in discussing several ideas. Direct them toward the correct plan of using number sentences to solve the problem.

3 Solve

Work through the problem using the student page with the class. Show how to solve it step-by-step.

4 Check

Discuss why the answer makes sense. Try to develop a sense of reasoning.

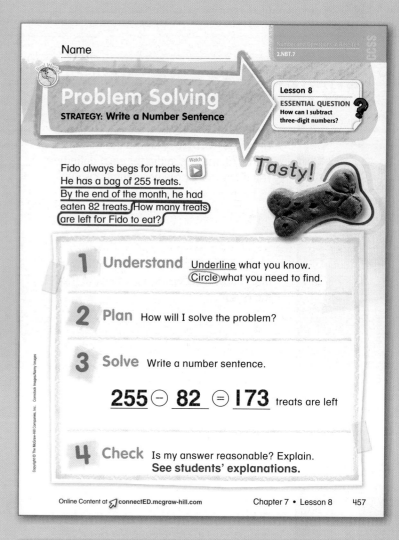

Name _____   2.NBT.7   CCSS

Problem Solving
STRATEGY: Write a Number Sentence

Lesson 8
ESSENTIAL QUESTION
How can I subtract three-digit numbers?

Fido always begs for treats. He has a bag of 255 treats. By the end of the month, he had eaten 82 treats. How many treats are left for Fido to eat?

Tasty!

1 Understand Underline what you know. Circle what you need to find.

2 Plan How will I solve the problem?

3 Solve Write a number sentence.

$$255 - 82 = 173$$ treats are left

4 Check Is my answer reasonable? Explain.
See students' explanations.

Online Content at connectED.mcgraw-hill.com   Chapter 7 • Lesson 8   457

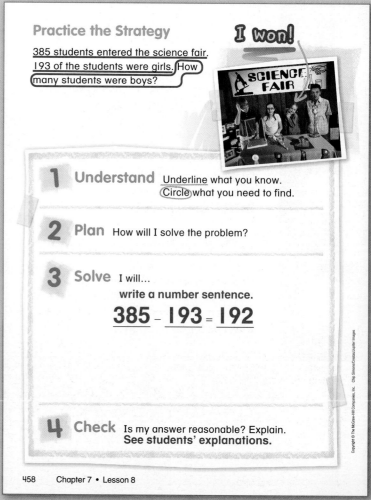

Practice the Strategy
I won!

385 students entered the science fair. 193 of the students were girls. How many students were boys?

1 Understand Underline what you know. Circle what you need to find.

2 Plan How will I solve the problem?

3 Solve I will...
write a number sentence.
$$385 - 193 = 192$$

4 Check Is my answer reasonable? Explain.
See students' explanations.

458   Chapter 7 • Lesson 8

Name _____

Mathematical
PRACTICE

Apply the Strategy

1. It took 227 days to build railroad tracks over a mountain. It took 132 days to build tracks over flat ground. How many more days did it take to build over the mountain?

$$\underline{227} \ominus \underline{132} \ominus \underline{95} \text{ days}$$

2. The Fuller family is driving 475 miles. They have already gone 218 miles. How many miles are left to go?

$$\underline{475} \ominus \underline{218} \ominus \underline{257} \text{ miles}$$

3. Flora's class is trying to collect 850 cans. She has turned in 370 cans. How many cans are needed to reach the class goal?

$$\underline{850} \ominus \underline{370} \ominus \underline{480} \text{ cans}$$

Chapter 7 • Lesson 8   459

Review the Strategies

> **Choose a strategy**
> • Make a model.
> • Guess, check, and revise.
> • Write a number sentence.

4. Anna has been keeping track of the weather for 289 days. 196 of the days were sunny. How many days were not sunny?

$$\underline{93} \text{ days}$$

5. There are 836 flowers in the field. The children pick 398 of the flowers. How many flowers are left in the field?

$$\underline{438} \text{ flowers}$$

6. 423 fish are in the tank. 184 fish are removed from the tank. How many fish are in the tank now?

$$\underline{239} \text{ fish}$$

460   Chapter 7 • Lesson 8

---

③ PRACTICE & APPLY

Mathematical
PRACTICE 1 Apply the Strategy

Have students work through the exercises on these pages independently. You may choose to assign exercises based on the chart below.

DIFFERENTIATED ASSIGNMENTS

AL **Approaching Level** Guide students through the exercises. Help them to use manipulatives while working through the exercises.

OL **On Level** Complete the exercises independently.

BL **Beyond Level** Complete the exercises independently without manipulatives.

Review the Strategies

Students may use other strategies to solve these exercises.
• Make a model
• Guess, check, and revise

21ST CENTURY SKILLS

Collaboration

In this problem-solving lesson, have students work in pairs or small groups to determine which number sentence best expresses each problem. Make sure they discuss the possibilities and determine if they have the correct information to solve each problem. Emphasize that they should also determine if the answer they have makes sense in the context of the problem.

RESPONSE TO INTERVENTION
DIFFERENTIATED INSTRUCTION

AL **APPROACHING LEVEL**

IF my students struggle with problem solving,

THEN choose a resource:

→ Use the Reteach worksheet with small groups.

→ Go online for a Differentiated Instruction activity.

OL **ON LEVEL**

IF my students seem to know problem solving, but need more practice,

THEN choose a resource:

→ Assign My Homework.

→ Go online for a Differentiated Instruction activity.

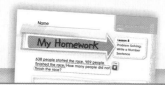

BL **BEYOND LEVEL**

IF my students have mastered problem solving,

THEN choose a resource:

→ Use the Enrich worksheet in cooperative groups.

→ Assign My Homework.

→ Go online for a Differentiated Instruction activity.

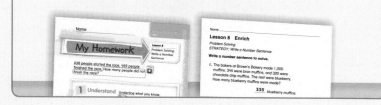

AL Name _____

Lesson 8   Reteach (1)
Problem Solving
STRATEGY: Write a Number Sentence

There were 185 apples growing on a tree. Andrew and his sister picked 62 apples and put them in the basket. How many apples are left on the tree?

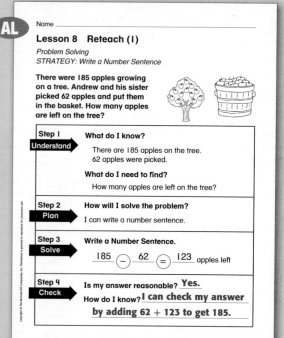

Step 1 Understand	**What do I know?** There are 185 apples on the tree. 62 apples were picked.
	What do I need to find? How many apples are left on the tree?
Step 2 Plan	**How will I solve the problem?** I can write a number sentence.
Step 3 Solve	**Write a Number Sentence.** 185 ⊖ 62 ⊜ 123 apples left
Step 4 Check	**Is my answer reasonable?** Yes. **How do I know?** I can check my answer by adding 62 + 123 to get 185.

AL Name _____

Lesson 8   Reteach (2)
Problem Solving
STRATEGY: Write a Number Sentence

Write a number sentence to solve.

1. Tara bought 79 paints at the art supply store. She bought 100 brushes. How many more brushes did she buy?

   __21__ brushes

2. Cameron's Corner Coffee Shop sold 962 cups of coffee in the morning and 491 cups in the afternoon. How many more cups of coffee did Cameron sell in the morning?

   __471__ cups of coffee

3. The school library has a goal to receive 800 books during a book drive. So far, they have received 543 books. How many more books do they need to reach their goal?

   __257__ books

4. Brayden took a math test with 200 questions. He got 188 questions right. How many questions did he miss?

   __12__ questions

BL Name _____

Lesson 8   Enrich
Problem Solving
STRATEGY: Write a Number Sentence

Write a number sentence to solve.

1. The bakers at Brown's Bakery made 1,000 muffins. 345 were bran muffins, and 320 were chocolate chip muffins. The rest were blueberry. How many blueberry muffins were made?

   __335__ blueberry muffins

2. Tristan bought a book with 573 pages. He read 202 pages. How many pages does he have left?

   __371__ pages

3. Beth saved $700. She spent $230 on vacation. How much money does she have left?

   __470__ dollars

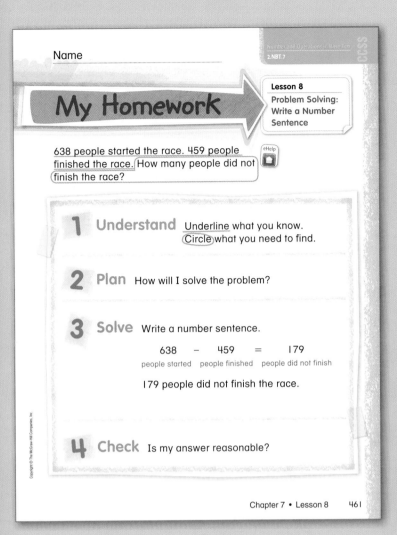

Name _____

My Homework

Lesson 8
Problem Solving:
Write a Number
Sentence

638 people started the race. 459 people finished the race. How many people did not finish the race?

1 Understand Underline what you know.
Circle what you need to find.

2 Plan How will I solve the problem?

3 Solve Write a number sentence.

638   −   459   =   179

people started   people finished   people did not finish

179 people did not finish the race.

4 Check Is my answer reasonable?

Chapter 7 • Lesson 8   461

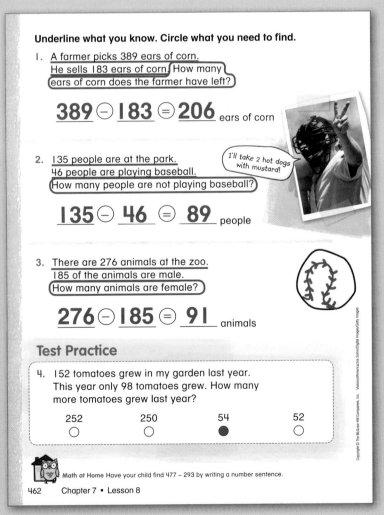

Underline what you know. Circle what you need to find.

1. A farmer picks 389 ears of corn. He sells 183 ears of corn. How many ears of corn does the farmer have left?

$389 − 183 = 206$ ears of corn

I'll take 2 hot dogs with mustard!

2. 135 people are at the park. 46 people are playing baseball. How many people are not playing baseball?

$135 − 46 = 89$ people

3. There are 276 animals at the zoo. 185 of the animals are male. How many animals are female?

$276 − 185 = 91$ animals

Test Practice

4. 152 tomatoes grew in my garden last year. This year only 98 tomatoes grew. How many more tomatoes grew last year?

252 ○   250 ○   54 ●   52 ○

Math at Home Have your child find 477 − 293 by writing a number sentence.

4 WRAP IT UP

My Homework

Assign homework after successful completion of the lesson. Students who understand the concepts may skip the **Homework Helper** section.

Test Practice

Diagnose Student Errors

Class trends in wrong answers may indicate common errors or misconceptions.

252 added incorrectly

250 added

54 correct

52 subtracted incorrectly

Formative Assessment

Ask students the following question.

How can I solve 847 − 62? See students' work. *What is the answer?* 785

LESSON 9
Subtract Across Zeros
OBJECTIVE Subtract from numbers ending in zero.

What's the Math?

 Common Core State Standards
DOMAIN: Number and Operations in Base Ten

Standards: 2.NBT.7, 2.NBT.9
The wording of these standards can be found on page 406.

What Students Should Understand

• When subtracting with three-digit numbers, subtract the ones, the tens, and then the hundreds, regrouping when needed.

• When the first number ends with two zeros and the second number does not have zeros in the ones or tens places, the first step you will take is to regroup 1 hundred as 10 tens and 1 ten as 10 ones.

• You can use base-ten blocks to help you regroup and find the difference.

What Students Should be Able to Do

Find 300 − 137.

Step 1

Subtract the ones. You cannot subtract 7 ones from 0 ones. There are no tens to regroup. Look at the hundreds. Regroup 1 hundred as 10 tens. Then regroup 1 ten as 10 ones.

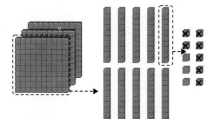

	hundreds	tens	ones
			10
	3̸	0̸	0̸
−	1	3	7
			3

Step 2
Subtract the tens.

	hundreds	tens	ones
		9	10
	3̸	0̸	0̸
−	1	3	7
		6	3

Step 3
Subtract the hundreds.

	hundreds	tens	ones
	2	9	10
	3̸	0̸	0̸
−	1	3	7
	1	6	3

So, 300 − 137 = 163.

Developing Vocabulary

 Review Vocabulary

zero

Review Activity

• Write the review word on the board. Ask students what they know about subtracting using zeroes.

• Have students browse the lesson and identify where the review word occurs.

 ELL Support Strategy Use this vocabulary activity to assess students' ability to read for understanding.

My Vocabulary Cards

Have students use a blank card to review a vocabulary word, such as *zero*.

 Building on the Essential Question

In this lesson, students will build upon the skills and concepts needed to answer the chapter's Essential Question "How can I subtract three-digit numbers?"

Plan Online
Plan for your lesson by using the resources at
connectED.mcgraw-hill.com

Digital Dashboard

Interactive Whiteboard Ready

Vocab

The eBook **Glossary** shows the definition of the word and has audio for each definition. The **eGlossary** provides definitions in 13 languages.

Watch

Watch as concepts are brought to life through **animations**, **songs**, and a variety of visual instruction.

Tools

Virtual Manipulatives with work mats allow teachers and students to model the lesson.

Check

Use **eAssessment** for online assignments and customized assessments.

Use the **Common Core Quick Check** before the lesson to assess students' retention of previously learned concepts.

Use the interactive **Self-Check Quiz** after the lesson to provide immediate feedback on lesson concepts.

eHelp

Digital and print resources assist students and parents in completing My Homework.

Games

Online games and **apps** provide extra practice for lesson concepts.

PD

Professional development videos help teachers gain a deeper understanding of the lesson concepts and strategies.

RtI

Support for **approaching**, **on-** and **beyond-level** students as well as **English Language Learners**.

Masters

Reteach and **Enrich** worksheets, **Manipulative Masters**, the **Problem of the Day**, and other blackline masters are available for each lesson.

---

1 LAUNCH THE LESSON
CCSS

If your students are well-versed in subtracting across zeros, you may choose to begin instruction with Step 2, **TEACH**.

You will need
☐ base-ten blocks

Mathematical PRACTICE 4 Modeling the Math

Have students work in groups of four. Have one student use base-ten blocks to model 400. Have a second student regroup 1 hundred as 10 tens.

> *When you regroup 1 hundred as 10 tens, how many tens do you have?* 10 tens *How many hundreds do you have?* 3 hundreds

Have the third student regroup 1 ten as 10 ones.

> *How many ones do you have?* 10 ones *How many tens?* 9 tens *How many hundreds?* 3 hundreds

Have the fourth student show that the final amount equals 4 hundreds.

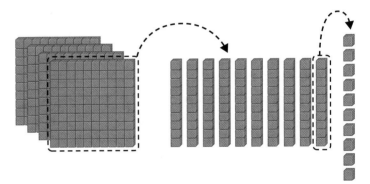

Begin core instruction here.

You will need
- ☐ base-ten blocks
- ☐ Work Mat 7

Explore and Explain

Read the directions that are at the bottom of the student page.

You need to find how many of the animals were not mammals. How can you do this? Find 200 − 126.

Draw a place value chart on the board. Write 200 − 126 in the chart. Point to the number 200.

Which base-ten blocks are you going to use to show this number? 2 hundreds flats *Subtract the ones first. Do you need to regroup?* Yes

Explain to students how to regroup across zeros.

When there are no tens to regroup, you will need to regroup 1 hundred as 10 tens. Now you have tens to regroup. Regroup 1 ten as 10 ones.

As you use base-ten blocks to model the math, show the work on the board.

How many ones are there after you regroup? 10 ones *What is 10 ones − 6 ones?* 4 ones

Have students take away 6 unit cubes. Write 4 in the difference in the ones place on the board.

Now continue the process for the tens and hundreds.

So, how many of the animals were not mammals?
74 animals

See and Show

Help students work through the example at the top of page. Work through this page as you have before. Use base-ten blocks and Work Mat 7.

Have them trace the dashed numbers as they work through the problems.

Mathematical PRACTICE 3  **Talk Math**

Discuss with students "How is subtracting from 400 different than subtracting from 435?" Sample answer: You cannot subtract from 0 so you have to go on over to the hundreds and start regrouping from there.

Name _____

Number and Operations in Base Ten
2.NBT.7, 2.NBT.9 CCSS

Subtract Across Zeros

Lesson 9
ESSENTIAL QUESTION
How can I subtract three-digit numbers?

Explore and Explain Watch ▶ Tools

"Yippee, I'm a mammal!"

"Me too!"

74 animals

Teacher Directions: Model using base-ten blocks. We have learned about 200 different kinds of animals. 126 of those animals were mammals. How many of the animals were not mammals? Draw the blocks. Write the number.

Online Content at connectED.mcgraw-hill.com   Chapter 7 • Lesson 9 463

See and Show

Mathematical PRACTICE

You can subtract across zeros.

Find 400 − 234.
Step 1 Subtract the ones. You cannot subtract 4 ones from 0 ones. There are no tens to subtract from. Look at the hundreds. Regroup 1 hundred as 10 tens. Then regroup 1 ten as ten ones.

hundreds	tens	ones
□	□	10
⁴	⁰	⁰
− 2	3	4
		6

Step 2 Subtract the tens. There are 9 tens left. Subtract 3 tens from 9 tens.

hundreds	tens	ones
□	9	10
⁴	⁰	⁰
− 2	3	4
	6	6

Step 3 Subtract the hundreds. There are 3 hundreds left. Subtract 2 hundreds from 3 hundreds.

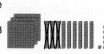

hundreds	tens	ones
3	9	10
⁴	⁰	⁰
− 2	3	4
1	6	6

400 − 234 = **166**

Talk Math How is subtracting from 400 different than subtracting from 435?

464 Chapter 7 • Lesson 9

Name _____

On My Own

Use Work Mat 7 and base-ten blocks. Subtract.

1.
hundreds	tens	ones
7	9	10
8	0	0
− 5	3	2
2	6	8

2.
hundreds	tens	ones
6	9	10
7	0	0
− 6	1	4
	8	6

3. 100
 − 76
 24

4. 900
 − 287
 613

5. 400
 − 167
 233

6. 700
 − 444
 256

7. 300
 − 16
 284

8. 800
 − 477
 323

9. 900
 − 876
 24

10. 500
 − 54
 446

11. 800
 − 691
 109

12. 200
 − 75
 125

13. 500
 − 321
 179

14. 600
 − 312
 288

Problem Solving

15. 400 bees are in the hive. 145 bees leave the hive. How many bees are still in the hive?

225 bees

16. 300 girls took gymnastics last year. This year 193 girls take gymnastics. How many more girls took gymnastics last year than this year?

107 girls

HOT Problem 500 people signed up for soccer. 123 people stopped playing. Then 154 more people stopped playing. How many people still play soccer? Explain.

Sample answer: 223, You have to subtract 123 from

500 first. Then subtract 154 from that difference.

500 − 123 = 377; 377 − 154 = 223

Have s_____ _____ _hrough the exercises on this page independent__ ___ _u may choose to assign exercises based on the chart below.

DIFFERENTIATED ASSIGNMENTS

AL Approaching Level Guide students through the exercises in On My Own. Help them to use manipulatives while working through the exercises.

OL On Level Complete the exercises independently.

BL Beyond Level Complete the exercises independently without manipulatives.

Common Error!

Students may forget to regroup more than one time when they subtract across zeros. Allow these students time to work with the base-ten blocks. Have them work in pairs to check each others' work.

Problem Solving

Have students work through the problem-solving exercises on this page independently.

Mathematical **PRACTICE** → In Exercise 16, students **make sense of problems and persevere in solving them.**

HOT Problem This exercise asks students to build upon their understanding of concepts needed to answer the chapter's Essential Question.

AL APPROACHING LEVEL

IF my students struggle with subtracting across zeros,

THEN choose a resource:

→ Use the Reteach worksheet with small groups.

→ Go online for a Differentiated Instruction activity.

→ **Rewrite the Problem** Write 800 – 315 vertically. Circle the hundreds and tens places in 800, which is the number 80. Cross out the 80 and write one number less, which is 79. Then add a 1 in front of the 0 in the ones place to make it 10. Now you can subtract to find the difference.

OL ON LEVEL

IF my students seem to know how to subtract across zeros, but need more practice,

THEN choose a resource:

→ Assign My Homework.

→ Go online for a Differentiated Instruction activity.

BL BEYOND LEVEL

IF my students have mastered subtracting across zeros,

THEN choose a resource:

→ Use a Differentiated Instruction activity from p. 405D.

→ Use the Enrich worksheet in cooperative groups.

→ Assign My Homework.

→ Go online for a Differentiated Instruction activity.

Name _____

AL
Lesson 9   Reteach
Subtract Across Zeros

You can use place-value charts to help you regroup across zeros.

Find 305 – 176.

Step 1
Subtract the ones. No tens to regroup. Regroup the hundreds.

Step 2
Regroup the tens.

Step 3
Subtract the ones, tens, and hundreds.

hundreds	tens	ones
2	10	
3̸	0̸	5
– 1	7	6

hundreds	tens	ones
	9	
2	1̸0̸	15
3̸	0̸	5̸
– 1	7	6

hundreds	tens	ones
	9	
2	1̸0̸	15
3̸	0̸	5̸
– 1	7	6
	1	2	9

Subtract. Check your answer.

1. 106
   – 28
   78

2. 503
   – 167
   336

3. 405
   – 218
   187

4. 601
   – 378
   223

5. 200
   – 145
   55

6. 205
   – 92
   113

7. 308
   – 175
   133

8. 300
   – 56
   244

9. 505
   – 90
   415

10. 802
   – 132
   670

11. 500 – 418 = **82**   12. 206 – 138 = **68**

13. 801 – 482 = **319**   14. 100 – 33 = **67**

15. 607 – 527 = **80**   16. 700 – 19 = **681**

Name _____

BL
Lesson 9   Enrich
Subtract Across Zeroes

Find the missing numbers in each subtraction pinwheel. Remember to regroup when subtracting across zeros.

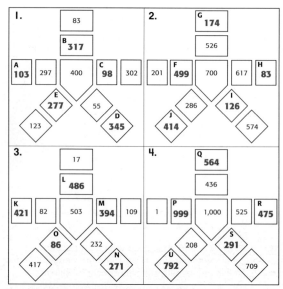

5. Match the difference with a number shown under the lines below. Write the letter of the difference on the line to write a mystery message.

r e g r o u p
475 277 174 475 86 792 999

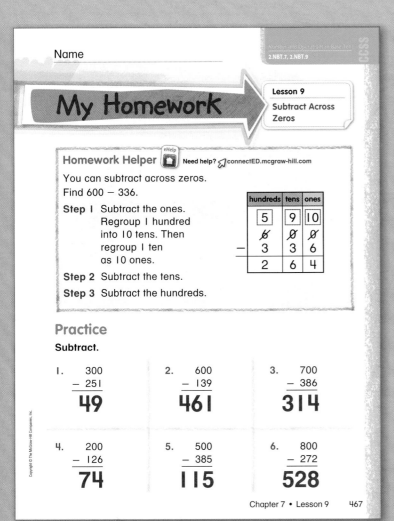

My Homework

Assign homework after successful completion of the lesson. Students who understand the concepts may skip the **Homework Helper** section.

Test Practice

Diagnose Student Errors

Class trends in wrong answers may indicate common errors or misconceptions.

889 added

311 correct

301 subtracted incorrectly

489 subtracted without regrouping

Formative Assessment

Dennis and Patty are playing a video game. Dennis scored 800 points for eliminating the red monster. Patty scored 317 points for eliminating the green monster. How many more points did Dennis score? 483 points

As students line up for recess, lunch, or dismissal, ask them to explain how the previous lessons on regrouping has helped them with subtracting across zeros.

Line Up!

Left worksheet (page 467)

Name _____

My Homework →

Lesson 9
Subtract Across Zeros

2.NBT.7, 2.NBT.9

Homework Helper 📱 Need help? connectED.mcgraw-hill.com

You can subtract across zeros.
Find 600 − 336.

Step 1 Subtract the ones. Regroup 1 hundred into 10 tens. Then regroup 1 ten as 10 ones.

hundreds	tens	ones
5	9	10
6̸	0̸	0̸
− 3	3	6
2	6	4

Step 2 Subtract the tens.

Step 3 Subtract the hundreds.

Practice

Subtract.

1. 300
 − 251
 49

2. 600
 − 139
 461

3. 700
 − 386
 314

4. 200
 − 126
 74

5. 500
 − 385
 115

6. 800
 − 272
 528

Subtract.

7. 100 − 89
```
  1 0 0
−   8 9
-------
  1 1
```

8. 600 − 564
```
  6 0 0
− 5 6 4
-------
    3 6
```

9. 500 − 268
```
  5 0 0
− 2 6 8
-------
  2 3 2
```

10. 900
 − 432
 468

11. 700
 − 364
 336

12. 200
 − 147
 53

13. 400 pineapples are planted in a row. 293 pineapples get picked. How many pineapples are still in the row?

107 pineapples

I spiked my hair!

Test Practice

14. Find 600 − 289.

889 ○   311 ●   301 ○   489 ○

Math at Home Have your child explain how to subtract 392 from 800.

My Review

Use these pages to assess your students' understanding of the vocabulary and key concepts in this chapter.

Vocabulary Check

Ask students how they could categorize the three vocabulary words in the word bank. Sample answer: Each word can be used to describe subtracting numbers.

ELL **ELL Support Strategy** Use the activity described in Vocabulary Check to develop students' ability to categorize items into networks of meaning.

Concept Check

If students need reinforcement of skills after completing this section, use the Reteach worksheet to review the concepts again.

Exercises	Concept	Review Lesson
4–8	Subtract hundreds	2
9–14	Subtract three-digit numbers	6
15–17	Rewrite subtraction	7
18–20	Subtract across zeros	9

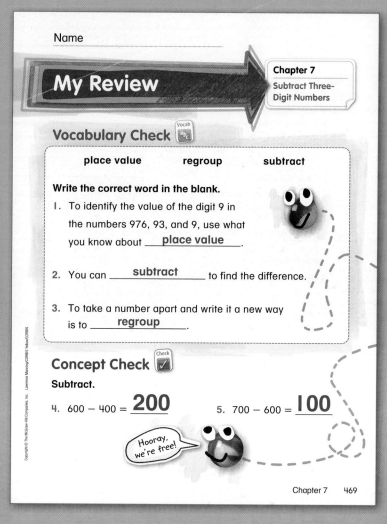

Name _____

My Review

Vocabulary Check

place value	regroup	subtract

Write the correct word in the blank.

1. To identify the value of the digit 9 in the numbers 976, 93, and 9, use what you know about ___place value___.

2. You can ___subtract___ to find the difference.

3. To take a number apart and write it a new way is to ___regroup___.

Concept Check

Subtract.

4. $600 - 400 =$ **200**   5. $700 - 600 =$ **100**

Hooray, we're free!

Chapter 7   469

Subtract.

6.
$$\begin{array}{r} 800 \\ -\ 400 \\ \hline \mathbf{400} \end{array}$$

7.
$$\begin{array}{r} 900 \\ -\ 600 \\ \hline \mathbf{300} \end{array}$$

8.
$$\begin{array}{r} 773 \\ -\ 100 \\ \hline \mathbf{673} \end{array}$$

9.
$$\begin{array}{r} 261 \\ -\ 10 \\ \hline \mathbf{251} \end{array}$$

10.
$$\begin{array}{r} 938 \\ -\ 329 \\ \hline \mathbf{609} \end{array}$$

11.
$$\begin{array}{r} 885 \\ -\ 16 \\ \hline \mathbf{869} \end{array}$$

12.
$$\begin{array}{r} 357 \\ -\ 189 \\ \hline \mathbf{168} \end{array}$$

13.
$$\begin{array}{r} 987 \\ -\ 598 \\ \hline \mathbf{389} \end{array}$$

14.
$$\begin{array}{r} 201 \\ -\ 124 \\ \hline \mathbf{77} \end{array}$$

Rewrite the problem. Subtract.

15. $385 - 166$
$$\begin{array}{r} 3\ 8\ 5 \\ -\ 1\ 6\ 6 \\ \hline 2\ 1\ 9 \end{array}$$

16. $247 - 189$
$$\begin{array}{r} 2\ 4\ 7 \\ -\ 1\ 8\ 9 \\ \hline 5\ 8 \end{array}$$

17. $925 - 638$
$$\begin{array}{r} 9\ 2\ 5 \\ -\ 6\ 3\ 8 \\ \hline 2\ 8\ 7 \end{array}$$

Subtract.

18.
$$\begin{array}{r} 400 \\ -\ 254 \\ \hline \mathbf{146} \end{array}$$

19.
$$\begin{array}{r} 700 \\ -\ 443 \\ \hline \mathbf{257} \end{array}$$

20.
$$\begin{array}{r} 300 \\ -\ 165 \\ \hline \mathbf{135} \end{array}$$

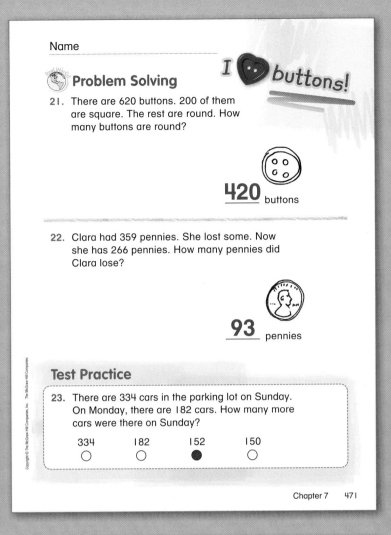

Name _____

Problem Solving   I ♥ buttons!

21. There are 620 buttons. 200 of them are square. The rest are round. How many buttons are round?

420 buttons

22. Clara had 359 pennies. She lost some. Now she has 266 pennies. How many pennies did Clara lose?

93 pennies

Test Practice

23. There are 334 cars in the parking lot on Sunday. On Monday, there are 182 cars. How many more cars were there on Sunday?

   334   182   152   150
    ○   ○   ●   ○

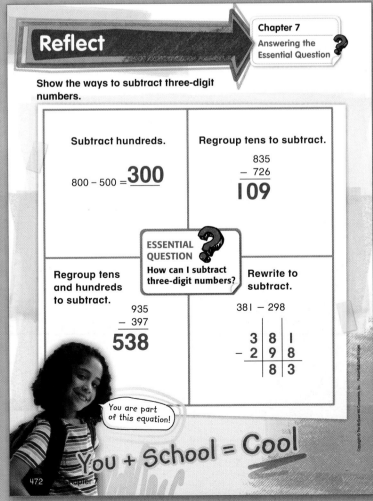

Reflect

Chapter 7
Answering the
Essential Question

Show the ways to subtract three-digit numbers.

Subtract hundreds.

$800 - 500 = $ **300**

Regroup tens to subtract.

835
− 726
109

ESSENTIAL QUESTION
How can I subtract three-digit numbers?

Regroup tens and hundreds to subtract.

935
− 397
538

Rewrite to subtract.

$381 - 298$

$$\begin{array}{c|c|c} 3 & 8 & 1 \\ -2 & 9 & 8 \\ \hline & 8 & 3 \end{array}$$

You are part of this equation!

You + School = Cool

Problem Solving

Remind students of the four-step plan for problem solving. For students who need help in reading comprehension, have them work with another student to read the problem aloud before attempting the four-step plan.

Test Practice

Diagnose Student Errors

Class trends in wrong answers may indicate common errors or misconceptions.

334   this is the number of cars on Sunday only
182   this is the number of cars on Monday only
152   correct
150   subtracted wrong

Reflect

Display this chapter's vocabulary on the Virtual Word Wall. Ask students to refer to the words as they complete the graphic organizer.

You may choose to have your students use a different graphic organizer for review.

Summative Assessment

Use these alternate leveled chapter tests from the Assessment Masters to differentiate assessment for the specific needs of your students.

Chapter Tests		
Level	**Type**	**Form**
AL	Multiple Choice	1A
AL	Multiple Choice	1B
OL	Multiple Choice / Free Choice	2A
OL	Multiple Choice / Free Choice	2B
BL	Free Choice	3A
BL	Free Choice	3B
Additional Chapter Resource Masters		
OL	Vocabulary Test	
OL	Listening Assessment	
OL	Oral Assessment	

Glossary/Glosario

Vocab [abc] → Go online for the eGlossary.

Aa

English	Spanish/Español

A.M. The hours from midnight until noon.

a.m. Las horas que van desde la medianoche hasta el mediodía.

add (addition) Join together sets to find the total or sum. The opposite of *subtract*.

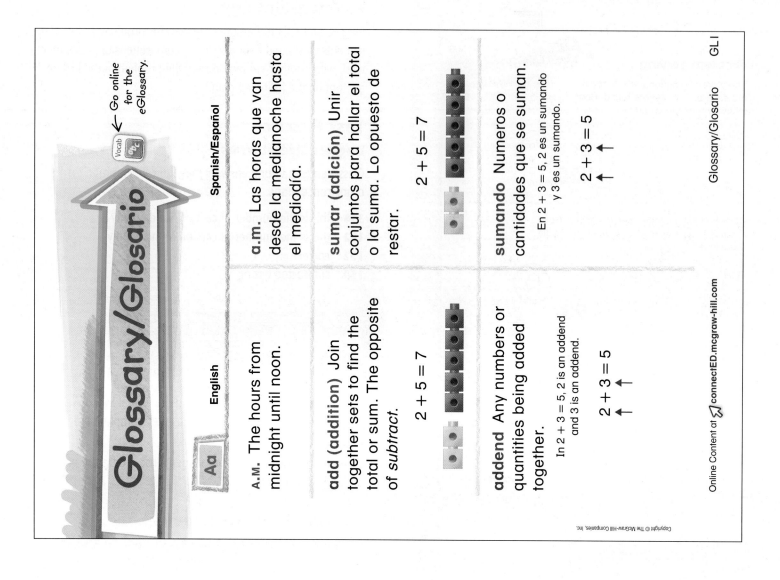

$$2 + 5 = 7$$

sumar (adición) Unir conjuntos para hallar el total o la suma. Lo opuesto de restar.

$$2 + 5 = 7$$

addend Any numbers or quantities being added together.

In 2 + 3 = 5, 2 is an addend and 3 is an addend.

$$2 + 3 = 5$$

sumando Numeros o cantidades que se suman.

En 2 + 3 = 5, 2 es un sumando y 3 es un sumando.

$$2 + 3 = 5$$

Online Content at connectED.mcgraw-hill.com

Glossary/Glosario   GL1

Aa

after Follow in place or time.

5 **6** 7 8

6 is just *after* 5

analog clock A clock that has an hour hand and a minute hand.

minute hand — hour hand

angle Two sides on a two-dimensional shape meet to form an angle.

array Objects displayed in rows and columns.

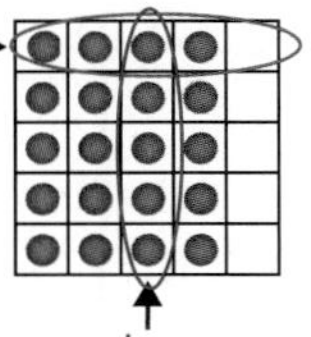

row — column

después Que sigue en lugar o en tiempo.

5 6 7 **8**

6 está justo *después* del 5

reloj analógico Reloj que tiene una manecilla horaria y un minutero.

minutero — manecilla horaria

ángulo Dos lados de una figura bidimensional se encuentran para formar un ángulo.

arreglo Objetos organizados en filas y columnas.

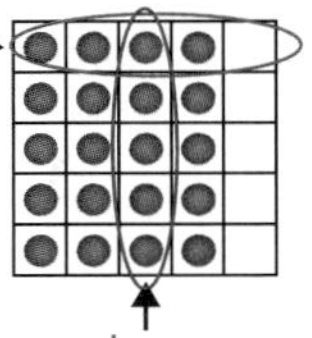

fila — columna

Bb

bar graph A graph that uses bars to show data.

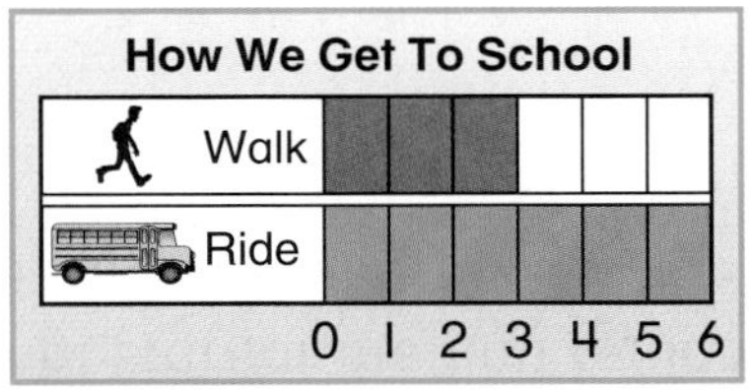

How We Get To School

	0	1	2	3	4	5	6
Walk							
Ride							

gráfica de barras Gráfica que usa barras para ilustrar datos.

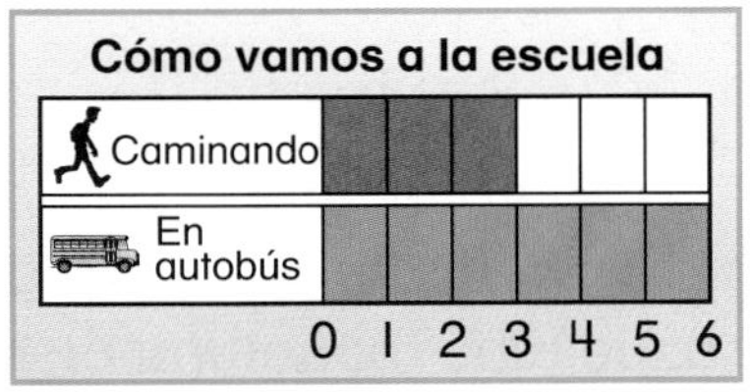

Cómo vamos a la escuela

	0	1	2	3	4	5	6
Caminando							
En autobús							

before

5 **6** 7 8

6 is just *before* 7

antes

5 **6** 7 8

6 está justo *antes* del 7

between

47 48 **49** 50

49 is *between* 48 and 50

entre

47 48 **49** 50

49 está *entre* 48 y 50

Cc

cent

1¢   1 cent

centavo

1¢   1 centavo

Online Content at ⌐ connectED.mcgraw-hill.com

---

cono Figura tridimensional que se estrecha hasta un punto desde una base circular.

cone A three-dimensional shape that narrows to a point from a circular face.

contar hacia atrás En una recta numérica, comienza en un número mayor (5) y cuenta (3) hacia atrás.

$$5 - 3 = 2$$

2 3 4 **5** 6

count back On a number line, start at the greater number (5) and count back (3).

$$5 - 3 = 2$$

2 3 4 **5** 6

seguir contando En una recta numérica, comienza en el primer sumando (4) y cuenta (2) hacia delante.

$$4 + 2 = 6$$

3 4 5 6 7

count on On a number line, start at the first addend (4) and count on (2).

$$4 + 2 = 6$$

3 4 5 6 7

Online Content at connectED.mcgraw-hill.com

Glossary/Glosario   GL5

---

cent sign (¢) The sign used to show cents.

1¢   5¢

signo de centavo (¢) El signo que se usa para mostrar centavos.

1¢   5¢

centimeter (cm) A metric unit for measuring length.

0 1 2 3 4 5
centimeters

centímetro (cm) Unidad métrica para medir la longitud.

0 1 2 3 4 5
centímetros

circle A closed, round two-dimensional shape.

círculo Bidimensional redonda y cerrada.

compare Look at objects, shapes, or numbers and see how they are alike or different.

comparar Observar objetos, formas o números para saber en qué se parecen y en qué se diferencian.

GL4   Glossary/Glosario

cube / cubo

cube A three-dimensional shape with 6 square faces.

cubo Figura tridimensional con 6 caras cuadradas.

cylinder / cilindro

cylinder A three-dimensional shape that is shaped like a can.

cilindro Figura tridimensional que tiena la forma de una lata.

data / datos

data Numbers or symbols, sometimes collected from a survey or experiment, that show information. *Data* is plural.

Name	Number of Pets
Mary	3
James	1
Alonzo	4

datos Números o símbolos que se recopilan mediante una encuesta o experimento para mostrar información.

Nombre	Número de mascotas
María	3
James	1
Alonzo	4

day / día

day 1 day = 24 hours Examples: Sunday, Monday, Tuesday, Wednesday, Thursday, Friday, Saturday

día 1 día = 24 horas Ejemplos: domingo, lunes, martes, miércoles, jueves, viernes y sábado

difference / diferencia

difference The answer to a subtraction problem.

$$3 - 1 = 2$$

The difference is 2.

diferencia Resultado de un problema de resta.

$$3 - 1 = 2$$

La diferencia es 2.

digit / dígito

digit A symbol used to write numbers. The ten digits are

0, 1, 2, 3, 4, 5, 6, 7, 8, 9.

dígito Símbolo que se utiliza para escribir números. Los diez dígitos son

0, 1, 2, 3, 4, 5, 6, 7, 8, 9.

digital clock / reloj digital

digital clock A clock that uses only numbers to show time.

reloj digital Reloj que marca la hora solo con números.

Glossary/Glosario

GL8-GL9

Dd

dime dime = 10¢ or 10 cents

head   tail

moneda de 10¢ moneda de diez centavos = 10¢ o 10 centavos

cara   cruz

dollar one dollar = 100¢ or 100 cents. It can also be written as $1.00 or $1.

front

back

one dollar = $1 or $1.00

dólar un dólar = 100¢ o 100 centavos. También se puede escribir $1.00.

frente

revés

un dólar = $1 o $1.00

dollar sign ($) The sign used to show dollars.

signo de dólar ($) Símbolo que se usa para mostrar dólares.

doubles (and near doubles) Two addends that are the same number.

6 + 6 = 12 ← doubles

6 + 7 = 13 ← near doubles

dobles (y casi dobles) Dos sumandos que son el mismo número.

6 + 6 = 12 ← dobles

6 + 7 = 13 ← casi dobles

Ee

edge The line segment where two *faces* of a three-dimensional shape meet.

edge →

arista Segmento de recta donde se encuentran dos caras de una figura tridimensional.

arista →

equal groups Each group has the same number of objects.

There are four equal groups of counters.

grupos iguales Cada grupo tiene el mismo número de objetos.

Hay cuatro grupos iguales de fichas.

equal parts Each part is the same size.

This sandwich is cut into 2 equal parts.

partes iguales Cada parte es del mismo tamaño.

Este sándwich está cortado en 2 partes iguales.

Online Content at ⬛ connectED.mcgraw-hill.com

Ff

cara La parte plana de una figura tridimensional.

El cuadrado es la cara de un cubo.

familia de operaciones Enunciados de suma y resta los cuales tienen los mismos números.

$6 + 7 = 13 \qquad 13 - 7 = 6$
$7 + 6 = 13 \qquad 13 - 6 = 7$

pie Unidad usual para medir longitud.

1 pie = 12 pulgadas

cuartos Cuatro partes iguales de un todo. Cada parte es un cuarto, o la cuarta parte del todo.

---

face The flat part of a three-dimensional shape.

A square is a face of a cube.

fact family Addition and subtraction sentences that use the same numbers.

$6 + 7 = 13 \qquad 13 - 7 = 6$
$7 + 6 = 13 \qquad 13 - 6 = 7$

foot (ft) A customary unit for measuring length. Plural is feet.

1 foot = 12 inches

fourths Four equal parts of a whole. Each part is a fourth, or a quarter of the whole.

Online Content at connectED.mcgraw-hill.com

Ee

igual a =

$6 = 6$

6 es *igual o* lo mismo que 6.

estimar Hallar un número cercano a la cantidad exacta.

47 + 22 se redondea a 50 + 20.
La estimación es 70.

número par Los números que terminan en 0, 2, 4, 6, 8.

forma desarrollada La representación de un número como suma que muestra el valor de cada dígito. También se llama *notación desarrollada*.

536 se escribe como 500 + 30 + 6.

---

equal to =

$6 = 6$

6 is *equal to* or the same as 6.

estimate Find a number close to an exact amount.

47 + 22 rounds to 50 + 20.
The estimate is 70.

even number Numbers that end with 0, 2, 4, 6, 8.

expanded form The representation of a number as a sum that shows the value of each digit. Sometimes called *expanded notation*.

536 is written as 500 + 30 + 6.

Gg

greater than >

7 > 2

7 is greater than 2.

group A set of objects.

1 group of 4

mayor que >

7 > 2

7 es mayor que 2.

grupo Conjunto o grupo de objetos.

1 grupo de 4

Hh

half hour (or half past) A unit to measure time. Sometimes called *half past* or *half past the hour.*

a half hour = 30 minutes

halves Two equal parts of a whole. Each part is a half of the whole.

hexagon A 2-dimensional shape that has six sides.

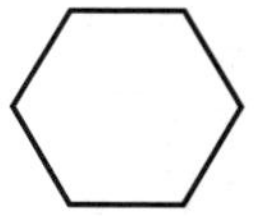

media hora (o y media) Unidad para medir tiempo. A veces se dice *hora y media.*

media hora = 30 minutos

mitades Dos partes iguales de un todo. Cada parte es la mitad de un todo.

hexágono Figura bidimensional que tiene seis lados.

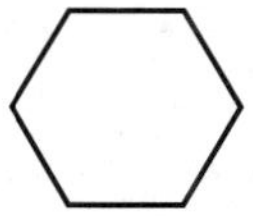

Online Content at connectED.mcgraw-hill.com

pulgada (pulg) Unidad usual para medir longitud.

12 pulgadas = 1 pie

operaciones inversas Operaciones que se oponen una a otra.

La suma y la resta son operaciones inversas u opuestas.

clave Indica qué o cuánto representa cada símbolo.

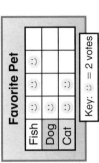

Animal doméstico favorito

Pez	☺	☺	☺
Perro	☺	☺	
Gato	☺		

Clave: ☺ = 2 votos

---

ii

inch (in) A customary unit for measuring length. The plural is *inches*.

12 inches = 1 foot

inverse Operations that are opposite of each other.

Addition and subtraction are inverse or opposite operations.

Kk

key Tells what (or how many) each symbol stands for.

Favorite Pet

Fish	☺	☺	☺
Dog	☺	☺	
Cat	☺		

Key: ☺ = 2 votes

Hh

hour A unit to measure time.

1 hour = 60 minutes

hour hand The hand on a clock that tells the hour. It is the shorter hand.

hour hand

hundreds The numbers in the range of 100–999. It is the place value of a number.

365

3 is in the hundreds place.
6 is in the tens place.
5 is in the ones place.

---

hora Unidad para medir tiempo.

1 hora = 60 minutos

manecilla horaria Manecilla del reloj que indica la hora. Es la más corta.

manecilla horaria

centenas Los números en el rango de 100 a 999. Es el valor posicional de un número.

365

3 está en el lugar de las centenas.
6 está en el lugar de las decenas.
5 está en el lugar de las unidades.

Mm

measure To find the length, height, weight, capacity, or temperature using standard or nonstandard units.

medir Hallar la longitud, altura, peso, capacidad o temperatura usando unidades estándares o no estándares.

meter (m) A metric unit for measuring length.

1 meter = 100 centimeters

metro (m) Unidad métrica para medir longitud.

1 metro = 100 centímetros

minute (min) A unit to measure time. Each tick mark is one minute.

1 minute = 60 seconds

minuto (min) Unidad para medir tiempo. Cada marca es un minuto.

1 minuto = 60 segundos

minute hand The longer hand on a clock that tells the minutes.

minute hand

minutero La manecilla más larga del reloj. Indica los minutos.

minutero

Ll

length How long or how far away something is.

length

longitud El largo de algo o lo lejos que está.

longitud

less than <

4 < 7

4 is less than 7.

menor que <

4 < 7

4 es menor que 7.

line plot A graph that shows how often a certain number occurs in data.

diagrama lineal Una gráfica que muestra con qué frecuencia ocurre cierto número en los datos.

moneda de 5¢ moneda de cinco centavos = 5¢ o 5 centavos

cara   cruz

recta numérica Recta con marcas de números.

0 1 2 3 4 5

nickel nickel = 5¢ or 5 cents

head   tail

number line A line with number labels.

0 1 2 3 4 5

en punto El momento en que comienza cada hora.

Son las 7 en punto.

o'clock At the beginning of the hour.

It is 7 o'clock.

números impares Los números que terminan en 1, 3, 5, 7, 9.

odd number Numbers that end with 1, 3, 5, 7, 9.

Online Content at ✏ **connectED.mcgraw-hill.com**

Glossary/Glosario   **GL19**

---

missing addend The missing number in a number sentence that makes the number sentence true.

9 + ☐ = 16

The missing addend is 7.

month A unit of time. 12 months = 1 year

April

Sunday	Monday	Tuesday	Wednesday	Thursday	Friday	Saturday
	1	2	3	4	5
6	7	8	9	10	11	12
13	14	15	16	17	18	19
20	21	22	23	24	25	26
27	28	29	30			

This is the month of April.

near doubles Addition facts in which one addend is exactly 1 more or 1 less than the other addend.

sumando desconocido El número desconocido en un enunciado numérico que hace que este sea verdadero.

9 + ☐ = 16

El sumando desconocido es 7.

mes Unidad de tiempo. 12 meses = 1 año

Abril

domingo	lunes	martes	miércoles	jueves	viernes	sábado
	1	2	3	4	5
6	7	8	9	10	11	12
13	14	15	16	17	18	19
20	21	22	23	24	25	26
27	28	29	30			

Este es el mes de abril.

casi dobles Operaciones de suma en las cuales un sumando es exactamente 1 más o 1 menos que el otro sumando.

GL18 Glossary/Glosario

Online Content at ✈ **connectED.mcgraw-hill.com**   Glossary/Glosario   **GL18-GL19**

patrón Orden que sigue continuamente un conjunto de objetos o números insertar punto.

unidad de patrón

pattern An order that a set of objects or numbers follows over and over.

pattern unit

moneda de 1¢ moneda de un centavo = 1 ¢ o 1 centavo

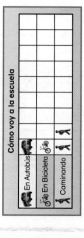

cara   escudo

penny penny = 1 ¢ or 1 cent

head   tail

pentágono Polígono de cinco lados.

pentagon A polygon with five sides.

gráfica con imágenes Gráfica que tiene diferentes imágenes para ilustrar la información recopilada.

picture graph A graph that has different pictures to show information collected.

Cómo voy a la escuela						
En Autobús						
En Bicicleta						
Caminando						

How I Get to School						
Bus						
Bike						
Walk						

Oo

ones The numbers in the range of 0-9. A place value of a number.

65

5 is in the ones place.

unidades Los números en el rango de 0 a 9. Valor posicional de un número.

65

El 5 está en el lugar de las unidades.

order

1, 3, 6, 8, 10

These numbers are in order from least to greatest.

orden

1, 3, 6, 8, 10

Estos números están en orden de menor a mayor.

Pp

P.M. The hours from noon until midnight.

p.m. Las horas que van desde el mediodía hasta la medianoche.

parallelogram A two-dimensional shape that has four sides. Each pair of opposite sides is equal and parallel.

paralelogramo Figura bidimensional que tiene cuatro lados. Cada par de lados opuestos son iguales y paralelos.

partition To divide or "break up."

separar Dividir o desunir.

Qq

quarter quarter = 25¢ or 25 cents

head   tail

quarter hour A quarter hour is 15 minutes. Sometimes called *quarter past* or *quarter til*.

Rr

rectangle A plane shape with four sides and four corners.

moneda de 25¢ moneda de 25 centavos = 25¢ o 25 centavos

cara   cruz

cuarto de hora Un cuarto de hora es 15 minutos. A veces se dice hora y cuarto.

rectángulo Figura plana con cuatro lados y cuatro esquinas.

Online Content at connectED.mcgraw-hill.com

Glossary/Glosario   **GL23**

Pp

place value The value given to a *digit* by its place in a number.

1,365

1 is in the thousands place.
3 is in the hundreds place.
6 is in the tens place.
5 is in the ones place.

pyramid A three-dimensional shape with a polygon as a base and other faces that are triangles.

Qq

quadrilateral A shape that has 4 sides and 4 angles.

valor posicional El valor dado a un *dígito* según su posición en un número.

1,365

1 está en el lugar de los millares.
3 está en el lugar de las centenas.
6 está en el lugar de las decenas.
5 está en el lugar de las unidades.

pirámide Figura tridimensional con un polígono como base y otras caras que son triángulos.

cuadrilátero Figura con 4 lados y 4 ángulos.

Rr

suma repetida Usar el mismo sumando una y otra vez.

repeated addition To use the same addend over and over.

rombo Paralelogramo con cuatro lados de la misma longitud.

rhombus A shape with 4 sides of the same length.

redondear Cambiar el *valor* de un número a uno con el que es más fácil trabajar.

24 redondeado a la decena más cercana es 20.

round Change the *value* of a number to one that is easier to work with.

24 rounded to the nearest ten is 20.

Ss

lado Uno de los segmentos de recta que componen una figura.

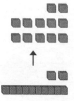

El pentágono tiene cinco lados.

side One of the line segments that make up a shape.

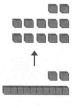

A pentagon has five sides.

Rr

rectangular prism A three-dimensional shape with 6 faces that are rectangles.

prisma rectangular Figura tridimensional con 6 caras que son rectángulos.

regroup Take apart a number to write it in a new way.

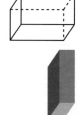

1 ten + 2 ones becomes 12 ones.

reagrupar Separar un número para escribirlo de una nueva forma.

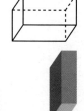

1 decena + 2 unidades se convierten en 12 unidades.

related fact(s) Basic facts using the same numbers. Sometimes called a *fact family*.

$4 + 1 = 5 \quad 5 - 4 = 1$
$1 + 4 = 5 \quad 5 - 1 = 4$

operaciones relacionadas Operaciones básicas en las que se usan los mismos números. También se llaman *familias de operaciones*.

$4 + 1 = 5 \quad 5 - 4 = 1$
$1 + 4 = 5 \quad 5 - 1 = 4$

Online Content at connectED.mcgraw-hill.com

Ss

cuadrado Figura bidimensional que tiene cuatro lados iguales. También es un rectángulo.

square A two-dimensional shape that has four equal sides. Also a rectangle.

restar (sustracción) Eliminar, quitar, separar o hallar la diferencia entre dos conjuntos. Lo opuesto de *sumar*.

$$5 - 5 = 0$$

subtract (subtraction) Take away, take apart, separate, or find the difference between two sets. The opposite of *add*.

$$5 - 5 = 0$$

suma Resultado de la operación de sumar.

$$2 + 4 = 6$$

sum The answer to an addition problem.

$$2 + 4 = 6$$

Ss

skip count Count objects in equal groups of two or more.

2, 4, 6, 8, 10

0 1 2 3 4 5 6 7 8 9 10

slide To move a shape in any direction to another place.

slide

sphere A three-dimensional shape that has the shape of a round ball.

contar salteado Contar objetos en grupos iguales de dos o más.

2, 4, 6, 8, 10

0 1 2 3 4 5 6 7 8 9 10

deslizar Traslador una figura a una nueva posición.

deslizar

esfera Figura tridimensional que tiene la forma de una pelota redonda.

Ss

survey Collect data by asking people the same question.

Favorite Animal	
Dog	|||||	
Cat	||||

This survey shows favorite animals.

symbol A letter or figure that stands for something.

$+$

This symbol means to add.

tally marks A mark used to record data collected in a survey.

|||| |||

tally marks

---

encuesta Recopilar datos al hacer las mismas preguntas a un grupo de personas.

Animal favorito	
Perro	|||||	
Gato	||||

Esta encuesta muestra los animales favoritos.

símbolo Letra o figura que representa algo.

$+$

Este símbolo significa sumar.

marca de conteo Marca que se utiliza para registrar los datos recopilados en una encuesta.

||||| |||

marcas de conteo

Tt

tens The numbers in the range of 10–99. It is the place value of a number.

65

6 is in the tens place.
5 is in the ones place.

thirds Three equal parts.

thousand(s) The numbers in the range of 1,000–9,999. It is the place value of a number.

1,365

1 is in the thousands place.
3 is in the hundreds place.
6 is in the tens place.
5 is in the ones place.

three-dimensional shape A shape that has length, width, and height.

---

decenas Los números en el rango de 10 a 99. Es el valor posicional de un número.

65

6 está en el lugar de las decenas.
5 está en el lugar de las unidades.

tercios Tres partes iguales.

millar(es) Los números en el rango de 1,000 a 9,999. Es el valor posicional de un número.

1,365

1 está en el lugar de los millares.
3 está en el lugar de las centenas.
6 está en el lugar de las decenas.
5 está en el lugar de las unidades.

figura tridimensional Que tiene tres dimensiones: largo, ancho y alto.

Tt

trapezoid A two-dimensional shape with four sides and only two opposite sides that are parallel.

trapecio Figura bidimensional de cuatro lados con solo dos lados opuestos que son paralelos.

triangle A three-dimensional shape with three sides and three angles.

triángulo Figura tridimensional con tres lados y tres ángulos.

two-dimensional shape The outline of a shape - such as a triangle, square, or rectangle - that has only *length* and *width*.

figura bidimensional Contorno de una figura, como un triángulo, un cuadrado o un rectángulo, que solo tiene *largo* y *ancho*.

Vv

vertex

vertex
vertex
vertex
vertex

vértice

vértice
vértice
vértice
vértice

Ww

week A part of a calendar. 1 week = 7 days

Sunday	Monday	Tuesday	Wednesday	Thursday	Friday	Saturday

semana Parte de un calendario una semana = 7 días

domingo	lunes	martes	miércoles	jueves	viernes	sábado

whole The entire amount or object.

el todo La cantidad total o el objeto completo.

Yy

yard (yd) A customary unit for measuring length.

1 yard = 3 feet or 36 inches

year A way to count how much time has passed or will pass. 1 year = 12 months

January, February, March, April, May, June, July, August, September, October, November, December

yarda Unidad usual para medir la longitud.

1 yarda = 3 pies o 36 pulgadas

año Un período insertar punto, un año = 12 meses

enero, febrero, marzo, abril, mayo, junio, julio, agosto, septiembre, octubre, noviembre, diciembre

Work Mat 1: Ten-Frame

3+6=9 in all

Work Mat 1: Ten-Frame   WM1

Online Content at connectED.mcgraw-hill.com

Work Mat 1 Ten-Frame   WM1

Work Mat 2: Ten-Frames

Work Mat 2: Ten-Frames

Work Mat 2 Ten-Frames

Name WS

Work Mat 3: Number Lines

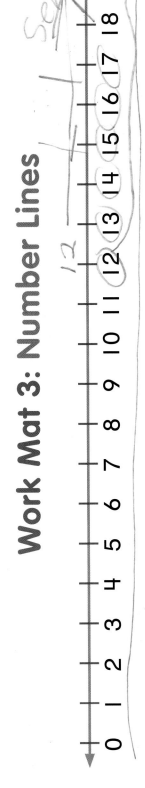

0 1 2 3 4 5 6 7 8 9 10 11 12 13 14 15 16 17 18 19 20

Seko

12

21 22 23 24 25 26 27 28 29 30 31 32 33 34 35 36 37 38 39 40

41 42 43 44 45 46 47 48 49 50 51 52 53 54 55 56 57 58 59 60

Work Mat 4: Number Lines

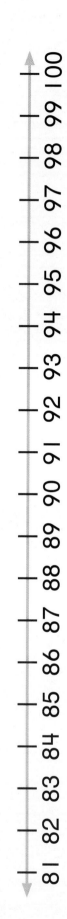

Name _____

Work Mat 5: Part-Part-Whole

Part	Part

Whole

Work Mat 5: Part-Part-Whole   WM5

Work Mat 6: Tens and Ones Chart

Tens	Ones

Name _____

Work Mat 7: Hundreds, Tens, and Ones Chart

Hundreds	Tens	Ones

Work Mat 7: Hundreds, Tens, and Ones Chart   **WM7**

Work Mat 8: Thousands, Hundreds, Tens, and Ones Chart

Thousands	Hundreds	Tens	Ones

Index

Magenta font indicates Teacher Edition pages.

Act It Out, 44, 122, 270, 398, 503–506, 507–508, 608

Activity Cards, (see My Learning Stations)

Add/addition, 4, 5–6, 11–14, 15–16, 17–20, 21–22, 23–26, 27–28, 29–32, 33–34, 35–38, 39–40, 41–44, 45–46, 47–48, 75–78, 79–80, 81–84, 85–86, 87–90, 91–92, 93, 95–97, 98, 127–130, 131–132, 133–136, 137–138, 145–148, 149–150, 160, 165–168, 169–170, 171–174, 175–176, 177–180, 181–182, 183–184, 185–188, 189–190, 191–194, 195–196, 197–200, 201–202, 203–204, 207–208, 209–210, 211–213, 214, 223–226, 227–228, 261–264, 265–266, 347–348, 351–354, 355–356, 357–360, 361–362, 363–366, 367–368, 369–370, 371–374, 375–376, 377–380, 381–382, 383–386, 387–388, 389–392, 393–394, 395–398, 399–400, 401–403, 404

  Addends, 5–6, 11–14, 15–16, 22, 35–38, 39–40, 47–48, 95, 102, 145–148, 149–150, 160, 165–168, 169–170, 347–348

  Addition-subtraction relationship, 69–72, 73–74

  Arrays, 103–104, 105–106, 133–136, 137–138, 153–154, 156

  Break apart addends, 165–168, 169–170, 183, 211

  Break apart a number to add, 351–354, 355–356

  Commutative Property of Addition, 11–14, 15–16

  Counting on, 17–20, 21–22, 47–48

  Fact family, 7–8, 81–84, 85–86, 95–96, 98, 218, 223–226, 227–228, 247, 281

  Fluency Practice, 93, 151, 209–210

  Grouping addends, 35–38, 39–40

  Hundreds, 357–360, 361–362, 370

  Identity Property of Addition, 11–14, 15–16

Inverse operations, 69–72, 73–74, 95

Make a 10, 29–32, 33–34, 48, 98

Make a 100, 351–354, 355–356, 369

Mental addition, 363–366, 367–368, 404

Mentally add 10, 363–366, 367–368, 370

Mentally add 100, 363–366, 367–368, 370

Missing addend, 7–8, 75–78, 79–80, 98, 365, 368, 370

Near doubles, 7–8, 23–26, 27–28, 66

Number sentence, 11–14, 15–16, 29–32, 33–34, 41–44, 45–46, 47–48, 185–188, 189–190, 357, 377, 383, 389

On number lines, 17–20, 21–22

Plus sign (+), 4

Properties, 11–14, 15–16

Related facts, 7–8, 69–72, 73–74, 75–78, 79–80, 95

Repeated, 103–104, 127–130, 131–132, 133–136, 137–138, 153, 476

Sums, 7–8, 11–14, 15–16, 48, 60, 96, 102, 145–148, 149–150, 160, 183, 211, 218, 346, 347–348

Sums of equal addends, 145–148, 149–150, 154

3 addends, 35–38, 39–40

3 and 4 two–digit numbers, 196–200, 201–202

Three-digit numbers, 383–386, 387–388, 389–392, 393–394

To a two-digit number, 177–180, 181–182

Two-digit numbers, 185–188, 189–190, 191–194, 195–196, 197–200, 201–202, 212

Addends, 5–6, 11–14, 15–16, 22, 35–38, 39–40, 47–48, 95, 102, 145–148, 149–150, 160, 165–168, 169–170, 347–348

  Break apart addends, 165–168, 169–170, 183, 211

  Grouping, 35–38, 39–40

  Missing, 7–8, 75–78, 79–80, 98, 365, 368, 370

Afternoon, 586

A.M., 587–588, 591–592, 625–628, 629–630, 631–633, 634

Am I Ready?, 3, 101, 159, 217, 287, 345, 407, 475, 521, 585, 637, 727

Analog clocks, 587–588, 593–596, 597–598, 611–612, 631–633, 634

Analyzing

  Bar graphs, 555–558, 559–560, 580

  Data, 541–544, 545–546, 547–548, 555–558, 559–560, 573–576, 577–578, 580

  Line plots, 573–576, 577–578

  Picture graphs, 541–544, 545–546, 547–548, 580

Angles, 729–730, 745–748, 749–750, 757–758, 790

  Edges, 729–730, 757–758, 765–768, 769–770, 790

  Vertex (vertices), 765–768, 769–770, 790

Answering the Essential Question, (see Essential Question)

Approaching Grade Level, (see Differentiated Instruction)

Arrays, 103–104, 105–106, 133–136, 137–138, 153–154, 156

Assessment

  Am I Ready?, 3, 101, 159, 217, 287, 345, 407, 475, 521, 585, 637, 727

  Assess Prerequisite Skills, 3, 101, 159, 217, 287, 345, 407, 475, 521, 585, 637, 727

  Assess Readiness, 3–3A, 101–101A, 159–159A, 217–217A, 287–287A, 345–345A, 407–407A, 475–475A, 521–521A, 585–585A, 637–637A, 727–727A

  Check My Progress, 47–48, 67–68, 125–126, 183–184, 247–248, 313–314, 369–370, 431–432, 501–502, 547–548, 611–612, 663–664, 683–684, 757–758

  Concept Check, 47, 67, 96, 125, 154, 211, 282, 313, 339, 402, 470, 516, 580, 632, 663, 722, 790

  Diagnose Student Errors, 33–34, 39–40, 45–46, 47–48, 59–60, 65–66, 67–68, 91–92, 97–98, 111–112, 125–126, 149–150, 155–156, 169–170, 175–176, 181–182, 183–184, 189–190, 195–196, 201–202, 213–214, 227–228, 233–234, 239–240, 245–246, 247–248, 253–254, 259–260, 265–266, 277–278, 299–300, 305–306, 311–312, 313–314, 331–332, 341–342,

Bb

Cc

Index

Index